C0-AMZ-813

# CONVEYORS

*and Related Equipment*

# CONVEYORS

## *and Related Equipment*

WILBUR G. HUDSON

M.E., A.S.M.E.

*Second Edition*

NEW YORK · *John Wiley & Sons,* INC.

LONDON · *Chapman & Hall,* LTD.

SECOND EDITION
*Second Printing, July, 1950*

PRINTED IN THE UNITED STATES OF AMERICA

# PREFACE

I have endeavored to make this book useful to those who seek information regarding the kind of equipment to use to best advantage; to the student engineer who requires a better understanding of the applications and limitations of the various types of material-handling equipment and methods of storage; and to the architect, consultant, and plant engineer who must have a general knowledge of the art to weigh intelligently the recommendations of the manufacturer.

Little attempt is made to guide the draftsman through the details of design of chains, bearings, shafting, gearing, etc. All manufacturers have established standards which their draftsmen follow. Unfortunately the draftsmen in a large organization have little opportunity to ascertain costs since the estimating and designing are in separate departments with tenuous contacts, but relative costs have a bearing on the selection of equipment. Where possible, comparative costs are indicated.

It is hoped that the book may be of value to the engineering contractor. He relies on the engineering skill and experience of the manufacturer and does not dictate specifications; but, as he is vitally interested in the proper erection and adjustment that he includes as part of his work, information along these lines has been included wherever the author's personal experience has provided data of value.

Material handling is so broad a subject that it cannot be covered comprehensively in one volume; consequently those machines are discussed which most frequently enter into the average problems. A brief historical outline, when it is of interest, is included, and then the more detailed discussion proceeds with the technicalities of layout, the performance possibilities, and maintenance suggestions.

The author of a work of this kind faces a dilemma. If it is to be useful to the student engineer it must include elementary matter which is dull reading to the plant engineer, the architect, or the consultant, but if the discussion is on the level of interest to them it will lack clearness for the student. A compromise has been attempted. It is assumed that the student, through study of the catalogues and other matter furnished by the manufacturers, will be familiar with the different types of equipment and, in a general way, with their applications. Perhaps it is more important to know their misapplications, but that knowledge unfortunately comes through painful and costly experience.

I appreciate that many of my statements are personal opinions based on my observation and experience and not necessarily indisputable, but as far as it has been possible to do so these observations have been checked through consultations with associates.

The student engineer approaching this art may get the impression that it has reached its limitations — that there are no more frontiers. Scanning the catalogues of thirty years ago we see the same types of elevators, flight conveyors, skip hoists, belt conveyors, crushers, etc., as are illustrated today. Actually, great progress has been made, and more is to come. The introduction of V-belts and high-speed drive chains, alloy steels, hydraulic and pneumatic conveyors, vibrating screens and feeders, motorized reducers, powder metallurgy (compressing and heat-treating metallic powders), sealed anti-friction bearings, improved conveyor belts and rolls, en masse conveyors, and automatic controls create new possibilities in efficiency, long life, and reduced costs of handling. Certainly we have no reason to think that we have now reached the limits of development in this important field of engineering.

Since this book was first published in 1944 there have been some striking developments in materials-handling methods and machines. Wartime requirements led to a rapid growth of the use of industrial trucks, tractors, and trailers. The curtailment of the supply of natural rubber has been followed by the development of conveyor belts far stronger and better than prewar belts. The use of plastics and compressed metallic powders recently has forced our attention to the dust explosion risks in industrial installations. Certain sections of the book have been extended to analyze typical applications and misapplications of the machines under discussion.

Wilbur G. Hudson, M.E.

Chicago, Illinois
*March, 1949*

# CONTENTS

## CHAPTER 1

# GENERAL PRINCIPLES

Material handling plays an important part in industrial economy. Great steam plants would not be possible without coal-handling equipment, nor could steel, paper, chemical, cement, and manufacturing plants function without conveyors. Mass production in industry depends on the conveying system, and expansions in mass production invariably follow improvements in methods of handling the materials involved.

**Tricky Materials.** Most performance disappointments result from a failure on the part of the engineer to make a comprehensive study of the material and its reaction in a conveyor. Tricky materials are many; it is worth while to list a few of them.

Carbon-black pellets are extremely fragile, and if broken up they are useless for certain purposes. Gentle handling is essential, and any conveyor having a grinding action will be a failure.

Sulphur develops static electricity through friction, and when discharged along a chute it builds up a voltage later equalized by spark discharge. The disasters resulting from chuting sulphur into the hold of a vessel about to sail can readily be appreciated. Chutes must be lined with aluminum or aluminum bronze, and the conveying system must be such that the static charge will be dissipated harmlessly.

In certain brewing processes a mixture of ground malt and hulls has been found best in the vats. If the hulls are not ground up the liquor filters freely. If the hulls are ground up the whole process slows down, and the output of the plant is reduced. Special grinding machines have been developed which do not pulverize the hulls, but if this prepared mixture then is handled by a high-speed elevator, by a scraper conveyor, or even by a screw conveyor, the hulls suffer degradation and the processing is slow and costly.

Cement is an odd material, often causing the designer much grief. The capacity of a bucket elevator for handling cement is much less than its tabulated value. Air is trapped in the buckets as the cement enters. A few vents in the floor of each bucket will remedy this trouble to some extent, but oversize buckets should be selected Another curious characteristic is that, while aerated, cement flows freely, but after it has stood awhile in storage or in a car the air is squeezed out, and it will not flow.

Soda ash is even more lively when aerated. The author has seen soda ash freshly stored by pneumatic conveyor flow out of an opening in a bin in a way which approached the flow of water; that is, its angle of repose was almost zero. It has a troublesome habit of sticking to the buckets of a centrifugal discharge elevator and discharging back down the return leg, though it handles nicely in a slow-speed continuous bucket elevator. Since the dust has an irritating effect on the mucous membrane, dustless operation is essential. For unloading bulk soda ash from box cars the pneumatic conveyor, which functions like a vacuum cleaner, has advantages.

Engineers designing sewage-treatment plants have run into trouble in the selection of elevators for handling wet sludge. Conveying en masse fails utterly, as the sludge builds up on the walls of the duct and on the impellers, completely jamming the machine. It quickly chokes a bucket elevator by adhering to the buckets, and it contains a fine grit which soon cuts through the chain joints and sprocket wheels. Handling sludge is one of the most difficult conveying problems.

Fuller's earth in granular form, granulated slate for prepared roofing, granulated sugar, table salt, and the like must not be ground up or degraded. Food products, talc, face powder, tooth paste, etc., must not suffer discoloration or come in contact with lubricants. The shell or protective sheath of oats must not be damaged by rough handling. Some coals when damp are very corrosive to steel plate. Flaxseed at high velocity acts almost like a sand blast. Copra, under the high-velocity action of a pneumatic conveyor, may yield up its oil content, causing difficult deposits in the centrifugal receiver and reducing the quality of the copra. Ashes are abrasive, dusty, and troublesome when dry and corrosive when wet.

Borax, ground feldspar, and sand are highly abrasive. Aluminum oxide in finely powdered form has a cutting action just a little lower than diamond dust. If it gets into the chain joints, as it has an uncanny ability to do, the chain is soon ruined.

These are only a few of the tricky materials — the list is long. Table 1 mentions bulk materials that frequently enter into material-handling problems, with comments on their action when handled in conveyors.

**Dust Explosions and Dust Prevention.** With the extensive use of materials having an affinity for oxygen there is a growing dust hazard in connection with materials handling installations. The subject is covered at length in Chapter 22. All mechanical conveyors can be housed in so that dust will not be scattered; for example, a cover plate may be placed over the carrying run of a flight conveyor or upon the trough of a screw conveyor. Continuous-flow conveyors are inherently dustless. Belt conveyors with trippers are difficult; they are discussed in Chapter 10. Pneumatic conveyors are dustless except at the discharge from the receiver or dust collector, but there is an internal risk that a fragment of steel in a finely divided combustible material might strike a spark by impact against the wall of the duct.

**Plant Layout and Conveyor Layout.** The type of conveyor is only one part of the layout of a plant. There may be, and usually are, several equally effective types of material-handling equipment, but the flow of material through the plant — that is to say the *engineering* of the conveying system — has a far-reaching effect on the cost of production. Savings or losses in every department may depend on the material-handling scheme. Too often first cost receives more attention than reliability. As a rule it takes only two or three breakdowns of a badly engineered conveying system to wipe out the difference in cost for the best machine that might have been installed.

**Price vs. Quality.** The responsible conveyor manufacturer with a reputation to maintain will not cheapen his product to compete with something he knows to be inferior. It is not difficult to find an assembled skip hoist, drag scraper, etc., cheaper than the product of a first-class manufacturer, since the drum, sheaves, shaft, and bucket can be purchased here and there from small shops which at the moment need work. If the assembled equipment fails, the seller may sidestep responsibility. The subcontractor has been paid and is not inclined to lose a few dollars he made on a part whose application he knew nothing about. The user holds the bag, as under the circumstances he should. His headache can be avoided if he weighs reputation against price differential.

States and municipalities must purchase from the lowest bidder, and maintenance guarantees are rarely required. Maintenance costs are usually lower in the privately owned plant because, for the sake of his own reputation, the works engineer as a rule buys the best equipment. Two installations stand out in the author's memory. In 1907 a pivoted bucket carrier was purchased by an Illinois institution on a mandatory competitive basis. It handled about 12,000 tons of coal and 1000 tons of ashes per year. The cost of maintenance was high, and finally in 1938 the equipment was in such generally bad condition that bids were asked for a practically complete replacement. It so happened that in 1908 a carrier costing about 20 per cent more, almost identical in size, layout, and tonnage handled, was installed in a neighboring manufacturing plant. In 1938 it was still in fine condition with a maintenance cost averaging $50 per year (material only).

**Engineering Responsibility.** Considerations of suitability are of even greater importance to the consulting engineer than to the manufacturer or contractor, whose guarantee may be limited to quality or capacity. On one occasion it was required to unload slate granules from box cars to an overhead bin at 40 tons per hour. This slate was a clean sharp product, screened to about 1/4-in. cubes, used for facing roofing paper. The consulting engineers specified a pneumatic system, with the usual guarantees of quality and capacity. When the equipment was placed in operation it was immediately apparent that the high velocity, the jostling in the nozzle and flexible hose, and the impact at the elbows so degraded and rounded the particles that the slate was unusable. The contractor sued for the 10 per cent balance due him, and the purchasers sued for the return of the 90 per cent already paid. Quality and capacity were acknowledged. The court held that the responsibility rested with the consulting engineer who specified the type of equipment and who should have studied the manufacturing requirements; that it was not the responsibility of the contractor to determine whether the pneumatic system specified by the engineer would make the material unsuitable. He was required merely to unload the material at 40 tons per hour, and he did so. Eventually a set of power shovels was installed, with a belt conveyor alongside the track, and a belt and bucket elevator, which functioned with very little damage to the granules.

**Capacity.** "Handling capacity" may have different meanings to different persons. The engineer must be specific in his statements. If it is desired to unload ten 50-ton cars in 10 hours, a conveyor capacity of 50 tons per hour will not suffice. If an unloading capacity of 100 tons per hour is specified, that does not mean that two 50-ton cars will be unloaded, because time is lost in spotting the cars, or if power shovels are involved the car-door bulkheads must be removed. If a 50-ton-per-hour pneumatic unloader is used the cleanup of the last few tons in each car is done at a fraction of that rate, and then the emptied car must be moved out and a loaded car moved in.

**Samples Important.** It is a good idea to save a sample of the material for which you are asked to specify a conveyor. Memory sometimes is amazingly short when things do not work out exactly as expected by the purchaser. In a pneumatic system, for instance, if the material proves to have different characteristics from those for which the velocity and volume of air were determined, the results may be quite different from expectations.

**Importance of Clearance around Machinery.** One of the most irritating circumstances is lack of comfortable headroom and clearance around machinery. An overhead girder, or a pipe which scrapes the head, or scant lateral clear space which results in a smear on the clothes, is a defect in design. It may be a serious factor should a man be injured and bring suit for damages.

**Importance of Engineering.** It is often a temptation to use a standard machine for a job which seems to call for no engineering. It is true that by so doing the engineering cost is eliminated, but the engineering cost may be only a small part of the total cost, and the purchaser should carefully consider whether the all-round efficiency of his installation is best assured by having standardized equipment intended to fulfill average requirements. It may be that such a machine will do the job, but if it does not the saving in engineering cost soon evaporates.

Each manufacturer maintains a staff of specialists, skilled through years of experience. The purchaser or engineer who develops a project without seeking their cooperation may let himself in for serious troubles and large losses. The engineering of material-handling installations is not always as elementary as it appears to be.

**Liberality of Design.** Possibly this designation requires an explanation. When a specification calls for a certain capacity the contractor receives no additional compensation, except a sense of pleasure, if that capacity is exceeded. He may be in serious difficulties if his installation fails even by a small margin to meet the guarantee. This is especially true in government work where the inspector has no discretion as regards approval.

A coal bunker may be specified for 500-ton capacity figured at 50 lb. per cu. ft.; but coal often weighs less than 50 lb. per cu. ft., and if it does the capacity is too small. The angle of repose of a material may have been assumed to be 35° and then may be found to be 45° when the material is deposited in a container with a cone top, and so there is a vacant space at the top of the container. The capacity cannot easily be increased. The handling capacity of conveyors is definitely specified, but many materials weigh less than expected, owing to aeration, and the conveyor is not quite up to capacity. Play safe and leave a margin in your design to take care of contingencies. Your final check will come along sooner.

**Specifications.** The specifications of consulting or project engineers are nearly always fair to both parties of a contract, but it is advantageous for the bidder to read through the "small print." This is true particularly with government specifications, which sometimes have odd angles. On one contract including a coal-storage structure adjacent to the boiler house and a larry runway from beneath the bin through the boiler house, the author completed the bin structure and notified the government engineer that, as soon as the boiler house framework was erected so that the larry track could be suspended therefrom, the job could be wound up at once. The contract carried a penalty of $100 per day. Two months later the government advised that the work could be finished and a week later the job was wound up and accepted. In due course final payment, less $6000 penalty, was received. The engineer agreed that the contractor could not hang the larry runway from sky hooks but pointed to a clause in " small print " which required the contractor to ask for an extension of time should his work be interrupted, and the Comptroller General gave him no alternative but to assess the penalty clause since written application for an extension had not been filed. It took the energetic intervention of a United States senator to get that $6000.

**Selection Chart.** It is impossible to state flatly which conveyor is or is not best suited to a given material, for conditions vary. Table 2 shows the types usually selected. Of course there are several different conveyors adapted to any one material, and only experience can guide in selecting the best one for a given set of circumstances. The table refers to materials frequently met in material-handling problems. There are many others.

TABLE 1

CHARACTERISTICS OF MATERIALS IN RELATION TO THEIR BEHAVIOR IN CONVEYORS

*Note.* Power calculations for flight conveyors involve the coefficient of friction of the material in contact with steel plate. In calculating pneumatic conveyors, use the " specific weight," not the weights given in this table.

| Material | Weight per Cubic foot | Comment |
|---|---|---|
| Acid phosphate | 90 | Very tricky because sticky. Pneumatic handling impossible. |
| Alum, lumpy | 60–65 | Abrasive. Contamination may be objectionable. |
| Ammonium nitrate | 62 | Actively hygroscopic. In contact with copper, zinc, or brass it forms a salt which sensitizes it. Not affected by steel or iron. Very sticky when damp. It is an insensitive explosive. |
| Aluminum oxide | 60 | One of the most abrasive materials. Rated 9 in Mohs' scale.[1] Fine white powder, 180–300 mesh. |

[1]Mohs' scale: 1. Talc. 2. Gypsum. 3. Calc spar. 4. Fluorspar. 5. Apatite. 6. Feldspar. 7. Quartz. 8. Topaz. 9. Sapphire. 10. Diamond.

TABLE 1—*Continued*

| Material | Weight per Cubic foot | Comment |
|---|---|---|
| Arsenic salt | 100–130 | Heavy. Poisonous. Compact. Difficult. |
| Ashes, dry | 35–40 | Abrasive when dry; corrosive when |
| wet | 45–55 | wet. |
| Bauxite, crushed | 75–85 | Abrasive. |
| Bentonite | 50 | Sluggish. |
| Bone meal | 55–60 | Difficult at times. |
| Borax | 50–70 | Extremely abrasive. |
| Bran | 16 | Easily handled except when oily. |
| Brewer's grains, wet | 55 | Sometimes actively corrosive when hot. |
| Carbon | 50 | If for certain purposes, as for dry batteries, must be kept from contamination by iron dust, etc. |
| Carbon black | 25 | Extremely fragile if pelletized. |
| Cement | 85–100 | Entrains air. Compacts in storage. Dusty and abrasive. Must not come in contact with moisture or surfaces which may sweat. En-masse conveyors not advised. |
| Chalk, pulverized | 70–75 | Tricky. |
| Charcoal | 12–20 | Dusty; dust is explosive. |
| Clays | 35–52 | Sluggish. Sometimes abrasive. Adheres to metals. |
| Coal | 40–50 | Some are corrosive when wet. Dust is explosive. Degradation may be objectionable. Lignite very fragile. |
| Cocoa | 35–40 | Hygienic precautions. Sometimes sticky. Cocoa shells abrasive. |
| Coffee beans | 32–35 | Hygienic precautions. Gentle handling. |
| Copra cake | 25–30 | Oily. Not difficult. |
| Copra meal | 40 | Sticky. Often sandy and abrasive. Oil may exude if handled by pneumatic conveyor. |
| Cork, ground | 5–15 | Sluggish. May be discolored by con- |
| crushed | 6–12 | tact with iron or steel. |
| Corn, shelled | 45 | Easily handled. Abrasive. |
| Corn meal | 40 | Hygienic precautions. |
| Cottonseed | 35–40 | Will not flow when fuzzy. Hulls and meal easily handled. |
| Cullet | 80–100 | (Broken glass, sometimes heated and sprayed with water.) Small particles work into chain joints, causing severe abrasion and sometimes corrosion. Cullet and aluminum oxide are leaders in destructive action on conveyor chains. |
| Face powder | 30–40 | Must not be discolored. |
| Feldspar, crushed | 100 | Extremely abrasive. |

TABLE 1—*Continued*

| Material | Weight per Cubic foot | Comment |
|---|---|---|
| Flaxseed | 45 | Abrasive. Free flowing. |
| Flour | 35–40 | Hygienic precautions. Explosive dust. |
| Flue dust (flue dirt) | 100 | Abrasive. |
| Fluorspar | 100 | Abrasive. |
| Fly ash | 30–45 | Tricky when aerated. Not abrasive except when mixed with flue dirt. |
| Foundry sand | 90–110 | Abrasive. May be sticky. |
| Fuller's earth, granular | 35 | Fragile. Slightly abrasive. May be oily and sticky. |
| spent | 60 | |
| Glass batch, soda ash, lime, fine sand | | Abrasive. |
| Glue, granular | 45 | Must be kept cool and dry. |
| Graphite, flake | 40 | Easily handled. Self-lubricating. |
| flour | 25 | |
| Grass seed | 11–15 | Reasonably gentle handling. |
| Gypsum, calcined | 55–60 | Handles readily except when extremely fine. |
| pulverized | 80 | |
| lumpy | 90 | |
| Iron ore | 150 | Abrasive. May be in large fragments. |
| Lead oxides | 60–150 | Lead salts are poisonous. Dustless operation essential. |
| Lead sulphates | 100 | Abrasive. Dusty. |
| Lime, pebble | 55 | Sometimes sluggish. |
| hydrated | 32–40 | |
| pulverized | 32–40 | |
| Limestone, dust | 85 | Abrasive and dusty. |
| screenings | 90–95 | Abrasive. |
| Linseed meal | 44 | Easily handled. |
| Malt, dry | 20–30 | Easily handled. |
| Mica, pulverized | 13–15 | Dusty. Somewhat sticky. |
| Molybdenum concentrates | 110 | Sticky and difficult. Abrasive. |
| Oats | 25 | Shell is fragile. Degradation is objectionable. |
| Peanuts, shelled | 35–40 | Hygienic handling. Fragile. Oily. |
| whole | 15–20 | Often sandy. Belt elevator best. |
| Petroleum coke | 42 | Not particularly abrasive. |
| Pitch, dry | 50–62 | Dusty. Lumps fragile. |
| Pumice | 45 | Abrasive. Polishes. |
| Pumicite | 40–47 | 300 mesh, abrasive. |
| Quartz, ground | 110 | Extremely abrasive. |
| Rice | 45–50 | Hygienic precautions. Fragile. |
| Rubber scrap, ground | 30 | Sluggish and difficult. |
| Salt, coarse | 45–50 | Hygroscopic. Adheres to iron and steel. Difficult when wet and when hot. Corrosive. |
| fines | 75–80 | |
| Salt cake | 75–95 | Flows very freely. |
| Sawdust and pulverized wood | 14–20 | Floating dust may be explosive. |
| Shellac | 80 | Dust dangerously explosive. |

TABLE 1—*Continued*

| Material | Weight per Cubic foot | Comment |
|---|---|---|
| Silica flour | 80 | Sluggish. Abrasive. |
| Sludge, sewage | 40–50 | Sticky, sandy, abrasive. Extremely difficult for any type of conveyor. |
| Soap flakes (Rinso, etc.) | 10–20 | Granular. Fragile. Sticky when hot. |
| Soap powders | 30–40 | Gentle handling necessary. |
| Soda ash, heavy | 55–65 | Caustic. Dustless operation essential. |
| light | 20–35 | Sluggish but not difficult. May be as hot as 400° F., which means reduced tension in chains subjected to this heat. |
| Sodium aluminum sulphate | 75 | Must not come in contact with oil. |
| Soybeans, cake | 45 | Abrasive when sandy. Some of the |
| meal | 40 | processed products are sticky, e.g., |
| spent | 28 | " expeller foots." |
| Starch, pulverized | 40–45 | Dust extremely explosive. |
| Sugar, raw | 55–65 | Hygienic requirements. Sometimes |
| refined | 50–55 | sticky. Sheen of refined product must not be impaired. |
| Sulphur, coarse | 60–70 | Danger from static sparks. Risk of |
| pulverized | 60 | ignition. Corrosive when wet. |
| Talc | 50–60 | Semi-abrasive. Discoloration objectionable. Adheres to metal. |
| Tanbark | 60 | Sluggish. Sometimes corrosive. |
| Tobacco stems | 25 | Stringy and sluggish. |
| Wheat | 48 | Hygienic conditions as with all food products. |
| Wood, " hog-fuel " | 15–30 | Difficult because of slivers, especially in flight and screw conveyors. |
| Wood chips, dry | 18–20 | Fluffy when dry and not difficult if |
| wet | 55 | screened. Sometimes mildly corrosive. |
| Zinc and other metallic dusts | | Hazardous with en-masse conveyors. |
| Zinc oxide | 20–35 | Avoid discoloration. Tends to pack. |
| Zinc sulphate | 60 | Not difficult. |

TABLE 2

SELECTION CHART

| | Ashes, Wet | Ashes, Dry | Coal, Average | Coal, Corrosive | Coke | Coke Breeze | Flue Dirt | Fly Ash | Grains | Granular and Pulverized Materials | Hog Fuel | Ores, Light | Ores, Heavy | Rock | Sand and Gravel | Sawdust | Sticky Material | Material at High Temperature |
|---|---|---|---|---|---|---|---|---|---|---|---|---|---|---|---|---|---|---|
| *Conveyors* | | | | | | | | | | | | | | | | | | |
| Apron | | | * | * | * | * | | | | | * | * | * | * | | | | * |
| Belt | | | * | * | * | * | * | | * | * | * | * | * | * | * | * | | Woven wire OK |
| En masse | | | * | | | | | * | * | * | | | | | | * | | * |
| Flight | | | * | | | * | | * | | * | * | | | | | * | | * |
| Drag chain | * | * | | * | * | * | | * | | | | | | | | * | | * |
| Pneumatic | | * | * | | | * | | * | | * | * | * | | | | * | | * |
| Vibrating | | | * | * | * | * | | | | * | * | * | * | | * | * | | * |
| *Elevators* | | | | | | | | | | | | | | | | | | |
| Centrifugal discharge | * | * | * | * | | | * | * | * | * | * | * | | | * | * | | * |
| Continuous bucket | | | * | | | * | | * | * | * | * | * | * | * | * | * | * | * |
| Gravity discharge | | | * | | | | | * | | | | | | | | | | |
| Pivoted bucket | * | * | * | * | * | * | * | | | * | | | | | | | | * |
| *Screw conveyors* | | | * | | | * | | | | | | | | | | | | |
| Steel flight | | | * | | | | | * | * | * | * | * | | | | * | | * |
| Cast-iron flight | * | * | | * | * | | * | * | | | | * | | | | | | * |
| Ribbon | | | | | | | | * | | * | * | * | | | | * | * | * |
| *Steam jet conveyors* | | * | | | | | * | * | | | | | | | | | | |
| *Skip hoists* | * | * | * | * | * | * | * | * | | * | | * | | * | * | | | * |
| *Crushers* | | | | | | | | | | | | | | | | | | |
| Roll | | | * | * | * | | | | | | | | | | | | | |
| Jaw and gyratory | | | | | | | | | | | | * | * | * | | | | |
| *Screens* | | | | | | | | | | | | | | | | | | |
| Revolving | | | | | * | * | | | | | | * | * | * | * | | | |
| Shaker | | | * | * | * | * | | | | | * | | | | | | | |
| Vibrating | | | * | * | * | * | | | * | * | * | * | * | * | * | * | | * |

# CHAPTER 2

## SCREW CONVEYORS

The screw conveyor usually consists of a long-pitch plate-steel helix mounted on a shaft or spindle carried in bearings within a U-shaped trough. As the element rotates, the material fed to it is moved forward by the thrust of the lower part of the helix and is discharged through openings in the trough bottom or at the end. This conveyor does not always find favor with engineers, but properly applied it does a good job and often its cost will be about one-half that for any other type of conveyor. It is a simple machine to maintain, replacements are inexpensive, and it is readily made dust tight. For many functions it is the best type of conveyor.

**Construction.** A well-designed screw conveyor for non-abrasive, non-corrosive materials has a steel helicoid, cold rolled in one continuous strip between bearings, rather than in short sections. By cold rolling the helicoid attains a tapered section with greatest thickness at the shaft and with the thin outer edge taking a hardness about double that of the original strip. If the conveyor is to handle food products, toilet powder, moist cork, or other material which may be discolored through contact with steel plate, the rotating parts or the entire conveyor may be of stainless steel, bronze, aluminum, Monel metal, etc., though at a considerable increase in first cost.

If it is desired to churn or mix materials the helix is made segmental or bladed, like a succession of marine screw propellers, and is then referred to as a paddle mixer. One such application is mixing water with ashes when discharging from a storage bin to reduce the dust nuisance.

For ashes, clinker, ores, etc., the helix may be of cast-iron sections bolted to the shaft and the trough may be made of cast iron or hardened-face concrete. For sticky material, like molasses, hot tar, or asphalt, a ribbon helix is preferable. This construction prevents build-up along the line between helix and shaft where it would cause loss of handling capacity.

Thrust bearings should if possible be located at the discharge end of a conveyor so that the shaft will be in tension. Anti-friction bearings may be provided which take thrust in either direction; they are well worth the difference in cost over sleeve bearings, as they are in housings with seals to keep out dust and retain the lubricant.

Care should be exercised when ordering a screw to specify whether it is to be right-hand or left-hand. A right-hand screw is one in which the material moves toward you when you stand at the discharge end of the conveyor with the helix rotating clockwise (Fig. 2-1).

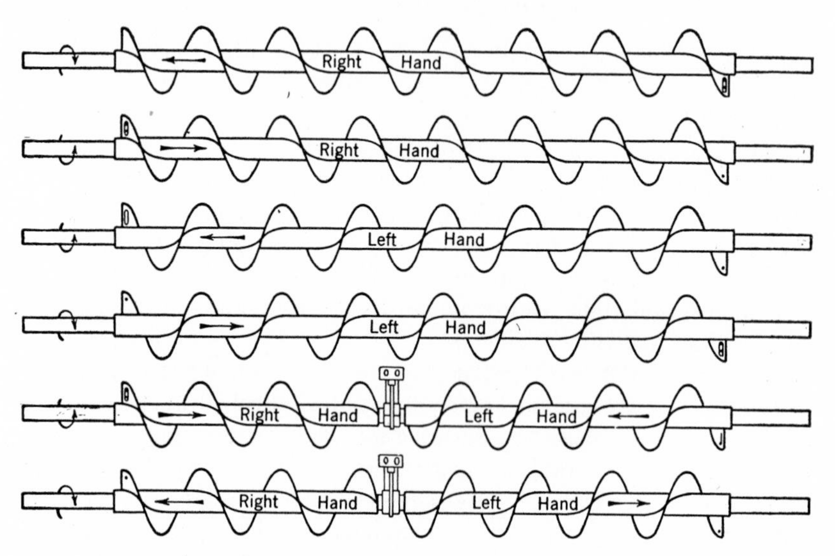


Fig. 2-1. Method of designating screw conveyors as right or left hand.

**Inclined Conveyors.** Screw conveyors can be operated with the path inclined upward, but the capacity decreases rapidly as the inclination increases (Fig. 2-2). A standard pitch screw inclined at 15° with the horizontal has 70 per cent of its horizontal capacity; if it is inclined 25° the capacity is reduced to 40 per cent; if it is inclined 45° the material will move along the floor of the trough but at a greatly reduced rate. For steep inclines the helix may have a short pitch, and the trough may be made tubular; then the capacity loss is less. Thus with a jam feed and 45° incline such a conveyor has a capacity about 50 per cent of its capacity when horizontal.

The bearing hangers of inclined conveyors should be of T design to reduce the interference with the flow of the material. It may be desirable to use a few turns of double helix each side of the bearing hangers. With suitable forced feed a screw conveyor in a vertical position will lift material if the rotating speed is high and there are no intermediate bearings. Such a conveyor is not self-clearing and should not be used for material which will sour or spoil.

**Capacity.** Because of the manner in which the material is moved in a screw conveyor the allowable loading and the speed are controlled by the characteristics of the material; thus light free-flowing non-abrasive materials may fill the trough deeply, and the rotating speed may be higher than with heavier and more abrasive materials. The recommendations of the manufacturers should be followed. Those of the Link-Belt Company will be used for illustration.

Figure 2-3*A*. For materials which are light, free flowing, and non-abrasive, such as dry grains, flaxseed, malt, cornmeal, and pulverized coal, the maximum loading is 45 per cent of the vertical cross section

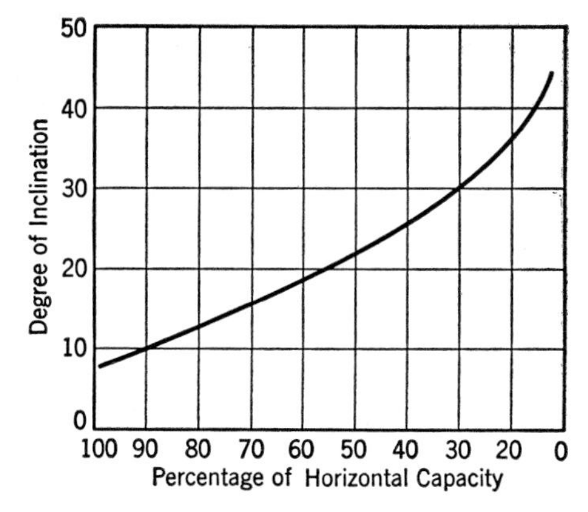


FIG. 2-2. Capacity change as related to inclination with standard pitch conveyors.

of the helix as shown by the diagram on the chart. Maximum speed depends upon the diameter. Thus a 4-in. screw may operate at 180 r.p.m., and 45 per cent loading will give a capacity of 100 cu. ft. per hr. If the diameter is 24 in. (usually the largest standard size), maximum speed is about 95 r.p.m., and 45 per cent loading will give a capacity in excess of 10,000 cu. ft. per hr. Multiplying the number of cubic feet per hour by the weight per cubic foot and dividing by 2000 gives the capacity in tons per hour.

Figure 2-3*B*. For non-abrasive materials of medium weight containing fines and small lumps, such as alum, beans, soybeans, slack coal, hydrated lime, coffee, corn grits, shelled corn, and cottonseed bulbs, the maximum loading is 38 per cent of the vertical cross section of the helix, and the maximum speeds are within the limits of 120 and 70 r.p.m.

Figure 2-3*C*. For semi-abrasive granular materials with small lumps and weighing 40 to 80 lb. per cu. ft., such as lumpy lime, asbestos, borax, carbon black, sized coal, fly ash (not mixed with flue dust), wet

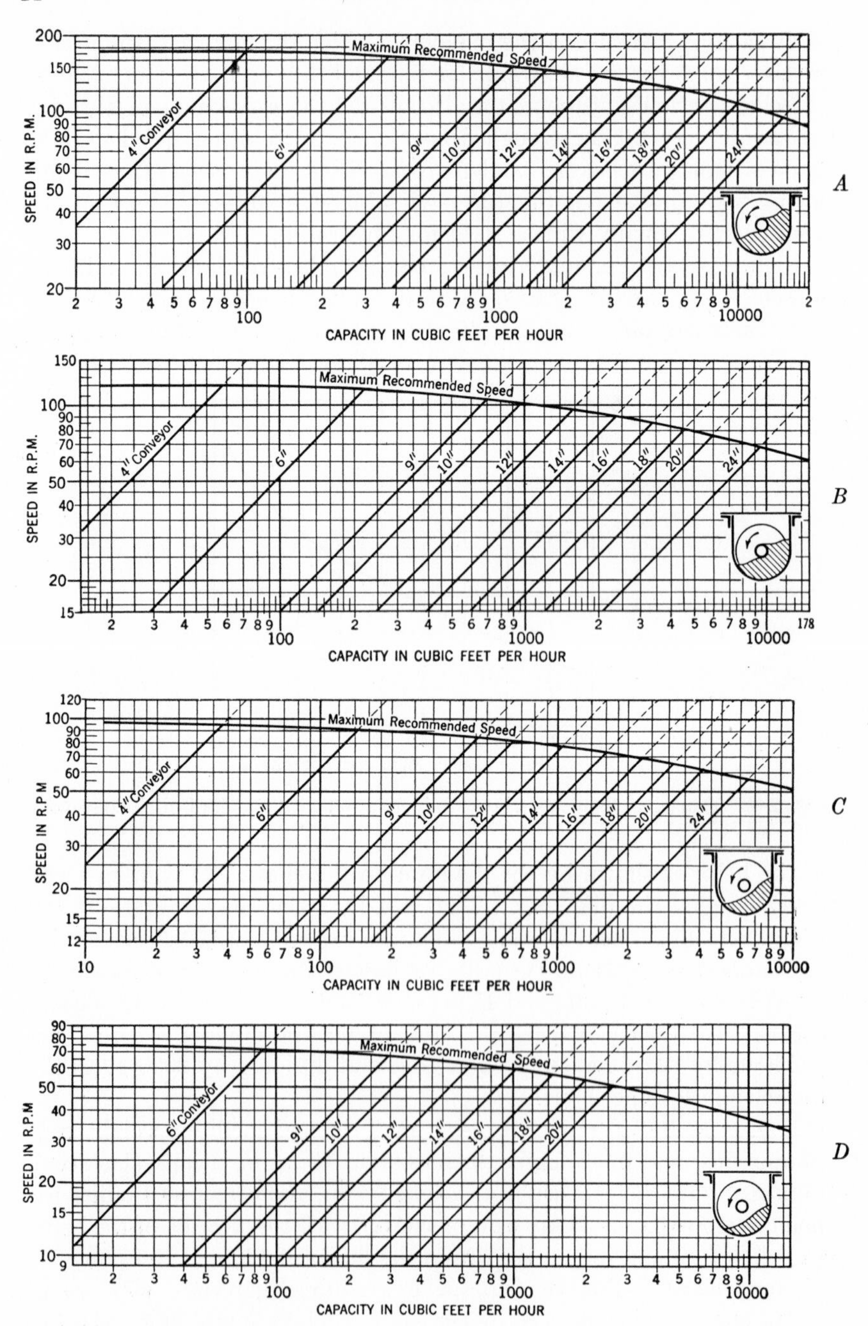


FIG. 2-3. Speed-capacity charts. (Link-Belt.) (*A*) Loading 45 per cent. (*B*) Loading 38 per cent. (*C*) Loading 31 per cent. (*D*) Loading 25 per cent.

malt, salt, and tankage, the maximum loading is 31 per cent of the vertical cross section of the helix, and the maximum speeds are within the limits of 95 and 60 r.p.m.

Figure 2-3*D*. For abrasive and semi-abrasive materials, such as cement, crushed bauxite, gypsum, zinc oxide, fluorspar, foundry sand, limestone dust and screenings, acid phosphate, raw sugar, sulphur, and ground clay, the maximum loading is 25 per cent of the vertical cross section of the helix, and the maximum speeds are within the limits of 70 and 50 r.p.m.

For materials such as flue dirt, silica sand, and ashes, the loading should be further reduced, and the point is approached where special construction or some other type of conveyor should be specified.

**Additional Factors Affecting Size and Pitch.** A screw conveyor may have a discharge zone of considerable length if the trough is made with an open bottom so that the material flows out over a continuously advancing crest. This is a convenient arrangement in a conveyor above a storage bunker. However, as the "drag" across the surface of the discharged material may throttle its forward movement, if such a conveyor is fed by another conveyor or an elevator, the feeding unit must have a capacity not in excess of that throttled capacity.

When the feed is fairly uniform, as from a screen, crusher, or mixer, as distinguished from a "head" above the helix at the inlet, the material may be chuted directly (Fig. 2-4*A*), with only the precaution that the feed be not located directly above a hangar. If there are several simultaneous feed points the screw capacity should exceed the combined rate of feed. If the feed is under a "head," as from a storage bin or hopper, the pitch of the helix in the loading zone should be less than the pitch of the conveying section beyond (Fig. 2-4*B*) or should have a smaller outside diameter. The feed zone is loaded to full capacity as shown in section *A-A*, while beyond the feed section the helix is uniformly loaded to about 40 per cent as seen in section *B-B*.

The screw conveyor serves as an efficient feeder when so arranged, unless the material is fluffy, aerated, or tends to arch. Figure 2-5 illustrates a neat installation handling stoker coal from a storage bin to a weigh larry. Since the receiving end of the conveyor has a smaller diameter it acts as a feeder. Two contactors on the larry are connected in the motor circuit: one is actuated when the larry is pushed to the end of the runway and starts the conveyor; the other breaks the circuit when the hopper dips slightly under full load.

**Lump Size.** The size and percentage of lumps in the material influence the size of the screw as shown in Table 1. With a high percentage

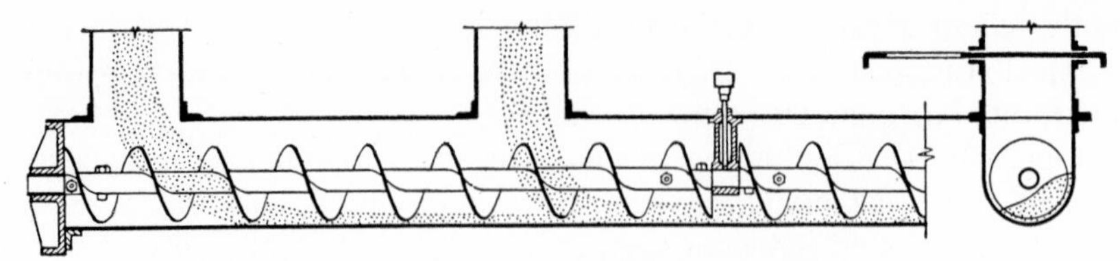

Fig. 2–4*A*. Controlled or Uniform Loading.

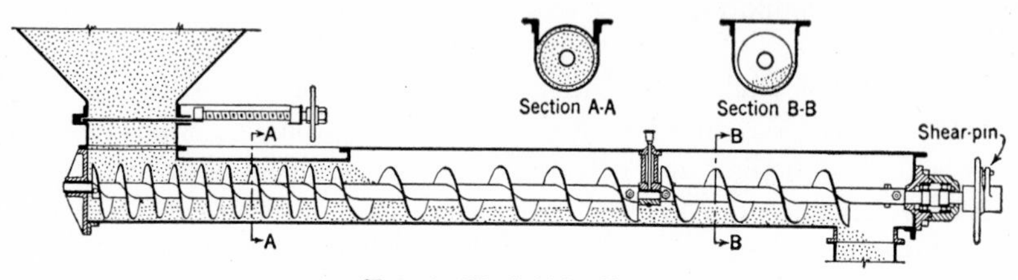


Fig. 2–4*B*. Self-feeding.

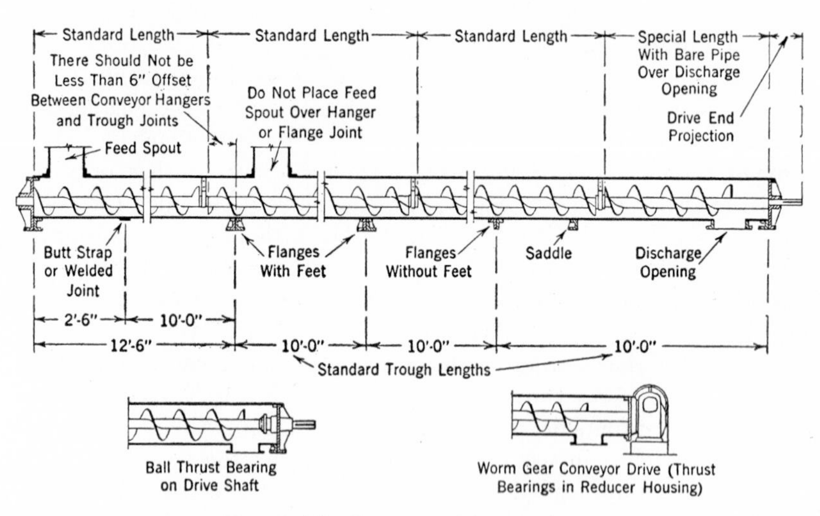


Fig. 2–4*C*. Layout and installation.

of hard lumps it is desirable that the clearance between helix and trough equal the size of the largest lumps so that they will not jam.

TABLE 1

Maximum Lump Sizes Handled by Screw Conveyors

| | Helix diameters, inches | | | | | | | | | |
|---|---|---|---|---|---|---|---|---|---|---|
| | 4 | 6 | 9 | 10 | 12 | 14 | 16 | 18 | 20 | 24 |
| 20 to 25% lumps, inches | ½ | ¾ | 1½ | 1½ | 2 | 2½ | 3 | 3 | 3½ | 3½ |
| All lumps, inches | ¼ | ½ | ¾ | ¾ | 1 | 1¼ | 1½ | 2 | 2 | 2½ |

**Power Determination.** The power required to drive a screw conveyor depends on the characteristics of the material handled, the length of the conveyor, and the rate of handling. For normal conditions the horsepower input to the conveyor shaft will approximate

$$\text{Horsepower} = \frac{CLWF^*}{33{,}000}$$

where $C$ = capacity of conveyor in cubic feet per minute.
$L$ = conveyor length in feet.
$W$ = weight of material in pounds per cubic foot.
$F$ = the material factor.

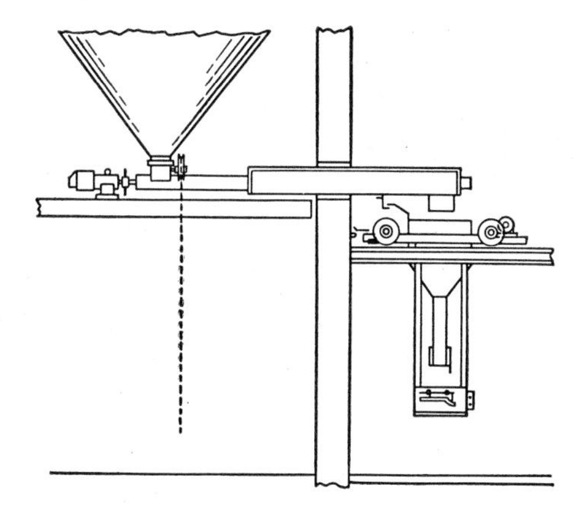

Fig. 2–5. Feed control by smaller diameter screw. Automatic start and stop.

For materials similar to those in Fig. 2-3*A*, $F$ = 1.2.
For materials similar to those in Fig. 2-3*B*, $F$ = 1.4 to 1.8.
For materials similar to those in Fig. 2-3*C*, $F$ = 2 to 2.5.
For materials similar to those in Fig. 2-3*D*, $F$ = 3 to 4.

The motor should be selected with a margin for drive loss, momentary overloads, and packing or "setting" of the material between runs. If the conveyor is inclined upward, allowance must be made for the power required to lift the material. When the above formula is used for a conveyor with a small power requirement — less than 2 hp. — the result must be multiplied by 2; if the requirement is between 2 and 4 hp., the result must be multiplied by 1.5. When a conveyor receives its load from an overhead bin, allowance must be made for friction

*If the conveyor is lightly loaded or has a length exceeding 100 ft. the horsepower by this formula should be increased 10 to 15 per cent.

and jamming at the loading point. An allowance of ½ to 1 hp. will usually suffice.

To illustrate the foregoing, assume a screw conveyor feeding 1½ by ½-in. slack coal from a bin to a stoker hopper with a capacity of 380 cu. ft. per hr. The length is 40 ft. horizontally. If the coal weighs 50 lb. per cu. ft. the capacity is 9.5 tons per hour. Referring to the charts we see that we can select a 14-in., a 12-in., or a 10-in. screw. The first is unnecessarily large, and the 10-in. at 48 r.p.m. might be used. However, if, we adopt the smaller diameter for the feed section under the bin it will be too small for 1½-in. lumps. A reduction from the 12-in. to 10-in. is better, so we adopt the 12-in. at 30 r.p.m. For the power we have

$$HP = \frac{6.3 \times 40 \times 50 \times 1.8}{33{,}000} = 0.69 \qquad \text{say, 0.7 hp.}$$

As stated, since the horsepower is less than 2 we will multiply by 2 and add 1 hp. for the jam feed from the overhead bin, making a total of 2.4 hp., for which the nearest standard size motor is 3 hp.

Assume somewhat different conditions: required, a horizontal screw conveyor to distribute 1½-in. slack coal to a bunker over a discharge length of 25 ft. The total length of the conveyor is 50 ft. The conveyor is fed by a bucket elevator having a capacity of 25 tons per hour. We will use an open-bottom trough over the bunker, and since the feed is from an elevator there can be no surges or jam loads. By Fig. 2-4*B*, for 25 tons per hour or 1000 cu. ft. per hr., we may use a 12-in. screw at 70 r.p.m. We can use 60 r.p.m., but as there is a slowdown in capacity when dragging the coal across that in the loaded section of the bunker we will use the higher rotating speed.

By the formula the power requirement is:

$$HP = \frac{16.7 \times 50 \times 50 \times 2}{33{,}000} = 2.53 \text{ hp.}$$

$F$ is taken as 2 in view of the discharge drag. Allowing 90 per cent for the efficiency of the drive, we have 2.8 hp.; since the requirement is between 2 and 4, we multiply by 1.5 and obtain a motor horsepower of 4.2. for which the nearest standard motor is 5 hp. For the speed of 70 r.p.m. we may use a standard 10.3: 1 reducer with roller chain drive having 17 and 40 tooth sprockets and a 1750-r.p.m. motor.

**Limiting Lengths for Screw Conveyors.** The limit of length depends on the torque capacity of the pipe shaft, couplings, and coupling bolts, that is, on the twist at the drive end.

The horsepower may be converted into torque by the formula

$$T = \frac{63{,}000 \times HP}{N}$$

where $T$ = torque in inch-pounds.
$N$ = speed in revolutions per minute.

Or we may convert torque capacity into horsepower:

$$HP = \frac{T \times N}{63{,}000}$$

Link-Belt gives the torque capacities for standard screw conveyors as shown in Table 2. If the torque is found to exceed these figures

TABLE 2

MAXIMUM TORQUE CAPACITIES FOR STANDARD SCREW CONVEYORS

| Nominal Diameter of Screw, inches | Inside Diameter of Pipe, inches | Maximum Torque Capacity, inch-pounds[1] |
|---|---|---|
| 6 | 1½ | 3,060 |
| 9 | 1½ | 3,060 |
| 9 | 2 | 6,100 |
| 10 | 1½ | 3,060 |
| 10 | 2 | 6,100 |
| 12 | 2 | 6,100 |
| 12 | 2½ | 9,270 |
| 12 | 3 | 16,400 |
| 14 | 2½ | 9,270 |
| 14 | 3 | 16,400 |
| 16 | 3 | 16,400 |
| 18 | 3–3½ | 16,400 |
| 20 | 3½ | 16,400 |
| 20 | 4 | 25,600 |
| 24 | 4 | 25,600 |

[1]Maximum torque for standard construction with standard couplings and bolts.

special sizes of pipe and couplings are provided substantially increasing the maximum.

Assume the requirement of a 20-in. screw conveyor to handle 40 tons per hour of slack coal weighing 50 lb. per cu. ft. at 75 r.p.m. May a standard conveyor have a length of 150 ft.? The power has been determined 12.5 hp. at the head shaft. From the formula,

$$T = \frac{63{,}000 \times 12.5}{75} = 10{,}500 \text{ in-lb.}$$

From Table 2 the 20-in. conveyor with standard 3½-in. pipe has a maximum torque capacity of 16,400 in-lb.

Let us assume a material which comes under Fig. 2-3*D*, say cement at 90 lb. per cu. ft. The horsepower for a 14-in. conveyor at 50 r.p.m. with $F = 3.5$ is 24 hp., and

$$T = \frac{63{,}000 \times 24}{50} = 30{,}300 \text{ in-lb.}$$

This is far beyond the 16,400-in-lb. limit in Table 2. It would be better to specify a slow-speed 16-in. belt conveyor requiring 1.5 hp. In a long screw conveyor there is another consideration. Should a bearing bind or should there be a slight misalignment of the trough, the torque will vastly increase.

**Comment.** In Chapter 1, cast-iron screw conveyors are listed as suitable for wet or dry ashes. Broadly this is true, but ashes may be so wet that they will build up on the helix, and sometimes dry ashes are extremely abrasive, grinding down the helix to a feather edge which then breaks off. Even then as long as there is a trace of helix left the conveyor manages to move the ashes along, though of course at reduced capacity.

Some stringy materials such as chips with bark strips, licorice roots, and cotton waste are troublesome, as they wind around the spindle or catch between helix and trough. Material which sets requires careful attention so that the residue after a run will not jam the helix. A screw conveyor beneath an open track hopper exposed to rain and intended for cement or gypsum would be unworkable for that reason.

The manufacturers publish comprehensive literature on screw conveyors which should be studied before deciding on the size, speed, loading, and other factors, though it is best to ask their advice.

## CHAPTER 3

## FLIGHT AND APRON CONVEYORS

The *flight conveyor* has an endless chain or twin chains passing around sprockets at the head and foot ends, with spaced transverse scrapers or "flights" which push the material along a trough.

The *apron conveyor* almost invariably has twin chains on which overlapping pans are mounted to carry the material instead of scraping it. An apron conveyor used for controlling the rate of feed, as from a track hopper, is called an "apron feeder."

In addition to the screw and belt conveyors we thus have two machines for transporting bulk materials horizontally or on an inclined path limited only by the cost and the working limit of the chains. The apron conveyor costs more per foot of length than the flight conveyor and as a rule more than a belt conveyor.

**Flight conveyors** may be several hundred feet in length, but as the material is scraped along a trough they are not suited to abrasives like ashes or sand. A modified type called the drag-chain conveyor is specifically adapted for ashes. Flight conveyors will operate on an upward slope of 40° to 45° but at a greatly reduced capacity. If the slope is greater than 25° the flight depth must be sufficient to prevent backward cascading of the material, as will readily be seen by laying out the incline, depth, and slope of the material, assuming a reasonable backing-up against the flight. On a downward slope the conveyor may be used to retard or check the flow of material along a path too long for a chute. A common example is presented by a coal preparation plant at the foot of a hill where the mine dump is at the crest. The motor starts the conveyor, then acts as a brake pumping current back into the line.

Two or more materials may be handled by a single conveyor by means of longitudinal partitions which divide the trough into two or more channels, the flights being slotted to correspond. One difficulty is that if the materials have widely different coefficients of friction, as with sized coal and refuse, the wear and stretch on the heavy side chain will exceed that on the other. In a three-compartment conveyor the material with the highest coefficient of friction should be carried in the center compartment.

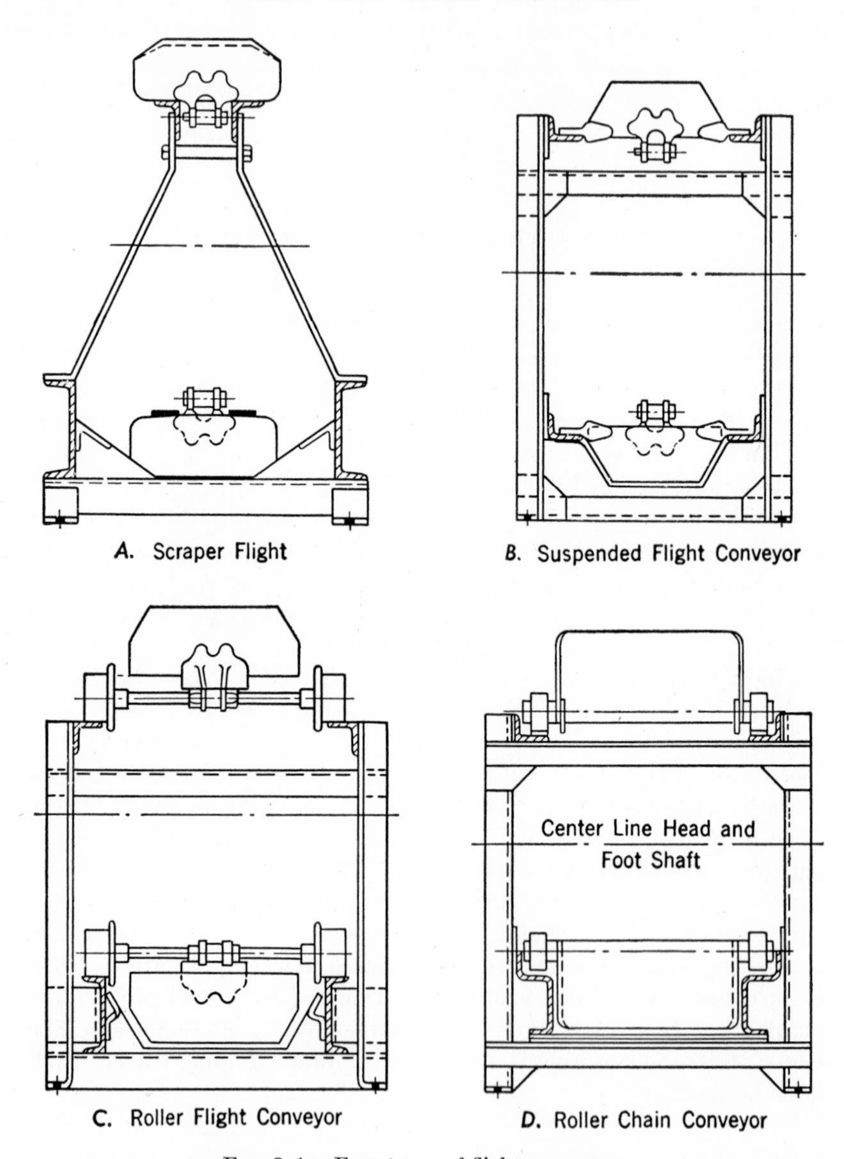


FIG. 3-1. Four types of flight conveyors.

*Construction.* Figure 3-1*A* is a cross section of a single-strand scraper flight conveyor, in which the flights are drawn along the trough bottom. Figure 3-1*B* is a single-strand suspended flight conveyor with wearing shoes attached to the flights to carry them clear of the trough along the carrying run and support them along the return run.

Figure 3-1*C* is similar to the suspended flight conveyor except that rollers are substituted for shoes — the roller flight conveyor. Figure 3-1*D* is a double-strand conveyor with roller chains to carry the flights — the roller chain suspended flight conveyor.

The trough may be of forged steel plate or built up with channel sides and renewable steel-plate bottom. For corrosive materials the trough

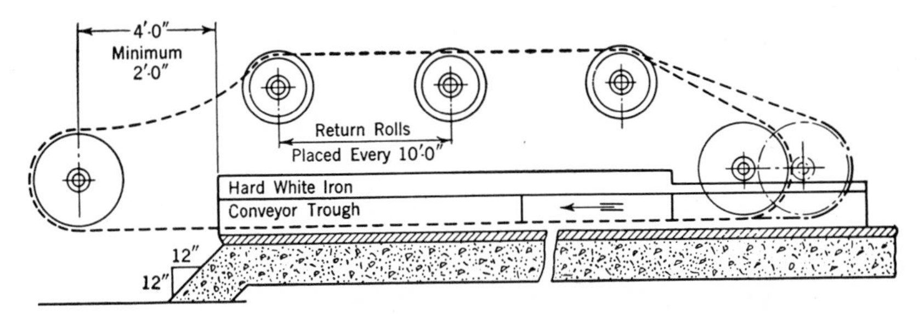


The drag chain conveyor.

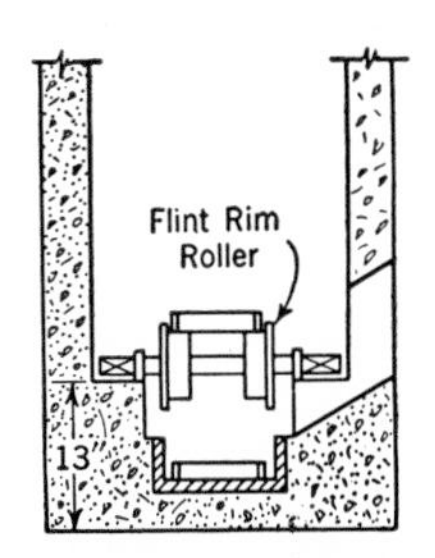


Section through drag chain conveyor.

Fig. 3-2.

may be of cast-iron sections. If the material is very light, like wood chips or sawdust, the trough may be of hardwood planks.

The flights are steel plate or malleable iron with thickened edges. In the double-strand conveyor with wide flights they are reinforced by angles for stiffness.

Discharge gates are operated by rack and pinion with hand wheel. Usually they open against the flow of material, but they may open crosswise.

Drag chain conveyors, Fig. 3-2, do not have flights as the open links serve to move the material. The trough is of cast iron or hardened-face concrete, with T-rails set flush. These conveyors operate at slow speeds, generally 20 ft. or less per minute. One typical application is for quenching hot material. The trough is horizontal and filled with water, but it curves upward toward the discharge end where the water drains backward as the material moves up the incline.

*Protection.* If a conveyor is protected by shear pin and is fed by a previous unit, the shear pin holder should be so arranged that it will trip a lever-connected relay which will stop the preceding motor when the pin shears. Interlocking the motors electrically does not suffice since the released motor continues to run.

A well-designed flight conveyor, properly employed, is a long-lived machine with fairly low maintenance and power requirement. It is suited to a wide variety of conditions and will stand a lot of abuse; it is not unusual to see a conveyor with the flights deeply buried from end to end of the carrying run and still pulling. It should not be applied to materials with a high coefficient of friction or to abrasives, nor is it suited to corrosives unless specially designed for them. The manufacturers list their standard sizes, spacing of flights, and other limitations, and their recommendations should be followed.

*Selections, Capacities, and Lump Sizes.* For moderate duty, low capacities, and small lumps, the single-strand scraper flight conveyor suffices. For large capacities and active service a double-strand suspended flight conveyor with replaceable wearing parts may be selected, but careful consideration should be given to a belt conveyor as a possible alternative. There is no hard and fast rule for the type to be chosen. Wide flights attached to a single strand of chain are insecure and may break off the attachment. With two strands the flight is supported at both ends, and the attachment is more secure. The chain stress may be so great that the pressure per square inch in the articulation point will cause galling as the chain rounds the head sprocket unless the pin bearing is sufficiently large, regardless of the strength of the chain. The pull per chain is halved in the two-strand conveyor. As a single chain to some extent blocks the feed to the trough and lumps may ride the chain or jam in the links, this type of conveyor is limited to material with few and small lumps. Flight spacing is varied to suit the size of lumps and the capacity and slope of the conveyor. Double-strand conveyors with widely spaced flights are best for the larger lumps. Heavy flights, of course, should not be of the scraper type. Table 1 shows the capacities for several standard conveyor sizes with coal, which is the material commonly handled by flight conveyors. For other materials the capacity is in direct proportion to their weight as compared with the weight of coal, but the power must be determined for it depends not only on the rate of handling but also on the coefficient of friction of the material against steel plate, the length, and the path.

TABLE 1

Capacity and Size of Lumps Handled by Flight Conveyors

| Flight Width and Depth, inches | Amount of Material per Foot of Conveyor, cubic feet | Approximate Capacity for 50-Lb. Material at 100 Ft. per Min.,[1] tons per hour | Lump Size, inches (Lumps not to exceed 10% of total volume) Single Strand | Double Strand |
|---|---|---|---|---|
| 12 by 6 | 0.40 | 60 | 3½ | 4 |
| 15 by 6 | 0.49 | 73 | 4½ | 5 |
| 18 by 6 | 0.56 | 84 | 5 | 6 |
| 24 by 8 | 1.16 | 174 | ... | 10 |
| 30 by 10 | 1.60 | 240 | ... | 14 |
| 36 by 12 | 2.40 | 360 | ... | 16 |

[1]If the conveyor is inclined, multiply the horizontal capacity by 0.90 for 20° to 25°, by 0.80 for 25° to 30°, by 0.70 for 30° to 36°. Free-flowing materials may avalanche backwards.

Drag chain conveyors may be loaded to considerable depth. The speed should be low. Table 2 shows the capacities for various widths of trough, the material having a depth of 6 in. and the conveyor speed being 10 ft. per min., for material weighing 50 lb. per cu. ft. (Ashes when wet weigh about 50 lb. per cu. ft. and when dry about 35 lb.)

*Power Determinations.* Since the material is scraped along a trough it is necessary that the coefficient of friction be known to determine the power required to drive the conveyor. Table 3 gives these coefficients for a number of materials. Some of these materials would not be handled by a flight conveyor, but they are included for convenient reference.

TABLE 2

Capacities, Drag Chain Conveyors

Speed, 10 ft. per min. Depth, 6 in. Weight, 50 lb. per cu. ft.

| Trough Width, inches | Capacity, tons per hour |
|---|---|
| 10½ | 4.5 |
| 13 | 6. |
| 16 | 7.5 |
| 20 | 9.5 |

The coefficient of friction of flights against trough, or of flight shoes against guides, may be taken as 0.33, designated by $F$ in the formulas to follow. If the guides are lubricated, $F$ may be reduced to 0.20, but lubrication cannot be relied upon. When the flights are carried clear of the trough by rollers the friction is a function of the relative diam-

TABLE 3

COEFFICIENTS OF FRICTION FOR VARIOUS MATERIALS ON STEEL PLATE

| Material | Coefficient | Material | Coefficient |
|---|---|---|---|
| Anthracite coal | 0.33 | Hydrated lime | 0.65 |
| Bituminous coal | 0.59 | Magnesium chloride | 0.70 |
| Cement | 0.93 | Pulverized limestone | 0.58 |
| Clay | 0.60–0.70 | Sand and damp ashes | 0.68 |
| Coke | 0.36 | Sawdust, wet | 0.60 |
| Copra (varies) | 0.40 | Soda ash | 0.65 |
| Grains | 0.30–0.40 | Starch | 0.78 |
| Ground cork | 0.65 | Sugar, fine, granulated | 0.67 |
| Hog fuel (dry) | 0.60 | Wood chips | 0.35 |

eters of pin and roller, or

$$RF = \frac{d}{D} \times 0.33 + 2\frac{Y}{D}$$

where $RF$ = rolling friction.
$d$ = diameter of the pin.
$D$ = diameter of the roller.
0.33 = coefficient of friction of steel against steel (roller bore against pin),
$Y$ = rolling friction of the roller against the track (0.03).

This rolling friction, $RF$, approximates 0.1 unless the rollers are mounted on anti-friction bearings.

We first determine the pull on the chain. For a horizontal scraper flight conveyor the pull is

$$C_p = (2 \times W \times L \times F) + (W_1 \times L \times F_1)$$

where $C_p$ = chain pull, or resistance to turning at the radius of head sprocket, in pounds.
$W$ = weight per foot of the sliding parts of the conveyor.
$L$ = length in feet from head to foot shafts.
$F$ = coefficient of friction for sliding parts of the conveyor.
$W_1$ = weight of material per foot of conveyor, or load per foot.
$F_1$ = coefficient of friction between material and trough (Table 3).

If instead of scraper flights we have the element carried clear of the trough by rollers, the chain pull is

$$C_p = (2 \times W \times L \times RF) + (W_1 \times L \times F_1)$$

If the conveyor is inclined there is a difference between the chain pull and the resistance to turning at the radius of the head sprocket, since the downhill pull of the chain in the return run reduces the turning effort and the power but does not reduce the pull. The turning effort, with the element sliding, is

$$\begin{aligned}&(W \times L)\,[(\cos\theta \times F) + \sin\theta]\\ &+ (W_1 \times L)\,[(\cos\theta \times F_1) + \sin\theta]\\ &+ (W \times L)\,[(\cos\theta \times F) - \sin\theta]\end{aligned}$$

The chain pull is the pull required for the equivalent horizontal path plus that required for the lift.

To illustrate, assume a scraper conveyor handling bituminous coal at 150 tons per hour, inclined upward at 23°. Centers, 150 ft. Assume the weight of chain and flights at 60 lb. per lineal foot and the weight of the material at 50 lb. per ft. of conveyor (loaded run). Using the coefficient of friction in Table 3, namely, 0.59 for material against trough and 0.33 for flights against trough, we have

$$\begin{aligned}\text{Turning effort in pounds} &= 9000 \times [(0.92 \times 0.33) + 0.39] = 6242\\ &+ 7500 \times [(0.92 \times 0.59) + 0.39] = 6996\\ &+ 9000 \times [(0.92 \times 0.33) - 0.39] = -778\\ &\text{Net turning effort} = 12{,}460 \text{ lb.}\end{aligned}$$

The return run is assisting the turning effort by 778 lb.

To determine the motor horsepower we use the net turning effort plus 10 per cent for friction in the head and foot bearings plus 10 per cent for loss in the reduction gearing plus 10 per cent (or more depending on the conditions) for starting loads or surges. Designate this figure for convenience as "gross turning effort," and the motor horsepower is

$$\text{Motor } HP = \frac{\text{Gross turning effort} \times \text{Speed in feet per minute}}{33{,}000}$$

We assumed that the material weighed 50 lb. per ft. of conveyor, and, since the capacity is 5000 lb. per min., the speed is 100 ft. per min. Therefore

$$\text{Motor } HP = \frac{16{,}583 \times 100}{33{,}000} = 50.25 \quad \text{(50-hp. motor)}$$

The horizontal projection of the 150-ft. conveyor is 138 ft. The lift is 58 ft., and the weight lifted is the element plus material, or 60 + 50 = 110. Thus for the chain pull we have

$$\begin{aligned}C_p &= \text{Horizontal pull for element} & 60 \times 138 \times 0.33 &= 2732\\ &+ \text{Horizontal pull for material} & 50 \times 138 \times 0.59 &= 4071\\ &+ \text{Vertical pull, } 58 \times 110 & &= 6380\\ & & \text{Chain pull} &= 13{,}183 \text{ lb.}\end{aligned}$$

Let us analyze a horizontal conveyor having roller chains. Assume 180-ft. centers with a capacity of 200 tons per hour of bituminous coal at 66 ft. per min. From Table 1 we see that the flights may be 36 by 12 in., and we will space them between two strands of 24-in.-pitch engineering chains with 5-in. rollers on 1-in. pins located at mid pitch to carry the element clear of the trough and drive collars at the articulation points. The head sprockets are six tooth, and for a speed of 66 ft. per min. the head shaft makes 5.5 r.p.m. Because of the long-pitch chains an equalizing gear and pinion are desirable as the first reduction to eliminate pulsation. An equalizing gear has the same number of sectors as there are teeth in the head sprockets, namely, six, and so the reduction is 6 : 1 or a countershaft speed of 33 r.p.m.

The weight of 10 ft. of element, or 20 ft. of chain with five flights and ten center pins with rollers, is found from the catalogues to be 800 lb., so that $W \times L = 14{,}400$. The $W_m$ for 200 tons per hour at 66 ft. per min. is approximately 100 lb. per ft. of conveyor. For the rolling friction we have

$$RF = \frac{d}{D} \times 0.33 + 2\frac{Y}{D} = \frac{1}{5} \times 0.33 + 2 \times \frac{0.03}{5} = 0.078$$

Substituting in the formula for chain pull we have

$$C_p = (2 \times 14{,}400 \times 0.078) + (100 \times 180 \times 0.59) = 12{,}866 \text{ lb.}$$

Adding 10 per cent for friction loss and 10 per cent drive loss gives us 31 for motor horsepower, enabling us to use a standard 30-hp. motorized reducer, which is rated to take care of momentary overloads. The next larger size is 40 hp., which costs much more. If we use a standard 11.4 : 1 reducer on a 1750-r.p.m. motor, the output shaft has 153.5 r.p.m., which gives a convenient reduction, by roller chain drive, of 4.7 : 1 to the 33-r.p.m. countershaft. Finally we should check the bearing area of the pins of the chain selected for the conveyor to see that we do not have an excessive pressure per square inch with the chain pull of approximately 6500 lb. per chain (½ of $C_p$).

It is interesting to see just what advantage is gained by suspending the flights on rollers as compared with a conveyor with scraper flights.

Substituting in the formula, reducing $W$ to 10,800 lb. because of the omission of the center rollers with their pins and bushings, we have

$$C_p = (2 \times 10{,}800 \times 0.33) + (100 \times 180 \times 0.59) = 17{,}748 \text{ lb.}$$

whence

$$HP = \frac{17{,}748 \times 66}{33{,}000} = 35.5 \qquad \text{and} + 10\% + 10\% = 42.9 \text{ motor hp.}$$

We require not only a larger motorized reducer but also heavier chains to take care of the added pull of 4882 lb.

Specifications for flight conveyors are standardized for average conditions, and the manufacturers give complete data on sizes, weights, capacities, recommended speeds, and power requirements. However, a specification for a high-grade flight conveyor follows.

Capacity, 250 tons per hour of bituminous coal. Distance between centers, 200 ft. Speed, 100 ft. per min. The chains are 12-in. pitch, 36,000 lb. ultimate strength, with 2 by 3/8 in. side bars of high-carbon steel. Pins, 0.75-in.-diameter high-carbon heat-treated steel in case-hardened bushings. The rollers are single-flanged chrome iron 3.5 in. in diameter. The flights are 0.25 by 12 by 30 in. steel, spaced 24 in. apart and stiffened with angles. The head shaft is 5 15/16 in. in diameter of forged steel mounted in anti-friction bearings and connected through roller chain to a 40-hp. motorized reducer. The trough has 3/16-in. side plates with a replaceable 3/8-in. high-carbon steel bottom plate.

There is an advantage in having the rollers which carry the chain clear of the trough located midway in the links rather than at the points of articulation; the rollers are easily replaced without disconnecting the chain and may be mounted on anti-friction bearings since the roller spindle is much smaller than the chain pins and these bearings are not subjected to the shock of the drive. The coefficient of friction for sleeve bearing rollers is about 0.09; for anti-friction bearings it is about 0.03. In a long conveyor with high capacity, such bearings not only save power but also, by reducing the $P_c$, often permit the use of a lighter chain, offsetting to some extent the higher price of this type of chain.

**Apron Conveyors.** The alternative to a flight conveyor may be an apron conveyor. An apron conveyor can handle abrasive materials that cannot be scraped along a trough, and as the loading is readily controlled it may be used as a feeder. As an alternative to a rubber belt it can handle materials at a temperature higher than 300° F. that cannot be handled on rubber.

The apron conveyor consists of overlapping beaded steel pans supported between, or mounted upon, two strands of roller chain, and with the usual head and foot assembly. The speed usually is less than 100 ft. per min., and if the conveyor is to serve as a picking table the speed must be quite slow; apron feeders operate at 10 to 30 ft. per min. Apron conveyors and feeders commonly have fixed side plates or "skirt boards" which protect the chains and permit the load to be carried at considerable depth without spilling over the edge of the apron. Except in a picking table, it is better to carry a thick bed at slow speed than a thin bed at high speed. The limit of inclination is about 25° because with a steeper slope the material will slide backward unless the apron is provided with cleats.

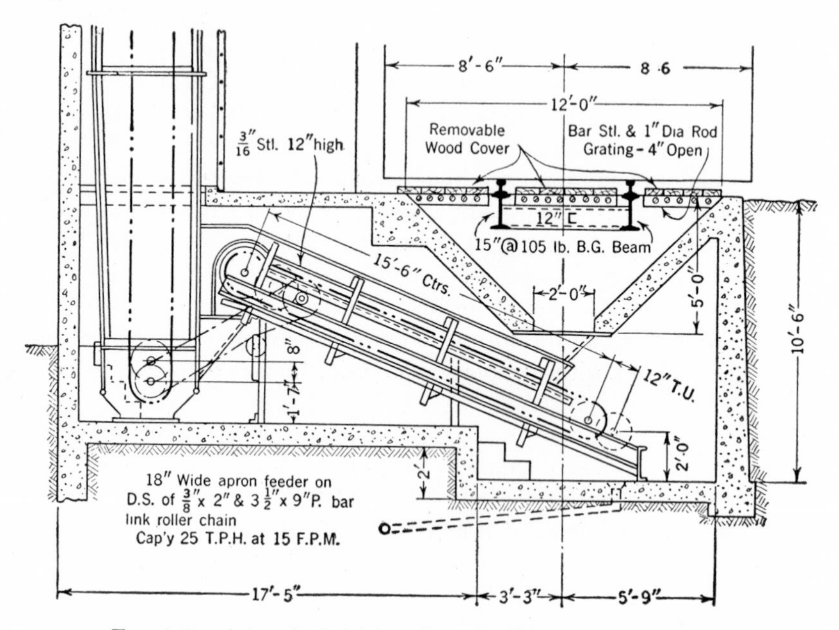


FIG. 3–3. Apron feeder driven from foot shaft of elevator.

An apron feeder to control the rate of flow from a track hopper has the advantage that with an upward slope the depth of track-hopper pit is substantially reduced. This is demonstrated by Fig. 3-3, showing an 18-in. apron feeder driven from the foot shaft of an elevator. The feeder speed is 15 ft. per min. for a capacity of 25 tons per hour of stoker coal. The depth of pit is 10 ft. 6 in.

Figure 3-4 shows the assembly for mine-run coal with a crusher between feeder and elevator. As the crusher may be by-passed, crusher and feeder are driven by separate motors. The capacity is 45 tons per hour with a pit depth of 11 ft.

If an apron is to withstand heavy shock at the loading point, as by rock or ore, it may be of manganese steel or high-carbon steel with impact rails about 3/16 in. below the bottom of the apron so that as the pans yield under impact they bring up against the rails before permanent deflection occurs.

Mention should be made of the *bar-flight* feeder, Fig. 3-5, sometimes advantageous where the pit depth must be a minimum. As here shown the depth is but 2 ft. ½ in. This type of feeder is merely a double-strand flight conveyor with shallow flights. The return run is beneath a shield so that the flow is direct to the lower run.

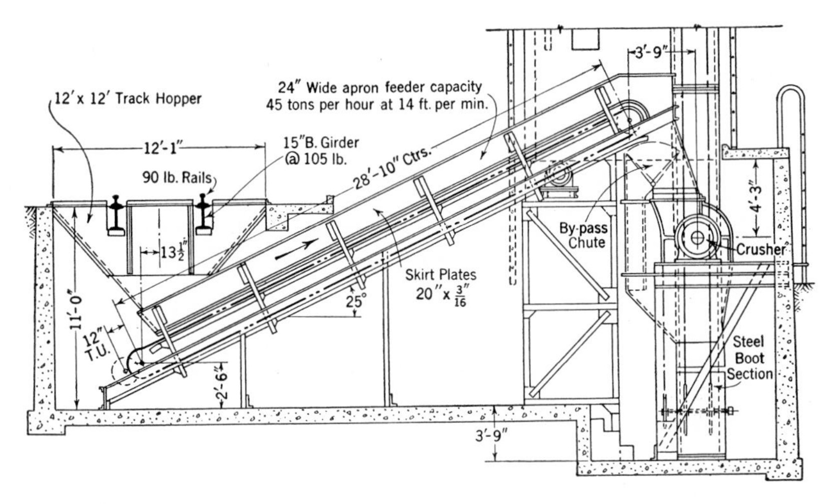


Fig. 3-4. Assembly of apron feeder, crusher, and elevator. Discharge from feeder may be by-passed direct to elevator.

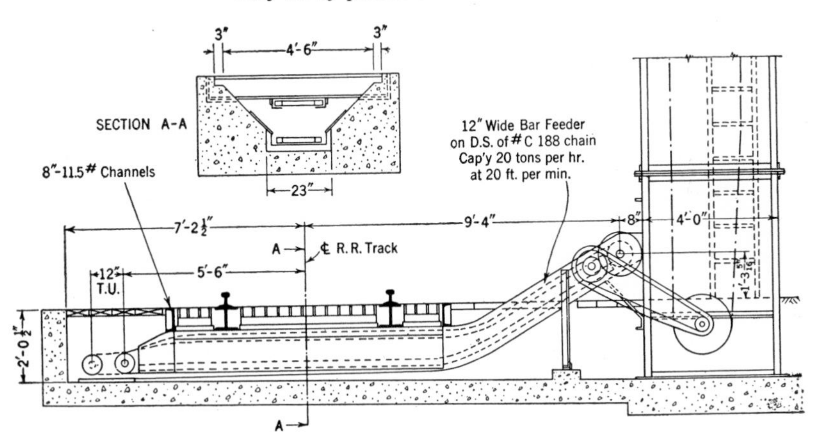


Fig. 3-5. Bar-flight feeder and shallow track hopper.

The bar-flight feeder is limited to material without large lumps, to rather small capacities, and to use in connection with comparatively narrow track hoppers.

*Capacity.* The capacity at a given speed is a function of the depth of the load, its weight, and the width between skirts. An allowance is made for slip due to the drag against the skirts. In a horizontal conveyor a nominal factor is 75 per cent, or

$$\text{Tons per hour} = \frac{75\% \times \text{Load section in sq. ft.} \times \text{Wt. per cu. ft.} \times \text{Ft. per hr.}}{2000}$$

Table 4 gives capacities at 20 ft. per min. with materials weighing 50 lb. per cu. ft. and the permissible lump sizes.

TABLE 4

CAPACITIES OF HORIZONTAL APRON CONVEYORS AND FEEDERS AT 20 FT. PER MIN. WITH MATERIAL WEIGHING 50 LB. PER CU. FT. AND SIZE OF LUMPS PERMISSIBLE

| Width of Apron between Skirts, inches | Depth of Material on Apron, inches | Capacity at 20 Ft. per Min., tons per hour | Lumps[1] Avg. inches | Lumps[1] Max. inches |
|---|---|---|---|---|
| 24 | 12 | 45 | 4 | 6 |
| 30 | 12 | 56 | 6 | 8 |
| 30 | 15 | 70 | 6 | 10 |
| 36 | 12 | 68 | 8 | 12 |
| 36 | 18 | 102 | 8 | 14 |
| 42 | 12 | 79 | 8 | 14 |
| 42 | 24 | 158 | 10 | 18 |
| 48 | 12 | 90 | 8 | 18 |
| 48 | 24 | 180 | 12 | 24 |
| 60 | 12 | 113 | 12 | 18 |
| 60 | 24 | 225 | 15 | 28 |

[1]Large percentage of lumps assumed.

Since there is only rolling friction except for the side rub against the skirts which depends on the material and its depth, the required power is much less than in a flight conveyor which scrapes its load. The skirt

TABLE 5

RESISTANCE OR DRAG OF MATERIAL AGAINST SKIRT BOARDS OF APRON CONVEYOR IN POUNDS PER FOOT OF CONVEYOR

| | Depth of Load on Apron in Inches | | | | |
|---|---|---|---|---|---|
| | 12 | 15 | 18 | 24 | 30 |
| Anthracite coal | 6 | 9 | 13 | 22 | 35 |
| Bituminous coal | 6 | 9 | 13 | 22 | 35 |
| Coke | 3 | 5 | 7 | 12 | 20 |
| Lime, hydrated | 8 | 12 | 20 | 30 | 40 |
| Limestone, pulverized | 8 | 12 | 20 | 30 | 40 |
| Wood chips and hog fuel | 3 | 4 | 6 | 8 | 10 |

drag may be disregarded in the average apron feeder, but in long apron conveyors it should be taken into consideration when estimating the power requirement. The allowances in Table 5 will suffice for average conditions.

*Determination of Power.* The chain pull for a horizontal apron conveyor is that due to the rolling friction against the rails supporting the conveyor plus the drag against the skirt boards, or

$$C_p = RF \times (2W_c + W_m \times L) + D_s \quad \text{in pounds}$$

where $W_c$ = the weight of one run of the element.

$W_m$ = the weight of material per foot of apron.

$L$ = distance between centers.

$D_s$ = the skirt drag multiplied by length, Table 5.

$RF$ values are as noted for suspended flight conveyors.

To illustrate, assume a horizontal apron conveyor of 100-ft. centers and 2 ft. between skirts, with the load 12 in. deep. Speed, 100 ft. per min. Material, bituminous coal. Assume further that the weight of apron is 60 lb. per lineal foot and the weight of load 100 lb. per lineal foot. The apron rollers are of 6-in. diameter, turning on 1½-in. bushings.

$$RF = \frac{d}{D} \times 0.33 + 2\frac{Y}{D} = \frac{1.5}{6} \times 0.33 + \frac{0.06}{6} = 0.1, \text{ approximately}$$

The chain pull $C_p = 0.1 \times (12{,}000 + 10{,}000) + 600 = 2800$ lb.

The required horsepower is $\dfrac{2800 \times 100}{33{,}000} = 8.48$ hp.

If we add 10 per cent for friction loss in the head and foot bearings and 10 per cent for reduction loss we have the motor horsepower as 10.26, or if starting loads or surges may be severe we should add another 10 per cent.

If the apron is inclined upward, allowance is made for the lift, just as with the inclined conveyor.

Under the assumed conditions the conveyor is handling

$$\frac{0.75 \times 2 \times 50 \times 100 \times 60}{2000} = 225 \text{ tons per hour.}$$

*Tramp Iron.* A magnetic head assembly may be applied to an apron conveyor by mounting the unit between the head sprockets. The head-end skirtboards should then be of non-magnetic material. The apron becomes magnetized as it approaches the head end, and fragments of tramp iron adhere for several feet along the return run before dropping off.

One difficulty is that since the depth of load on the apron may be a foot or more the pull may not suffice to draw the fragments through the cascade at the discharge. In the great copper smelting plants where it is essential to eliminate stray but infrequent iron pieces, a permanent magnet is sometimes balanced just above the load on the apron. A buried fragment dips the magnet sharply, actuating an emergency stop and causing a puff of talcum to squirt upon the load. A few trials suffice to establish how far beyond the powder spot the fragment should be looked for. Of course the device is suited only to infrequent functioning.

*Comment.* Care is essential in the erection of a flight or apron conveyor if it is to function properly. The head and foot shafts must be in line. Twin sprockets should be checked for lateral spacing, and it should be noted whether the twin chains match exactly, both when starting up and subsequently. A check should be made for loose flights or pans and missing chain cotters. If the chain is unidirectional it should be assembled to run in the proper direction; that is, as each link engages the tooth of the drive sprocket there should be no movement between the barrel and the tooth but only between barrel and pin (Fig. 19-4).

Proper adjustment of the chain is important, as excessive tension wastes power and causes severe wear in the chain joints. Many of us can recall the extra effort required to propel a bicycle when the chain was too tight. If there is too much slack in the chain it may snag at the leaving side of the sprocket, especially when the chain is new and fits the sprocket snugly. Lubrication of roller chains may or may not be advisable. Dust tends to work into the bushings and out again, but with lubricated joints the dust remains in and if abrasive the pitch of the chain is soon increased. Felt seals in anti-friction bearings have a tendency to trap the dust and grind grooves in the pins.

# CHAPTER 4

## THE BUCKET ELEVATOR

A bucket elevator consists of an endless chain or a belt to which are attached buckets for elevating pulverized, granular, or lumpy materials along a vertical or a steeply inclined path.

The elements of a bucket elevator are: head assembly, including drive, head shaft and bearings, head sprocket or pulley and the supports; foot assembly, including foot shaft, foot sprocket or pulley and adjustable bearings or take-ups (the take-ups may be at the head end). The casing is usually of steel plate and may have internal chain guides. It has a receiving hopper or boot and provision for receiving and discharging the load. The elevating element may be a single strand of chain or twin chains or a belt, to which the buckets are attached.

**Applications and Limitations.** Bucket elevators will handle practically all loose materials if the lumps are not too large for the buckets. The elevator is not suited to material which is sticky or which will not flow, and with light fluffy material at high temperature the up-draft or chimney action in the casing may cause trouble. Vertical elevators usually are preferable, as inclined elevators require carrying idlers or supporting rails along the loaded run and the return-run catenary may be awkward.

**Chain and Bucket Elevators.** The types in common use are as follows:

Type 1. *Centrifugal Discharge* (Fig. 4-1*A*), with buckets of malleable iron or steel plate spaced at intervals by bolting to the chain attachments. Material enters by flowing along the floor of the boot from which it is scooped up by the digging action of the buckets as they round the foot wheel. The material is discharged by centrifugal action as the buckets pass over the head wheel. The proper speed, diameter of the head wheel, and position of the head chute are important for clean action. The centrifugal-discharge elevator is a high-speed machine because of the method of discharge.

Type 2. *Perfect Discharge* (Fig. 4-1*B*). The buckets are carried between two strands of chain snubbed under the head wheels to bring them into an inverted position above the discharge chute. This is a slow-speed machine for fragile, sticky, or slow-flowing materials. The method of loading is similar to that in the centrifugal-discharge elevator.

TYPE 3. *Continuous Bucket* (Fig. 4-1*C*), *Single Strand.* This is a slow-speed machine. The buckets are mounted continuously along the chain. They are loaded after they round the foot wheel and line up for

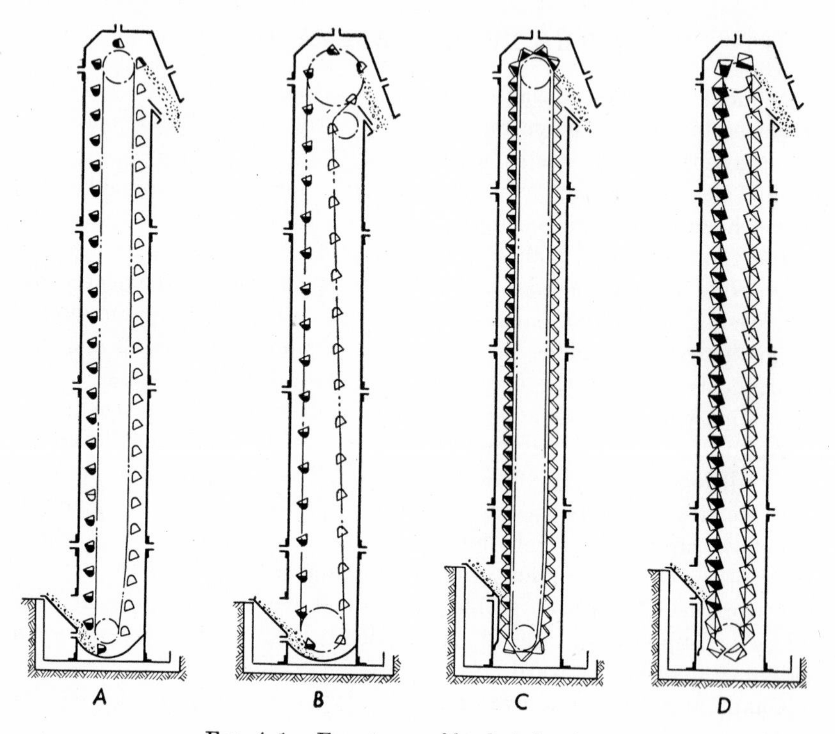


FIG. 4–1. Four types of bucket elevators.

the ascent — a "loading leg," as it is called. At the head the discharge from each bucket is over the front of the preceding bucket which forms a chute or guide to the fixed discharge spout.

TYPE 4. *Continuous Bucket* (Fig. 4-1*D*), *Double Strand.* The buckets are carried between two strands of chain and thus may extend rearward, permitting larger buckets in a casing of a given size than is possible with type 3. Material is loaded and discharged as in type 3. It is often referred to as the "supercapacity continuous-bucket elevator."

TYPE 5. *Gravity Discharge* (Fig. 4-2). This is the name given to the double-strand elevator conveyor with spaced V-section buckets. It may follow almost any path in a vertical plane. Its principal advantage is with fragile materials since it eliminates a transfer from one unit to another. It is a slow-speed machine. Material is loaded as in type 1, but discharge is through gates in a trough as in the flight conveyor. If the horizontal leg of an inverted-L-path gravity-discharge elevator has considerable length the cost usually is higher than for the vertical elevator with a tandem conveyor of the screw or flight type.

*Selecting a Bucket Elevator.* The centrifugal-discharge elevator is lowest in first cost. The continuous-bucket elevator operates at slower speed and thus with less wear on the buckets, chains, and wheels; therefore the maintenance cost is lower. Friable materials

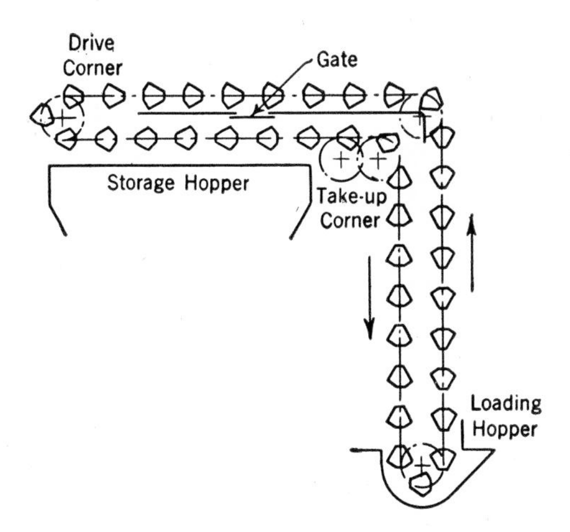


FIG. 4–2. Gravity-discharge elevator conveyor.

can be handled with less breakage than by the centrifugal-discharge type since both the loading and discharge operations involve less shock.

Perfect discharge elevators are used only with materials which discharge sluggishly. Supercapacity elevators are used for the largest capacities. The larger buckets are suited to fines, larger lumps, or both.

Gravity-discharge elevator conveyors are nicely adapted to conditions such as illustrated by Fig. 4-2, where a lift is followed by a short horizontal run. They are less frequently specified than formerly.

*Elements of Design.* Each manufacturer standardizes his drive or head groups, and the designer uses one or the other of these standardized arrangements. Sealed anti-friction bearings have the advantage that they require infrequent lubrication. A motorized reducer, or a motor with herringbone gear reducer with drive to the head shaft through enclosed roller chain, has superseded the old arrangement of gears and countershafts. Shear-pin protection against overloads is unnecessary since a circuit breaker gives sufficiently prompt release for the usual overload build-up, and a sudden shock, as when a crowbar enters the boot, would rip off several buckets before the shear pin would function. It is necessary, however, to provide an automatic backstop to prevent reversal when the elevator stops under load.

The foot assembly provides for adjustment as the chain stretches or wears. Adjustment is by screw take-up bearings or by automatic weighted take-ups. Sometimes it is desirable to maintain a fixed position of the foot shaft, as when a conveyor or feeder is driven from this shaft, when the foot shaft is inaccessible, or when it is desired to maintain a fixed relation between the buckets and the bottom plate of the boot. Then the head shaft is mounted in take-up bearings.

The casings are of 14-gauge to ¼-in. steel plate suitably reinforced by angles. Welded casings are preferred as they give a neater appearance than riveted casings and they cost less. The cross-section dimensions should be such that the sway of the chain will not bring the buckets into contact with the front or back plates. In elevators of extreme lift it may be desirable to provide one or more chain-guide sections to restrict the sway.

If the material is corrosive, such as damp salt or wet high-sulphur coal, a corrosion-resisting casing should be specified, or the inside of a steel-plate casing may be given a protecting coating of an anti-corrosive compound. A wood casing will resist some corrosives but presents an objectionable fire risk. Asbestos-cement sheets (Transite, etc.) give complete protection. If the casing is directly against a concrete silo it will be found that the casing can be formed as the silo is poured at a cost less than for a steel-plate casing. A concrete casing has an indefinitely long life but by itself is too costly.

*Chains.* Both the type and the size of the chain must be chosen with care. For light duty, moderate centers, and small capacities, the ordinary "Ewart" or detachable malleable chain suffices. The so-called Class C chain (page 369) or combination chain is most frequently specified for elevators in the middle range of capacity and lift. It has durability and is simple, rugged, and low in cost. For severe service and abrasive materials — ashes, for example — we may use the bushed chains with hardened-steel pins and renewable hardened-steel bushings which contact the sprocket teeth. In general, the wider, heavier malleable-iron chains have larger wearing surfaces and higher tensile strengths than the lighter narrower chains and are best suited for heavy duty. Elevators of extremely large capacity use the so-called engineering chains (page 369). These are used also in gravity discharge elevators. The rollers support the element along the horizontal runs.

Engineering chains have hardened wearing surfaces, high-carbon heat-treated renewable pins, case-hardened bushings, and chrome-iron rollers. It is essential that the bushings be shouldered and locked fast in the inner side bars; otherwise the holes gradually widen, and the side bars must be replaced when the bushings are reversed. In cheap chains the bushing holes are punched; in well-made chains they are broached to close fit.

Lubrication should be through an Alemite fitting in the end of the pin with counterbore to the bushing. The lubricant thus is forced outward and forms a grease seal.

An inclined elevator should be double strand with the chains guided along the carrying run by side guides or tracks. Sliding shoes waste power and eventually wear through the guides. Roller chains should have flanged rollers, preferably midway in the length of the link rather

TABLE 1

VERTICAL CENTRIFUGAL-DISCHARGE ELEVATORS

Sizes of buckets; maximum lumps; capacities, buckets 75 per cent filled.

| Bucket Spacing, inches | Size, Length by Width | Speed, feet per minute | Max. Lumps All Lumps | 10% Lumps | Capacity in Tons per Hour 35-Lb. Material | 50-Lb. Material | 100-Lb. Material |
|---|---|---|---|---|---|---|---|
| 13 | 6 × 4 | 225 | ½ | 2½ | 5 | 7 | 14 |
| 16 | 8 × 5 | 230 | ¾ | 3 | 9 | 13 | 27 |
| 16 | 10 × 6 | 230 | 1 | 3½ | 16 | 23 | 47 |
| 18 | 12 × 7 | 268 | 1¼ | 4 | 27 | 38 | 77 |
| 18 | 14 × 7 | 268 | 1¼ | 4 | 32 | 46 | 92 |
| 19 | 16 × 8 | 262 | 1½ | 4½ | 44 | 63 | 127 |

Horsepower. Motor horsepower for centrifugal discharge elevators closely approximates

$$\frac{\text{Tons per hour} \times 2 \times \text{Lift in feet}}{1000}$$

than at the points of articulation so that the rollers may be replaced without disconnecting the chain — a far tougher job with a heavy elevator than with a horizontal conveyor. These rollers carry a load made up of the reaction against the guides of half the weight of a bucket plus half a bucket loading; thus the spindle of the roller is small, permitting the use of low-cost anti-friction bearings. This is a very desirable detail. A 12-in.-pitch roller chain so equipped costs about 50 per cent more than the standard chain, or if the pitch is 24 in. the increased cost is about 40 per cent.

Heavy-duty elevators should have wide hardened cast-steel driving collars in the chains. Cast-steel head sprockets with flame-hardened teeth are preferable to chilled cast iron, because under heavy impact the soft iron core penes out and the chilled surface breaks down. In selecting a chain consideration should be given to the bearing area of the pin; some chains have a high ultimate strength without corresponding bearing area and may gall as discussed in Chapter 19.

*Charts of Capacity and Power.* When selecting an elevator the designer uses the tables furnished by the manufacturers, which show the maximum size of lumps for each size of bucket, the capacities for different weights of materials with the listed speeds, and the motor horsepower required.

Table 1 gives the data for centrifugal-discharge elevators. In the third column the usual speed for each size is noted. The speed may be somewhat higher but should not be less than listed. If the material is fluffy or entrains air the capacity should be reduced by 25 per cent below the tabulated capacities.

Table 2 gives the data for perfect discharge elevators at 120 ft. per min. This speed may be reduced to any desired lower speed. The capacity is proportional to the speed.

Table 3 gives the data for gravity-discharge elevators at 100 ft. per min. Lower speeds are advantageous.

Tables 4 and 5 give the data for vertical continuous-bucket elevators. In Table 4 the speed is 125 ft. per min. Lower speeds are desirable. Supercapacity elevators, Table 5, are used for the larger capacities, and the speed is shown as 100 ft. per min., though a slower speed is advantageous.

**Belt and Bucket Elevators.** Belt and bucket elevators are either centrifugal discharge or continuous bucket. They are more susceptible to damage than chain elevators as the belt may be cut or burned by an overload causing slip at the head pulley. The head pulley must be lined up accurately and inspected occasionally to see that the surface is clean and the belt running centrally. A flanged head pulley will not function since any deflection of the belt will cause it to ride the flange. A ribbed belt (Chapter 10) might be effective in maintaining a true run, but this is questionable. A crown face pulley may strain the attachment bolts.

With the chain and bucket elevator for coal and similar materials, the slow-speed continuous bucket elevator is better than the high-speed centrifugal-discharge elevator. With the belt and bucket elevator, maintenance costs have been found to be less with the high-speed centrifugal-discharge elevator because there is less wedging of material between buckets and belt where it causes trouble with the attachment bolts.

## TABLE 2[1]

### Perfect Discharge Elevators

Sizes of buckets; maximum lumps; capacities, speed 120 ft. per min. and buckets 75 per cent filled; horsepower at head shaft.

| Bucket Spacing, inches | Size of Buckets | Maximum Lumps | | Capacity in Tons per Hour | | | Horsepower required | | | | | |
|---|---|---|---|---|---|---|---|---|---|---|---|---|
| | | | | | | | 35-Lb. Material | | 50-Lb. Material | | 75-Lb. Material | |
| | | All Lumps | 10% Lumps | 35-Lb. Material | 50-Lb. Material | 75-Lb. Material | For Terminals | For Each Foot of Centers | For Terminals | For Each Foot of Centers | For Terminals | For Each Foot of Centers |
| 20 | 8 × 5 × 5½ | ¾ | 3 | 4 | 6 | 8 | 0.2 | 0.01 | 0.2 | 0.01 | 0.2 | 0.02 |
| 20 | 10 × 6 × 6½ | 1 | 3½ | 7 | 10 | 15 | 0.2 | 0.01 | 0.3 | 0.02 | 0.4 | 0.03 |
| 20 | 12 × 6 × 6½ | 1¼ | 3½ | 8 | 11 | 17 | 0.2 | 0.01 | 0.3 | 0.03 | 0.4 | 0.03 |
| 24 | 14 × 8 × 8½ | 1¼ | 4 | 14 | 20 | 30 | 0.5 | 0.03 | 0.6 | 0.04 | 0.9 | 0.05 |
| 24 | 16 × 8 × 8½ | 1½ | 4½ | 16 | 23 | 34 | 0.5 | 0.04 | 0.7 | 0.04 | 1.0 | 0.06 |
| 24 | 18 × 8 × 8½ | 1½ | 4½ | 18 | 26 | 40 | 0.6 | 0.04 | 0.8 | 0.05 | 1.2 | 0.07 |
| 24 | 20 × 8 × 8½ | 1¾ | 5 | 20 | 29 | 44 | 0.6 | 0.04 | 0.9 | 0.06 | 1.3 | 0.08 |
| 24 | 24 × 8 × 8½ | 1¾ | 5 | 24 | 34 | 52 | 0.7 | 0.05 | 1.0 | 0.07 | 1.5 | 0.09 |

[1] Source: Link-Belt Company.

TABLE 3[1]

GRAVITY-DISCHARGE ELEVATORS

(Used primarily for bituminous coal)
Capacities in tons per hour at 100 ft. per min. Buckets loaded to 80 per cent of level full.

| Size of Bucket, inches $L \times W$ | Capacity in tons per Hour at 100 Ft. per Min. | | | Horsepower[2] with Material at 50 Lb. per Cu. Ft. | | | | | |
|---|---|---|---|---|---|---|---|---|---|
| | Bucket Spacing, inches | | | Per 10-Ft. Vertical Lift | | | Per 100-Ft. Horizontal Run | | |
| | | | | Spacing of Buckets, inches | | | | | |
| | 18 | 24 | 36 | 18 | 24 | 36 | 18 | 24 | 36 |
| 16 × 15 | 46 | 35 | 23 | 0.59 | 0.44 | 0.30 | 5.32 | 4.24 | 3.04 |
| 20 × 15 | 58 | 44 | 29 | 0.74 | 0.56 | 0.37 | 6.32 | 4.97 | 3.54 |
| 24 × 15 | 70 | 52 | 35 | 0.90 | 0.67 | 0.45 | 7.34 | 5.74 | 4.04 |
| 20 × 20 | 104 | ... | 52 | 1.30 | ... | 0.66 | 9.20 | ... | 4.85 |
| 24 × 20 | 125 | ... | 63 | 1.60 | ... | 0.80 | 10.92 | ... | 5.74 |
| 30 × 20 | 159 | ... | 79 | 2.00 | ... | 1.00 | 13.70 | ... | 7.08 |
| 36 × 20 | 191 | ... | 95 | 2.42 | ... | 1.21 | 16.30 | ... | 8.40 |

[1]Source: Link-Belt Company.
[2]Add 5 per cent to horsepower for each bend in path of loaded run.

Although the inclined chain and bucket elevator involves the risk of eventual trouble from worn supporting rails, the inclined belt and bucket elevator (Fig. 4-3) is often preferred to the vertical type as it loads and discharges better and is supported safely along the carrying run by spaced rolls with anti-friction bearings. The return run is allowed to hang free in a flat catenary. The loading point should be fixed carefully to feed directly into the buckets after they have lined up for the lift and with minimum impact against the belt. The drive of the belt elevator is similar to that of the chain elevator and should have overload protection and automatic brake.

The take-up tension, which must be sufficient to prevent skidding at the head, is a certain percentage of the horsepower tension. Conditions vary so widely that definite values cannot be set up, but the approximate values in Table 6 (United States Rubber Company) illustrate the need of heavy slack-side tension. Automatic or weighted take-ups are best as they adjust themselves to variations in belt length due to temperature changes or starting loads. Inclined elevators require sufficient take-up tension to eliminate excessive sag in the free return run.

TABLE 4

VERTICAL CONTINUOUS BUCKET ELEVATORS[1]

Bucket sizes; maximum lumps; capacities; horsepower. Capacities with buckets 75 per cent full; speed, 125 ft. per min.

| Buckets | | Max. Lumps | | Capacity in Tons per Hour | | | | Horsepower Required | | | | |
|---|---|---|---|---|---|---|---|---|---|---|---|---|
| | | | | | | | | | For Each Foot of Centers | | | |
| Size | Gauge of Steel | All Lumps | 10% Lumps | 35-Lb. Material | 50-Lb. Material | 75-Lb. Material | 100-Lb. Material | For Terminals | 35-Lb. Material | 50-Lb. Material | 75-Lb. Material | 100-Lb. Material |
| 8 × 5 × 7¾ | 12 | ¾ | 2½ | 12 | 17 | 25 | 34 | 0.1 | 0.02 | 0.03 | 0.04 | 0.05 |
| 10 × 5 × 7¾ | 12 | ¾ | 2½ | 15 | 21 | 32 | 42 | .1 | .03 | .04 | .05 | .07 |
| 10 × 7 × 11⅝ | 12 | 1 | 3 | 19 | 27 | 41 | 54 | .1 | .03 | .04 | .07 | .09 |
| 12 × 7 × 11⅝ | 10 | 1 | 3 | 23 | 32 | 49 | 65 | .1 | .04 | .05 | .08 | .10 |
| 14 × 7 × 11⅝ | 10 | 1 | 3 | 26 | 38 | 57 | 76 | .1 | .04 | .06 | .09 | .12 |
| 12 × 8 × 11⅝ | 10 | 1¼ | 4 | 27 | 39 | 58 | 78 | .2 | .05 | .07 | .11 | .13 |
| 14 × 8 × 11⅝ | 10 | 1¼ | 4 | 32 | 45 | 68 | 91 | .2 | .05 | .08 | .12 | .14 |
| 16 × 8 × 11⅝ | 10 | 1½ | 4½ | 36 | 52 | 78 | 104 | .2 | .07 | .09 | .13 | .16 |
| 18 × 8 × 11⅝ | 10 | 1½ | 4½ | 41 | 58 | 88 | 117 | .2 | .08 | .11 | .14 | .18 |

[1] Source: Link-Belt Company.

TABLE 5

VERTICAL SUPERCAPACITY ELEVATORS

Sizes of buckets; maximum lumps, based on 10–20 per cent of lumps in material; capacities at 100 ft. per min. with buckets 75 per cent full; horsepowers at head shaft.

| | Size of Buckets, inches | Maximum Lumps[2] | Capacities in Tons per Hour | | | Horsepower | | | | | |
|---|---|---|---|---|---|---|---|---|---|---|---|
| | | | | | | 50-Lb. Material | | 75-Lb. Material | | 100-Lb. Material | |
| | | | 50-Lb. Material | 75-Lb. Material | 100-Lb. Material | Terminals | Each Foot of Centers | Terminals | Each Foot of Centers | Terminals | Each Foot of Centers |
| Chain | 12 × 8 × 11½ | 6 | 60 | 90 | 120 | 0.37 | 0.09 | 0.55 | 0.14 | 0.74 | 0.19 |
| pitch[1] | 16 × 8 × 11½ | 6 | 80 | 120 | 160 | 0.49 | 0.12 | 0.73 | 0.18 | 0.98 | 0.24 |
| 12 in. | 20 × 8 × 11½ | 6 | 100 | 150 | 200 | 0.61 | 0.15 | 0.92 | 0.23 | 1.23 | 0.31 |
| | 16 × 12 × 17½ | 8 | 115 | 175 | 230 | 0.77 | 0.17 | 1.15 | 0.26 | 1.54 | 0.34 |
| Chain | 20 × 12 × 17½ | 8 | 145 | 220 | 290 | 0.99 | 0.22 | 1.48 | 0.33 | 1.97 | 0.44 |
| pitch | 24 × 12 × 17½ | 8 | 175 | 260 | 345 | 1.19 | 0.27 | 1.73 | 0.40 | 2.38 | 0.53 |
| 18 in. | 30 × 12 × 17½ | 8 | 215 | 320 | 425 | 1.44 | 0.32 | 2.16 | 0.48 | 2.89 | 0.64 |
| | 36 × 12 × 17½ | 8 | 255 | 385 | 510 | 1.73 | 0.38 | 2.60 | 0.58 | 3.47 | 0.77 |
| Chain | 24 × 17 × 23½ | 10 | 230 | 345 | 460 | 2.11 | 0.35 | 3.16 | 0.53 | 4.22 | 0.71 |
| pitch | 30 × 17 × 23½ | 10 | 285 | 430 | 570 | 2.65 | 0.44 | 3.97 | 0.66 | 5.29 | 0.88 |
| 24 in. | 36 × 17 × 23½ | 10 | 345 | 520 | 690 | 3.20 | 0.52 | 4.79 | 0.79 | 6.39 | 1.06 |

[1] These are the long-pitch engineering chains.
[2] Not over 20 per cent large lumps.

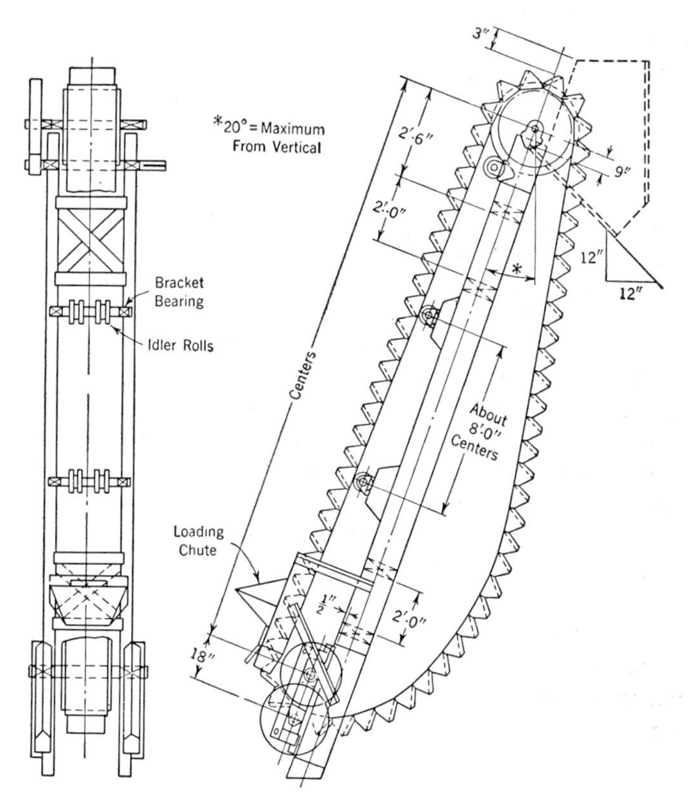


FIG. 4–3. Belt elevator. Continuous bucket type.

TABLE 6

PERCENTAGES OF SLACK-SIDE TENSION TO HORSEPOWER TENSION

180° arc of contact

| | Bare Pulley | | Lagged Pulley | |
|---|---|---|---|---|
| Pulley Condition | Dry | Wet | Dry | Wet |
| Clean | 60% | 85% | 45% | 60% |
| Fine grit, as rock dust | 80–90% | 80–120% | 80–100% | 80–150% |
| Fine dust, as clay, etc. | 100–130% | 120–170% | 120–170% | 100–170% |
| Sharp sand | 80–150% | 80–120% | 60–100% | 60–100% |

*Belt Selection.* We will follow the recommendations of the United States Rubber Company for elevator belts. The belt must have sufficient body to prevent the bolts from tearing through, to resist cracking by lumps caught between the boot pulley and the belt, and to have a reasonable margin for wear and resistance to absorption of moisture.

Elevator belts have strong tightly woven duck and sufficient plies to give thickness and body. The duck recommended for various services are:

32 oz. Most commonly used. Suitable for light non-clogging materials as grain and for moderately coarse materials.

36 oz. Needed for body strength and cushioning when handling heavy lump materials; for marine legs and rugged service.

35 oz. Hard woven. For wet and abrasive conditions as elevating wet fine ore. With sufficient number of plies is suitable for heavy lump materials.

28 oz. Seldom used. Too light and flexible except for very light duty. See also page 237.

*Belt Tension.* The maximum tension in an elevator belt may be high because of the dead weight of belt, buckets, and load. The maximum tension occurs at the point where the belt enters the head pulley. The horsepower tension is equal to the peak $HP \times 33{,}000$ divided by the speed in feet per minute. If the actual horsepower is not known the horsepower tension may be taken as the maximum load on the rising side plus boot friction. Boot friction may be taken as the maximum load on 25 ft. of belt for centrifugal-discharge elevators or on 10 ft. of belt for continuous bucket elevators.

The number of plies required for the tension is checked by dividing the maximum tension by the width of belt in inches and keeping within the permissible tensions in Table 7.

TABLE 7

Maximum Tensions per Ply-Inch

| | | |
|---|---|---|
| 28 oz. | 24 lb. per ply-in. | |
| 32 oz. | 27 lb. per ply-in. | |
| 36 oz. | 30 lb. per ply-in. | |
| 35 oz. | 32 lb. per ply-in. | (hard woven) |

More plies may be advisable to bring the belt up to minimum ply thickness as required for body. The greater the weight of material scooped up per bucket or the greater the projection of the buckets out from the belt, the greater the carcass thickness must be to hold the attachment bolts. High speed increases the shock. Rubber covers should be on both sides of the belt.

*Pulley Diameter.* This should be at least 4 in. for each ply of belt, and the pulley width should be 2 in. more than the transverse length of the buckets. Lagging the head pulley is good insurance as it increases the traction and cushions against stray lumps.

**Speeds** of belt elevators are far higher than are permissible with chain elevators. Table 8 gives the recommendations for speeds and related head pulley diameters.

Maximum lumps with centrifugal discharge elevators and the capacities in tons per hour, with the bucket spacing and speeds noted, are given in Table 9.

The designer should be conservative in using the rated capacities of elevator buckets listed by the manufacturer. As the struck capacity is larger than the actual load-carrying capacity, the percentages in Table 10 are recommended.

*An Elevator or a Belt Conveyor?* This choice arises frequently in material-handling layouts. If the capacity is small or moderate the elevator has an advantage over the inclined belt conveyor in first cost and cost of up-keep. With larger capacities the elevator becomes a bulky machine and the inclined belt may be better. The heavy elevator will in time require reversal of the chain pins and bushings, the replacement of worn rollers if these serve as drive collars, and the replacement of an occasional bucket. The belt conveyor requires practically no replacements for eight or ten years of active service, barring accidents, but when a new belt is necessary the cost is considerable.

The belt conveyor costs about half as much as the bucket elevator of large capacity if the supporting structures are not included, but the conveyor costs considerably more than the elevator if the inclined bridge of one and the casing of the other are taken into account.

A chain and bucket elevator is immune to serious accident. A belt conveyor may suffer serious accident from a detached chute plate, fragment of tramp iron, etc. However, the inclined belt is generally preferred if it is suited to the job layout and the capacity is large.

*An Elevator or a Skip Hoist?* Chain and bucket elevators seem to be preferred to the skip hoist for materials whose action is not too severe as regards impact, abrasion, and corrosion, and where the lift is not extreme. Skip hoists have distinct advantages for extreme lifts, as in mine shafts where the depths may be several thousand feet. In the layout of steam-plant coal-handling installations the bucket elevator will as a rule fit in more conveniently, especially where coal is to be stocked out and reclaimed from reserve ground storage. Moreover with the extensive use of small sizes the layout at the track hopper is easier, especially when the coal may be received in flat-bottom cars from which it is removed by crane and grab bucket. For limestone, cement clinker, castings, scrap wire, gravel, crushed rock, and the like, although the skip hoist is usual, the bucket elevator is by no means unsuitable; but it must be of rugged construction. The machine shown in Fig. 6-1 operated for 19 yr. with limestone before replacements of pins, bushings, and collars were made.

With a high lift, the weight of two runs of chain, the buckets, and

## TABLE 8

### Belt and Bucket Elevators

Centrifugal-discharge types; recommended speeds; head pulley diameters.

| Head Pulley Diameters, inches | High Speed, with Fine Free-Flowing Materials — Grains, Dry Sand, etc., feet per minute | Moderate Speed, for Coal, Stone, Cinders, Cement, etc., feet per minute |
|---|---|---|
| 18 | 270 | 220 |
| 20 | 285 | 230 |
| 24 | 315 | 260 |
| 30 | 355 | 290 |
| 36 | 390 | 320 |
| 42 | 430 | 350 |
| 48 | 465 | 375 |
| 60 | 525 | 425 |
| 84 | 630 | 515 |

## TABLE 9

### Maximum Lumps and Capacities

| Bucket Spacing, inches | Size, Length by Width | Speed, feet per minute | Maximum Lumps | | Capacity in Tons per Hour | | |
|---|---|---|---|---|---|---|---|
| | | | All Lumps | 10% Lumps | 35-Lb. Material | 50-Lb. Material | 100-Lb. Material |
| 13 | 6 × 4 | 225 | ½ | 2½ | 5 | 7 | 14 |
| 16 | 8 × 5 | 258 | ¾ | 3 | 11 | 15 | 30 |
| 16 | 10 × 6 | 258 | 1 | 3½ | 18 | 26 | 52 |
| 18 | 12 × 7 | 298 | 1¼ | 4 | 30 | 42 | 85 |
| 18 | 14 × 7 | 298 | 1¼ | 4 | 36 | 52 | 103 |
| 18 | 16 × 8 | 298 | 1½ | 4½ | 53 | 114 | 152 |

Link-Belt recommends 32-oz. belt up to and including 10-in. buckets.

Horsepower: Motor horsepower for centrifugal-discharge elevators closely approximates

$$\frac{\text{Tons per hour} \times 2 \times \text{Lift in feet}}{1000}$$

## TABLE 10

### Buckets — Working Capacity in Percentage of Struck Capacity

| | Per Cent |
|---|---|
| Light, fine, free-flowing materials, grain, etc. | 80–85 |
| Same if loading above the foot shaft | 85–90 |
| Heavy, coarse, moderately free-flowing materials, coal, ores, etc. | 65–75 |
| Minerals, pulps, liquids | 35 |

Where the capacity is figured in bushels, 1 bu. = 1.25 cu. ft.

the casing becomes many times the weight of a skip bucket, guides, and loader. Large lumps call for very large elevator buckets. The maintenance costs of a skip hoist are limited to cable replacements and occasional repairs to bucket, loader, sheaves, and bearings. Replacement costs in an elevator will usually be larger, especially with abrasive materials.

There are no hard-and-fast rules dictating the choice of an elevator, a skip hoist, or an inclined belt conveyor, as circumstances vary endlessly. Each will do a fine job if well designed, carefully fabricated, and properly erected. In the author's experience, the factor tending most seriously to interfere with the perfect operation of a chain-and-bucket elevator, otherwise suitable, is carelessly erecting the elevator out of plumb laterally. This causes faulty action where the chain enters the sprocket teeth at the head and severe wear on the chain side bars. In a belt-and-bucket elevator exact alignment is even more important. Moreover the discharge action should always be checked carefully when the belt-and-bucket elevator is placed in operation. Not infrequently a slight increase or decrease in the speed of a centrifugal-discharge elevator will eliminate any small discharge down the return leg, a condition seriously affecting the life of the belt.

# CHAPTER 5

## THE SKIP HOIST

In simplest form the skip hoist consists of a guided bucket raised and lowered by a cable attached to a hoisting machine, with provision for loading the bucket at the lower point of travel and discharging it at the top of the run. The path of travel is determined by the guides. The diagrams (Fig. 5-1) show the paths for industrial installations, to which we will limit our discussion.

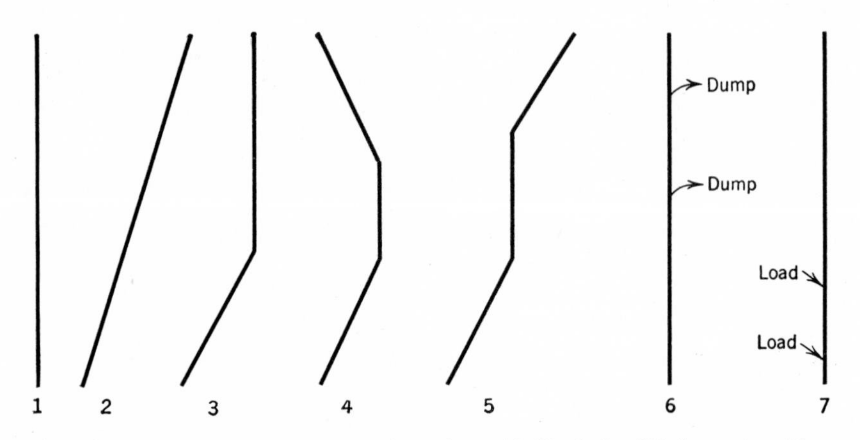


Fig. 5-1. Typical paths for the skip hoist. (1) Vertical. Discharge to either side. (2) Inclined. (3) Incline and vertical. (4) C-path. (5) S-path. (6) Vertical with two dumping positions. (7) Vertical with two loading stations.

**Applications and Limitations.** The outstanding advantages of the skip are: its few moving parts; its ability to handle material which contains large lumps or is abrasive or corrosive; and its adaptability to high lifts and large capacities. With high lift and large capacity the first cost will as a rule be less than for any other type of mechanical conveyor. The skip is easily adapted to the formation of reserve storage as an auxiliary function either through a by-pass at the head or by an intermediate discharge point to form a pile, on the far side of a track hopper, which is then spread out and reclaimed by a bulldozer, caterpillar crane, or drag scraper.

Frequently the selection of a machine for elevating lies between a skip, a bucket elevator, and an inclined belt conveyor. If the material is corrosive or quite abrasive or has a high temperature, the skip may be best. If the lift is high and the capacity large, the skip probably will be best. For comparatively low lifts either the inclined belt or the bucket elevator has the advantage. Large lumps are handled better in the large bucket of the skip than in the smaller buckets of an elevator.

**Types.** There are three types of skip hoists:

Uncounterweighted, in which the bucket is pulled up to the point of discharge where it tips, discharges its load, and descends by gravity. Some form of brake is needed to control the descent. Usually this is dynamic braking — driving the motor as a generator.

Counterweighted, in which a counterweight cable is attached to the drum but winds in the reverse direction from the bucket cable. The counterweight equals the weight of the bucket plus half the load in the bucket; thus the load on the motor is the equivalent of half the useful load for travel in either direction, and the hoisting unit is smaller than if the load were not counterweighted.

Balanced, in which two buckets are operated from one drum and travel in opposite directions. This nearly doubles the capacity with corresponding increase in the motor horsepower though not in the size of the hoisting machine.

There have been variations from the standard machines of today, but they do not seem to survive. There was the vertical skip in which the bucket did not tip but had a hinged front plate, held shut or released by a guide rail along the run. There was the skip bucket pivotally mounted in a four-wheel carriage, thus permitting a horizontal run through the basement of a boiler house followed by an incline up to the point of discharge while the bucket remained upright. It had limited application. There was the inclined skip with the motor mounted on the rear axle of the bucket, thus eliminating cables and sheaves. The bucket will skid unless the incline is quite flat, but it does have advantages.

**Loading.** Each type may be loaded by an automatic loader (Fig. 5-2) which controls the flow to the bucket. The three general types of such loaders are:

Damming type, in which the down swing of the loader permits the material to flow into the bucket until checked by the angle of repose. However, if the control of the movement of the bucket is automatic, the bucket will start upward after an interval whether a load has entered or not.

Full-bucket control type, in which the bucket will start upward only after it is loaded to capacity. This has the advantage that the skip does not make useless trips.

Weight-of-load-in-bucket type, in which the bucket starts upward, cutting off the flow when it is loaded with a given *weight* of material. This is used if materials differing widely in weight are handled successively. The load on the hoist is unchanged regardless of the weight per cubic foot of the material.

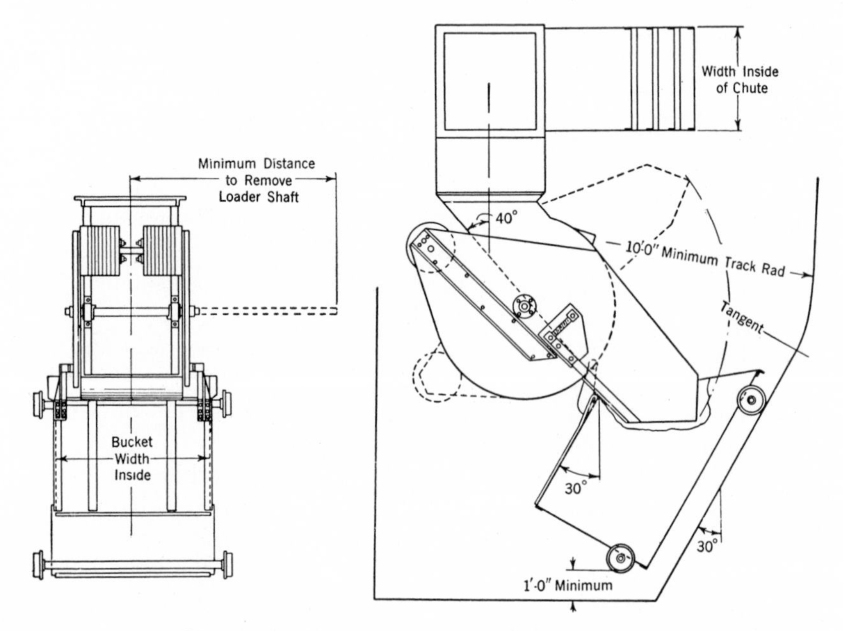


FIG. 5–2. The automatic loader of the skip hoist.

**Control.** There are two control methods: the semi-automatic, in which the bucket makes one round trip and stops, and the full automatic, in which the bucket repeats the cycle until stopped by the attendant. The method of control is tied in with the method of loading; thus with a manually loaded skip the control is never full automatic.

The limits of bucket travel are controlled by a traveling cam mounted on a spindle geared to the hoist drum shaft or countershaft. At the points determined by the contactors, the travel limits are fixed. Emergency stops just beyond the normal stop-points function if the automatic stop fails. A slack cable switch mounted on the hoist frame would function if the bucket should overrun when it reached the lower end of its path, if the cable should break, or if the descending bucket should stick in the guides. In the balanced and counterweighted skips a slack cable switch is applied to both cables.

The control panel is wired for the desired semi-automatic or full-automatic control, with overload and no-voltage protection and the necessary appurtenances for control of the bucket movement in connection with the traveling cam, and also to stop the motor if the bucket should engage the upper emergency stop or if the slack cable switch should open. With full-automatic control the loader contactors function through the traveling cam by means of magnetic switches to start the filled bucket upward or downward. A three-point push-button station is provided to stop the bucket at any point in an emergency or to cause a stationary bucket to continue upward or return.

**The Hoist.** This is the all-important part of a skip hoist, and it has reached a high state of development by various manufacturers. Figure 5-3 shows the standard hoist by Link-Belt. The grooves are machined and polished. The heavy drum shaft is carried in three anti-friction bearings, two of which are arranged to take end thrust. The intermediate shaft is mounted in two anti-friction bearings which permit centering of the herringbone gears. The high-speed shaft has two anti-friction bearings which will take any end thrust from the floating armature of the motor. All bearings are automatically lubricated, and outside bearings are sealed. The motor is either a direct-current compound-wound or an alternating-current high-torque squirrel cage, connected to the reducer high-speed shaft through flexible coupling which forms also the brake wheel of the solenoid brake. The traveling cam limit switch is connected by chain drive to the intermediate shaft. The base is a rigid welded steel frame with the joint between the upper and lower halves of the gear housing machined for an oil-tight fit. This description serves to indicate the careful engineering entering into the modern skip engine.

**The Bucket.** Skip buckets are of heavy steel plate in the form of an open-top rectangular box. They are rated in cubic feet water-level capacity with the bucket vertical. In a skip having a flat inclined path the working capacity of the bucket is reduced. Four flanged wheels guide it along the runway. As a rule the leading pair is set to a narrower gauge than the trailing pair so that when the bucket approaches the dumping point the forward end moves horizontally while the trailing end continues upward until the bucket reaches the discharge position. The " bale " or yoke is pivoted and extends slightly above the top of the bucket, where connection is made to the hoist cable. If loading is automatic, suitable steel roller arms on the front plate of the bucket engage the loader at the approach to the lower end of the run.

A skip bucket does not bottom when loading but is always suspended on the hoist cable, thus preventing slack which would cause the slack cable switch to open the motor circuit.

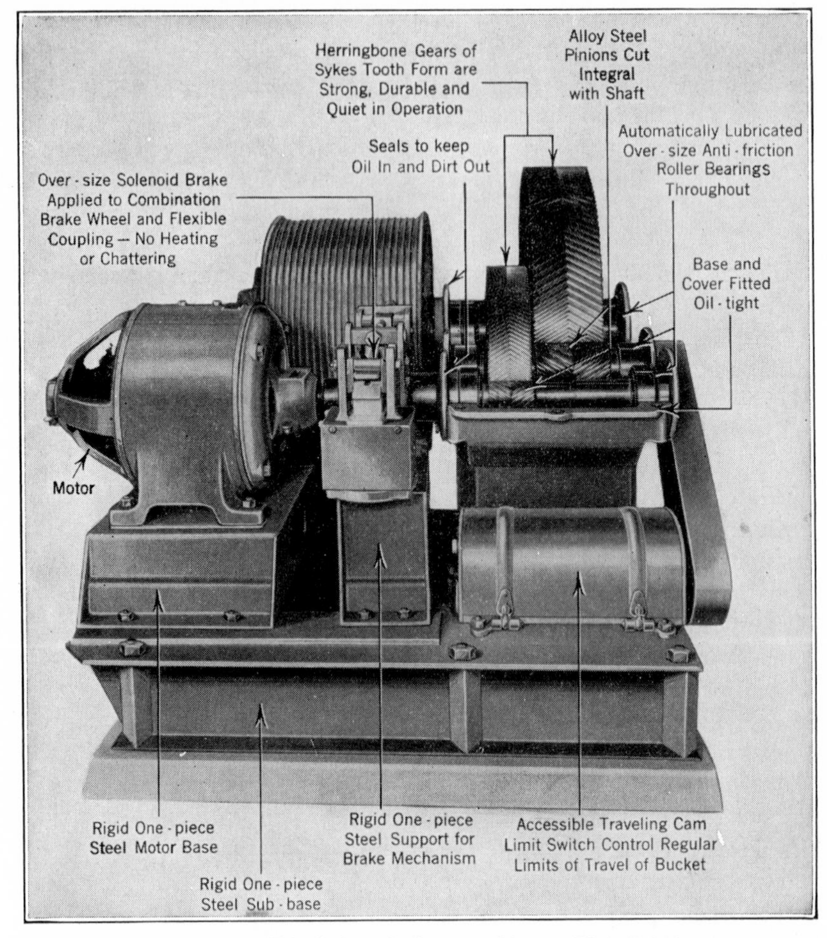


FIG. 5–3. Skip hoist winding machine. (Link-Belt.)

**The Counterweight.** As the bucket of a counterweighted skip enters the dumping rails at the top of the lift and tilts, much of the load is taken off the hoist cable. As the counterweight at this moment has nearly reached the lower limit of its travel, brackets are provided to lift off part of the weight sections and maintain balance. This is called the "compensating counterweight." A spring connection between counterweight and cable reduces the shock when starting and stopping.

**Cables and Sheaves.** The cables are the vulnerable part of a skip hoist and should be of the highest grade obtainable. Sheaves should be of ample diameter (Chapter 11). If the cables show damage from bending, a replacement with a cable of larger diameter is useless. The head sheaves are rather inaccessible, and anti-friction bearings are worth the higher cost.

**Capacities and Power Requirements.** For industrial applications the speeds are 100 ft. per min. or less for the slow-speed skip, 100 to 150 ft. for the medium-speed, and up to 450 ft. for the high-speed. The rate of handling is a function of the speed, the size of the bucket, the distance it travels, and the type of skip. As the machines are standardized the designer uses the data of the manufacturer he favors in making his selection. For the purpose of illustration we show the data of one manufacturer in Table 1. It will be noted that the skips have the above classifications of slow, medium, and high speed, with the further differentiation between automatic and semi-automatic control. The sizes of hoists are designated as RS-½, RS-1, RS-2, and RS-3 (the largest). It will be observed that the uncounterweighted skip requires much more power than the counterweighted and balanced skips for the same work. The high-speed skip should have automatic slowdown as the bucket approaches the limits of travel.

**Comment.** For small capacities and lifts, as for the removal of ashes from a small steam plant, the costly hoisting unit may be replaced by a head assembly consisting of a motorized reducer with a sprocket on the extended slow-speed shaft. A suitable chain is led from the bucket up over the sprocket, then down, and is attached to the bottom of the bucket. A limit switch at the top and bottom of the run and a start-and-stop-bucket station suffice for the control. Such a skip costs about one-third as much as the standard skip with geared hoist, etc., but may be applied only to very small capacities and lifts.

When the layout involves discharge to an overhead conveyor the skip is somewhat at a disadvantage compared with the elevator since a conveyor cannot receive a succession of large batches and there must be a surge hopper and feeder between skip and conveyor. This means that the head sheave must be at considerable height above the conveyor, and a heavy head structure may be required. Sometimes a shuttle car is in tandem with a skip with its cycle synchronized with that of the bucket so that it receives the bucket load and travels outward as the bucket descends, discharging automatically and returning to the loading position as the bucket ascends (Fig. 5-4). The combination is not so well adapted to conditions calling for varying points of delivery of the material.

A skip with automatic loader requires a deep track pit (Fig. 5-5). A 40-cu.-ft. bucket with 14 by 18 ft. track hopper calls for a pit depth of 19 ft., and a balanced skip with two 40-cu.-ft. buckets and a 14 by 30 ft. track hopper requires a pit depth of about 21 ft. The storage ca-

# TABLE 1[1]

## Capacities of Skip Hoists in Tons of Coal per Hour

| Type of Skip | Bucket Capacity, cubic feet | | Automatic Loading; Fully Automatic Operation | | | | | | | | | Automatic Loading; Semi-Automatic Operation | | | | | |
|---|---|---|---|---|---|---|---|---|---|---|---|---|---|---|---|---|---|
| | | | 20 | 30 | 40 | 60 | 80 | 100 | 120 | 150 | 200 | 20 | 30 | 40 | 60 | 80 | 100 |
| Slow-speed 80 ft. per min. uncounterweighted and counterweighted | Tons per hour | 40-ft. lift | 24 | 35 | 50 | 75 | 95 | 120 | 145 | 185 | 245 | 20 | 30 | 40 | 60 | 80 | 100 |
| | | 60 " " | 16 | 24 | 35 | 50 | 65 | 80 | 100 | 125 | 165 | 15 | 23 | 30 | 45 | 60 | 75 |
| | | 80 " " | 13 | 20 | 25 | 40 | 55 | 65 | 80 | 100 | 135 | 12 | 18 | 24 | 35 | 45 | 60 |
| | | 100 " " | 11 | 16 | 22 | 30 | 45 | 55 | 65 | 85 | 110 | 10 | 15 | 20 | 30 | 40 | 50 |
| | | 120 " " | 9 | 14 | 18 | 25 | 35 | 45 | 55 | 70 | 95 | 8 | 12 | 17 | 25 | 30 | 40 |
| | | 160 " " | 7 | 10 | 14 | 21 | 30 | 35 | 45 | 55 | 70 | 6 | 9 | 13 | 19 | 26 | 30 |
| | | 200 " " | 6 | 8 | 11 | 17 | 23 | 29 | 35 | 45 | 55 | 5 | 8 | 11 | 16 | 22 | 27 |
| | Total motor hp. | Uncounterweighted | 10 | 12 | 16 | 22 | 28 | 36 | 42 | | | 10 | 12 | 16 | 22 | 28 | 36 |
| | | Counterweighted | 5 | 5 | 5 | 8 | 9 | 11 | 14 | 17 | 22 | 5 | 5 | 5 | 8 | 9 | 11 |
| | Hoist machine | Uncounterweighted | RS-½ | RS-½ | RS-½ | RS-1 | RS-1 | RS-2 | RS-2 | | | RS-½ | RS-½ | RS-½ | RS-1 | RS-1 | RS-2 |
| | | Counterweighted | RS-½ | RS-½ | RS-½ | RS-1 | RS-1 | RS-1 | RS-2 | RS-2 | RS-3 | RS-½ | RS-½ | RS-½ | RS-1 | RS-1 | RS-1 |
| Medium-speed 140 ft. per min. uncounterweighted and counterweighted | Tons per hour | 40-ft. lift | 35 | 50 | 70 | 105 | 140 | 175 | 210 | 265 | 350 | 28 | 40 | 55 | 85 | 115 | 140 |
| | | 60 " " | 25 | 37 | 50 | 75 | 100 | 125 | 150 | 185 | 250 | 22 | 35 | 45 | 65 | 90 | 110 |
| | | 80 " " | 21 | 30 | 40 | 65 | 85 | 105 | 125 | 155 | 210 | 18 | 27 | 35 | 55 | 75 | 90 |
| | | 100 " " | 17 | 26 | 35 | 50 | 70 | 85 | 105 | 130 | 170 | 15 | 23 | 30 | 45 | 60 | 75 |
| | | 120 " " | 15 | 22 | 30 | 45 | 60 | 75 | 90 | 110 | 150 | 13 | 20 | 27 | 40 | 55 | 65 |
| | | 160 " " | 11 | 16 | 22 | 35 | 45 | 55 | 65 | 85 | 110 | 10 | 15 | 21 | 30 | 40 | 50 |
| | | 200 " " | 9 | 13 | 18 | 27 | 35 | 45 | 55 | 65 | 90 | 9 | 13 | 18 | 27 | 35 | 45 |
| | Total motor hp. | Uncounterweighted | 16 | 21 | 29 | 39 | 50 | 62 | 72 | | | 16 | 21 | 29 | 39 | 50 | 60 |
| | | Counterweighted | 5 | 6 | 8 | 12 | 16 | 20 | 24 | 30 | 39 | 5 | 6 | 8 | 12 | 16 | 20 |
| | Hoist machine | Uncounterweighted | RS-½ | RS-½ | RS-½ | RS-1 | RS-1 | RS-2 | RS-2 | | | RS-½ | RS-½ | RS-½ | RS-1 | RS-1 | RS-2 |
| | | Counterweighted | RS-½ | RS-½ | RS-½ | RS-1 | RS-1 | RS-1 | RS-2 | RS-2 | RS-3 | RS-½ | RS-½ | RS-½– | RS-1 | RS-1 | RS-1 |

TABLE 1[1] (*Continued*)

| Type of Skip | Bucket Capacity, cubic feet | | Automatic Loading; Fully Automatic Operation | | | | | | | | |
|---|---|---|---|---|---|---|---|---|---|---|---|
| | | | 20 | 30 | 40 | 60 | 80 | 100 | 120 | 150 | 200 |
| High-speed 260 ft. per min. uncounterweighted and counterweighted (two-speed) | Tons per hour | 80-ft. lift | | | 60 | 90 | 120 | 150 | 180 | 225 | 300 |
| | | 100 " " | | | 50 | 75 | 100 | 125 | 155 | 190 | 255 |
| | | 120 " " | | | 45 | 65 | 90 | 110 | 135 | 165 | 225 |
| | | 160 " " | | | 35 | 55 | 75 | 85 | 110 | 135 | 185 |
| | | 200 " " | | | 30 | 45 | 60 | 75 | 95 | 115 | 155 |
| | Total motor hp. | Uncounterweighted | | | 54 | 73 | 93 | 110 | 134 | | |
| | | Counterweighted | | | 15 | 22 | 29 | 36 | 44 | 55 | 73 |
| | Hoist machine | Uncounterweighted | | | RS-1 | RS-1 | RS-1 | RS-2 | RS-3 | | |
| | | Counterweighted | | | RS-1 | RS-1 | RS-1 | RS-1 | RS-2 | RS-2 | RS-3 |
| High-speed 260 ft. per min. balanced (two-speed) | Tons per hour | 80-ft. lift | | | 115 | 175 | 235 | 295 | 355 | 445 | 590 |
| | | 100 " " | | | 100 | 155 | 205 | 255 | 305 | 380 | 510 |
| | | 120 " " | | | 90 | 135 | 180 | 225 | 270 | 335 | 450 |
| | | 160 " " | | | 75 | 110 | 145 | 170 | 220 | 275 | 370 |
| | | 200 ' " | | | 60 | 90 | 125 | 155 | 185 | 235 | 310 |
| | Total motor hp. | | | | 29 | 44 | 58 | 73 | 87 | 108 | 145 |
| | Hoist machine | | | | RS-1 | RS-1 | RS-1 | RS-1 | RS-2 | RS-2 | RS-3 |

Tables given here are based on vertical lifts. For inclined runs, multiply horsepowers by the following:

80° — 0.985
70° — 0.940
60° — 0.866
50° — 0.766

[1] Source: Link-Belt Company.
When handling ashes, use 80 per cent of above capacities and horsepower.
Manual loading with semi and non-automatic operation figured for a minimum cycle of 2 min.
The weight of coal assumed at 50 lb. per cu. ft.
The weight of ashes is assumed at 40 lb. per cu. ft.
A ton is figured at 2000 lb.

pacity of the track hopper should be not less than 20 per cent of the rated hourly capacity of the skip.

The purchaser should secure the recommendations of a responsible manufacturer before deciding on the type of skip required for his plant. The major item of cost is the hoisting unit and the size of this unit de-

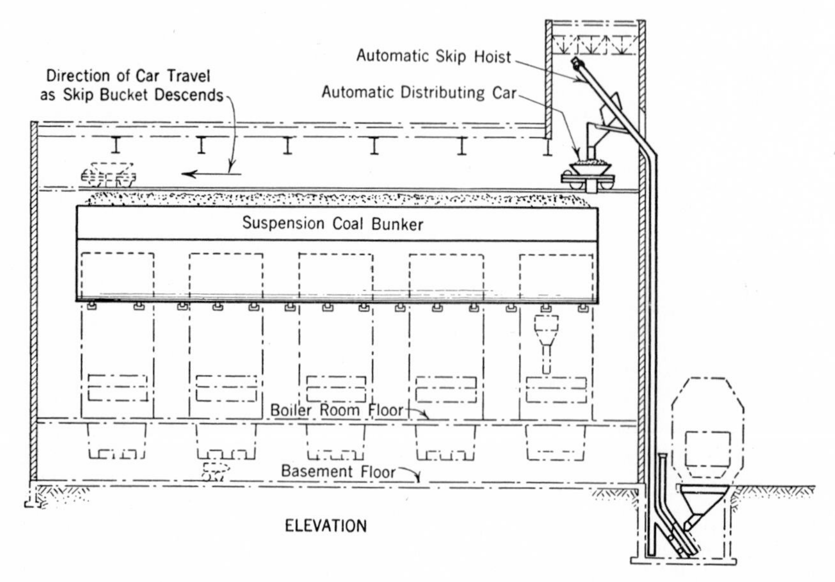


Fig. 5-4. Distributing car synchronized with skip hoist. (Bartlett and Snow.)

pends largely on the type of skip. Assume a requirement of hoisting 110 tons per hour with a lift of 160 ft. By referring to the high-speed hoists in Table 1 we find:

| Type of Hoist | Bucket Size, cubic feet | Hoist Size | Motor Horsepower |
|---|---|---|---|
| Uncounterweighted | 120 | RS-3 | 134 |
| Counterweighted | 120 | RS-2 | 44 |
| Balanced | 60 | RS-1 | 44 |

Let us select a skip, applying Table 1. It is desired to lift 40 tons per hour of mine-run coal, with lumps not larger than 10 in., along a straight run of 100 ft. inclined at 80° to the horizontal. We see that with a full-automatic skip with 60-cu.-ft. bucket and with a medium speed of 140 ft. per min. the listed capacity is 50 tons per hour. We can disregard the slight reduction in capacity due to the 80° slope. With either the counterweighted or uncounterweighted type the hoist

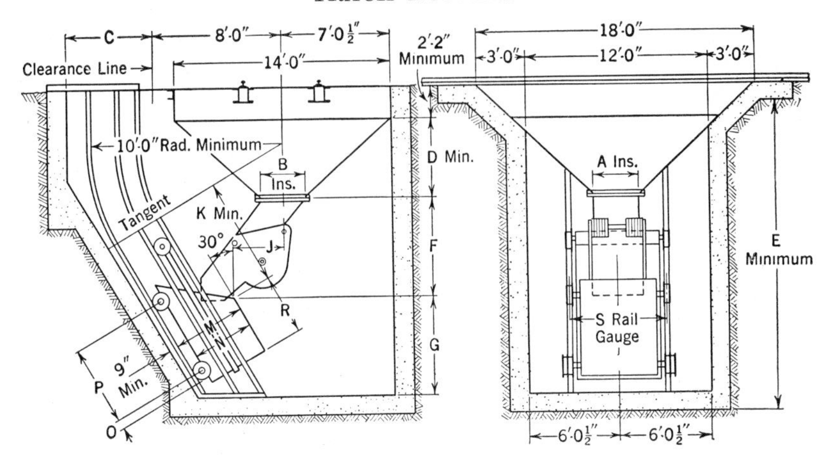


Single-Skip Track Hopper

14′ × 18′ Single-Skip Hopper

| Bucket Capacity, cubic feet | A | B | C | D | E | F | G | J | K | M | N | O | P | R | S |
|---|---|---|---|---|---|---|---|---|---|---|---|---|---|---|---|
| 40 | 2′-0″ | 2′-9⅞″ | 5′-6″ | 5′-3″ | 19′-2″ | 6′-5½″ | 5′-3½″ | 3′-4¾″ | 6′-6″ | 4′-0¾″ | 3′-6″ | 6″ | 4′-7″ | 3′-0″ | 4′-11¾″ |
| 60 | 2′-6″ | 2′-9⅞″ | 5′-6″ | 5′-1″ | 19′-10½″ | 6′-5½″ | 6′-2″ | 3′-4¾″ | 6′-9″ | 4′-0¾″ | 3′-6″ | 8″ | 5′-1″ | 4′-0″ | 5′-5¾″ |
| 80 | 3′-0″ | 2′-9⅞″ | 6′-2½″ | 5′-0″ | 20′-1″ | 6′-5½″ | 6′-5½″ | 3′-4¾″ | 7′-0″ | 4′-8¼″ | 4′-0″ | 12″ | 5′-3″ | 4′-0″ | 6′-1″ |
| 100 | 3′-0″ | 2′-9⅞″ | 6′-2½″ | 5′-0″ | 20′-11″ | 6′-5½″ | 7′-3½″ | 3′-4¾″ | 7′-3″ | 4′-8¼″ | 4′-0″ | 12″ | 5′-9″ | 5′-0″ | 6′-1″ |
| 120 | 3′-0″ | 2′-9⅞″ | 6′-2½″ | 5′-0″ | 21′-9½″ | 6′-5½″ | 8′-2″ | 3′-4¾″ | 7′-9″ | 4′-8¼″ | 4′-0″ | 12″ | 6′-9″ | 6′-0″ | 6′-1″ |

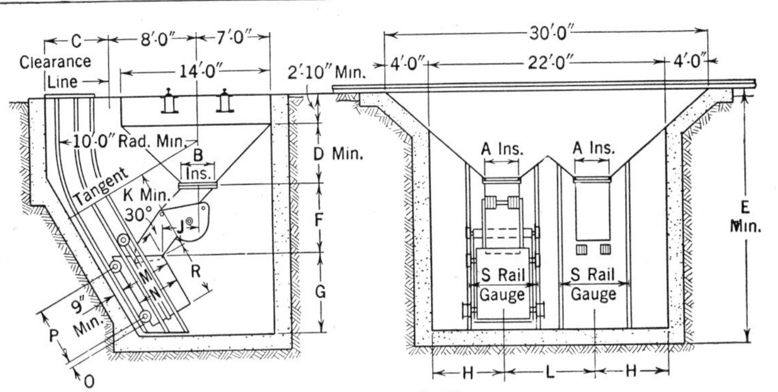


Balanced-Skip Track Hopper

14′ × 30′ Balanced Skip Hopper

| Bucket Capacity, cubic feet | A | B | C | D | E | F | G | H | J | K | L | M | N | O | P | R | S |
|---|---|---|---|---|---|---|---|---|---|---|---|---|---|---|---|---|---|
| 40 | 2′-0″ | 2′-9⅞″ | 5′-6″ | 6′-0″ | 20′-7″ | 6′-5½″ | 5′-3½″ | 7′-7″ | 3′-4¾″ | 6′-6″ | 6′-11″ | 4′-0¾″ | 3′-6″ | 6″ | 4′-7″ | 3′-0″ | 4′-11¾″ |
| 60 | 2′-6″ | 2′-9⅞″ | 5′-6″ | 5′-10″ | 20′-5″ | 6′-5½″ | 6′-2″ | 7′-4″ | 3′-4¾″ | 6′-9″ | 7′-5″ | 4′-0¾″ | 3′-6″ | 8″ | 5′-1″ | 4′-0″ | 5′-5¾″ |
| 80 | 3′-0″ | 2′-9⅞″ | 6′-2½″ | 5′-5″ | 21′-2″ | 6′-5½″ | 6′-5½″ | 6′-10″ | 3′-4¾″ | 7′-0″ | 8′-5″ | 4′-8¼″ | 4′-0″ | 12″ | 5′-3″ | 4′-0″ | 6′-1″ |
| 100 | 3′-0″ | 2′-9⅞″ | 6′-2½″ | 5′-5″ | 22′-0″ | 6′-5½″ | 7′-3½″ | 6′-10″ | 3′-4¾″ | 7′-3″ | 8′-5″ | 4′-8¼″ | 4′-0″ | 12″ | 5′-9″ | 5′-0″ | 6′-1″ |
| 120 | 3′-0″ | 2′-9⅞″ | 6′-2½″ | 5′-5″ | 22′-10½″ | 6′-5½″ | 8′-2″ | 6′-10″ | 3′-4¾″ | 7′-9″ | 8′-5″ | 4′-8¼″ | 4′-0″ | 12″ | 6′-9″ | 6′-0″ | 6′-1″ |
| 150 | 3′-0″ | 2′-9⅞″ | 9′-6″ | 5′-4″ | 23′-2″ | 6′-5½″ | 8′-6½″ | 6′-6½″ | 3′-6″ | 9′-0″ | 9′-0″ | 5′-5⅞″ | 4′-6″ | | | 6′-0″ | 7′-0″ |
| 200 | | | | | | | | | | | | | | | | | |

Fig. 5–5. Track hoppers for single and balanced skips. Dimensions are Link-Belt standards.

size is designated as RS-1, but the motor is 39 hp. for the uncounterweighted skip as against 12 hp. for the counterweighted skip. The next smaller size is the 40-cu.-ft. bucket. This has a capacity of 35 tons per hour at 140 ft. per min., and we might speed up this skip to secure the required capacity of 40 tons per hour and use the smaller RS-½ hoist with considerable saving in first cost.

Again, assume the problem of lifting 65 tons per hour of coal vertically 120 ft. We can specify a full-automatic counterweighted skip with 100-cu.-ft. bucket at a speed of 140 ft. per min., or a 60-cu.-ft. bucket at 260 ft. per min. Slow speed gives a gentler engagement with the loader, but the large bucket requires a more costly hoist tower. We could specify the high-speed machine with automatic slowdown at the ends of travel. Either requires the same size of hoist machine and approximately the same power.

Assume a more complex requirement: A lift of 160 ft. on an incline of 70° with the horizontal for a capacity of 150 tons per hour of minus ¼-in. coal which will be received in four-pocket, 70-ton cars. The job can be done with a counterweighted skip with a 200-cu.-ft. bucket geared to 260 ft. per min., for which 73 motor hp. will be required, but there is a bad feature. To secure a straight run for the counterweight, its guides might be mounted along the top chord of the bridge, a dangerous position. Or it might be a vertical run along the boiler-house wall. Since the run will be too short, we can hang the counterweight in a bight, introducing one more bend in the cable and doubling the weight, about 15 tons in this case. For the four-pocket cars the track hopper must be exceptionally deep to converge to a single loader. Consider the alternative of a balanced skip.

The capacity is attained by a two-speed balanced skip with 100-cu.-ft. buckets at about the same speed and motor hp., but the hoist machine will be smaller, and the track hopper with twin loaders will require less depth. The sides of the hopper for this small coal should be on at least a 50° slope, and it may be necessary to provide vibrators against the side plates if the coal is sluggish, as probably it will be.

One interesting application of the balanced skip was a tandem lift from beneath a track hopper to a Bradford breaker and then from beneath the breaker up to the bunker.

The first lift was 55 ft. and the speed 69 ft. per min. The second lift of 128 ft. was made at 160 ft. per min. Both buckets were 60-cu.-ft. capacity with the cables wound on a single drum whose diameter was stepped down for half its length to give the slower speed. The capacity of each lift is 40 tons per hour. It was good engineering, making one skip do a job for which two were contemplated.

Analyzing the operation and disregarding the slowdown at each end of the run, we see that the up-trip of the lower bucket at 69 ft. per min. requires 48 sec. In 48 sec. the upper bucket at 160 ft. per min. rises 128 ft. as required. Actually the motor was a two-speed machine for automatic slowdown to 80 ft. per min. at the ends of travel of the high-speed bucket. This made a corresponding terminal slowdown from 69 ft. to 35 ft. per min. in the lower skip, but this does not affect the cycle.

Consider the problem of elevating 70 tons per hour of calcined gypsum weighing 60 lb. per cu. ft. from cars to an adjacent storage bin with its top 100 ft. ground level. The bin is 50 ft. long with its axis at 90° with the railroad siding.

Several machines are available. One is an L-path continuous-flow elevator in combination with a distributing screw conveyor. The cross section of the elevator duct will be 136 sq. in. and the speed 55 ft. per min. The chain pull approximates 20,000 lb., which is extremely heavy, and the power requirement is 40 motor horsepower for the elevator and 15 for a 20-in. screw conveyor at 50 r.p.m.

Again we may specify an apron feeder and a gravity-discharge elevator conveyor with a vertical lift of 120 ft. and horizontal centers of 50 ft. Buckets, 20 by 20 in. spaced 18-in. centers. Speed, 70 ft. per min. This calls for a 15-hp. motor plus 5 hp. for the feeder.

A third possibility is a skip hoist. We require a lift of about 140 ft. to accommodate a surge hopper ahead of the distributing conveyor. The skip will be full automatic, counterweighted, with an 80-cu.-ft. bucket at 140 ft. per min.

We require a 20-hp. hoist plus 15 hp. for the screw.

The continuous-flow installation will cost least, but not if it is of special design suited to this material. The bucket elevator will be highest in cost. The skip cost is between the two, and its maintenance with calcined gypsum will be lowest.

At a sand-and-gravel preparation plant where it was desired to screen the incoming material and distribute it, after sizing, into eight silos for local trade (Fig. 5-6) it was found that a lift of 125 ft. was required, with a capacity of 100 tons per hour. For the capacity, with material weighing 100 lb. per cu. ft., we require a balanced skip with full-automatic control and 40-cu.-ft. buckets at 260 ft. per min.

The skip is the best machine here. The vertical-inclined path is not too good for a bucket elevator, and the skip will stand up better with sand and gravel than either a chain-and-bucket or belt-and-bucket elevator.

A somewhat different requirement is shown in Fig. 5-7 where a

Fig. 5–6. Full automatic balanced skip hoist. Two 40-cu.-ft. buckets, 125-ft. hoist, for 100 tons per hour of gravel and stone. (Link-Belt.)

stock pile of limestone weighing 96 lb. per cu. ft. is maintained back of a retaining wall opposite a battery of vertical kilns. A traveling skip was installed. Since the limestone must be manually loaded, a non-automatic balanced skip was specified. The lift is 100 ft. Buckets are 60-cu.-ft. capacity. Speed, 100 ft. per min. Each bucket makes one lift and stops with the other bucket in position for loading. Some modification of the arrangement of the stock pile which would permit loading with a small bulldozer would be an improvement here.

**Maintenance.** The cables are the vital part of the skip. If the valley of the sheave groove is too narrow the cable is pinched, and abrasion results. If the V is too wide the cables will flatten under

FIG. 5–7. Traveling skip hoist with non-automatic control. Two 60-cu.-ft. buckets for 100 tons per hour of limestone. Speed 100 ft. per min. (Link-Belt.)

service. Cables should be protected by applications of a heavy lubricant. Since it is difficult to determine the condition of a cable by inspection, it is well to play safe and install a new cable or reverse the cable when gradual elongation ceases. Operators learn to determine the condition from the tonnage handled as well as by inspection. The most frequent causes of cable trouble are small head and guide sheaves, worn grooves, and sheaves out of line.

The Bethlehem Steel Company advises:

The individual wires of a steel cable move relatively to each other and twist around their own axes. To protect these " bearing surfaces " from rust and wear, lubrication is necessary. Clean the cable carefully before applying the lubricant, removing dirt and grit with kerosene and a stiff brush, or pull the cable through a tightly wrapped swab. If the cable has been working in a wet atmosphere it may be covered with hydrated rust, a slimy film that cannot be removed until the cable has been throughly dried out. To apply oil or grease on top of hydrated rust is wasted effort.

A stiff cable with fewer, larger wires requires a heavier lubricant than a more flexible cable with many wires. When applying a heavy lubricant, thin it out by heating to get the desired penetration. The cable may be lubricated by pulling it slowly through a vat containing the heated lubricant or by a paint brush. Some lubricants have an acid base which actually corrodes wires. The lubricant should be one which will not "fight" with the lubricant already on the cable. Cables operating under high-temperature conditions require a lubricant that will hold its body at such temperatures.

Never let the cable rust or become dried out. Every type of cable presents its own lubrication problem. If the load is heavy, if the speed is high, if the bends (around sheaves) are frequent, or if the cable is exposed to corrosive fumes, special care in lubrication is essential.

The functioning of the automatic loader should be checked at intervals. If the counterweight which balances the rotating member is too heavy there is an excessive shock as the bucket engages the loader; if it is too light the loader may drop while the bucket is aloft, with possible severe damage. The traveling cam, the heart of the control, is enclosed and requires little attention except for adjustment as the cable stretches. Guides and bucket rollers and the clips which secure the cables to the bucket yoke and counterweight call for careful checking.

## CHAPTER 6

## BUCKET CARRIERS

**Open-Top Carriers.** If it is required to elevate material, but without an upper or lower horizontal run, there are available the bucket elevator and the open-top carrier. The latter is intended for flat inclines between 40 and 60° with the horizontal. It resembles (Fig. 6-1) a continuous bucket elevator but with deep pockets and skirt boards to prevent spillage. The particular installation shown was

Fig. 6–1. Heavy-duty open-top carrier. Designed for 800 tons per hour of limestone.

put into operation in 1913 to handle 800 tons per hour of limestone, and though it is more than 30 yr. old it is a well-engineered job by present standards. The long pitch chains have intermediate carrying rollers, the articulations have driving collars, and the twin drive gears have replaceable segments. The first replacement of chain pins, bushings, driving collars and pins for the flanged rollers were made in 1932 after 19 yr. of active service. Were this machine to be duplicated today about the only improvements that might be made would be anti-friction bearings in the flanged rollers and head shaft bearings.

**Horizontal Runarounds.** Not infrequently it is required to have a runaround path in a horizontal plant. For this the side pull Redler

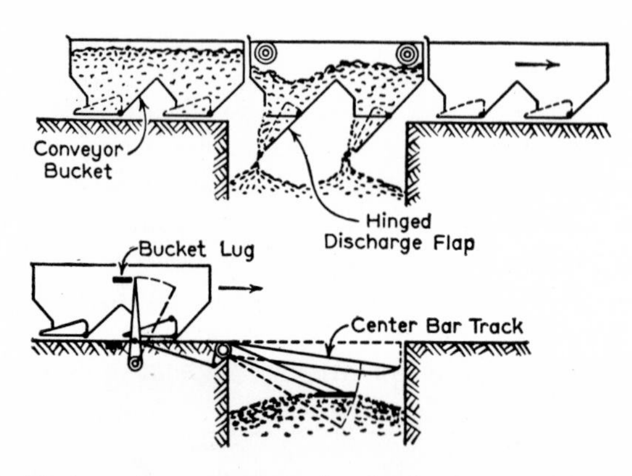


FIG. 6–2. Horizontal-runaround carrier for fragile material. (Link-Belt.)

conveyor (Figs. 8-12 and 20-9) may fulfil the requirements unless the material is quite fragile and will not stand pushing along a trough. With such material if degradation must be avoided the "side-car carrier" is indicated.

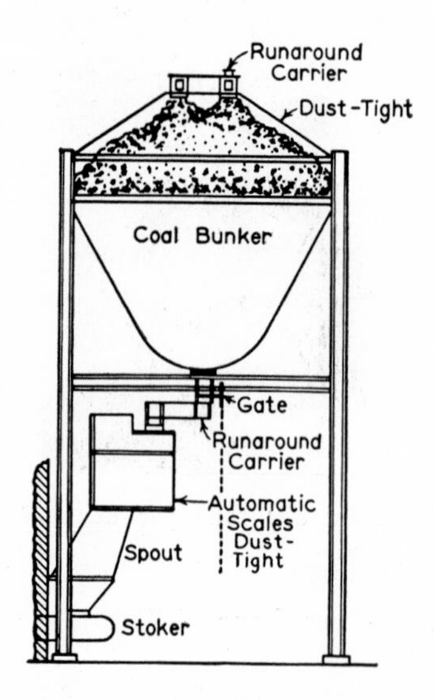


FIG. 6–3. Horizontal-runaround carriers as applied for loading to, and distributing from, bunker.

**Side-Car Carrier.** The machine was originated by Mr. N. L. Davis during the war, to meet the need for a horizontal closed circuit conveyor in the manufacture of metallic magnesium from magnesium chloride in the form of fragile flakes somewhat resembling corn flakes in fragility and extremely hygroscopic.

The chloride is fed continuously to a battery of chutes leading to the electric furnaces. It must not be degraded or pulverized or the efficiency of the furnaces is seriously reduced. The loads must feed out at a succession of outlets and any surplus recirculates.

Figure 6-2 shows the principle of operation. The buckets are attached to a single strand of roller chain and maintained level by an outside guide roller. Each bucket has hinged discharge flaps normally held shut by the floor of the trough but free to drop to discharge position as they cross the gaps leading to the retort chutes. Degradation during transit is almost completely eliminated, but it is still desirable that there be no drag across the material filling the chutes. A V-shaped arm crosses the top of each chute and is raised and dropped by a lever which contacts a lug on every tenth or twelfth bucket. A pad on the lower leg of the V, holds the upper leg of the V in a position to form a bridge across the gap when the material nears the top of the chute so that the flaps cannot drop until the level of material in the chute has lowered.

Each of these carriers as installed in the war plants has a length of several hundred feet between centers and operates 24 hr. per day. Figure 6-3 shows the application of two of these machines as developed by the Link-Belt Company for distributing coal in a storage bunker and from the bunker to the automatic scales hoppers.

The power requirement of this machine may be approximated by the formula

$$\text{Chain pull} = RF \times (2W_c + W_m \times L) + 0.33 \times W_m \times L' \text{ in pounds.}$$

$W_c$ = weight of one run of the element in pounds.

$W_m$ = weight of material per foot of conveyor in pounds.

$L$ = centers distance in feet.

$L'$ = maximum distance in feet the buckets travel with load.*

$RF$ = rolling friction in carrier rollers, 0.1 approximately.

$$HP = \frac{\text{Pull} \times \text{Speed in feet per minute}}{33{,}000}$$

In selecting the motor add 10 per cent for friction in the terminals and 10 per cent for drive loss.

**Pivoted Bucket Carrier.** This is intended for a closed-circuit path in a vertical plane. It consists of a train of overlapping buckets pivotally suspended between two strands of chain, with supporting rails or guides, turn wheels, drive, and a tripper or dumper to up-end the buckets for discharge.

**Historical.** About 1885, C. W. Hunt invented the Hunt carrier, with spaced, pivotally hung buckets between two strands of chain. Because of the gap between buckets a loader was necessary to deposit the charge into each bucket and avoid the spill through these inter-

* If carrier is loaded at one end of a run and feeds out at multiple points along this run, take $L'$ as $\frac{1}{2}L$. If loaded along one run with multiple feed out points along the return run, take $L'$ as $1.5L$.

spaces. Later George McCaslin invented the McCaslin carrier with overlapping buckets which eliminated the loader but required a device to reverse each bucket after it discharged to bring it into proper overlap before it re-entered the loading run. Then S. B. Peck invented the Peck carrier with the buckets hung between rearward extensions of the chain links so that they automatically lapped and unlapped properly (Figs. 6-4 and 6-5). With the expiration of the Peck patents other manufacturers adopted this arrangement, which is the standard carrier of today.

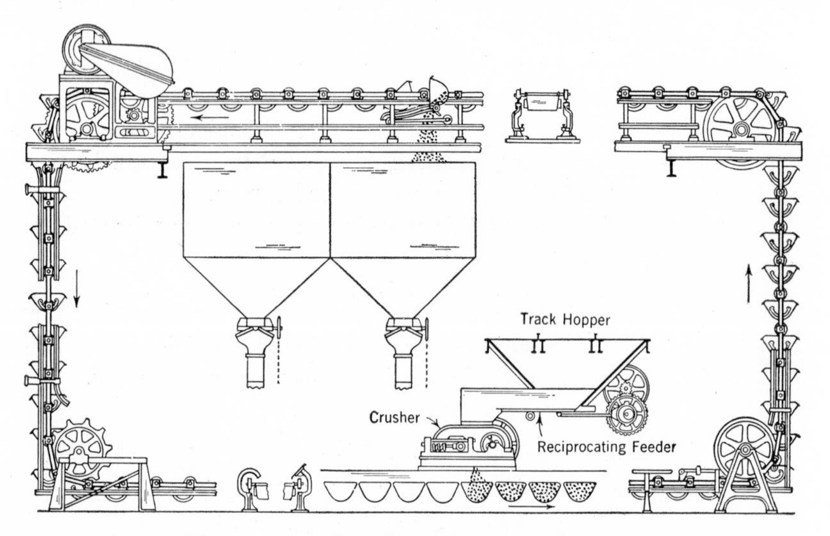


Fig. 6-4. Typical pivoted bucket carrier layout.

**Essential Elements.** The bucket sizes of standard Peck carriers range from 18 by 15 in. (length by width) up to 36 by 36 in. The chain pitch must be the same as the bucket length, so the long-pitch engineering chains are used. Spacer rods hold the two strands in alignment and serve as the pivot shafts from which the buckets are suspended. The center of gravity of the bucket, whether empty or filled, is below the pivot line; thus the buckets always remain upright except when tilted for discharge. Any part of the conveying element may be replaced when worn with little disturbance of the assembly. The bucket trunnions have renewable bearing blocks, and the buckets may be removed without detaching the cross rods. The flanged rollers have 400 Brinell rims. The chain bars are rigid, ribbed, malleable iron with heat-treated chrome-nickel pins locked in the sidebars. Pins, bushings, and rollers are lubricated through Alemite fittings in the ends of the pins. The bushings are seamless steel, case-hardened, and shouldered to act as spacers for the side bars at each articulation point. The buckets are one-piece malleable castings with malleable-iron dumping cams riveted to both ends.

This carrier is essentially a slow-speed machine usually operating at 40 to 60 ft. per min. The driving sprockets are driven through equalizing gears which compensate for the pulsations of the long-pitch chains. Complete protection is given by shear pin, automatic brake, and an

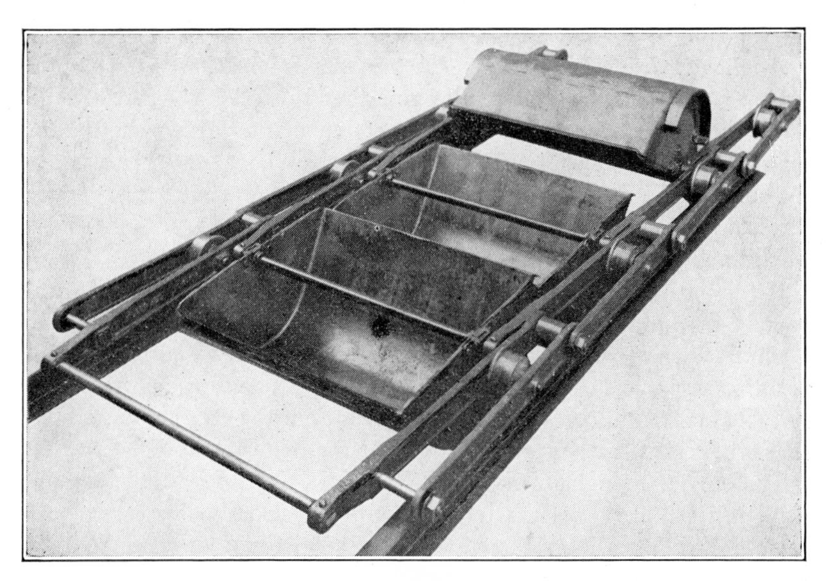

FIG. 6–5. Construction of 30 by 36 in. Peck carrier. Driving collars at articulations and flanged carrying rollers with anti-friction bearings. Buckets may be removed without disconnecting the chains. Capacity per Table 2, 115 to 155 tons per hour at 45 to 60 ft. per min.

emergency stop which acts should a bucket reverse or fail to level off after dumping. Carrying rails usually weigh 16 lb. per yd. If the material is corrosive the guards and casings are of copper-bearing steel or other resistant material.

The dumper, or tripper, may be stationary with provision for raising or lowering, or it may be mounted on a carriage to provide for discharge at any point along the upper run.

Figure 6-5 shows the modern pivoted bucket carrier with refinements in details. This is a section of a 30 by 36 in. heavy-duty carrier for hot, finely pulverized abrasive material. The drive sprockets engage with collars at the articulation points of the chain. Carrying rollers located opposite the bucket trunnions are carried on sealed anti-friction bearings. These rollers carry only the weight of the element along the horizontal runs and are not subjected to the shock of the drive. The figure indicates how any part of the carrier may be replaced without disturbing the assembly. When entering a curve in the path the cantilever extensions of the inner side bars of the chain to which the bucket trunnion rods are attached sweep in a wider arc than the articulations of the chain, thus unlocking the lips of the buckets and automatically lapping them in the proper position for tilting as they enter the top run.

**Applications and Limitations.** A frequent application of the pivoted bucket carrier is for a rectangular runaround path in a vertical plane, as for handling coal and ashes in a steam plant. However, it may follow almost any variation from this path. Where there is a vertical lift only, the bucket elevator has less dead weight and costs less. If the lift is extremely high, the skip hoist, which involves still less dead weight and costs less, will usually be the best selection.

If the path is a vertical lift followed by a short horizontal run, the gravity-discharge elevator conveyor is a good choice, but if the material is abrasive the carrier is much better since it carries the material instead of scraping it along a trough. An elevator in tandem with any suitable horizontal conveyor may cost less than the carrier; the preference will rest with the characteristics of the material.

The carrier is high in first cost. Its best feature is that, once installed, it will serve year after year with remarkably low cost of upkeep. Some installations have been in service for more than forty years and are still functioning. Table 1 shows a few actual maintenance costs for steam-plant runaround carriers. The figures are by no means exceptional.

TABLE 1

MAINTENANCE COSTS OF PIVOTED BUCKET CARRIERS

| Material Handled | Years Covered | Tons per Year | Annual[1] Repairs | Maintenance per Ton Handled |
|---|---|---|---|---|
| Coal and ashes | 6 | 25,000 | $12 | $0.0004 |
| Coal and ashes | 5 | 81,000 | 26 | 0.0003 |
| Coal | 13 | 242,000 | 130 | 0.0005 |

[1]Material only, not including labor.

Few types of conveyors can show records approaching these. In recent years the application of carriers to handling coal and ashes in steam plants has been somewhat restricted because of the introduction of pulverized fuel and the development of sluicing and pneumatic systems for the disposal of the slag and fly ash. In the chemical field, for hot, abrasive, or corrosive materials, the carrier has an important place, often fulfilling the severe requirements better than any other type of conveyor. For food products, as tomatoes from trucks to vats, the buckets are lined with porcelain or similar material not affected by acid and readily sterilized.

**Capacities and Power Requirements.** Table 2 shows the standard sizes of pivoted bucket carriers with capacities and recommended maximum speeds. These capacities are conservative, as they are based on

TABLE 2

Capacities of Pivoted Bucket Carriers with Coal or Similar Material Weighing 50 Lb. per Cu. Ft. at Speeds Noted

| Bucket Pitch × Width, inches | Pitch of Chain, inches | Capacity of Bucket in Cubic Feet Level Full | Capacity in Tons of Coal per Hour | Speed, feet per minute |
|---|---|---|---|---|
| 18 × 15 | 18 | 0.74 | 15–20 | 30–40 |
| 18 × 18 | 18 | 0.89 | 20–25 | 30–40 |
| 18 × 21 | 18 | 1.04 | 25–30 | 30–40 |
| 24 × 18 | 24 | 1.55 | 35–45 | 40–50 |
| 24 × 24 | 24 | 2.08 | 50–60 | 40–50 |
| 24 × 30 | 24 | 2.55 | 60–75 | 40–50 |
| 24 × 36 | 24 | 3.09 | 70–90 | 40–50 |
| 30 × 24 | 30 | 3.65 | 80–105 | 45–60 |
| 30 × 30 | 30 | 4.55 | 95–130 | 45–60 |
| 30 × 36 | 30 | 5.47 | 115–155 | 45–60 |
| 36 × 36 | 36 | 8.00 | 160–255 | 50–80 |

loading the buckets to 80 per cent capacity. A carrier with longer pitch and narrower buckets will cost less than one of the same capacity but with shorter pitch and wider buckets.

**Determination of Motor Size.** The horizontal and vertical centers being known, the size of the motor can be determined from the charts (Fig. 6-6). The tabulated horsepower figures are for material weighing 50 lb. per cu. ft.

To illustrate the use of the charts assume a carrier with a 240-ft. horizontal and 50-ft. vertical centers to handle 65 tons of coal per hour, and ashes alternately. Since ashes weigh less than coal the operation with coal will determine the size of motor. From Table 2 we see that the carrier should be 24 by 30 in. with a speed of 40 ft. per min. Referring to Fig. 6-6, chart 2, the lines for the horizontal and vertical centers intersect between 15 hp. and 20 hp.; we will use a 20-hp. motor.

Unless the center distances are exceptionally large the horsepower

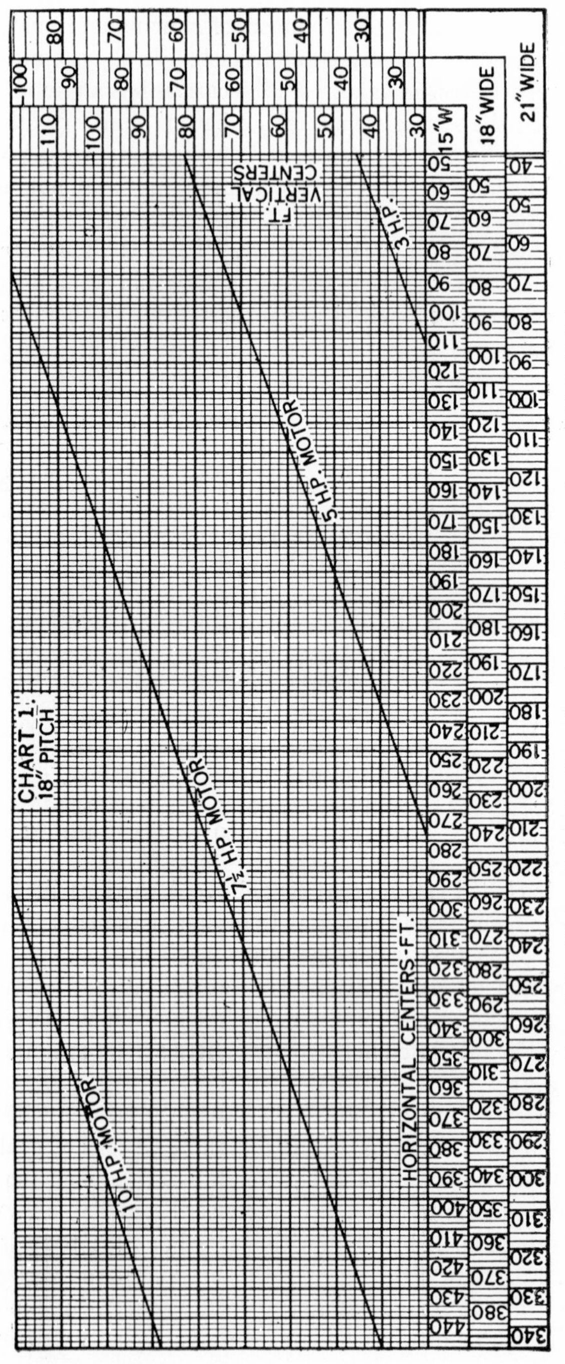


Fig. 6–6. Motor determinations for pivoted bucket carriers. (Link-Belt.)

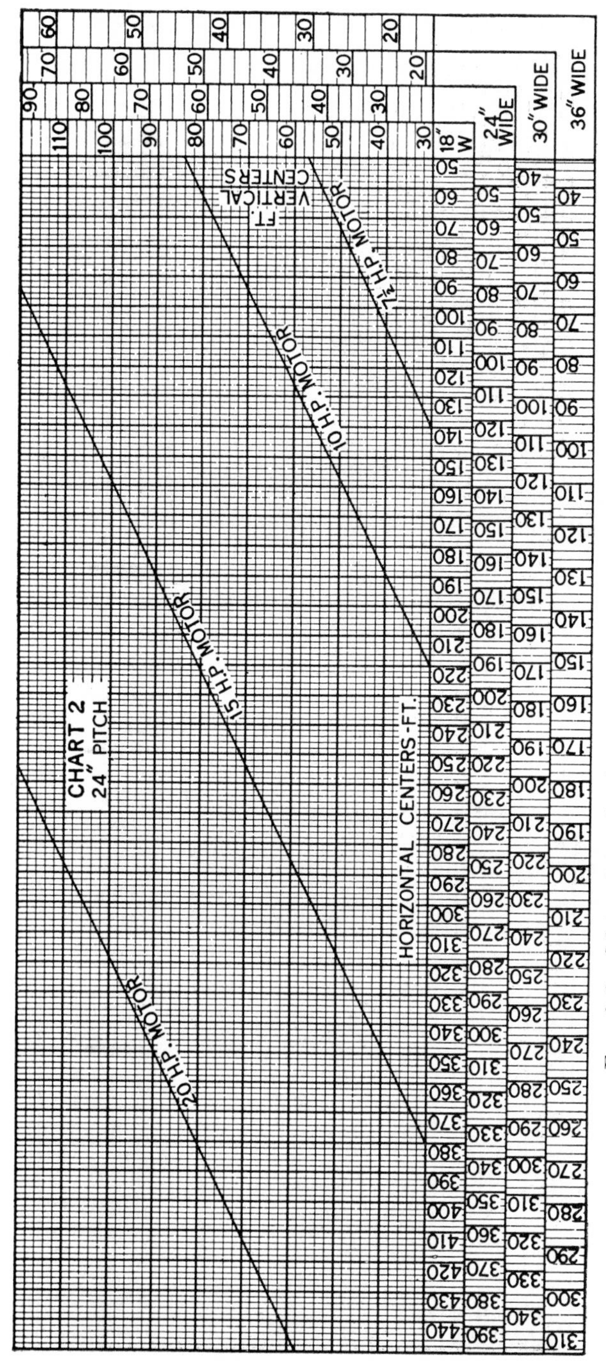


FIG. 6-6. Motor determinations for pivoted bucket carriers. (Link-Belt.)

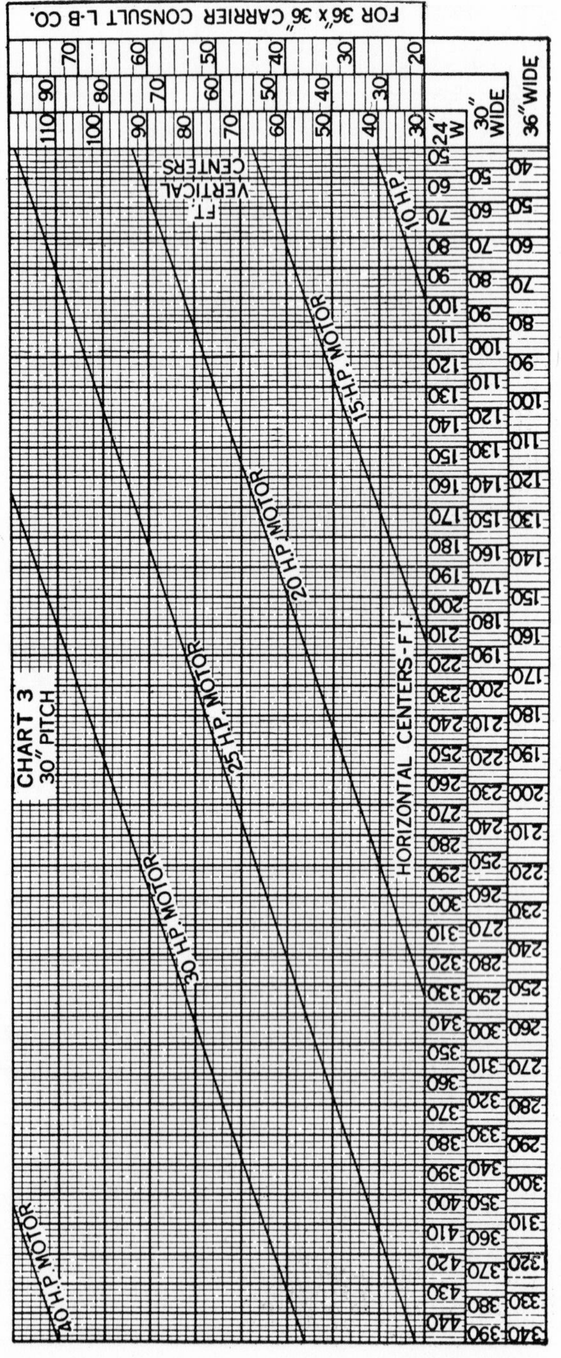


Fig. 6-6. Motor determinations for pivoted bucket carriers. (Link-Belt.)

TABLE 3

WEIGHTS FOR PIVOTED BUCKET CARRIER INSTALLATIONS

| Size of Carrier, inches | Weight of Drive Machinery | | Weight of Upper Corner Machinery | *A* | *B* | *C* | *D* | *E* | *F* |
|---|---|---|---|---|---|---|---|---|---|
| | With Head Frames | Without Head Frames | | | | | | | |
| 18 × 15 | | 3,500 | 1,000 | 45 | 69 | 93 | 135 | 155 | 175 |
| 18 × 18 | | 3,550 | 1,025 | 51 | 80 | 109 | 145 | 170 | 195 |
| 18 × 21 | | 3,600 | 1,050 | 56 | 88 | 123 | 155 | 185 | 215 |
| 24 × 18 | 10,600 | 9,300 | 2,650 | 114 | 153 | 192 | 220 | 260 | 300 |
| 24 × 24 | 10,700 | 9,390 | 2,700 | 122 | 173 | 224 | 230 | 280 | 330 |
| 24 × 30 | 10,800 | 9,480 | 2,750 | 131 | 195 | 259 | 235 | 295 | 355 |
| 24 × 36 | 10,900 | 9,570 | 2,800 | 139 | 216 | 293 | 240 | 315 | 390 |
| 30 × 24 | 22,900 | 19,600 | 6,200 | 136 | 208 | 280 | 255 | 330 | 400 |
| 30 × 30 | 23,000 | 19,700 | 6,275 | 149 | 238 | 327 | 280 | 370 | 455 |
| 30 × 36 | 23,100 | 19,800 | 6,350 | 155 | 262 | 369 | 295 | 400 | 510 |
| 36 × 36 | | 31,000 | 11,000 | 275 | 408 | 541 | 450 | 575 | 700 |

*A*. Weight per foot of chain and buckets, with buckets empty.
*B*. Weight per foot of chain and buckets, with buckets full of coal at 50 lb. per cu. ft.
*C*. Weight per foot of chain and buckets, with buckets full of material at 100 lb. per cu. ft.
*D*. Weight per foot of upper run including cross channels, walk, hand railing, rails, rail chairs, chain and buckets, with buckets empty.
*E*. Weight per foot of upper run including cross channels, walk, hand railing, rails, rail chairs, chain and buckets, with buckets full of coal at 50 lb. per cu. ft.
*F*. Weight per foot of upper run including cross channels, walk, hand railing, rails, rail chairs, chain and buckets, with buckets full of material at 100 lb. per cu. ft.

allowance for materials heavier than coal needs to be increased beyond the figures in Fig. 6-6 only by the horsepower required to lift such material over that required to lift 50-lb. material.

**Weights of Carriers.** When laying out the frame of a building which will house a carrier the engineer must know the loads involved. The weights in Table 3 refer to Peck carriers but are substantially correct for all standard carriers. The structural supports at the two upper corners carry considerable load. In addition to the weight of the machinery parts at these points there is the weight of the chain and buckets suspended from the drive sprockets, and at the opposite end there is the weight of chain, buckets, and material in the ascending run.

**Operation and Maintenance.** The pivoted bucket carrier is so nearly trouble proof that attention is routine. The attendant should see that the pressure lubrication of the chains maintains a grease collar where dust might enter the joints and that the take-ups are adjusted for a slight play in the chains. Occasional tests should be made of the protective devices — the automatic brake which prevents reversal of motion should the current fail and the cutout which stops the motor should a bucket fail to level off; otherwise these may not function on the rare occasions on which they are called upon.

Infrequently it happens that the horizontal and vertical centers are such that the chordal movements of the long-pitch chains at two or more corner wheels synchronize with cumulative effect, so that while the equalizing gears eliminate pulsation back of the drive sprockets a serious pulsation builds up along the lower run. The operator should observe first whether the bearing supports are yielding. If the supports are rigid a slight shift in the corner positions or change in centers may correct the difficulty.

# CHAPTER 7

## UNIT LOADS

We use the term *unit loads* to cover generally the handling of boxes, bags, packaged materials, castings, paper rolls, and, in general, integrated items as distinguished from pulverized, granular, and lumpy bulk materials. In the field of miscellaneous freight handling this subject is of major importance, calling for much study by the materials-handling engineer.

Where a direct lowering of packaged or boxed materials is involved, the *spiral chute* may provide the simplest method and lowest cost. The pitch of the spiral must be fixed to suit the flowability of the loads, and so this lowerer is not well suited where these vary widely. In department stores where the spiral frequently passes through six or eight floors to a basement shipping department, it is necessary to sort out the packages on the loading floors; otherwise a package of flour placed between two boxes of canned goods may fare rather badly.

Incidently a spiral chute is a very good fire escape for hospitals for the insane. A patient placed in the chute will be deposited gently at ground level, regardless of his performance en route.

**Roller Conveyors.** Either gravity-roll or power-roll conveyors may solve the problem of horizontal and inclined movements more economically than is possible with any other machine. Figure 7-1 shows an installation by the Logan Company. Incoming merchandise moves from the car into the building on a gravity-roll unit and is conveyed to the second floor on a 45° incline by pusher flights (the incline is too steep for power rolls). From this storage room the loads are lowered to the machine floor by a spiral chute and moved onward by a live-roll conveyor to the machines. The boxed product, placed on a live-roll conveyor, is delivered to cars for shipment, or it may be sent to trucks or to storage by shifting a switch in the conveyor line.

When two or more roller conveyors are tributary to a trunk line, it is necessary to prevent collisions by an interceptor as shown in Fig. 7-2. Here workers are stationed at two batteries of packing machines and set the packages on gravity-roll conveyors. The interceptor is actuated by a package on either the tributary conveyor or the trunk conveyor and serves to hold back one package momentarily until the

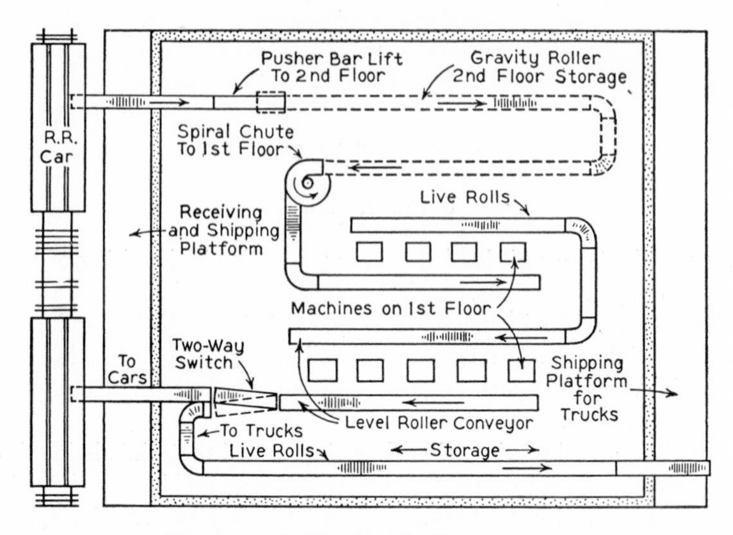


FIG. 7–1. Application of roller conveyors.

FIG. 7–2. Automatic interceptor, controlling delivery of boxes from gravity roll conveyor to belt conveyor.

other has cleared. The package on the belt conveyor having more traction will take the right of way over that on the gravity rolls.

Roller conveyors are standardized by various manufacturers, and the engineer should avoid changing standard constructions based on experience. *Gravity conveyors* are best adapted for boxes or cartons with unyielding riding faces, approximate uniformity in weight, and not over 100 lb. each. It is usual to have the rolls spaced so that not less than three rolls are always under the unit load. An incline of ½ in. per ft. is usually required for cartons, ⅜ in. per ft. for wood boxes weighing less than 75 lb., and less for heavy rigid loads.

*Pallet Chain Conveyors.* Figure 7-3 shows typical installations for handling bottles. At the top is a Chain Belt Company conveyor for transferring bottled beer from the filling and capping line to the boxing station, using a "table-top" chain. In the foreground is a rotating disc which, with the guide plates, serves to shift the bottles from the approach line to the reverse line. These bottle conveyors are quite widely used in bottling plants, sometimes with pans or trays attached to a single strand of chain, as shown in the central illustration, a Link-Belt Company installation, and sometimes, as shown in the bottom picture, on a pallet chain designed to articulate both horizontally and vertically.

**Belt conveyors** for unit loads may be similar to the standard flat-belt conveyor, but with closely spaced carrying idler rolls, or the belt may slide on a deck. Almost any type of unit loads, not destructive to the belt, may be so handled. For sliding belts the best decking is dressed maple, unless fireproof construction is required. A steel deck should have spaced perforations (2- or 3-in. holes) because of a tendency of the belt to stick to the deck by suction. The return run should be carried on idler rolls spaced 8- or 10-ft. centers.

The horsepower at the head shaft for horizontal conveyors is approximately

$$HP = \frac{(W + w) \times f \times S}{33{,}000}$$

where $W$ = weight of load on belt in pounds.
$w$ = weight of belt in pounds.
$f$ = friction coefficient (see below).
$S$ = speed in feet per minute.

(The horsepower for the return run is negligible.)

*A*

*B*

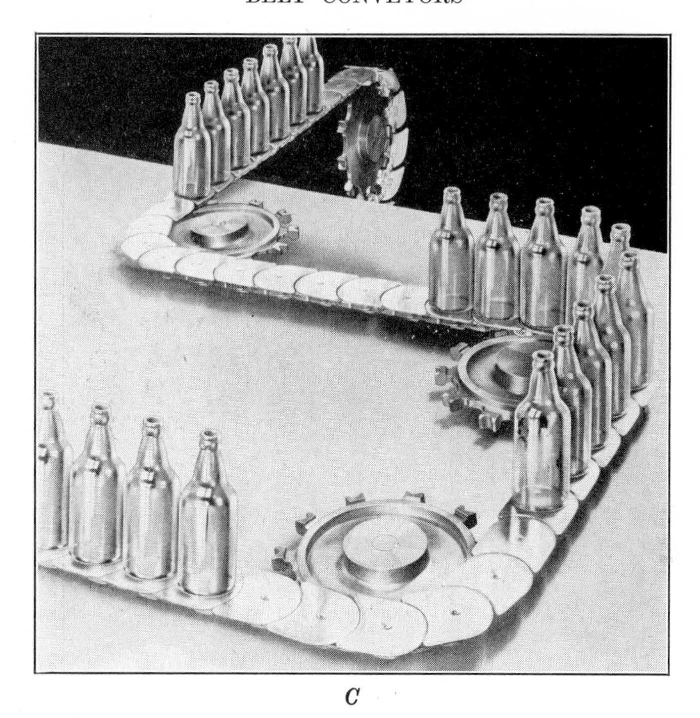

*C*

Fig. 7-3. Bottle conveyors. (*A*) Pallet chains and turntable. (Chain Belt.) (*B*) Horizontal runaround conveyor. (Link-Belt.) (*C*) Universal carrier chain, flexing in two planes. (Link-Belt.)

Values for *f*

| | Cotton or Untreated Canvas Belting, per cent | Rubber Impregnated Canvas Belting, per cent |
|---|---|---|
| Roller-supported belt | 3 to 5 | 3 to 5 |
| Steel deck | 20 | 20 |
| Hardwood deck | 25 | 30 |

Cotton and untreated canvas belts are satisfactory unless humidity conditions vary widely. If the conveyor has a length of several hundred feet a gravity take-up is preferable to a screw take-up as automatically maintaining the proper belt tension regardless of shrinkage or elongation. For conveyors exposed to the elements, rubber-covered belts may be specified but always roller supported.

The illustrations grouped in Fig. 7-4 show other types of unit handling equipment. Of interest is the overhead tow line for trucks. If the materials so transported can be palletized as discussed later in this chapter, low-lift fork trucks having the advantage of self loading

FIG. 7–4. (*A*) Overhead tow line for trucks. (*B*) Pallet conveyor for barrels. (*C*) Platform or apron conveyor.

and self discharge may provide a substantial reduction in handling costs, in fact after this plant was taken over by the Government, the change was made.

Where a sustained output of fragmentary materials which are abrasive or hot, such as scrap steel, castings, steel chips, and so on, is to be moved horizontally the best machine may be the vibrating trough, sometimes referred to as the *grasshopper conveyor* (Fig. 7-5). This

FIG. 7–5. Grasshopper conveyor. A Link-Belt installation handling hot castings from a mold conveyor to a shake-out screen where the castings are freed from sand.

consists of a flexibly mounted steel trough of rectangular cross section, oscillated by an eccentric drive at a speed adjusted to produce a forward movement of 20 to 50 ft. per min. for most materials, depending on their weight. The capacity depends on the width of the trough. There is no spillage because the material levels off as it moves along. Trough wear is slight. Although it is a straight line conveyor, separately driven sections may be set at an angle with one section discharging to the next.

When stacks or batches of magazines are to be lifted or lowered, there are several types of *tray elevators* or *lowerers* available. Sometimes these are loaded or unloaded manually and sometimes automatically. The trays in the automatic loader have a forked floor into which the auxiliary enters. The loads must be synchronized with the tray spacing so that each tray is in position to receive its batch as delivered. When unloading, the trays need not be synchronized, but the two machines should be electrically or mechanically inter-

FIG. 7–6. Power unloader for tray lowerer.

locked. The unloader (Fig. 7-6) functions nicely if the speed is not above 50 ft. per min., but at higher speeds the tendency is to slide the bottom book out before the stack begins to move, especially when the covers are glossy. An alternative which eliminates this difficulty is a bank of light rollers (roller-skate wheels serve very well), adjustably inclined at about 5°. The stacks start outward by gravity flow without any noticeable upsetting tendency.

Unloaders are of limited length as a rule, and one or more attendants transfer the stacks to skids or pallets which are moved to storage or to the shipping room by fork trucks. A normal pallet load is 2000 to 3000 lb.

As an alternative to batch handling, the Cutler-Hammer wire-cable elevator-conveyor for newsprint may be mentioned (Fig. 7-7). It has parallel assemblies of special wire cables guided by grooved rollers so that any combination of horizontal and vertical travel is possible. The papers enter the element as a continuing stream, with every fiftieth or one hundredth paper kicked out slightly to facilitate batching at the delivery end.

**Overhead Trams and Conveyors.** Manufacturing operations, the movement of materials through the shops, and the transfer to the shipping platform, may preferably be by overhead transport, keeping the aisles clear and eliminating damage to the floors. Two types of equipment are available, the tramrail and the trolley conveyor. Not much can be said of their engineering as they are standardized. However, some engineering details are interesting since they so frequently provide substantial reductions in costs.

**The tramrail,** or monorail system, consists of a carrier suspended from an overhead I-beam track or runway usually suspended from the ceiling beams except in the larger units where it is supported from below. The track may be extended indefinitely in any direction. It may have switches, turnouts, and a weighing section. Though usually level, the runway may have a moderate grade.

*Runway.* Figure 7-8 shows the standard track or runway sections commonly used. The flanges should be symmetrical with the web. Beams are preferably the same weight throughout the system. In curved sections 2 ft. of tangent are allowed between any curve and an adjacent switch. Supports are spaced sufficiently close to eliminate any vertical or lateral deflection due to the weight of the load and the impact caused by moving the load, and the top flange is reinforced if necessary to avoid risk of buckling. Supports for curved beams are spaced so that the middle ordinate from the curve to the chord brace does not exceed 8 in.

If wheel loads travel on the lower flange of a standard section medium steel I-beam, bending or peining will occur; and, if the wheel treads are coned to fit the flange, partial sliding and tread wear will result. If the wheels are set at an angle, lateral thrust increases the friction in the wheel bearings.

FIG. 7–7. Wire-cable elevator-conveyor for newspapers. A Cutler-Hammer installation.

*The carrier* may be hand propelled or motor operated. If motor operated, control may be remote or from a cage attached to the frame. The smaller trucks have four wheels in pairs connected by a yoke, as in the Cleveland Tramrail Company machine shown in Fig. 7-9, with the load suspended from the midpoint of the yoke. These carriers have a capacity up to 3000 lb.; with two units coupled in tandem the capacity becomes 6000 lb.

*The hoist* or lifting mechanism is suspended from the yoke. It may be a differential chain hoist or an electric hoist. The electric hoist is furnished in several standard speeds. The Cleveland Company has developed a chart, reproduced as Chart 1, which it is claimed indicates the type of hoist best suited to a particular job. On the assumption that a hoist should last at least five years, if the savings in five years are more than the difference in cost between a hand hoist and an electric hoist, the investment in the electric hoist is warranted.

To illustrate: If castings weighing 750 lb. each are handled at the rate of 75 per hour and lifted 4 ft., the work per hour is

$$750 \times 75 \times 4 = 225{,}000 \text{ ft-lb. per hr.}$$

Locating the value on Chart 1, we find that the cost of doing this work with an electric hoist geared to lift at 40 ft. per min. is 1.7 cents. The cost with a spur geared chain hoist is 46 cents. The annual saving is

$$44.3 \times 8 \times 300 = \$1063$$

Labor is taken at 50 cents per hour; current, at 2 cents per kw-hr. Average hoist costs are used. The charted figures include labor, material, and power but not overhead.

Two installations by the American Monorail Company are shown in Figs. 7-10*A* and *B*. In one, handling steel rods, the machine is controlled from the floor; in the other, the operator rides in a trailer.

Figure 17-2 shows a Shepard Crane and Hoist Company monorail hoist equipped with trailer cage and grab bucket. The cage is hung from a trailer trolley connected by drawbar to the hoist unit.

**Overhead conveyors,** or trolley conveyors, consist of a power-propelled chain traveling at moderate speed, suspended by trolleys from a suitable track, and provided with attachments of various forms adapted to the work to be done. The loads are not concentrated as in the tramrail system, and so the track is much lighter. The motor is usually connected by roller chain or V-belt to a vertical-type worm gear or through a variable-speed drive which permits adjustment to suit varying operating conditions.

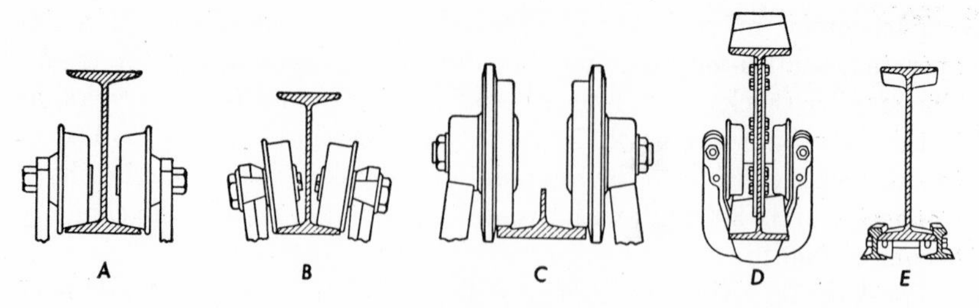


Fig. 7–8. Monorail runways.

*A*. Wheels coned to fit lower flanged of standard I-beam. Sliding and uneven track wear.

*B*. Wheels set at an angle. Lateral thrust against wheel bearings.

*C*. Wheels vertical and resting on thickened track. Cleveland Crane and Engineering Company.

*D*. Special I-beam runway; 12 by 4 in. section of high-carbon manganese steel with diagonal splice joints. American Monorail Company.

*E*. Standard T-rails clamped to bottom flange of runway I-beam. Shepard Crane and Hoist Company.

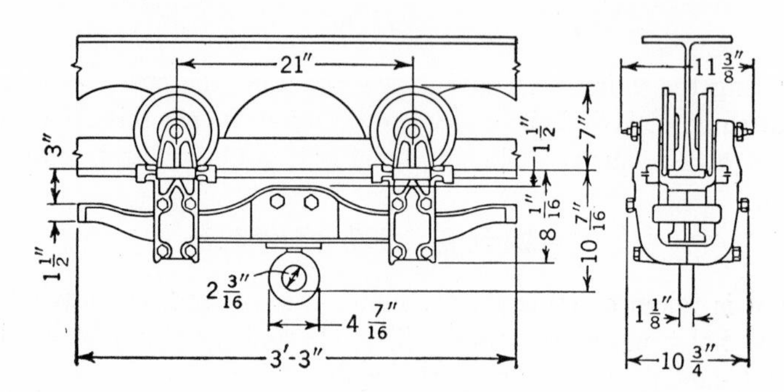


Single Unit Carrier.

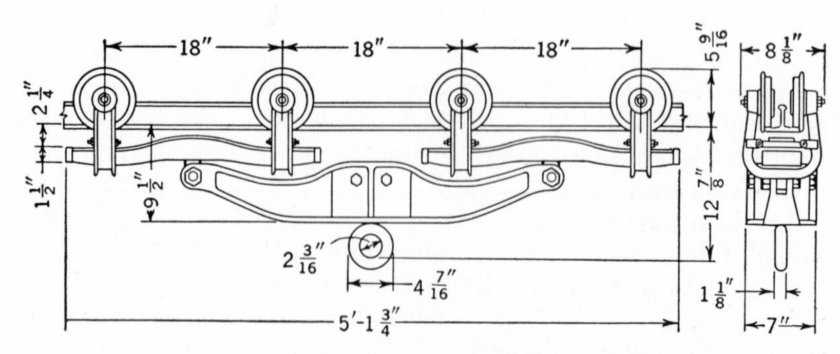


Double Unit Carrier.

Fig. 7–9. Overhead trams.

## CHART 1

### Determination of Hand- or Power-Operated Hoist

$A$ = weight of material handled.
$B$ = lift of load.
$C$ = foot-pounds of work done per hour.
$D$ = number of times load is lifted per hour.

Average working days per month = 25. 300 working days per year.
Work per hour = $C = A \times B \times C \times D$.
Work per 8-hr. day = $C \times 8$.
Work per month = $C \times 25$.
Work per year = $C \times 300$.

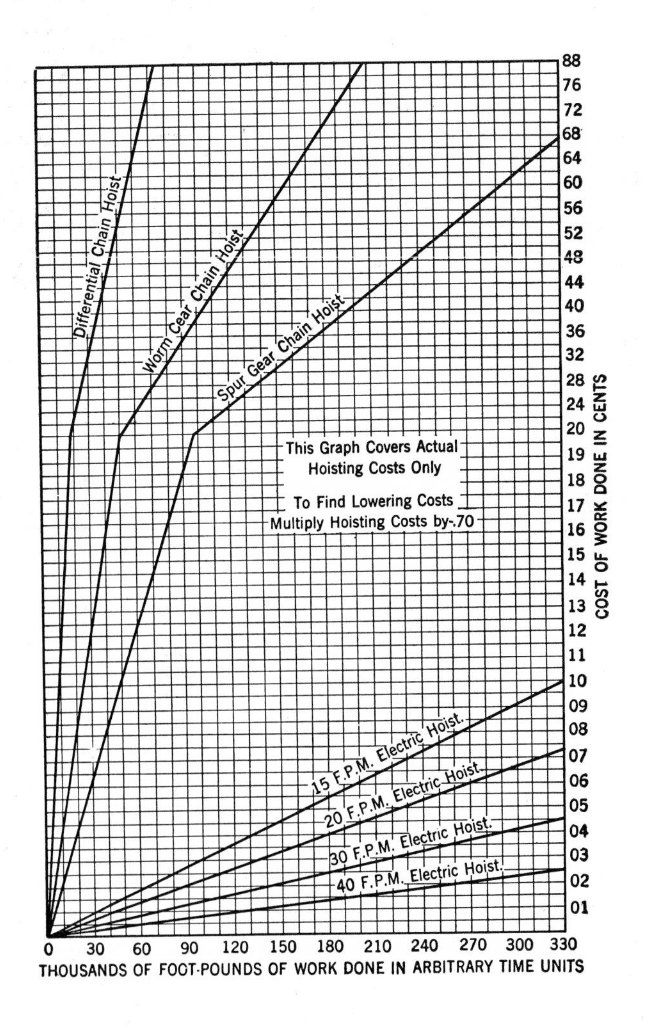

FIG. 7–10*A*. Trailer-controlled, power-operated tram. Machine is handling a 4-ton load on a 5 per cent grade.

*The path* may follow almost any course, up or down steep inclines or around short-radius curves. At the loading zone the track may dip downward, then rise to give headroom beneath. Automatic or direct control may be provided, and the usual requirements for safety in connection with exposed machinery are essential.

*Chains.* Several standard chains are available:

Figure 7-11*A* shows the Ewart detachable chain with attachments made integral with the links and provided with wheels for operating in a double angle track, adapted only to monoplane layouts.

Figure 7-11*B* shows the pintle chain (No. 477, etc.) with attachment links provided with extended lugs for pairs of trolley wheels adapted to an I-beam track. It may be used for monoplane or multiplane layouts.

Figure 7-11*C* shows the rivetless chain. Trolleys for an I-beam track are attached to the center links and can operate on monoplane or multiplane layouts. This is used for heavier loads and long paths since it is well adapted to multiple drives.

FIG. 7-10*B*. American monorail, motor operated with floor control. Trolleys mounted on side of I-beam runway.

Figure 7-11*D* shows the SS roller chain. The trolley attachment may be swiveled as shown. Flanged wheels operate on double T-rails with either monoplane or multiplane layouts. This type is used for heavy service and with either sprocket wheel or booster drives.

Trolley wheels are self-lubricated bronze bushed, ball bearing, or roller bearing. The bronze bushing is cheapest, but the coefficient of friction with anti-friction flanged rollers is 50 per cent less. If the trolleys pass through a hot chamber or washing zone, automatic relubrication is applied just beyond.

*Corners and Turns.* The chains are guided around corner turns either by idlers or by small, closely spaced rollers. The idlers are preferable as having only one lubrication point and fewer parts.

*Drives.* The drive may be located at a corner or anywhere along a straight run when the radii at the corners are too large for a sprocket. A multiple-point drive consists of a common power unit with two or more drive points located so that the total chain pull is divided. Individual booster drives distribute the load automatically. In long, heavy-duty installations the booster motors may be of the direct-current series-wound type, which, in addition to distributing the pull, serve to eliminate pulsation in the element.

*Load Carriers.* These are of various types of hooks and trays suspended from one or more trolleys. With multiple suspension there is the complication of "shortening" at horizontal corners (difference in length between chord and curve), but it is possible to compensate for this by a link between trolley and carrier.

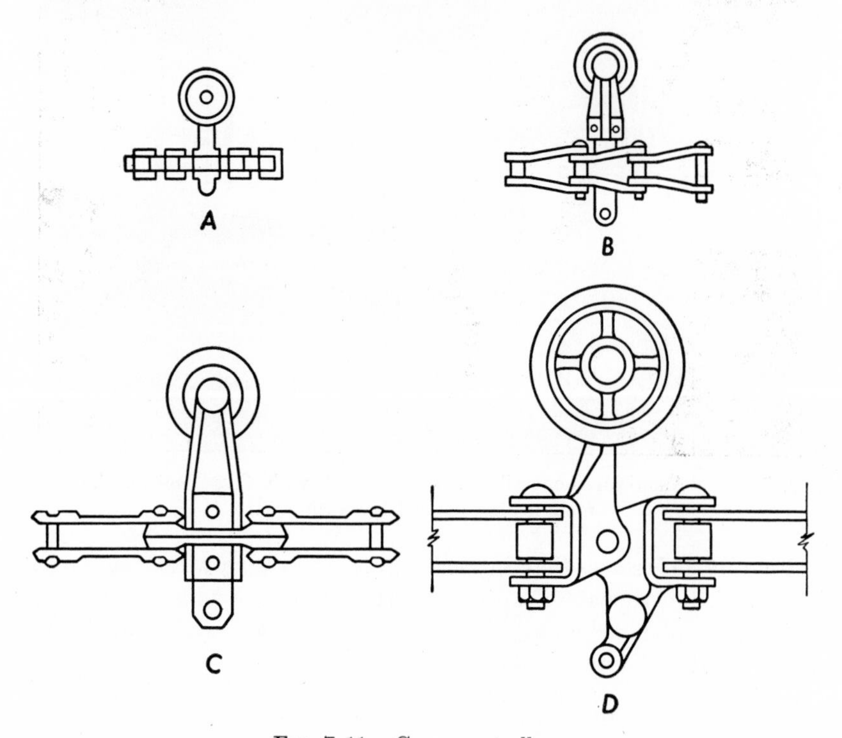


Fig. 7–11. Conveyor trolleys.

*Chain Pull and Horsepower.* The chain pull may be approximated by multiplying the weight of the element and maximum loading by a friction coefficient of 3 per cent. After the pull and speed are determined the horsepower at the head shaft is computed by the conventional formula, and this figure is doubled for the motor horsepower. In multiplane conveyors with relatively high chain pull, allowance must be made for the lifts and superposed radial thrust at vertical curves, depending on chain pull, spacing of trolleys, and radius of curve. The designer usually checks this thrust in connection with the size of trolley;

however, as a rule, the horsepower based on the total lift and horizontal pull, disregarding the reduction in horsepower due to the "downhill" runs, can be used safely in figuring the chain pull and trolley size. In general, trolley conveyors have 3-in., 4-in., or 6-in. pitch chains on a 3-in., 4-in., or 6-in. I-beam track, respectively. The 3-in. trolleys are rated up to a maximum load of 150 lb. The 4-in. is the most popular and costs little more. Speeds are often very low — not infrequently 3 ft. per min. or less — and so the power required for horizontal systems is remarkably small. It is not unusual to see a system of substantial length driven by a ¾-hp. motor.

**Comment.** In conveyors of considerable length there is an initial lengthening of the chain until the articulations become seated, so that several links may be removed before the take-up adjustment can be utilized.

Overhead supports and connectors are standardized and adapted to various conditions, but floor supports are available, as when the runway crosses a crane bay. Ninety per cent of installations are supported from above, usually by suspension rods with braces at intervals to prevent side sway.

If with expanding plant operations certain processes must be shifted or separated, either the overhead tram or the trolley conveyor offers a convenient tie-in. They may span streets or railroads, pass from floor to floor, or travel along loading platforms. With the overhead conveyor, cooling, drying, washing, or pickling operations may be done en route.

**Trucks, Tractors, and Trailers.** Wartime industrial requirements gave a remarkable impetus to the handling of grouped loads by trucks, tractors, and trailers. Although such machines are not conveyors in the strict sense of the term, as material-handling equipment whose use is rapidly expanding, a full knowledge of the possibilities is essential for the engineer responsible for the movement of materials through the plant.

The tremendous volume of shells, crates, boxes, packaged food stuffs, machinery parts, and other products made the transportation of these and many other articles impossible except by grouping them on skids and pallets and transferring them at shipping points in lots rather than singly. And yet only a small fraction of the materials which might be are as yet so handled, only about 1 per cent according to an estimate of the Tariff Commission, which listed 3000 kinds of packaged products that might be packed or shipped on skids or pallets. This method frees the loading and unloading operations from the

Fig. 7-12. Overhead conveyor handling chilled hogs up an incline from cooler to cutting floor.

limitations of manual handling through the use of fork or platform trucks and tractors with trains of trailers. In evaluating the analyses which follow it should be recognized that there are factors which cannot be covered adequately here. Present methods of handling and storing manually may sometimes be wrong, and study by the plant engineer may provide correction and cost savings without mechanical equipment. Again, conditions range all the way from decidedly in favor of industrial trucks to decidedly in favor of a conveyor or overhead tramrail, and in between are the borderline problems where it is impossible to predetermine the best system or method, especially since the functioning of industrial trucks depends so directly on the degree of skill attainable by the available personnel.

In a large plant more tonnage may be involved in non-production functions than in production. An advantage in the industrial truck is its availability for action in any of the plant operations as contrasted with a conveyor which is fixed in its location and its field of operation. Other factors to be taken into consideration are the conditions which will exist, whether explosive dusts or vapors may be present or whether the material is inflammable, as with baled cotton. Then suitable motors and switches must be specified.

**Pallets and Skids.** Frequently loads handled by trucks and tractors are mounted on or strapped to pallets and skids. Pallets (Fig. 7-13) are simple platforms providing top and bottom bearing surfaces and a minimum slot for insertion of the lifting device. In quantities they cost about $4 each. Among postwar developments are pallets of aluminum, of steel rolled sections, and of expanded metal. Skids are platforms equipped with runners or four legs that hold the platform 6 to 8 in. off the floor to provide clearance for the platform of a lift truck. Skids are commonly all wood, all steel, or steel and wood construction. In quantities they cost (1948) about $8 each. Boxes, racks, or dump bodies may be mounted on or built integral with any type of platform for convenience in making up unit loads. Where transfer inside the plant is involved, loaded pallets may be stacked more readily than loaded skids.

Adoption of the pallet system rarely increases packaging costs more than a very small percentage and sometimes reduces them. In many instances the loads may be paper wrapped and steel strapped or wired to the pallets, thus saving the cost of boxes and crates. Some forms of pallets are so cheap that they are considered expendable and not worth returning to the shipper. Note that the term "palletization" as used here may apply merely to putting handles on bundles or grouped freight as well as to mounting on a pallet.

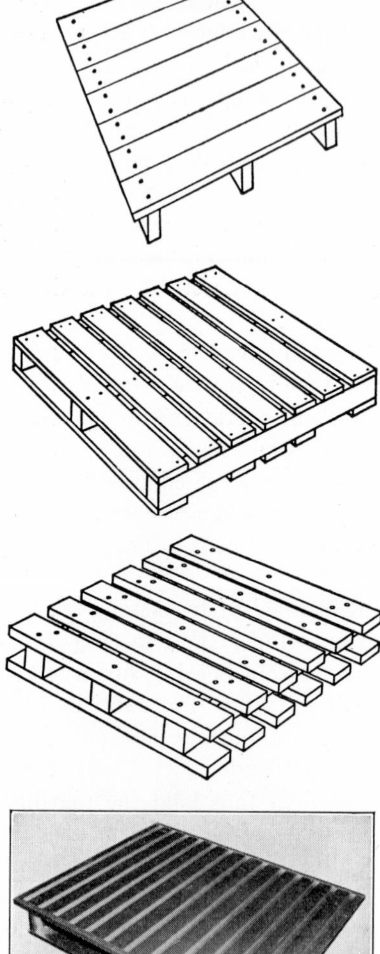

*A*. Single-faced pallet. Platform is sufficiently high above floor for entering the forks of truck.

*B*. Two-way double-faced pallet with bottom openings for hand truck and end spacings for entering forks.

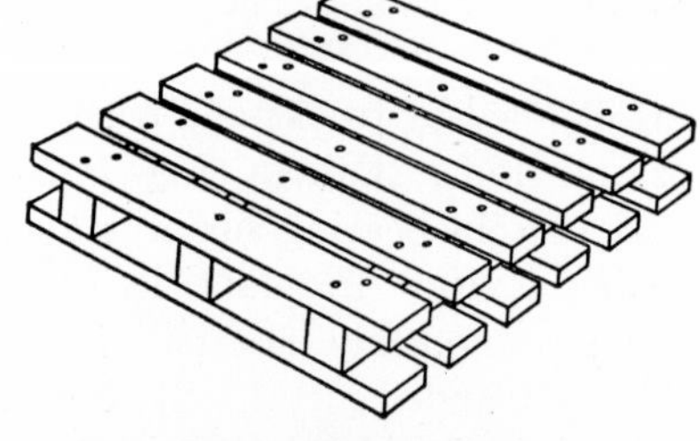

*C*. Stevedore pallet for lifting by cargo sling, as when loading to ships.

*D*. Cast-aluminum pallet. (Reynolds Aluminum Co.)

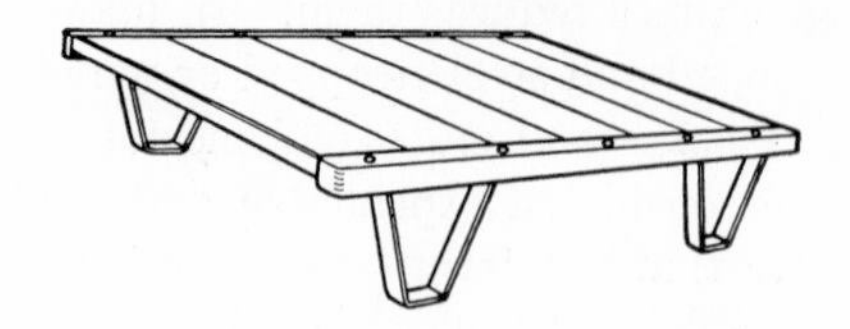

*E*. Single-face skid, steel bound, rounded corners, flush angles, and countersunk bolts.

FIG. 7–13.

**Trucks and tractors** usually can handle to best advantage materials that have been mounted on skids or pallets at the point of shipment or at destination. High-lift platform and fork trucks (Fig. 7-14) are used when loads are to be piled or tiered. Low-lift platform trucks are usual when the loads are to be deposited on the floor. If the distances are moderate and the traffic volume small, motorized hand trucks with manually raised or lowered platforms or forks will often suffice. Several motorized hand trucks now have power lift as well as traction (Fig. 7-15). For greater volume the power-operated truck, either with gasoline engine or storage battery and motor, with the operator riding the truck, is selected. Speeds of such driver-ride types of truck range from 400 to 600 ft. per min. These trucks cost from three to four times as much as the motorized hand trucks. Driver-ride power trucks equipped with suitable extension masts, of both platform and fork type, can stack boxes, crates, and so on, up to 10 ft. in the standard models, or higher when specially designed. When awkwardly shaped loads, not unitized, such as sheet-steel stacks, castings, and paper rolls, are to be removed from boxcars, the high-lift truck may be equipped with either a horizontal boom or a gooseneck. With side-door cars such a truck can enter and maneuver within. Carloads of paper rolls weighing up to 3000 lb. per roll, wound on pipe cores and stacked two deep in a boxcar can be unloaded by an operator and two helpers (to insert the stubs into the core) in 2 hr.

*The tractor-trailer system* is especially useful when large quantities of materials are to be collected at one point and moved to other points, as for example in handling carload freight. The tractor forms the trailer into trains, transfers them, and drops them off at designated points. One tractor may suffice for several trailer trains, as the tractor is freed to avoid time loss while the trailers are being loaded or unloaded possibly by fork or platform truck. Sometimes the trailers are taken into the cars, thus keeping the loads on wheels for the trip.

**Trailers** are of three types, all having four wheels but differing in the method of wheel mounting. They are: (1) caster, (2) fifth-wheel-steer, and (3) four-wheel-steer. The caster trailer has two swiveling wheels, the other two being mounted on a fixed axle. It is well adapted to power haulage in trains or local manual movement, and it is lowest in cost. The fifth-wheel trailer has one fixed axle and one swiveling axle with tongue attached for coupling to a tractor or tandem trailer. It also is nicely adapted to train haulage and heavy-duty operations. The four-wheel-steer trailer has all four wheels on steering knuckles connected by link bars, though sometimes these have two fifth-wheel axles interlocked. All wheels take the proper position for rounding a

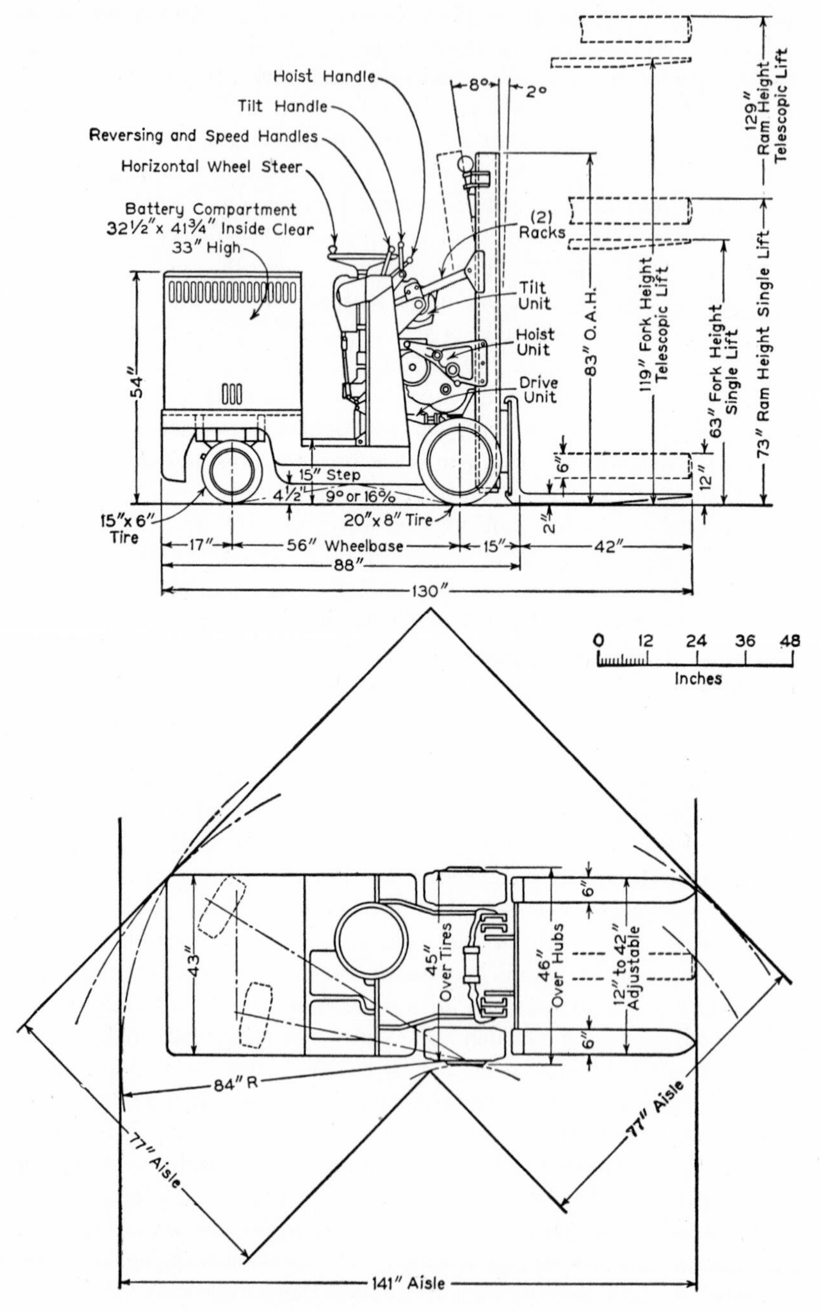


FIG. 7–14. High-lift fork truck. (Yale and Towne.)

curve, even of short radius, without causing a radial inward thrust or side skid due to the pull of the tractor. This is the most costly of the three and the most flexible in its possibilities.

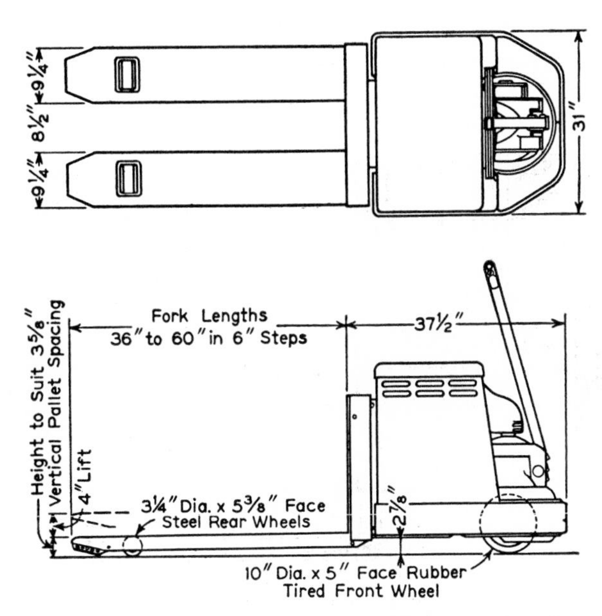


FIG. 7–15. Yale and Towne "Worksaver" pallet lift truck. Operator walks. Lifting forks will enter under pallet with 4-in. clearance. Lift is 4 in., power operated. Hydraulic load release. Capacities up to 2000 lb. Maximum battery size: lead, 6 cells, 23 plate; nickel alkaline, 10 cells, C-8.

**Power.** Industrial trucks may be classified as regards power as:

(1) Battery electric, which is powered by a storage battery and employs electric control and transmission.

(2) Gas electric, which is powered by an engine generator but otherwise is the same as the battery electric.

(3) Gas mechanical, which is powered by a gasoline engine and employs mechanical control and transmission, like an automobile.

The average cost of operation, including losses, maintenance, and fixed charges, is approximately in the ratio of two, three, and four, in the order given above. The greater economy of the battery electric truck is due mainly to the low cost of electric power and the absence of loss during idle periods. Sometimes, however, a costly charging station must be taken into consideration. The field of the gas mechanical type is where electric power is not available or where the trucks are moved from point to point and cannot be kept near a charging station. It has advantages also where the operations are intermittent, involving a day or two of work and then inactivity for a week or two while maintenance and adjustments are made.

The field of the gas electric type is the same as that for the gas mechanical type. Its transmission is flexible and efficient, especially for starting up under heavy loads. It eliminates the clutch and gear shift.

FIG. 7–16. Trailer train being loaded by low-lift truck.

**Speeds.** Industrial trucks can be engineered to operate over a wide range of speeds, but speeds of 90 to 500 ft. per min. are best adapted to the usual conditions and are most common. Because of the relatively short travel distances, narrow aisles, short turns, and the usual circumstances of plant operations, it is rare that higher speeds are either useful or safe. The good ton-foot performance of the industrial truck is due more to quick positioning for contact with the loads, quick pick-up and release of loads, and maneuverability, than to rapid travel. Also, from an operating cost standpoint, it is desirable to keep the speeds as low as possible. Operations are essentially stop and go, with repeated accelerations, and the energy consumed by acceleration is proportional to the square of the attained speed. So also is tire wear.

In the discussion that follows, the author is quoting freely from the data of the Electric Industrial Truck Association, whose manual, *Material Handling Handbook,* is well worth study by every materials-handling engineer.

**Charging Batteries.** In general, the time required to charge a motive-power battery that has delivered its rated capacity in powering a truck during a shift is 6 to 8 hr. Whether a single battery per truck was employed with sufficient capacity for the duty cycle of each day or more batteries were necessary to provide the daily capacity, it was considered desirable to have enough batteries available to keep the average discharge cycles at not more than 300 per yr. However, the trend now is toward evaluating the job to be done in ton-feet of horizontal and vertical movement or travel. Base load, frictional resistance, acceleration, and pay loads require energy that can be specified in horsepower or kilowatt-hours. Electric trucks are thus work-evaluated, and the battery compartments are usually designed to hold sufficient battery capacity for at least one full shift of hard work. The kilowatt-hours to do a specified job can be determined with a meter. A 4000-lb. capacity fork truck moving and tiering will use 10 to 14 kw-hr. of battery energy in an 8-hr. shift.

This is one of the first things to consider in the layout of the charging station, since it determines the maximum number of batteries for which space must be provided at one time. Of course, if no trucks are operated more than 8 hr. in 24, the number of batteries will ordinarily be the same as the number of trucks plus a spare or two, and the batteries may remain in the trucks while charging. Then the trucks are parked along the wall opposite the charging outlets. If the trucks employ replacement batteries, the charging room may be laid out to provide space for the batteries only, with charging benches of ample size to accommodate the batteries in one or more rows. Where operations are conducted on two or more floors, it may be found advisable to provide a power hoist so that the exchanges can be made without lowering or raising the truck to the charging station for servicing. Either single- or multiple-circuit units are available for charging one or a number of batteries simultaneously. Thus the facilities may readily be increased, as required by the growth of the truck fleet. Direct-current source of supply at voltages used in industrial trucks is unusual. A 24-volt battery cannot be efficiently charged from a 220-volt line directly. Where plant power supply is direct current, a motor generator set offers the most efficient means of providing charging current. Where alternating current is available, efficient dependable service can be secured from motor generators or rectifier-

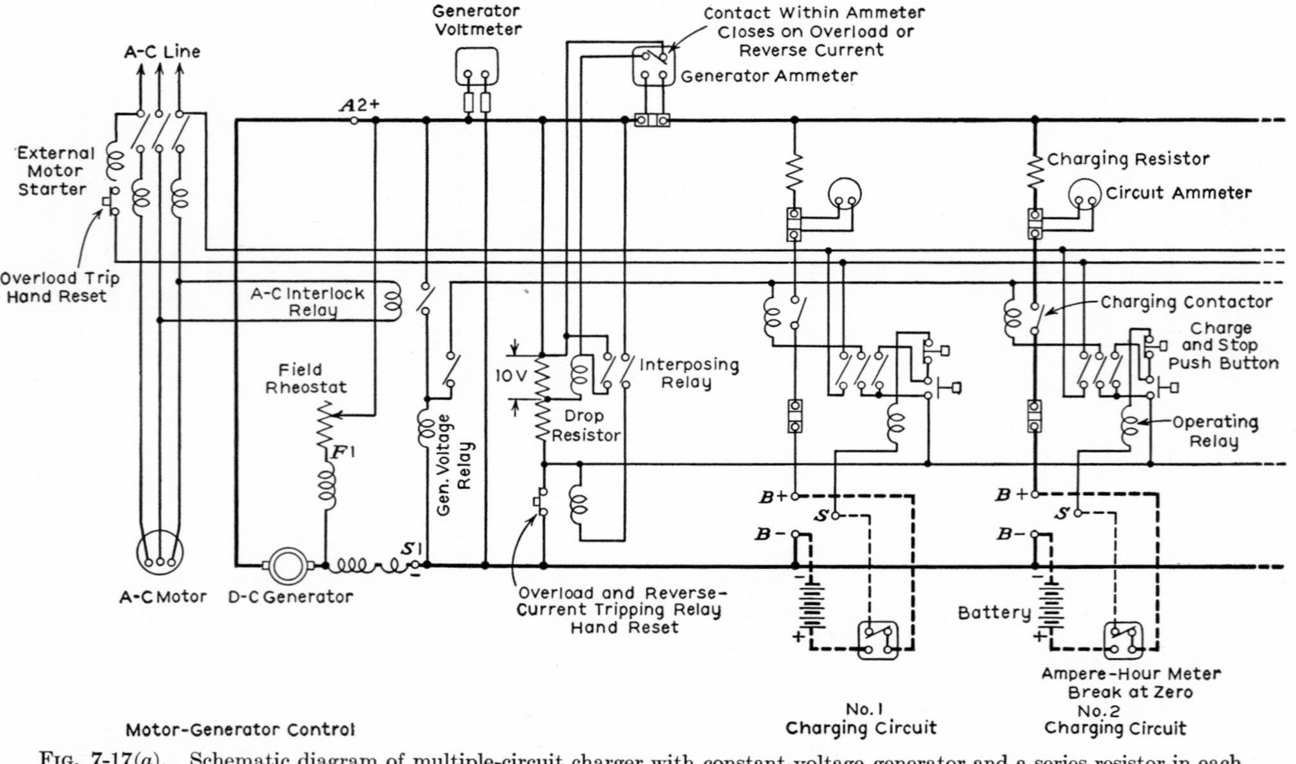


FIG. 7-17(*a*). Schematic diagram of multiple-circuit charger with constant-voltage generator and a series resistor in each battery circuit.

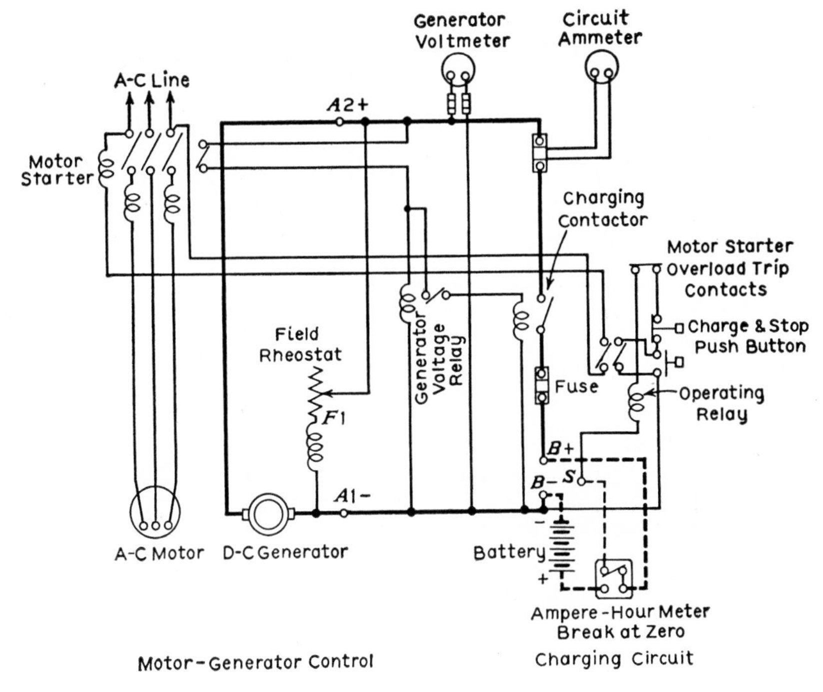


FIG. 7–17(*b*). Single charging circuit from A-C source.

type equipment. The recent pamphlet of the Electric Industrial Truck Association gives specifications which are advisable to follow.

With gas electric or gas mechanical trucks certain ventilation standards must be observed in the areas where these are operated. All trucks that carry the Underwriters laboratory labels are equipped with condensing mufflers and suppressers to prevent flame backfire. These do not in any way eliminate carbon monoxide, but they minimize the possibility of fire caused by the exhaust. Carbon monoxide results from incomplete combustion, and the more perfect the carburation of an engine, the less the danger from this scource. Tests have shown that when an engine with a good carburetor is idling at about 400 r.p.m. from 3 to 5 per cent of the exhaust gas is carbon monoxide. This diminishes as the speed or load in horsepower increases until it practically disappears at full speed. As far as the author knows, no device has been perfected to absorb exhaust carbon monoxide. Good housekeeping and careful maintenance will assure minimum fire risk.

**Routing and Dispatching.** Methods of routing and dispatching trucks are determined by the flow of work and the necessity of having trucks available when and where the flow of work demands and achieving this result as simply and directly as possible. In heavy industries, where one or more trucks are frequently employed continuously in transporting the work from one machine to another, this is a simple routine. It is more complex where there are separate functions for each truck or group of trucks, a circumstance that also requires careful study of the type of truck best suited to all the functions involved. For serving departments between which the traffic is relatively small, the scheduling of trips at regular intervals is preferred to the plan of dispatching trucks as called for by the foreman concerned. With schedules properly established and dependably maintained, foremen find it easy to plan accordingly in requisitioning supplies and in preparing outgoing materials for pick-up. Also better service is given than could possibly be rendered by the same number of trucks operating under a less orderly dispatch system. Centralized dispatching has much merit. It keeps the load factor high and minimizes the fixed charges.

The conditions at the receiving end of a plant are different and usually involve activity at more or less irregular intervals. This situation necessitates a separate allocation of equipment, and the number of trucks is dependent on the character of the incoming shipments and determinable only by trials, the cooperation of the manufacturer's expert, and possible arrangements with suppliers to ship in unit loads.

The shipping department of the plant may or may not be adjacent to the receiving end. If it is, the same truck fleet may be available for handling both incoming and outgoing shipments. Receiving and shipping conditions vary too widely to permit a discussion of the requirements.

**Truck Engineering.** As with other mechanized equipment, the industrial truck performs best when it is applied correctly to the type of work it will be called on to do. The truck manufacturers maintain staffs of field engineers whose advice should be requested, but the materials-handling engineer may wish to make confirming calculations in view of his intimate knowledge of his own plant operations. The units and abbreviations used in the discussion which follows are:

Tractive Effort, *TE*
Tractive Resistance, *TR*
Grade Resistance, *GR*

*Tractive effort, TE,* is the motive force exerted at the driving wheels of a truck or tractor in overcoming resistance to motion. It is commonly expressed in pounds and may be taken from the manufacturer's specifications.

*Tractive resistance, TR,* is a result of rolling friction and is commonly expressed in pounds per ton of gross weight of truck or tractor plus all loads. It varies with the kind and condition of the runway surface approximately as follows:

| Kind of Surface | Resistance[1] pounds per ton |
|---|---|
| Smooth concrete or wood block | 30 to 50 |
| Smooth, hard mastic | 30 to 50 |
| Granite block, poor brick, etc. | 50 to 70 |
| Gravel | 60 to 75 |
| Clay or sand | 200 to 300 |

[1]These values are based on use of anti-friction bearings.

For modern well-maintained industrial floors, an average value is 40 lb. per ton, and use of this value in traction calculations will usually give sufficiently accurate results for practical estimating purposes. However, the actual *TR* of any surface may easily be determined by pulling a trailer of known weight and, by means of a spring scale, observing the force necessary to maintain it in motion at a uniform speed on a level. *Example:* a trailer weighing 500 lb. is pulled through a scale which registers that a force of 10 lb. is being exerted. As the gross weight is ¼ ton, the *TR* per ton is 4 × 10 or 40 lb.

*Grade resistance, GR,* amounts to 20 lb. per ton for each 1 per cent of grade, the per cent of grade being the feet of vertical rise per 100 horizontal feet.

**Number of Trucks Required.** We must first determine the best size of unit load for the commodity to be handled. This indicates the required size or load-carrying capacity of the trucks, whereas the length or number of trips per day, plus an allowance for maneuvering and other delays, will indicate the required number. However, if the number thus determined is the minimum number that will maintain plant operations, it is decidedly advisable to have one or more reserve trucks. If we assume that at the receiving end of the plant it is required that one carload of incoming material shall be unloaded each hour and that two trucks will do the job, then if one should be out of service through mishap or breakdown the plant operations are seriously interrupted unless there is a stand-by ready to take over.

Let us assume that 1200 two-ton loads mounted on skid platforms are to be moved 100 ft. in one 8-hr. shift. From manufacturers specifications a 2-ton low-lift elevating platform truck is selected, for which speeds are given as 400 ft. per min., loaded, and 500 ft. per min., empty. Time to pick up load is 4 sec. Time to release load is 3 sec.

On the basis of these specifications, the theoretical time for one round trip is:

| | Seconds |
|---|---|
| Pick up load | 4 |
| Carry load 100 ft. | 15 |
| Release load | 3 |
| Return light | 12 |
| Total | 34 |

**Delay factor.** Allowances must be made for acceleration, turning around, maneuvering into position to pick up or release loads, and unforseen delays, which collectively may be termed the delay factor. This factor is greater for short trips and smaller for long trips. It varies also with the skill of the operator. Typical values for lift and fork trucks are:

| Length of Route, feet | Delay Factor, Ratio of Elapsed to Running Time |
|---|---|
| 50 | 2.5 |
| 100 | 2.0 |
| 250 | 1.5 |
| 500 | 1.2 |

If we apply a delay factor of 2.0 to the present example, the time per round trip is increased from the theoretical 34 sec. to 68 sec. On this basis, one truck may be expected to make 53 trips per hour and 424 trips per 8-hr. shift. To handle 1200 loads, three trucks are indicated.

**Estimating Required Number of Tractors.** In the engineering of the tractor-trailer system, the best average size of the unit load determines the load-carrying capacity for the trailers to be used, whereas the number of trailers that can be conveniently handled in one train, together with the maximum combination of tractive, grade, and acceleration resistances, determines the maximum tractive effort, *TE*, that the tractor must provide.

A tractor developing ample *TE* can be selected from the manufacturers' specifications; but in order to estimate the work that can be done in a given period it is necessary to determine the speeds to be expected. Performance curves supply this information.

As an example of the use of these curves, let us assume that, in an 8-hr. period, 250 tons of package freight are to be transferred from a barge dock to a car platform. The freight can be conveniently handled in trailer loads averaging 2 tons each, four trailers per train. The trailers weigh ¼ ton each. The runway from dock to car platform is 400 ft. long, level except for a grade against the load of 2 per cent for 50 ft. The average haul on the barge dock is 50 ft. and on the car platform 200 ft. The haul thus totals 600 ft. on the level plus 50 ft. on a 2 per cent grade. All running surfaces are smooth concrete in good condition.

We must determine the *TE* a tractor must develop to haul the trains under the stated conditions and the number of tractors needed to transfer 250 tons in 8 hr. at 8 tons per trip, that is, 32 trips.

If it is assumed that 30 ft. per min. per sec. is the maximum safe rate of acceleration and 30 lb. per ton is allowed for acceleration resistance, the *TE* required to haul the train may be calculated as follows:

| | |
|---|---|
| Loaded trip: | |
| Weight of train, 2¼ tons × 4 | 9 tons |
| *TR* for travel on level | 40 lb. per ton |
| *TE* for travel on level, 9 × 40 | 360 lb. |
| *TR* + *AR* for accelerating on level, 40 + 30 | 70 lb. per ton |
| *TE* for accelerating on level, 9 × 70 | 630 lb. |
| *TR* + *GR* for travel up 2% grade, 40 + 40 | 80 lb. per ton |
| *TE* for travel up 2% grade, 9 × 80 | 720 lb. |
| *TR* + *AR* + *GR* for accelerating up 2% grade, 40 + 30 + 40 | 110 lb. per ton |
| *TE* for accelerating up 2% grade, 9 × 110 | 990 lb. |
| Light trip: | |
| Weight of train, ¼ ton × 4 | 1 ton |
| *TE* for travel on level, 1 × 40 | 40 lb. |
| *TE* for accelerating on level, 1 × (40 + 30) | 70 lb. |
| *TE* for travel down 2% grade, 1 × (40 − 40) | . . . |

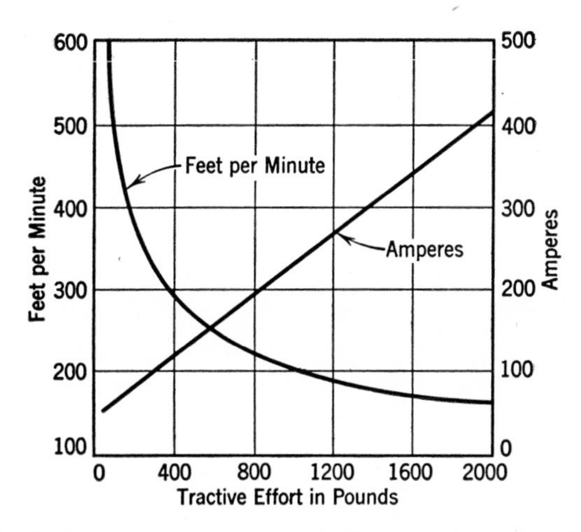


FIG. 7–18. Typical performance curve of three-wheel tractor having 36-volt power source. It gives a direct reading of the speed and current rate for a given tractive effort. Its use is explained in the text.

The maximum required *TE* is thus 990 lb. From the manufacturers' tables and performance curves, a 36-volt three-wheel tractor which develops the required *TE* with ample margin of safety is selected. Its performance curve is shown in Fig. 7-18, and, for the purposes of this example, its maximum *TE* is assumed to be 1800 lb. and its weight 1½ tons, including a 300-ampere-hr. battery and the operator. A portion of the *TE* developed is consumed in overcoming its own resistances. Under the severest conditions (110 lb. per ton), this amounts to $1\frac{1}{2}$ times 110 lb. per ton, or 165 lb., which added to the 990 lb. required for hauling the train under the same conditions gives 1155 lb. as the total maximum required *TE*. Thus the *TE* of 1800 lb. developed by the tractor selected affords a 645-lb. margin of safety.

Under the stated conditions the tractor is not required to start up on the grade where the *TE* is greatest, but it is desirable to allow for that contingency. Water or oil on the pavement would reduce the tractive grip of the wheels and is a possibility that should be allowed for. Good practice is to select a tractor developing a *TE* that shows an ample margin over the maximum calculated requirement.

Adding the *TE* required for hauling the train to the *TE* required by the tractor itself, we have:

| | Train | Tractor | Total |
|---|---|---|---|
| Loaded trip: | | | |
| *TE* for travel on level | 360 lb. | 60 lb. | 420 lb. |
| *TE* for accelerating on level | 630 | 105 | 735 |
| *TE* for travel up 2% grade | 720 | 120 | 840 |
| Light trip: | | | |
| *TE* for travel on level | 40 | 60 | 100 |
| *TE* for accelerating on level | 70 | 105 | 175 |
| *TE* for travel down 2% grade | ... | ... | ... |

**Travel Time.** To compare the time required for travel, the speeds are read from the performance curve by running verticals up from the tractive-effort scale until they intersect the speed curve and horizontals from these intersections to the speed scale at the left.

**Example.** If the required *TE* is 420 lb. a vertical from that value will intersect the speed curve at a point from which a horizontal to the speed scale will indicate 286 ft. per min. To compute the time required for acceleration, it may be assumed that acceleration is at a uniform rate of 30 ft. per min. per sec. and that the speed during acceleration is half the attained speed.

**Example.** If the attained speed is 286 ft. per min. the accelerating time is $286/30 = 9.53$ sec. $= 0.16$ min., and at an average of half the attained travel speed, or 143 ft. per min., the distance covered is 143 times $0.16 = 23$ ft. If the total distance is 600 ft., 23 ft. are covered at 143 ft. per min. and 577 ft. at 286 ft. per min.

We might make some allowance for deceleration that occurs when the loaded train starts climbing the grade and the acceleration as it leaves the grade, but the two balance off practically.

### Energy Calculations

*Travel*[1]

(1) On level, $TE = TR \times W$

(2) Upgrade, $TE = (TR + GR) \times W$

[1]Travel and acceleration formulas assume an efficiency of $66\frac{2}{3}$ per cent between battery and wheels.

(3) Downgrade, $TE = (TR - GR) \times W$
(4) $3\ TE$ = watt-hours required per mile
(5) $0.0568\ TE$ = watt-hours required per 100 ft
(6) $3\ TE \times$ m.p.h. = watts required
(7) $0.0341\ TE \times$ f.p.m. = watts required

where $TR$ = friction resistance in pounds per ton.
$GR$ = grade resistance of 20 lb. per ton for each per cent of grade.
$W$ = gross weight of truck or tractor in tons, including operator and all loads.
$TE$ = total required tractive effort in pounds.

*Acceleration*[1]

For acceleration from a stop to travel speed:

(10) Watt-hours required $= W \times (\text{f.p.m.})^2 \div 205{,}000$
(11) or $W \times (\text{m.p.h.})^2 \div 27$
(12) or $W \div C$

in which feet per minute or miles per hour = attained travel speed.
$C$ = acceleration factor given below.

| F.p.m. | $C$ | F.p.m. | $C$ | F.p.m. | $C$ |
|---|---|---|---|---|---|
| 20 | 512.5 | 220 | 4.2 | 420 | 1.16 |
| 40 | 127.5 | 240 | 3.52 | 440 | 1.06 |
| 60 | 56.5 | 260 | 3.02 | 460 | 0.96 |
| 80 | 32. | 280 | 2.7 | 480 | 0.89 |
| 100 | 20.5 | 300 | 2.27 | 500 | 0.815 |
| 120 | 14.15 | 320 | 2. | 520 | 0.755 |
| 140 | 10.4 | 340 | 1.77 | 540 | 0.7 |
| 160 | 8. | 360 | 1.57 | 560 | 0.675 |
| 180 | 6.25 | 380 | 1.415 | 580 | 0.61 |
| 200 | 5.125 | 400 | 1.275 | 600 | 0.565 |

A short-cut which gives fairly accurate results, if no grades are present, is to multiply the watt-hours required for travel by 1.75 for 50-ft. trips; by 1.60 for 75-ft. trips; by 1.50 for 100-ft. trips; by 1.40 for 150-ft. trips; by 1.30 for 250-ft. trips; and by 1.25 for 500-ft. trips. The result will be the watt-hours required for both travel and acceleration.

(Author's note: Throughout this discussion of performance and costs, it should be kept in mind that theoretical results may not be fulfilled in practice. The skill of operators varies widely and rest periods must be provided. Moreover accidental, or incidental delays occur which affect more or less the day by day performance.)

[1]Travel and acceleration formulas assume an efficiency of 66⅔ per cent between battery and wheels.

In our problem, the time required for one round trip is:

| Loaded trip: | *TE*, pounds | Speed, feet per minute | *Distance*, feet | *Time*, minutes |
|---|---|---|---|---|
| Acceleration on level | ... | 140 | 23 | 0.16 |
| Travel on level | 420 | 286 | 577 | 2.02 |
| Travel up 2% grade | 840 | 220 | 50 | 0.28 |
| Light trip: | | | | |
| Acceleration on level | ... | 250 | 70 | 0.28 |
| Travel on level | 100 | 500 | 530 | 1.06 |
| Travel down 2% grade | ... | 500 | 50 | 0.10 |

A fair allowance for making up trailers into trains and for miscellaneous delays would be 8 min. per round trip, bringing the estimated elapsed time to an average of approximately 12 min. At this rate one tractor could make about 40 trips per 8-hr. day which at 8 tons per trip would be more than ample for the transfer of 250 tons.

With reference again to the performance curve (Fig. 7-18) to estimate the battery capacity, the ampere values are read in connection with the time values previously computed. The ampere-hours required for a round trip may be estimated as follows:

| Loaded trip: | *TE*, pounds | Amperes | Minutes | Ampere-Minutes |
|---|---|---|---|---|
| Acceleration | 735 | 178 | 0.16 | 28.48 |
| Travel on level | 420 | 122 | 2.02 | 246.44 |
| Travel up 2% grade | 840 | 197 | 0.23 | 45.31 |
| Light trip: | | | | |
| Acceleration | 175 | 75 | 0.28 | 21.00 |
| Travel on level | 100 | 59 | 1.06 | 62.54 |
| Travel down 2% grade | ... | ... | ... | ... |
| | | | | 403.77 |

This gives us 6.73 ampere-hr. per trip and 215 for the required 32 trips. The rated capacity of the battery should therefore be not less than 215 times 1.25 = 268.75 ampere-hr. and it should consist of the required number of cells to deliver 36 volts. Thus the 300 ampere-hr. battery with which the tractor is equipped is of ample capacity for the job.

Ordinarily the performance curves are confined largely to tractor estimates. The ordinary traction-power formulas are sufficiently accurate for truck calculations. Truck travel distances are usually shorter, and much of the work done consists of lifting, so that the time consumed in travel is proportionally less.

**When Does Mechanical Handling Pay?** To arrive at the *total* cost of operating a truck, let us assume a 2-ton-capacity low-lift truck. A typical estimate would be:

| | |
|---|---|
| Net price of truck | $2000 |
| Cost of one set of tires | 100 |
| Depreciation basis | 1900 |

| | |
|---|---|
| Depreciation: 6% of $1900 | $123.50 |
| Annual tire cost | 100.00 |
| Net price of battery $450. 16½% | 74.25 |
| Cost of charging equipment $600. Depr. 5% | 30.00 |
| Maintenance of truck | 60.00 |
| Maintenance of battery | 30.00 |
| Maintenance of charging equipment | 10.00 |
| Charging current | 40.00 |
| Insurance | 10.00 |
| Total per year | $497.75 |
| Total per 8-hr. day, at 260 days per year | $1.91 |

We will assume that the cost per day will remain at $1.91, even though the truck works but a fraction of a day, and that the operator's wages are $1 per hour, and we have:

| Hours per Day | Total Trips Made | Tons Handled | Cost of Truck | Cost of Wages | Total per Day | Cost per 100 Ton-Ft. |
|---|---|---|---|---|---|---|
| ¼ | 13 | 26 | $1.91 | $.25 | $2.16 | 8.30 cents |
| ½ | 26 | 52 | 1.91 | .50 | 2.41 | 4.65 |
| 1 | 53 | 106 | 1.91 | 1.00 | 2.91 | 2.75 |
| 2 | 106 | 212 | 1.91 | 2.00 | 3.91 | 1.84 |
| 4 | 212 | 424 | 1.91 | 4.00 | 5.91 | 1.40 |

The total investment for truck and charging equipment is $3050. The amount earned on the investment may be estimated thus, for comparison with hand trucking: For the latter we will assume the laborer's wage at the low rate of 50 cents per hour. The cost on the basis of 3½ tons per hour will be 14.3 cents per ton.

| Hours per Day | Tons Handled | Power-Trucking Cost | Hand-Trucking Cost | Annual Saving | Per cent Return |
|---|---|---|---|---|---|
| ½ | 52 | $2.41 | $7.45 | $360. | 12 |
| 1 | 106 | 2.91 | 15.16 | 3,180. | 104 |
| 2 | 212 | 3.91 | 30.32 | 6,870. | 225 |
| 4 | 424 | 5.91 | 54.73 | 14,900. | 488 |

Hand-trucking cost remains substantially the same with increasing volumes until congestion occurs. Figure 7-19 shows the relation between hand trucking and power trucking along the lines developed in the foregoing table. Since trucking costs are intimately connected with the skill of the operators, which varies widely, the costs arrived at may require discounting, but there are actual instances in which the maximum return shown has been exceeded. Again, the corollary

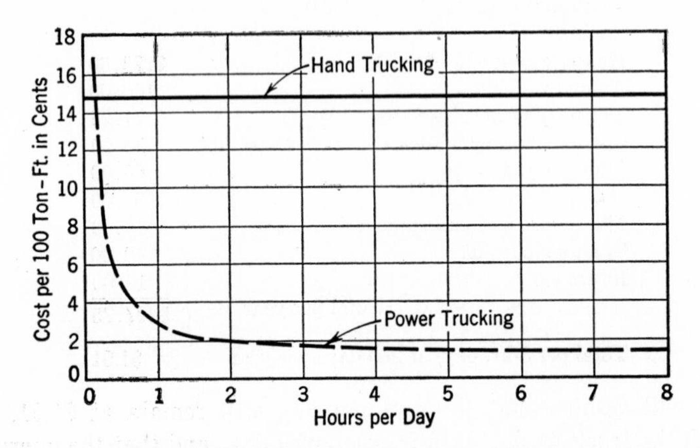


Fig. 7–19. Relation between power-trucking and hand-trucking costs.

profits from smooth flow of materials must be taken into consideration, these include savings in lost time of skilled machine operators and production machines, fewer accidents with lower compensation payments, less material and equipment damage, and decreased congestion in the production and storage areas through high tiering.

## CHAPTER 8

## THE CONTINUOUS-FLOW CONVEYOR

The continuous-flow, conveyor is a machine in which the material moves slowly within a duct as a continuous core as contrasted with the manner of movement of material conveyed by a screw or flight conveyor, pivoted bucket carrier, belt conveyor, or a bucket elevator.

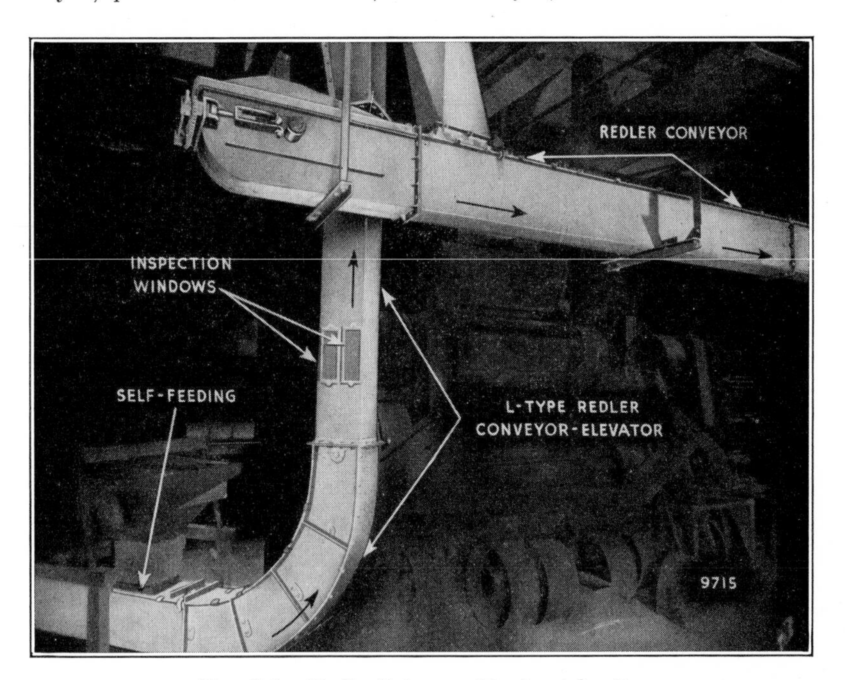


**Fig. 8-1.** Redler L-type and horizontal units.

Although these will convey all materials that can be conveyed en masse the continuous-flow conveyor may not be advisable for some materials or layouts.

**The Redler** (Fig. 8-1). The Redler, earliest of these, was invented by an Englishman of that name who devised the method of moving a flowable granular or pulverized material by means of spaced frames or skeletonized flights commonly attached to a steel cable, not by a direct push but by an induced movement due to the coherence of the mass in which the element is submerged.

The Redler conveyor was introduced to this country by the Stephens Adamson Manufacturing Company, which vastly improved the design and discarded the steel cable in favor of a simple detachable chain with the flight cast integral with the link. Though some of the early installations ran into difficulties, the manufacturers through research and experience soon determined both the limitations and the possibilities, and subsequent installations were uniformly successful.

*Method of Operation.* If material is fed to the duct by gravity flow it will move along with the skeleton flights since the frictional resistance to motion is much less than the pull of the submerged flight prongs. Usually the feed is to the upper or return run with a transfer to the carrying run immediately beyond. If the path leads upward, as in the L-type or loop type, the mass movement continues since the duct is filled to capacity and the material cannot slip backward. If the feed is from another machine, or is intermittent and so less than the capacity of the duct, spaced cleanout flights may be provided. Slip is not thereby completely eliminated, but when the feed is stopped the duct will be cleared of material after a few minutes' continued movement of the elevator — a desirable feature if the material will freeze, pack, or spoil.

The Redler is self-loading to capacity, cannot overload, and does not require a feeder. If the material is such that gravity loading somewhat less than the capacity of the duct is desired, the duct area may be reduced by a filler at the loading zone. If the material is sluggish and will not discharge as the flights emerge from the duct a plow extends into the path of the U-flights to press the mass outward (Fig. 8-2*A*).

**The Bulk Flo** (Fig. 8-3) as developed by the Link-Belt Company has a detachable malleable-iron chain with the characteristic peaked flight (Fig. 8-4) at each pitch. For complete cleanout there is an occasional modified flight (Fig. 8-5). As the flights are bolted to the chain attachment, various sizes may be provided for each size of chain. The chain is selected to suit the pull to which it is to be subjected, and the flight size depends on the desired capacity. The flights project outwardly from the chain, and substantially all the material discharges directly as they emerge from the duct. A small residue carries upward and discharges rearward across a Λ-shaped deflector (Fig. 8-6), then rejoins the main outflow. This applies to an elevator discharge, but in a conveyor the flights may be flat with a slight rearward slant to eliminate chatter.

The Bulk Flo is self-loading to capacity, cannot overload, and does not require a feeder. As there is only working clearance between the edges of the flights and the walls of the duct (except with lumpy mate-

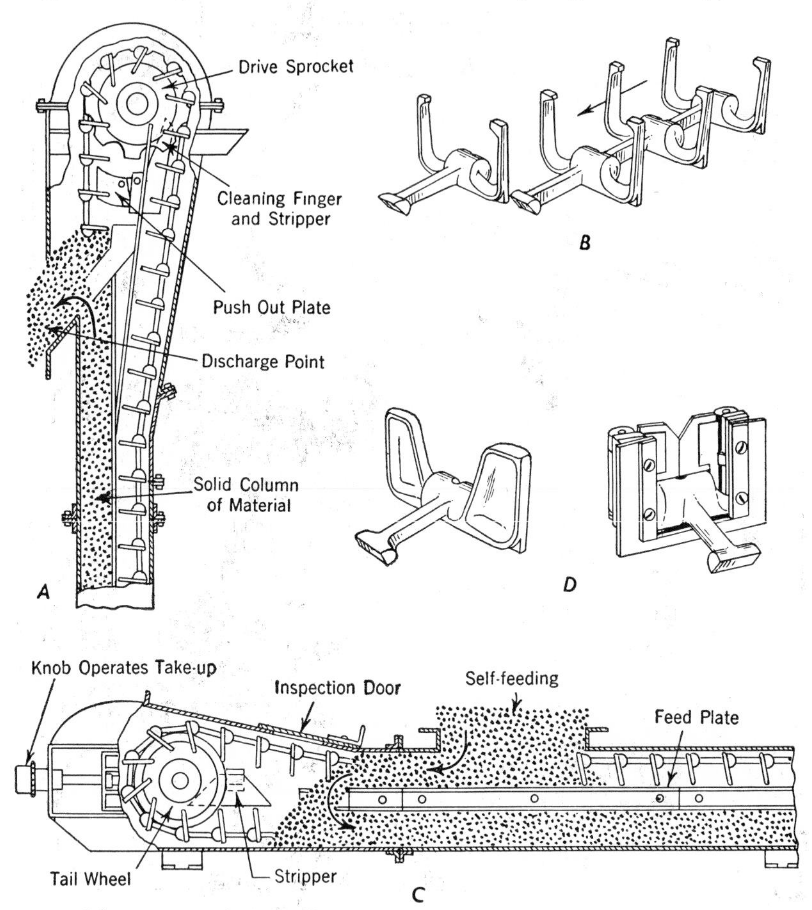


FIG. 8–2. Redler conveyor details. *A*. Sectional view at head of elevator. *B*. Skeleton flights. *C*. Loading end. *D*. Two types of cleanout flights.

rial) there is little slippage under part loading as the cells function equally well when partly filled.

In the loop-type Bulk Flo the loading zone is a tangent in the sweep of the curve of the loop, so that the load enters while the flights are parallel with each other. As they enter the turn they are radial with the unit cells expanded, and as they enter the following tangent they resume the relative position which they had while the load entered, thus eliminating any jamming action.

FIG. 8-3. Three loop-type Bulk Flos with automatic controls feeding coal from bin to stoker hoppers.

The effect of the peaked flight shape, with the long inner leg, is to give an outward thrust to the element in a loaded vertical run which counteracts the inward thrust due to the off-center position of the center of gravity of the load.

**The Uni-Flo** (Fig. 8-7) as developed by the Chain Belt Company has a projecting attachment on alternate links on which a horizontal pivoted flat flight rests. As the flights emerge from the duct they are tilted upward by a revolving cam, chain-driven from the head shaft, and the load discharges forward.

**The Flo-Master** (Fig. 8-8) as developed by the Gifford Wood Company has a carbon-steel chain of 6-in. pitch with steel flights riveted to alternate links extended to about midpitch of the following link,

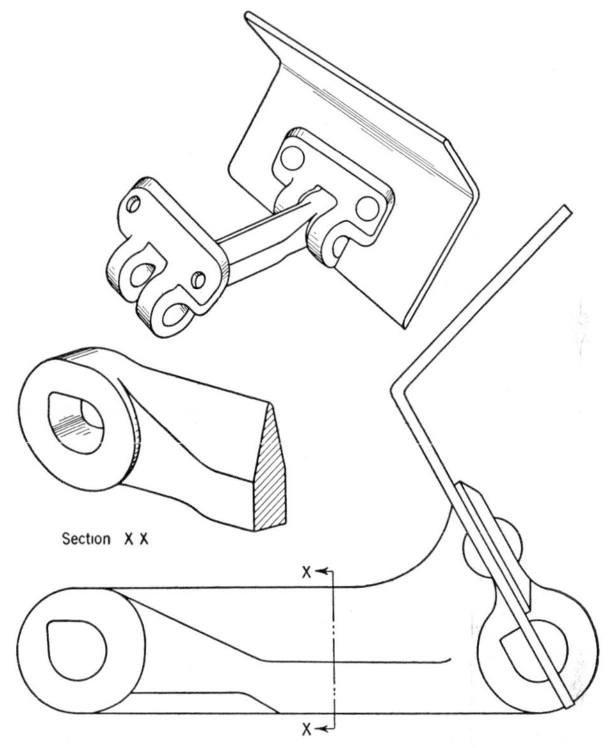


FIG. 8-4. The conveying element of the Bulk Flo. Peaked flights of various sizes are available for any size of chain, to suit the desired handling capacity.

providing a steep discharge angle as the ascending flights enter the head sprocket.

**The Mass-Flo** (Fig. 8-9) as developed by the Jeffrey Manufacturing Company has a chain somewhat similar to that of the Bulk Flo except that at every other pitch there is a projecting arm from which a flat flight is pivotally suspended. Discharge of the unit loads is accomplished by tilting the flights outward by a stationary cam projecting into the duct from the rear.

**The Hudson Helicoid** (Fig. 8-10) has an element consisting of an endless steel helicoid with spaced coils on which the material is carried in effect as a series of miniature hemispheres prevented from collapse by the wall of the encircling tubular duct. The helix pitch increases

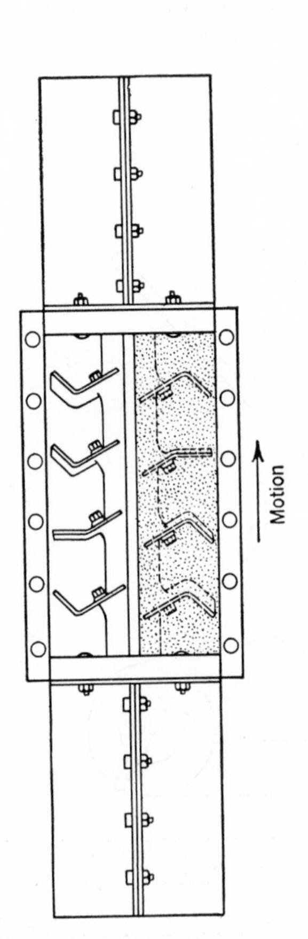


FIG. 8-5. The loaded and return runs of a Bulk Flo elevator. Near the middle of the return run is a cleanout flight used when complete cleanout of the duct is desired or when the material is fluid.

FIG. 8-6. Head section of the Bulk Flo, showing the flights emerging from the duct. Material is about to flow out. Behind the middle flight is the deflector which will divert any residue around the main discharge.

slightly from the loading point to the discharge point as the tension increases, relieving the congestion in the duct. At the point of dis-

FIG. 8-7. The head end of the Uni-Flo showing one of the flights tilted in discharge position by the revolving cam.

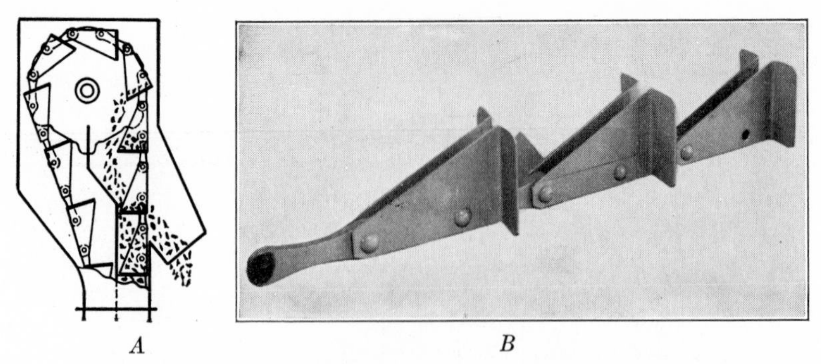


FIG. 8–8. (*A*) Discharge positions of the rearward-cantilevered flights of the Flo-Master. (*B*) Chain and flight assembly of the Flo-Master.

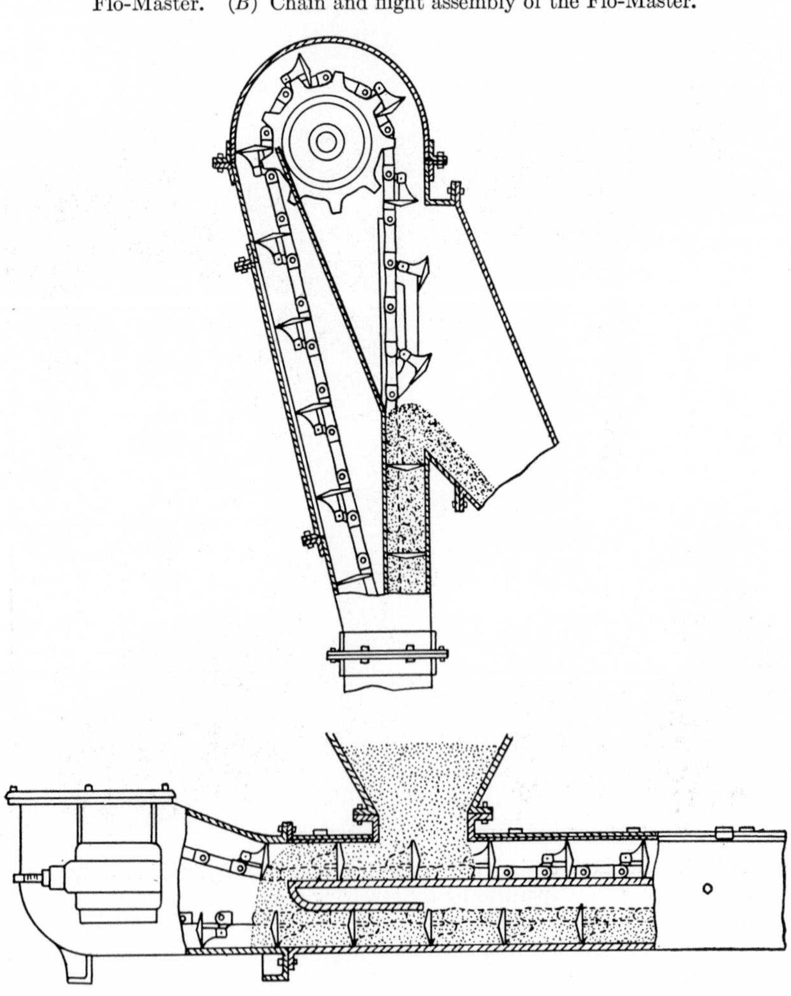

FIG. 8–9. The conveying element of the Jeffery Mass-Flo.

charge the unit loads collapse and the material flows radially outward. The speed of the element is limited only by the time interval between the end of the duct and the head wheel.

**Comparative Sizes.** Since the manufacturers of chain and flight en masse conveyors do not use the same method of designating their

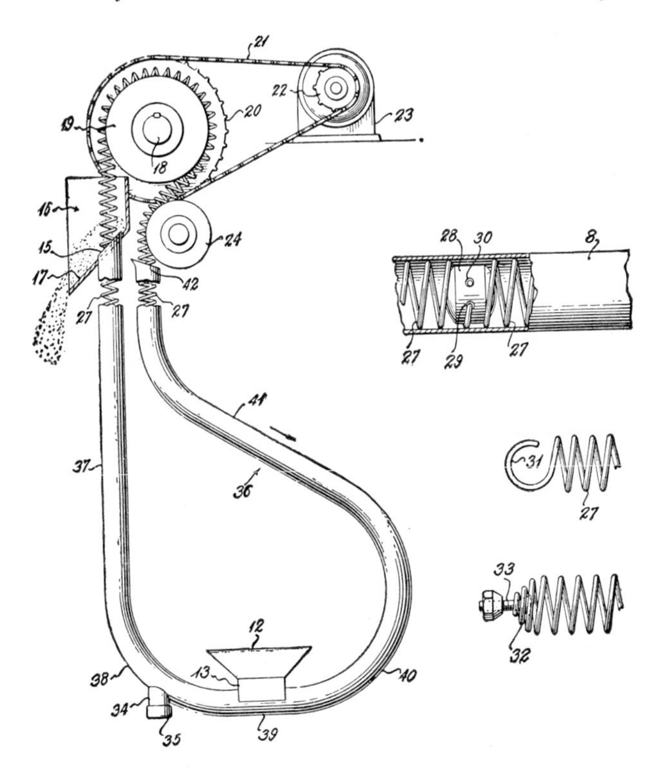


Fig. 8–10. Patent drawing of Hudson helicoid.

sizes, Table 1 lists the Redlers, Bulk Flos, Uni-Flos, Flo-Masters, and Mass-Flos according to the area of the duct.

**Applications and Limitations.** The continuous-flow conveyor will handle any pulverized or granular material unless it is actively abrasive, extremely fragile, or contains unbreakable lumps. It should be used with caution for any material that is sticky and will not flow, or that is corrosive, unless non-corroding metal is available. Since the material is in sliding contact with the walls of the duct and is subjected to more or less squeezing, fragile material will be pulverized to some extent. Hard lumps may jam between flights and casing. Coal presents no difficulty if the lumps are not too large to enter or discharge.

TABLE 1

COMPARATIVE SIZES OF CHAIN-FLIGHT CONTINUOUS-FLOW CONVEYORS[1]

| Conveyor | Size | Casing Area, square inches | Chain Pitch, inches |
|---|---|---|---|
| Redler | No. 3 | 10.5 | 3 |
| | 5 | 22.0 | 4 |
| | 7 | 40.7 | 5 |
| | 9 | 58.5 | 6 |
| | 11 | 85.2 | 7 |
| | 13 | 112.0 | 8 |
| | 15 | 144.0 | 9 |
| | 17 | 189.0 | 10 |
| | 19 | 240.0 | 11 |
| Bulk Flo | No. 35 | 22.0 | 4 |
| | 57 | 42.6 | 5 |
| | 610 | 69.8 | 6 |
| | 712 | 95.6 | 6 |
| | 913 | 136.5 | 8 |
| Flo-Master | No. 1 | 64.0 | 6 |
| | 2 | 96.0 | 6 |
| Uni-Flo | No. 5 | 22.0 | 5 |
| | 7 | 37.5 | 7 |
| | 9 | 57.0 | 9 |
| | 11 | 85.2 | 11 |
| | 13 | 113.4 | 13 |
| | 15 | 145.7 | 15 |
| Mass-Flo | No. 5 | 22.0 | 4 |
| | 7 | 37.5 | 5 |
| | 9 | 57.0 | 6 |
| | 11 | 85.2 | 7 |
| | 13 | 113.4 | 8 |
| | 15 | 145.7 | 9 |

[1]The use of the table: if a conveyor with a duct area of about 90 sq. in. is required, a Redler, a Mass-Flo or a Uni-Flo No. 11, a Bulk Flo No. 712, or a Flo-Master No. 2 may be selected.

Since the element is embedded in the material the articulations are subjected to damage if the material will corrode or grind them.

The continuous-flow conveyor is nicely suited to materials which should not come in contact with lubricants, must not be contaminated by exposure such as food products, or are harmful to breathe. If the material is to be held at nearly constant temperature the casing is insulated. Table 2 groups materials into three classes. Those in group 1 are easily handled. Those in group 2 are more or less difficult. Those in group 3 may be untouchable.

Many installations are in connection with coal of stoker size or smaller where the layout may be simplified and the investment substantially reduced through the en masse conveyor. The routine layout

TABLE 2

OPERATION OF CONTINUOUS-FLOW CONVEYORS WITH VARIOUS MATERIALS

Group 1. Easily handled

| | |
|---|---|
| Coal, if not corrosive | Ground bone |
| Coffee beans | Granulated sugar, if not sticky |
| Grains, wheat, etc. | Sawdust |
| Copra | Salt, dry |
| Corn, ground | Soybeans and products |
| Granulated cork | Soda ash |
| Wood chips | Fly ash, not containing flue dirt |

All flowable granular and pulverized materials which are not abrasive, corrosive, or do not contain unbreakable lumps.

Group 2. Sometimes difficult

| | |
|---|---|
| Bauxite | Hot salt |
| Burned lime | Some starch sours |
| Ground copra, when sticky | Wet coal in freezing temperatures |
| Brown sugar | Shelled corn |
| Hog fuel | Foundry dust |
| | Pumice[2] |

Group 3. Extremely difficult or unsuitable

| | |
|---|---|
| All corrosive materials[1] | Ground stone[2] |
| Ashes | Iron oxide |
| Bagasse, unless chopped up | Pulverized feldspar[2] |
| Carbon-black pellets | Molybdenum concentrates |
| Cement | Wet sewage sludge |
| Bug dust (coal dust and rock dust) | Borax[2] |
| Fuzzy cottonseed | Hot brewers' grains[1] |
| Gravel, sand, crushed stone | Heavy metallic dusts |

[1]May be handled with corrosion-resisting duct and chain.
[2]May be handled with provision against abrasion.

for transferring small coal from track hopper to a bin at 15 tons per hour is a 9-in. screw feeder driven from the foot shaft of an 8 by 5 in. centrifugal discharge elevator having a speed of 160 ft. per min. An L-type No. 57 Bulk Flo would be arranged as shown in Fig. 8-11; it would cost 40 per cent less than the other.

A unique feature of the conveyor is that a succession of feed-in openings will not overload the machine. The material will feed through the first opening of the loading run to the capacity of the duct, automatically stopping the feed from the following openings until the first feed ceases. Similarly, there may be a succession of discharge openings. The material will feed and fill successive chutes, or the width of the discharge slots may be adjustable for a succession of controlled discharges. There is a trend in boiler-house design toward an automatic feed to the stoker chutes or pulverizer hoppers from any section of an overhead bunker; this is an improvement over the larry method, which is by no means a dustless operation and requires the attendance of a man. A Redler is nicely adapted for a horizontal runaround or closed-

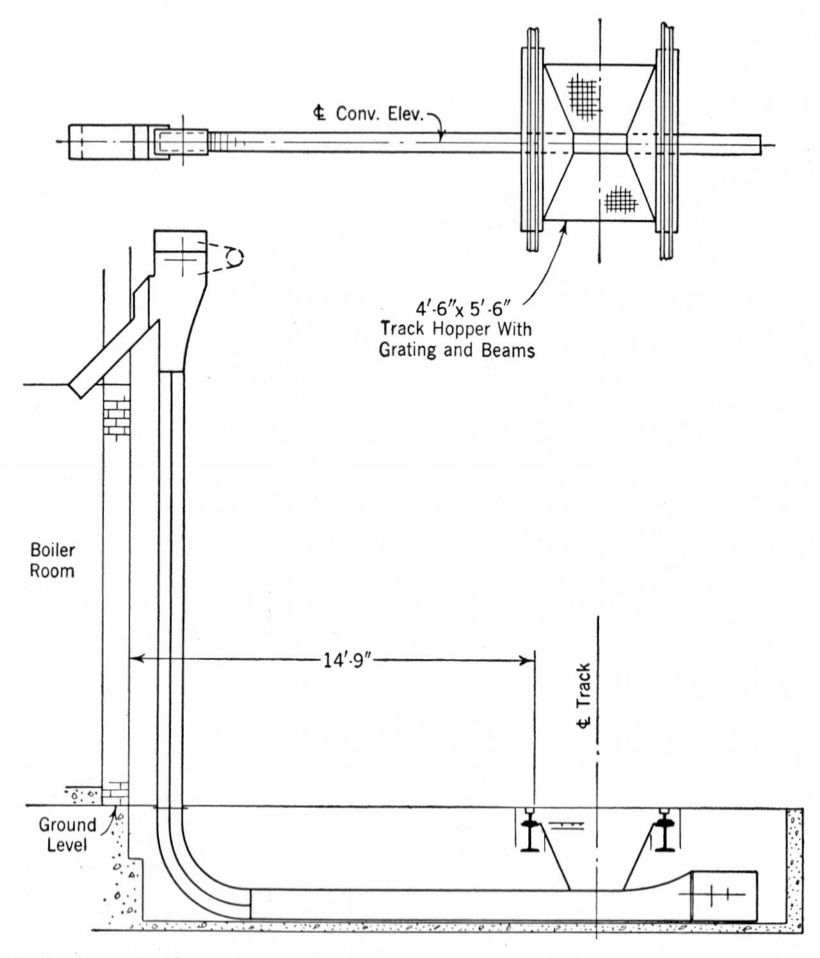


Fig. 8–11. Typical layout for L-type continuous-flow unit for transfer of coal from track hopper to storage bin.

circuit layout (Fig. 20-9). It operates at slow speed with a capacity slightly in excess of the maximum demand, and any surplus carries back and recirculates to the loading point where the duct is again filled to capacity; thus the coal from any section of a bunker is available for any boiler with completely dustless operation. It is not completely automatic, since it is difficult to feed more material to a conveyor than discharges, and if one or more boilers are off the line the runaround will tend to plug up. An overload stop or an overload signal is easily provided, and a variable-speed drive permits close adjustment of the speed to the demand.

For heavy-duty runarounds the Redler is now built as shown in Fig. 8-12 with malleable iron bushed chain supported on a hardened track

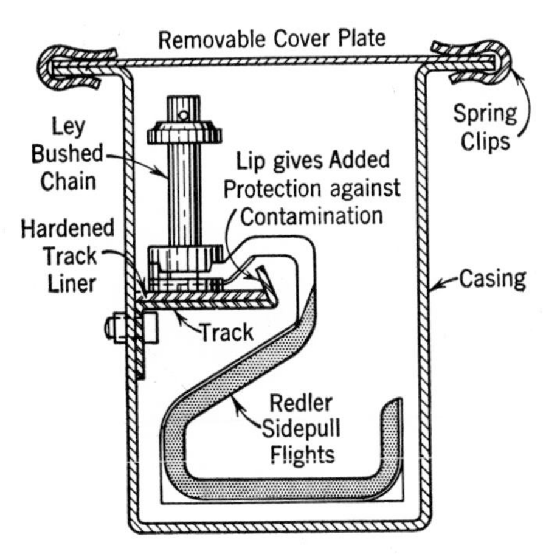


Fig. 8-12. Cross section of heavy-duty Redler horizontal runaround conveyor.

liner clear of the load. The skeleton flights likewise are carried clear of the trough.

**Track Hoppers.** When necessary the continuous-flow conveyor may have a track hopper with a depth substantially less than is required for the usual apron or reciprocating feeder. With fine, free-flowing materials the arrangement may be as in Fig. 8-13*A*, where the feed is direct to the load-carrying run. With a large track hopper it is possible to offset the duct as in Fig. 8-13*B*, so that if the conveyor is jammed by foreign material — large lumps, tramp iron, wood, etc. — the duct may be cleared more readily than if it is directly beneath the hopper. There should be the usual grid at track level, though material which can pass through a 3- or 4-in. grid may plug this type of conveyor.

**Tandem Units.** If an elevator discharges to a conveyor, or if two or more conveyors are in tandem, it is essential that when the speed of the first unit has been determined the second unit shall be given a higher speed. The first loads to the capacity of the duct, and if the tandem unit has 10 or 15 per cent greater speed its duct is more comfortably loaded, and frictional resistance is reduced.

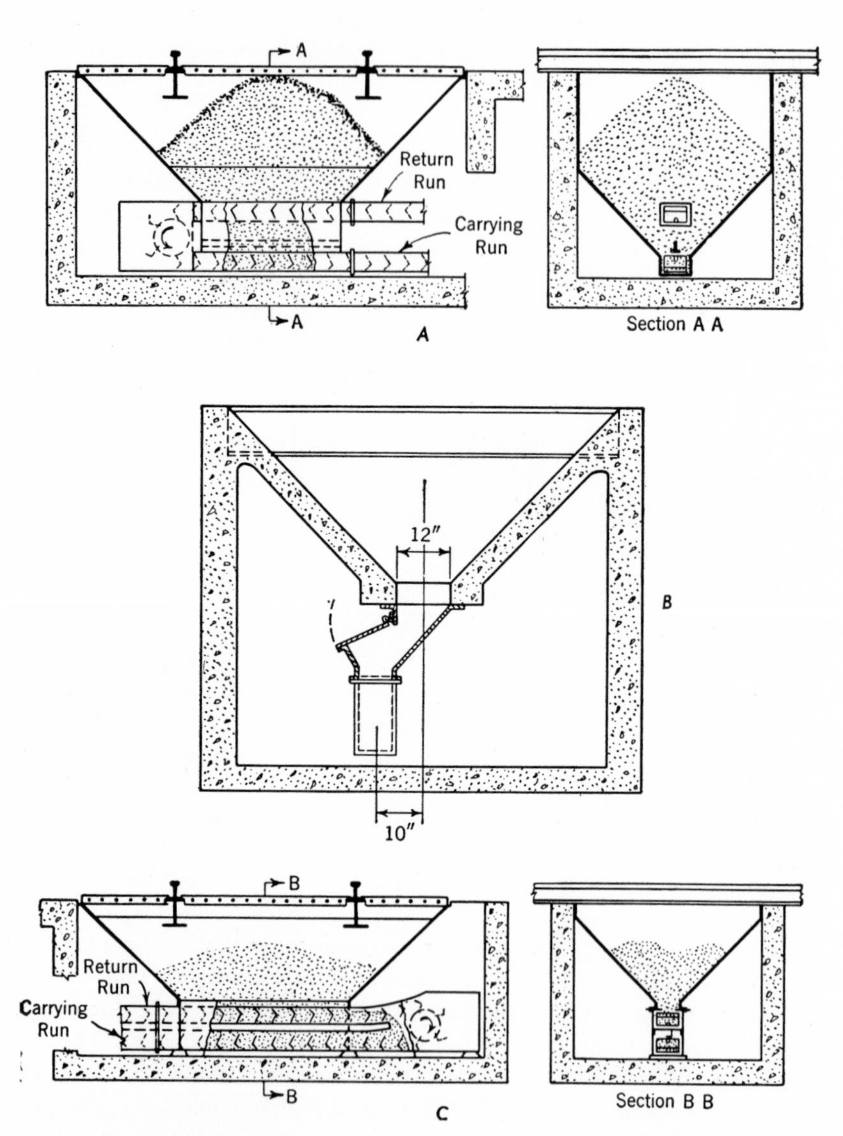


FIG. 8–13. Track hoppers. (*A*) Shallow track hopper with feed direct to carrying run. (*B*) Track hopper with conveyor off-set to facilitate clearing. (*C*) Shallow track hopper with feed to return run.

**Paths.** The continuous-flow conveyor is adapted to a wide variety of paths. If there is a long horizontal run followed by an upturn there should be a turn wheel at the bend to take the heavy radial thrust. If there is a vertical run followed by a horizontal run it is better to use tandem units.

**Additional Features.** There are situations which require not only that the conveyor be dustless but also that it be gas tight. This is a field in which the en masse conveyor is peculiarly adapted.

The conveyor properly applied does a good job, but there is always the temptation, because of its simplicity and low cost, to use it where some other type of conveyor is better. It requires more power than a flight conveyor or bucket elevator, but power is not important except where the capacity is large. In cross section it requires less space than a screw conveyor of the same capacity, about a third as much as a belt conveyor and about a fifth as much as a bucket elevator.

The continuous-flow elevator functions best when it is handling material at close to rated capacity, since under partial loading there may be a continuing slippage back through the impellers, but this maximum capacity is rigidly fixed by the size of the duct and the speed. The machine cannot, like a bucket elevator, handle surges. If a conveyor feeds to an elevator such adjustment to 100 per cent capacity introduces the necessity of a surge hopper between the two or an automatic stop in the motor circuit of the first machine, such as a diaphragm start-and-stop contactor attached to the side of the hopper or chute between the two.

With some materials it is of no consequence whether or not the elevator remains partly loaded at the end of a run, but self-clearing may be essential, as when handling damp coal in a location exposed to freezing temperatures or when handling a material that has a corrosive action in long contact with the walls of the duct. Substantially effective cleanout may be secured by running the elevator for several minutes after the work is done. However, if the material is one which sours or spoils, the continuous-flow machine is unsuitable, as complete cleanout cannot be attained except possibly by compressed-air jets.

**Determination of Power and Capacity.** *The Redler.* Figure 8-14 is the Redler speed-capacity chart published by the Stephens Adamson Manufacturing Company. Knowing the material weight per cubic foot, we enter the left-hand chart at the top or bottom and move vertically along the proper line to the intersection with the diagonal corresponding to the weight, then move across to the right to the diagonal corresponding to the type of machine (conveyor, elevator, etc.) and the type of material. We then move downward to the lower chart where

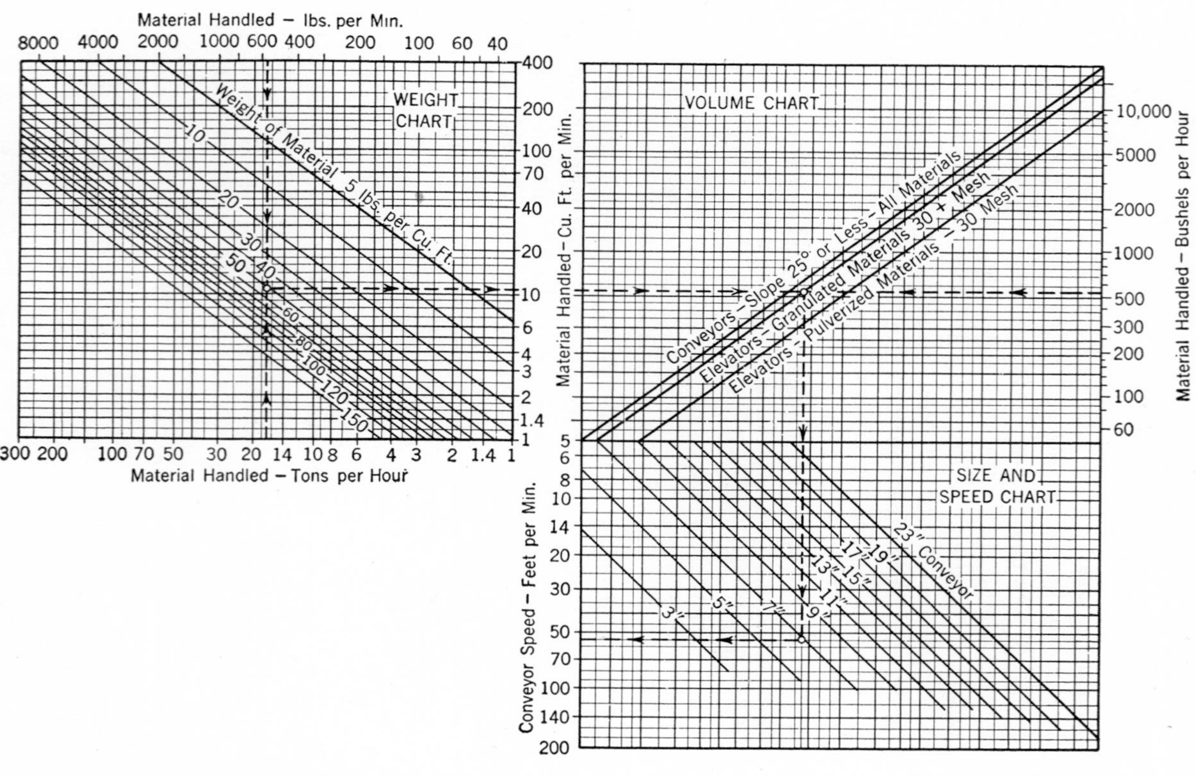


Fig. 8–14. Chart for determination of capacity and speed of Redler conveyors and elevators. (Stephens Adamson.)

TABLE 3

POWER FORMULAS FOR REDLER CONVEYORS AND ELEVATORS

Horizontal conveyor (no bends): $\text{Motor } HP = \dfrac{ELT}{1000}$

Inclined conveyor: $\text{Motor } HP = \dfrac{ELT + HT}{1000}$

L-path conveyor elevator: $\text{Motor } HP = \dfrac{FLT + GHT + KT}{1000}$

Loop-type elevator: $\text{Motor } HP = \dfrac{GT(H + \frac{1}{2}C)}{1000}$

where $L$ = length of horizontal run in feet.
$H$ = vertical run in feet.
$T$ = tons per hour.
$C$ = conveyor size.
$E$, $F$, $G$, $K$, are the factors in Table 4.

we intersect one or more diagonals which show the size of unit available and to the left to find the corresponding speed.

**Example.** The dotted line shows the procedure for a Redler to handle 17 tons per hour of coal. Enter the chart at 17 tons per hour and move upward to the diagonal for 50-lb. material. Moving horizontally to "elevators handling granulated material," then downward, we intersect the 7-in. diagonal and the corresponding speed of 50 ft. per min. The speed of 90 ft. per min. makes the 5-in. unit undesirable. If the lumps are large we can use a 9-in. at 35 ft. per min.

Having determined the size and speed we use the Table 3 formulas to find the motor horsepower. Since the type of material affects the power, it is necessary to use factors which reflect the coefficient of friction or drag of the material against the walls of the duct. These factors are given in Table 4.

**The Bulk Flo.** Figure 8-15 shows the capacity for each size of Bulk Flo for materials of various weights at various speeds. If we assume a material weighing 60 lb. per cu. ft. and a capacity of 50 tons per hour, a vertical line crosses the sizes from a No. 610 at 85 ft. to a No. 712 at 60 ft. per min. Again assume that we have a No. 712 machine. What is the capacity range with material weighing 60 lb. per cu. ft.? Following the No. 712 line from the left we see that the capacity ranges from about 17 tons per hour at a speed of 20 ft. to about 68 tons per hour at 80 ft. per min. Slow speeds are desirable; a conservative rating would be that corresponding to 40–60 ft. per min.

Figure 8-16 gives the formulas used in determining the motor horsepower for Bulk Flos. The maximum chain pull recommended for the No. 35 chains in malleable iron is 2200 lb.; for the No. 57 chains it is

# TABLE 4

## Redler Factors for Representative Materials

| Material | Weight per Cubic Foot, pounds | K | 3″ Units | | | 5″ Units | | | 7″ Units | | | 9″ Units | | | 11″ Units | | | 13″ Units | | | 15″ Units | | | 17″ Units | | | 19″ Units | | |
|---|---|---|---|---|---|---|---|---|---|---|---|---|---|---|---|---|---|---|---|---|---|---|---|---|---|---|---|---|---|
| | | | E | F | G | E | F | G | E | F | G | E | F | G | E | F | G | E | F | G | E | F | G | E | F | G | E | F | G |
| Beans, dry navy | 54 | 100 | 1.5 | 2.9 | 4.4 | 1.3 | 2.5 | 3.9 | 1.2 | 2.3 | 3.6 | 1.1 | 2.2 | 3.4 | 1.2 | 2.3 | 3.1 | 1.2 | 2.2 | 3.0 | 1.1 | 2.2 | 2.9 | 1.1 | 2.1 | 2.7 | 1.1 | 2.0 | 2.6 |
| Bicarbonate of soda, dry, pulverized | 55 | 0 | 3.0 | 6.9 | 8.1 | 2.6 | 5.7 | 7.1 | 2.4 | 5.2 | 6.4 | 2.3 | 4.9 | 5.8 | 2.4 | 5.2 | 5.4 | 2.3 | 5.1 | 5.1 | 2.3 | 4.9 | 4.8 | 2.2 | 4.7 | 4.5 | 2.2 | 4.6 | 4.3 |
| Bran | 26 | 0 | 4.1 | 8.3 | 3.8 | 3.3 | 6.6 | 3.4 | 3.0 | 6.0 | 3.2 | 2.8 | 5.5 | 3.0 | 3.0 | 5.9 | 2.8 | 2.9 | 5.7 | 2.7 | 2.8 | 5.5 | 2.6 | 2.7 | 5.3 | 2.5 | 2.6 | 5.0 | 2.4 |
| Cellulose acetate dry, coarse granular | 10 | 80 | 8.0 | 15.9 | 4.4 | 6.1 | 12.0 | 3.9 | 5.4 | 10.6 | 3.6 | 4.8 | 9.8 | 3.4 | 5.3 | 10.0 | 3.1 | 5.1 | 10.0 | 3.0 | 4.8 | 9.4 | 2.9 | 4.6 | 9.0 | 2.7 | 4.4 | 8.5 | 2.6 |
| Cement, dry Portland | 60–90 | 0 | 2.9 | 7.4 | 6.0 | 2.5 | 6.0 | 5.2 | 2.3 | 5.5 | 4.8 | 2.2 | 5.1 | 4.4 | 2.3 | 5.4 | 4.1 | 2.3 | 5.3 | 3.9 | 2.2 | 5.1 | 3.7 | 2.2 | 5.0 | 3.5 | 2.1 | 4.8 | 3.4 |
| Clay, dry lumpy | 40–100 | 80 | 3.1 | 5.9 | 4.6 | 2.6 | 4.9 | 4.1 | 2.4 | 4.5 | 3.8 | 2.3 | 4.2 | 3.5 | 2.4 | 4.5 | 3.3 | 2.3 | 4.4 | 3.2 | 2.3 | 4.2 | 3.0 | 2.2 | 4.1 | 2.8 | 2.1 | 4.0 | 2.8 |
| Clay, pulverized | 25–80 | 0 | 6.0 | 17.7 | 6.8 | 4.8 | 13.6 | 5.9 | 4.4 | 12.1 | 5.4 | 4.1 | 10.9 | 5.0 | 4.3 | 11.9 | 4.6 | 4.2 | 11.5 | 4.3 | 4.1 | 10.9 | 4.1 | 3.9 | 10.5 | 3.8 | 3.8 | 9.9 | 3.7 |
| Coal, minus ¼″ slack dry with l'ge proportion fines | 40–50 | 40 | 2.4 | 4.6 | 4.4 | 2.0 | 3.9 | 3.9 | 1.9 | 3.5 | 3.6 | 1.8 | 3.3 | 3.4 | 1.9 | 3.5 | 3.1 | 1.8 | 3.4 | 3.0 | 1.8 | 3.3 | 2.9 | 1.7 | 3.2 | 2.7 | 1.7 | 3.1 | 2.6 |
| Coal, minus ¼″ slack moderately wet | 45–55 | 40 | 3.3 | 6.1 | 5.4 | 2.8 | 5.1 | 4.8 | 2.6 | 4.7 | 4.4 | 2.5 | 4.4 | 4.1 | 2.6 | 4.7 | 3.8 | 2.5 | 4.6 | 3.6 | 2.5 | 4.4 | 3.4 | 2.4 | 4.3 | 3.2 | 2.3 | 4.2 | 3.1 |
| Coal, minus ¼″ slack very wet | 50–60 | 20 | 2.5 | 5.4 | 5.7 | 2.2 | 4.5 | 5.0 | 2.0 | 4.1 | 4.6 | 1.9 | 3.9 | 4.3 | 2.0 | 4.1 | 4.0 | 2.0 | 4.0 | 3.8 | 1.9 | 3.9 | 3.6 | 1.9 | 3.8 | 3.4 | 1.8 | 3.6 | 3.2 |
| Coal, minus 1½″ slack dry or damp | 40–50 | 40 | | | | | | | 2.1 | 3.8 | 3.6 | 1.9 | 3.5 | 3.4 | 2.0 | 3.7 | 3.1 | 2.0 | 3.6 | 3.0 | 1.9 | 3.5 | 2.9 | 1.9 | 3.4 | 2.7 | 1.8 | 3.3 | 2.6 |
| Coal, sized wet or dry | 40–50 | 80 | 2.2 | 4.1 | 3.8 | 1.9 | 3.4 | 3.4 | 1.7 | 3.1 | 3.2 | 1.6 | 2.9 | 3.0 | 1.7 | 3.1 | 2.8 | 1.7 | 3.0 | 2.7 | 1.6 | 2.9 | 2.6 | 1.6 | 2.8 | 2.5 | 1.5 | 2.8 | 2.4 |
| Coconut, shredded | 25 | 20 | 3.0 | 6.1 | 3.2 | 2.4 | 4.9 | 2.9 | 2.2 | 4.4 | 2.7 | 2.0 | 4.0 | 2.6 | 2.2 | 4.3 | 2.4 | 2.1 | 4.2 | 2.3 | 2.0 | 4.0 | 2.3 | 2.0 | 3.9 | 2.2 | 1.9 | 3.7 | 2.1 |
| Coffee, ground | 28 | 20 | 2.4 | 4.8 | 3.2 | 1.9 | 3.9 | 2.9 | 1.8 | 3.5 | 2.7 | 1.7 | 3.2 | 2.6 | 1.8 | 3.5 | 2.4 | 1.7 | 3.4 | 2.3 | 1.6 | 3.2 | 2.3 | 1.6 | 3.1 | 2.2 | 1.5 | 3.0 | 2.1 |
| Corn flakes | 12 | 0 | 3.8 | 7.9 | 2.3 | 2.9 | 6.0 | 2.1 | 2.6 | 5.3 | 2.0 | 2.4 | 4.8 | 1.9 | 2.6 | 5.2 | 1.9 | 2.5 | 5.0 | 1.8 | 2.3 | 4.8 | 1.8 | 2.2 | 4.6 | 1.7 | 2.1 | 4.3 | 1.7 |
| Flour, wheat | 30–40 | 0 | 3.2 | 7.1 | 3.5 | 2.6 | 5.6 | 3.2 | 2.4 | 5.1 | 2.9 | 2.2 | 4.7 | 2.8 | 2.4 | 5.0 | 2.6 | 2.3 | 4.9 | 2.5 | 2.2 | 4.7 | 2.4 | 2.2 | 4.5 | 2.3 | 2.1 | 4.3 | 2.3 |
| Fuller's earth, dry granular | 42 | 80 | 3.1 | 6.9 | 7.3 | 2.5 | 5.5 | 6.3 | 2.4 | 5.1 | 5.8 | 2.2 | 4.7 | 5.3 | 2.3 | 5.0 | 4.9 | 2.3 | 4.9 | 4.7 | 2.2 | 4.7 | 4.3 | 2.2 | 4.6 | 4.1 | 2.1 | 4.4 | 4.0 |
| Lime, burned or " quick " lump or " pebble " | 50 | 200 | 2.7 | 5.0 | 7.0 | 2.3 | 4.2 | 6.1 | 2.2 | 4.0 | 5.6 | 2.1 | 3.7 | 5.2 | 2.2 | 3.9 | 4.8 | 2.1 | 3.8 | 4.5 | 2.1 | 3.7 | 4.2 | 2.0 | 3.6 | 4.0 | 2.0 | 3.5 | 3.8 |
| Lime, dry burned small lumps and dust | 50 | 120 | 3.5 | 6.9 | 6.5 | 3.0 | 6.0 | 5.6 | 2.8 | 5.5 | 5.2 | 2.7 | 5.2 | 4.8 | 2.8 | 5.5 | 4.4 | 2.7 | 5.3 | 4.2 | 2.7 | 5.2 | 4.0 | 2.6 | 5.0 | 3.7 | 2.5 | 4.9 | 3.6 |
| Lime, fine with tendency to pack | 40–60 | 300 | 4.4 | 8.8 | 7.5 | 3.7 | 7.2 | 6.5 | 3.4 | 6.6 | 6.0 | 3.2 | 6.2 | 5.5 | 3.4 | 6.6 | 5.1 | 3.3 | 6.4 | 4.8 | 3.2 | 6.2 | 4.5 | 3.1 | 6.0 | 4.2 | 3.0 | 5.8 | 4.1 |
| Lime, hydrated | 10–25 | 0 | 11.1 | 35.5 | 7.0 | 8.4 | 27.3 | 6.1 | 7.5 | 23.0 | 5.6 | 6.7 | 20.4 | 5.2 | 7.3 | 22.5 | 4.8 | 7.1 | 21.6 | 4.5 | 6.7 | 20.3 | 4.2 | 6.4 | 19.3 | 4.0 | 6.0 | 18.1 | 3.8 |
| Salt, dry granulated | 80 | 80 | 1.9 | 3.8 | 5.7 | 1.7 | 3.3 | 5.0 | 1.6 | 3.1 | 4.6 | 1.5 | 2.9 | 4.3 | 1.6 | 3.1 | 4.0 | 1.5 | 3.0 | 3.8 | 1.5 | 2.9 | 3.6 | 1.5 | 2.9 | 3.4 | 1.5 | 2.8 | 3.2 |
| Salt rock | 75 | 100 | 1.9 | 3.5 | 6.5 | 1.7 | 3.1 | 5.6 | 1.6 | 2.9 | 5.2 | 1.5 | 2.8 | 4.8 | 1.6 | 2.9 | 4.4 | 1.6 | 2.8 | 4.2 | 1.5 | 2.8 | 4.0 | 1.5 | 2.7 | 3.7 | 1.5 | 2.6 | 3.6 |
| Sand, silica coarse dry | 90–100 | 160 | 2.1 | 4.2 | 7.0 | 1.9 | 3.7 | 6.1 | 1.8 | 3.4 | 5.6 | 1.7 | 3.3 | 5.2 | 1.8 | 3.4 | 4.8 | 1.7 | 3.4 | 4.5 | 1.7 | 3.3 | 4.2 | 1.7 | 3.2 | 4.0 | 1.7 | 3.2 | 3.8 |
| Sand very fine, dry | 90–100 | 120 | 2.4 | 5.2 | 7.3 | 2.1 | 4.5 | 6.3 | 2.0 | 4.2 | 5.8 | 2.0 | 4.0 | 5.3 | 2.0 | 4.1 | 4.9 | 2.0 | 4.1 | 4.7 | 2.0 | 4.0 | 4.3 | 1.9 | 3.9 | 4.1 | 1.9 | 3.8 | 4.0 |
| Sawdust, dry | 10–30 | 0 | 6.2 | 14.5 | 4.1 | 4.7 | 10.9 | 3.7 | 4.2 | 9.6 | 3.4 | 3.7 | 8.5 | 3.2 | 4.1 | 9.4 | 3.0 | 3.9 | 9.0 | 2.9 | 3.7 | 8.6 | 2.7 | 3.6 | 8.1 | 2.6 | 3.4 | 7.6 | 2.5 |
| Soda ash, light | 25–35 | 20 | 4.5 | 11.4 | 6.5 | 3.6 | 8.9 | 5.6 | 3.3 | 8.0 | 5.2 | 3.1 | 7.2 | 4.8 | 3.3 | 7.8 | 4.4 | 3.2 | 7.5 | 4.2 | 3.0 | 7.2 | 4.0 | 3.0 | 6.9 | 3.7 | 2.8 | 6.6 | 3.6 |
| Soybean meal | 40 | 20 | 2.2 | 4.8 | 4.6 | 1.9 | 3.9 | 4.1 | 1.7 | 3.6 | 3.8 | 1.6 | 3.3 | 3.5 | 1.7 | 3.5 | 3.3 | 1.7 | 3.4 | 3.2 | 1.6 | 3.3 | 3.0 | 1.6 | 3.2 | 2.8 | 1.5 | 3.1 | 2.8 |
| Starch, lump | 30 | 80 | 2.1 | 3.9 | 3.8 | 1.7 | 3.2 | 3.4 | 1.6 | 2.9 | 3.2 | 1.5 | 2.7 | 3.0 | 1.6 | 2.9 | 2.8 | 1.5 | 2.8 | 2.7 | 1.5 | 2.7 | 2.6 | 1.4 | 2.6 | 2.5 | 1.4 | 2.5 | 2.4 |
| Starch, pulverized | 25–45 | 0 | 5.4 | 15.9 | 6.0 | 4.3 | 12.2 | 5.2 | 4.0 | 10.9 | 4.8 | 3.7 | 9.8 | 4.4 | 3.9 | 10.7 | 4.1 | 3.8 | 10.3 | 3.9 | 3.7 | 9.8 | 3.7 | 3.5 | 9.4 | 3.5 | 3.4 | 8.9 | 3.4 |
| Sugar, dry granulated | 50 | 160 | 2.7 | 5.8 | 9.1 | 2.3 | 4.8 | 7.9 | 2.2 | 4.4 | 7.1 | 2.1 | 4.2 | 6.6 | 2.2 | 4.4 | 6.1 | 2.1 | 4.3 | 5.7 | 2.1 | 4.1 | 5.3 | 2.0 | 4.0 | 5.0 | 2.0 | 3.9 | 4.8 |
| Sugar, brown | 40–50 | 40 | 4.4 | 8.5 | 7.5 | 3.7 | 7.0 | 6.5 | 3.4 | 6.5 | 6.0 | 3.2 | 6.0 | 5.5 | 3.4 | 6.4 | 5.1 | 3.3 | 6.2 | 4.8 | 3.2 | 6.0 | 4.5 | 3.1 | 5.8 | 4.2 | 3.0 | 5.6 | 4.1 |
| Wheat, dry fairly clean | 48 | 40 | 1.7 | 3.3 | 5.2 | 1.5 | 2.7 | 4.5 | 1.4 | 2.5 | 4.2 | 1.3 | 2.4 | 3.8 | 1.3 | 2.5 | 3.6 | 1.3 | 2.5 | 3.5 | 1.3 | 2.4 | 3.3 | 1.3 | 2.3 | 3.1 | 1.2 | 2.2 | 3.0 |
| Wood chips, dry | 15–30 | 40 | 3.5 | 6.6 | 2.8 | 2.7 | 5.1 | 2.5 | 2.5 | 4.6 | 2.4 | 2.2 | 4.1 | 2.3 | 2.4 | 4.5 | 2.2 | 2.3 | 4.3 | 2.1 | 2 2 | 4.1 | 2.0 | 2.1 | 4.0 | 2.0 | 2.0 | 3.7 | 1.9 |

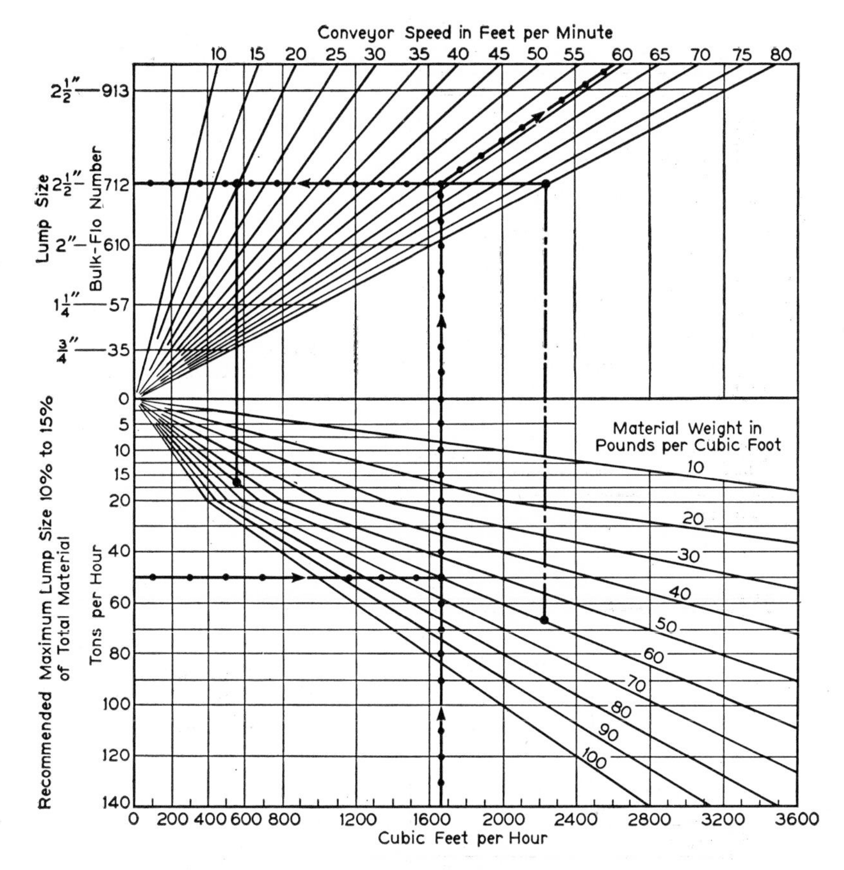


FIG. 8–15. Bulk Flo speed-capacity chart.

To determine Bulk Flo size and operating speed for a given capacity and weight of material, enter lower portion of chart from left side for capacities in tons per hour and move along a horizontal line to intersection with inclined material-weight line. From this point move vertically to intersection with first horizontal Bulk-Flo size line reached, in upper portion of chart.

Bulk Flo size is read at left-hand edge of upper chart. Conveyor speed is obtained by projecting a line up through the zero ordinate and the latter intersection point to the upper edge of the chart.

For capacities given in cubic feet per hour, enter chart at lower edge, disregard material-weight lines, and proceed to upper portion of chart on a vertical line to intersection with Bulk Flo size lines. Bulk Flo size and operating speed are then obtained in same manner as above.

Should speed obtained in this manner exceed the maximum recommended, repeat procedure, but select a Bulk Flo of next larger size operating at a correspondingly reduced speed.

Maximum-size lumps, constituting 10 to 15 per cent of total material, which may be handled in each size Bulk Flo, are listed to the left of the Bulk-Flo number.

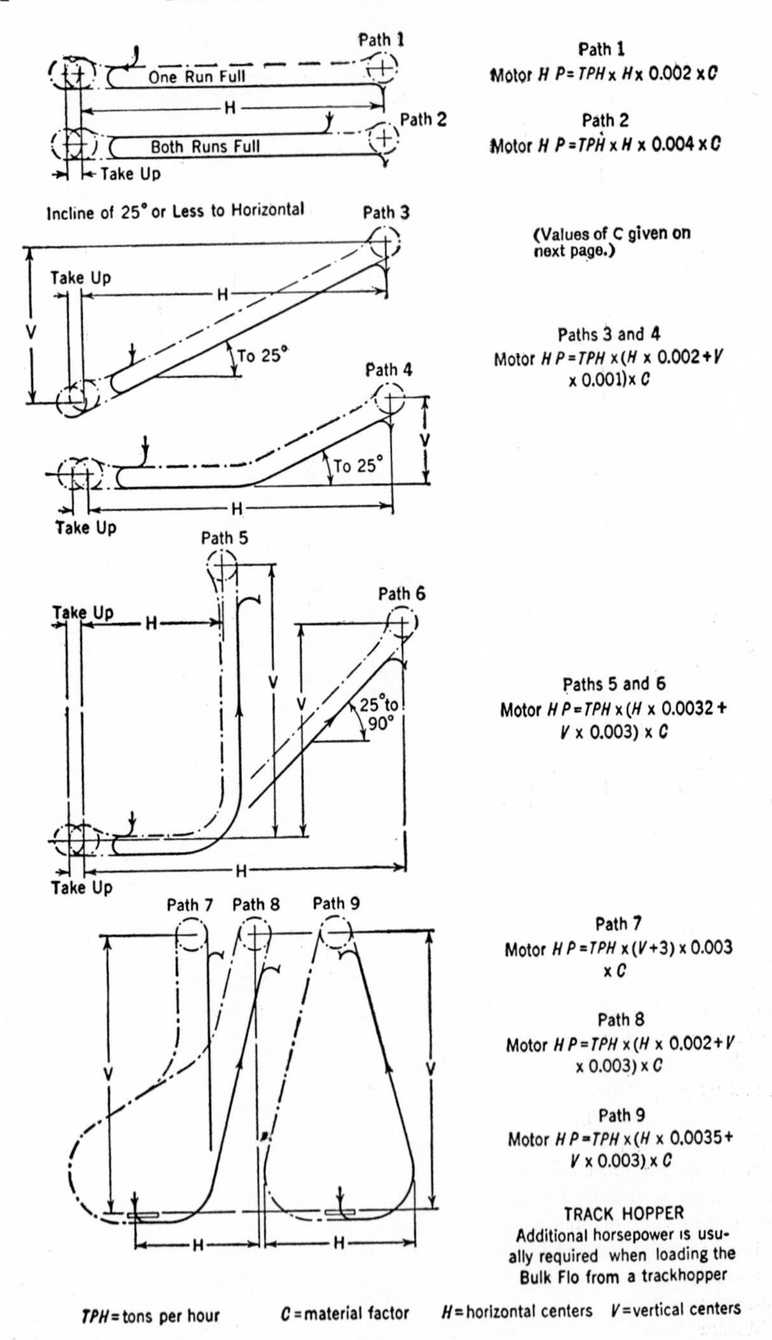


FIG. 8–16. Formulas for determining the motor horsepower of Bulk Flos having various paths.

TABLE 5

TABLE OF MATERIAL FACTORS

$C = 1$

| | | |
|---|---|---|
| Bran | Graphite flake | Soy beans |
| Coffee, ground | Nut kernels | Coconut, shredded |
| Cocoa beans | Soap flakes | Copra, ground |
| Flaxseed | | |

$C = 1.2$

| | | |
|---|---|---|
| Beans | Charcoal | Soybean meal 1.2–1.5 |
| Coal ¼ × 0 ¾ slack | Copra cake | Wheat |
| | Flour 1.2–1.5 | Wood chips (dry) |
| Coffee beans | Sawdust 1.2–1.5 | |

$C = 1.5$

| | | |
|---|---|---|
| Talc | Salt, pulverized (1.5–2) | Salt, rock |
| Starch, pulverized | | Wood chips (wet) |

$C = 2$

| | | |
|---|---|---|
| Clay (2.–2.5) | Starch, granular | Soda ash, light |
| Fly ash | Sugar, granular | Sugar, pulverized (2–2.5) |
| Lime, pebble | | Zinc oxide |

$C = 2.2$ to $2.5$

| | | |
|---|---|---|
| Alum | Lime, packs | Tobacco scraps |
| Borax | Soda ash, heavy | Limestone, pulverized |
| Cork, ground | | |

3500 lb.; for the No. 610 chains it is 5000 lb.; for the No. 712 chains it is 7000 lb.; and for the No. 913 chains it is 11,000 lb. With Promal these values may be increased by 25 per cent.

As might be expected the power requirements of the Redler and Bulk Flo are in practical agreement. Let us assume the requirement of 33.5 tons per hour of stoker coal with an L-type machine with 20-ft. horizontal and 50-ft. vertical legs. With a moderate speed of 45 to 50 ft. per min., we find that we can use an 11-in. Redler (area of duct 85.2 sq. in.), and from Tables 3 and 4 for the L-type machine we find:

$$\text{Motor } HP = \frac{3.7 \times 20 \times 33.5 + 3.1 \times 50 \times 33.5 + 40 \times 33.5}{1000} = 9 \text{ hp.}$$

For the Bulk Flo we find that we may use a No. 712 unit at 44 ft. per min. (area of duct 95.6 sq. in.), and, using the factor $C = 1.2$ for path 5,

$$\text{Motor } HP = 33.5\ (20 \times 0.0032 + 50 \times 0.003)\ 1.2 = 8.6 \text{ hp.}$$

**Chain Pull.** It is necessary to check the chain pull when making a selection. To illustrate, assume a loop-type Bulk Flo for 25 tons per hour of heavy soda ash, weighing 60 lb. per cu. ft. with a vertical lift of 47 ft. We select a No. 57 at 60 ft. per min. For the loop-type, Fig. 8-16:

$$\text{Motor } HP = 25(47 + 3) \times 0.003 \times C$$

The factor $C$ for heavy soda ash is 2.2 to 2.5; taking the larger figure, we have a motor horsepower of 9.4. That corresponds to a horsepower at the head shaft of about 8. At 60 ft. per min. the chain pull is 4400 lb. plus the weight of chain and flights in the return run, which reduces the horsepower but not the pull. The total chain pull will be about 4800 lb., which is too high for the No. 57. It is advisable to use the No. 712 at 45 ft. per min. with flights reduced in size, at which the chain pull will be about 6300 lb.

If the feed is controlled at 25 tons per hour we can speed up the No. 57 elevator to reduce chain pull; but if the loading is by gravity-flow from a bin or hopper the Bulk Flo will load itself to capacity, and the chain pull at a higher speed will not be less.

**Instructive Installations.** Engineers have had fewer opportunities to study the long-range performances, limitations, and possibilities of the continuous-flow conveyor than those of the old-line machines. In some ways it is a better machine. Sometimes it is not so good because it is misapplied or specified for a material for which it was not designed.

As a conveyor it requires about the same power as a flight conveyor. As an elevator the power requirement is substantially higher than that of a bucket elevator since the material slides instead of being carried. It has unique advantages in simplifying the layout, reducing the depth of a track hopper, eliminating the feeder, and automatically controlling the loading rate. Some typical applications are analyzed.

Figure 8-17 shows an installation at a roofing paper plant. Wood chips are stored in the bin at the left and feed out continuously by gravity flow, 24 hr. per day, to an L-path elevator. The discharge, after any small particles of iron have been culled out by a magnetized plate, is to the upper (outward) run of a horizontal conveyor which serves a battery of six piston-type digesters or defibrators. Each feed hopper must always be full to prevent blowout, and the requirement of each varies from 1 to 1½ tons per hour. The handling capacity of the elevator is 10 tons per hour.

Because only half the chips need be carried beyond the third hopper, a midlength by-pass halfway across the partition drops half the chips into feed hoppers 3, 2, and 1, while the remainder carries on to feed hoppers 6, 5, and 4. This by-pass reduces the power requirement by about 50 per cent. A surplus always carries back into the return run of the elevator, automatically reducing the feed from the bin.

One feature that is not so good is that this is a 24-hr.-a-day operation, and there is little opportunity for servicing. Figure 8-18 shows an installation better in this respect since it provides a 24-hr. chip

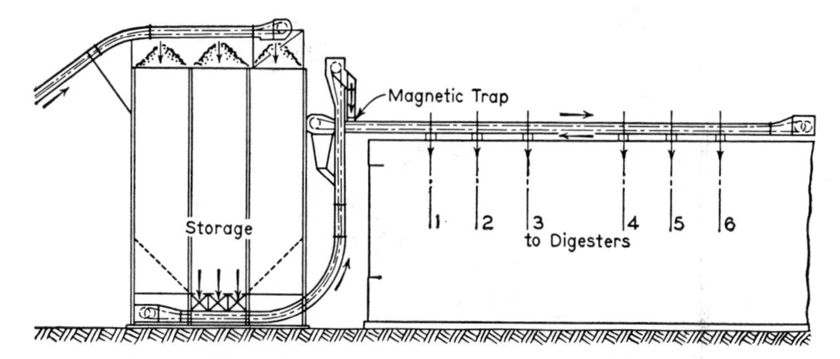


FIG. 8–17. Installation for handling wood chips.

storage above the digesters. Here the chips feed at 10 tons per hour from cars to a conveyor which discharges to a vibrating screen (Figure 8-19) to cull out slivers and blocks not readily digested by the defi-

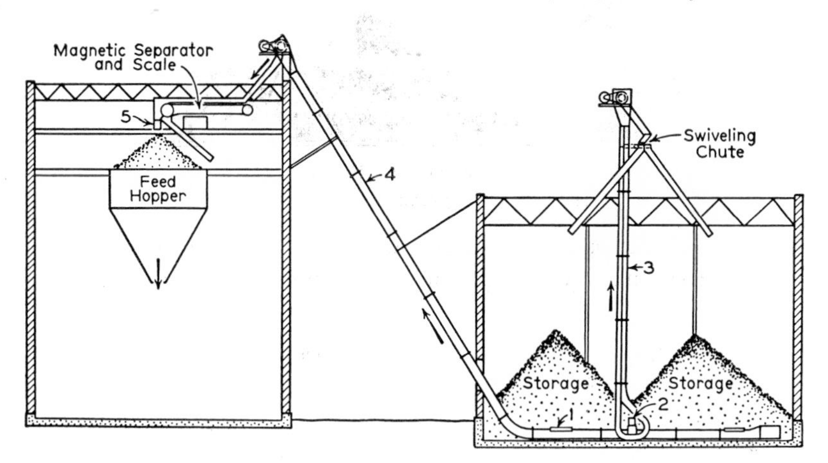


FIG. 8–18. Installation at paper-manufacturing plant. Conveyor 2 is discharge end of conveyor receiving wood chips from screen in Fig. 8–19.

brators; then they pass to conveyor 2 which extends along the ground for 200 ft. and conveys in the top run for convenience. It discharges either to the loop-type elevator 3 which forms the reserve storage pile in the building at the right or to elevator 4 which passes the chips through a weightometer and over a magnetic pulley to conveyor 5 above the storage bin. When the bin is nearly empty the last three units start automatically, taking chips from the storage pile unless conveyors 1 and 2 are operating. Delivery stops when the bin is full.

FIG. 8–19. Bulk Flo from track hopper feeding wood chips through vibrating screen to long ground-level conveyor.

A few hours run each day takes care of the requirements. Power tests on these units after they had been run in gave the following data:

| Unit | Speed, feet per minute | Installed Motor | Motor Horsepower by Formula | Motor Horsepower Input by Test |
|---|---|---|---|---|
| 1 | 65 | 5* | 2.4 | 1.98 |
| 2 | 65 | 7½ | 4.74 | 4.79 |
| 3 | 83 | 3 | 2.35 | 2.28 |
| 4 | 70 | 7½ | 6.1 | 4.33 |
| 5 | 70 | 2 | 0.75 | 0.89 |

* The allowance is liberal because of expected drag in feed from track hopper.

This type of machine lends itself to interesting requirements. At a New Orleans plant manufacturing wallboard, there are a chipper, storage bin, and battery of defibrators in sequence. The output of the chipper is 45 tons per hour. The requirement of the defibrators is less than 15 tons per hour. The problem of handling to storage, and from storage to the defibrator hoppers was solved by two Bulk Flo units. The first unit (No. 913) encircles the storage bin and is driven by a two-speed motor. When handling from the chipper to the bin at 45 tons per hour the speed is 66 ft. per min. When handling from the bin to the conveyor the speed is 33 ft. per min. The overhead conveyor has a capacity of 22 tons per hour. It carries out in the upper run and feeds out from the return run as described for Fig. 8-17, any surplus in this case falling into the bin. When handling the output of the chipper the elevator discharge may be direct to the conveyor to the limit of its self-controlled capacity, and the balance drops into the bin.

It is difficult to devise any combination of conveyors, other than the continuous-flow type, that so nicely fills the requirements.

In any such assembly of tandem units it is necessary to protect the installation by suitable interlocks. The usual starting interlock assures that the motors will start in proper sequence, first the distributing conveyor, then the elevator, the chipper, and finally the screen. The interlocks provide further for stopping any preceding unit, should one stop; thus, should the elevator stop, the chipper and screen must stop. This is better than stopping *all* units, since it discloses immediately where the trouble is.

Many of the older small plants have a coal vault paralleling the boiler fronts with apertures at floor level, from which coal is shoveled to the stokers. This makes a rather awkward condition for the installation of coal-handling equipment.

Figure 8-20 shows a neat arrangement at a midwest plant which solves the condition. There are four stoker-equipped boilers. It was desired to maintain a record of the coal delivered to each boiler. A self-feeding L-path continuous-flow conveyor extends along the floor and upward to a short screw conveyor. A 1200-lb.-capacity weigh larry traverses the line of stoker hoppers. This larry has two contactors. One functions to start the conveyors when the larry is pushed back against the wall beneath the discharge opening of the screw conveyor. The other functions to stop the conveyors when the filled larry hopper moves downward slightly as the scale beam poises. The larry is manually operated, since it is unnecessary to have motor propulsion when the hopper capacity is not over 1500 lb. if the wheels have anti-friction bearings. Only part of the vault storage will flow to the conveyor by gravity, but it is best not to locate a conveyor beneath piled coal. The rest of the coal is held in reserve and must be shoveled over if necessary. However, this is better than a buried conveyor, with repairs difficult and casing corrosion often severe.

Caution must be exercised with the heavy metallic dusts, such as zinc, brass, iron, and arsenic. Those that are free flowing tend to settle down in the ascending leg when the elevator is stopped and

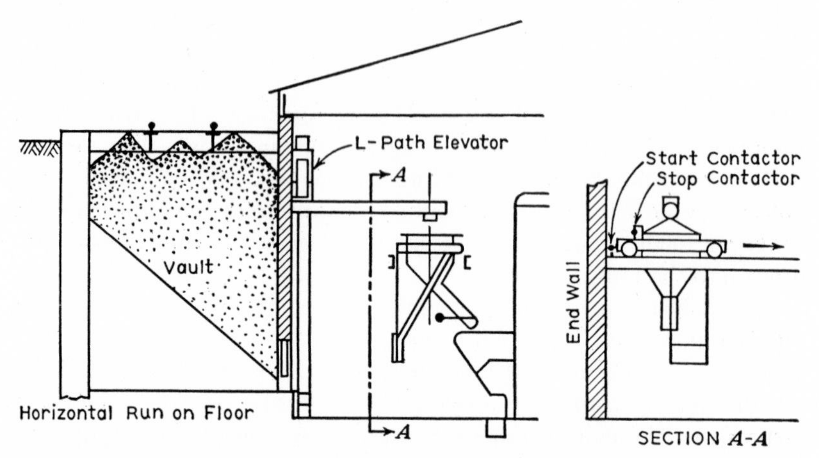


FIG. 8–20. Weigh larry automatically stops and starts coal-handling units.

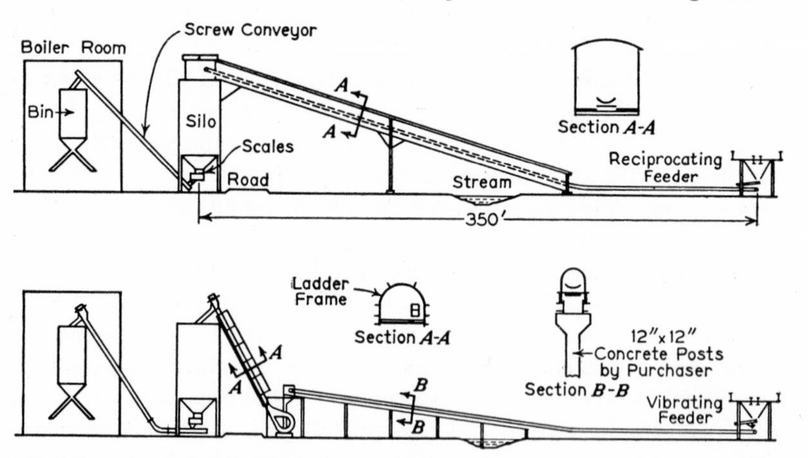


FIG. 8–21. Competitive layouts for handling, storing, weighing, and serving stoker-size coal.

cause heavy starting stresses. Those that are sluggish tend to pack and are difficult to dicharge. Sticky materials will not flow out at the point of discharge. In one installation, an L-path elevator for ammonium nitrate, the material refused to let go of the impellers and carried around almost 100 per cent. Fortunately compressed air was available, and two cross jets from $\frac{1}{16}$-in. nozzles gave complete discharge. The Redler has open impellers so that a plow can be provided to push out such material.

Without extended comment on the relative desirability of the selections made, let us see how the continuous-flow machines shape up competitively. In Fig. 8-21 are shown two propositions, submitted on an inquiry for equipment, to take small-size bituminous coal from a trestle 350 ft. distant to a purchaser's silo at 30 tons per hour and to weigh the coal automatically as it is withdrawn from storage to the boiler-house service bin at 10 tons per hour.

One proposition was a routine layout with reciprocating feeder, inclined belt conveyor with bridge and housing, automatic scales, and inclined short-pitch screw conveyor. The price quoted was $27,000 erected.

The other proposal cleverly took advantage of the specifications which stated that the purchaser would do all concrete work. It offered a vibrating feeder, a belt conveyor with only the belt housed, and an inclined loop-type elevator. Another continuous-flow elevator takes the coal from the automatic scales to the service bin. The price was $16,000 erected. It was accepted.

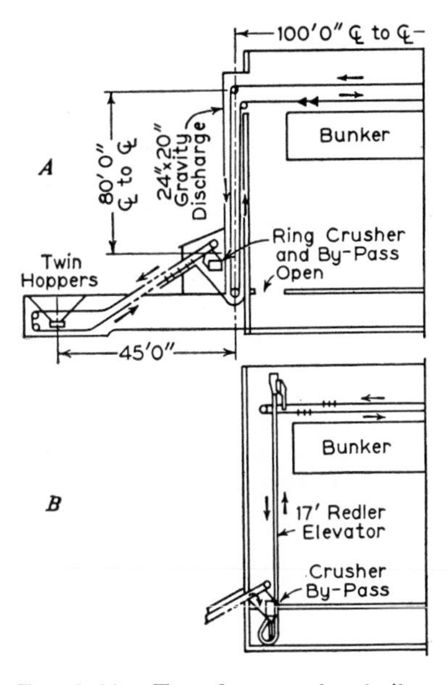


FIG. 8-22. Two layouts for boiler-house coal-handling project.

A major item of cost in the first proposition is in the belt-conveyor bridge, as compared with stringers and housing mounted on purchaser's concrete posts, even though the loop-type elevator is added. The vibrating feeder is better than a reciprocating feeder. An inclined screw is quite as good as the continuous-flow elevator for handling from storage and would make a further saving.

Figure 8-22*A* outlines a proposition for equipment to handle 75 tons per hour of coal, which at times requires crushing as a preliminary to sending it from bunker to unit pulverizers. It is conventional, with twin feeders discharging to a flight conveyor which delivers the coal either through or around a hammermill in a house outside the building. Coal is elevated 80 ft. and carried horizontally 100 ft. above the bunker by a 24 by 20 in. gravity-discharge elevator conveyor. The price was $24,000 erected. Figure 8-22*B* shows the competitive offer. Feeders and feeder conveyor are similar, but advantage is taken of the opening in the boiler-room floor to locate the crusher and elevator inside. The elevator is a 17-in. loop-type Redler at 50 ft. per minute, discharging to a single-strand suspended flight conveyor. The price quoted was $18,000 erected. It was accepted.

The gravity-discharge unit with long horizontal run is a costly machine, and it requires a support at the top or upper turn section and 80 ft. of casing. Moreover a house is required for the crusher.

The author has inspected many continuous-flow installations and questioned the operators to secure their opinions based on experience.

TABLE 6

| Material Handled | Comment |
|---|---|
| Four large units handling $\frac{3}{8} \times 0$. Bituminous coal. Capacities up to 150 tons per hour | O.K. |
| Damp sodium acetate. Z-path. Capacity $1\frac{1}{2}$ tons per hour. | O.K. |
| Hot dry aluminum sulphate. Selected because material must be kept hot and have no contact with oil | O.K. |
| Coal, $1\frac{1}{4} \times 0$. 30 tons per hour. Track hopper to bin. L-path | O.K. |
| Coal, 2 in. $\times$ 0, usually damp. L-type and tandem conveyor | Trough corroded under track hopper and chain wears |
| Dry coal, $\frac{5}{8}$ in. $\times$ 0. 75 tons per hour. Two elevators and overhead conveyors | O.K. |
| Zinc oxide and several other pulverized and granular materials at paint-manufacturing plant | Good with non-abrasives. Bad with abrasives |
| Borax. L-type. 10 tons per hour | Severe abrasion |
| Ground clay. L-type. 10 tons per hour | O.K. |
| Casein. 5 tons per hour | O.K. |
| (2) loop-type elevators for wet sewage sludge | Discarded. (Bucket elevators no better) |
| Granulated sugar and starch. Several at 10 tons per hour | O.K. |
| Shelled peanuts. 5 tons per hour | O.K. |
| Soap flakes. Vertical runaround | O.K. |
| Small loop-type elevator for ground stone | High maintenance |
| Flue dust. Smelter plant | Abrasion severe |
| Soybean meal, 10 tons per hour. Duct and chain coated with Bakelite because of gas action in bleaching | O.K. Bakelite lasts a year |
| 3-in. $\times$ 0 coal from crusher. Horizontal conveyor | O.K. after installing cast iron trough plates |
| 60-ft. loop-type elevator for 10 tons per hour rock salt | O.K. |
| Horizontal and inclined conveyor for wet corrosive coal from bin to stoker hoppers | O.K. after rebuilding with cast-iron plates |
| Wood chips. (Six installations) | O.K. |

TABLE 6—*Continued*

| Material Handled | Comment |
| --- | --- |
| Shelled corn. Loop-type elevator. 30 tons per hour | O.K. except for wear at loop |
| Ammonium nitrate. 2 tons per hour | O.K. Material sticky and discharged by air jets |
| Granulated sugar. 25 tons per hour | O.K. |
| Salt cake. 2 tons per hour | O.K. |
| Flake graphite. 6 tons per hour | O.K. |
| Copra meal. L-type. 15 tons per hour | O.K. |
| Face powder. Tooth powder. 1 ton per hour | O.K. |
| Hydrated lime. 3 tons per hour | O.K. |
| Hot brewers grains | Severe corrosion of malleable-iron chains |
| Horizontal conveyor for molybdenum concentrates | Discarded because of rapid wear |
| Zinc oxide, clay, talc. 10 tons per hour | O.K. |
| Dried tankage. 10 tons per hour | O.K. |
| Brass chips and dust. L-type 4 tons per hour | O.K. except for tendency of chain joints to become stiff |
| Silica flour. 4 tons per hour | O.K. |
| Bug dust, damp, 10 tons per hour. (Coal with rock dust, etc.) | Severe abrasion and corrosion in casing and chain |
| Coal. Z-path from track hopper, then vertically, and 45° incline to top of bin | Severe wear of duct at upper bend. Noisy |
| Z-path. Salt cake. 10 tons per hour | Very noisy, otherwise O.K. |
| Forty-eight miscellaneous installations handling bituminous slack. Capacities 10 to 65 tons per hour | Those handling clean dry coal O.K. Those handling wet or damp coal had high maintenance because of corrosion |
| Six installations handling wheat | All O.K. with little deterioration after 7 yr. operation |

Nearly all the installations listed had been in service for three years or more.

The opinion formed from these investigations was that the continuous-flow conveyor-elevator for harsh materials should be improved by casing sheets of either heavier-gauge steel or metal more resistant to corrosion and abrasion and that the chains could be improved, should be rated with lower pin-bearing loads, and should give better resistance to corrosion. Wartime regulations delayed these advancements, but the manufacturers are now improving their machines along these lines. It is not good engineering to specify the machine, merely because it costs less, for a material with which some other type of conveyor or elevator will give a lower maintenance cost. The standardized continuous-flow machine performs satisfactorily with pulverized and granular non-corrosive non-abrasive free-flowing materials, but, as with all other types of material-handling equipment, heavier construction is often necessary.

# CHAPTER 9

## PNEUMATIC AND HYDRAULIC CONVEYORS

**Pneumatic Conveyors.** The pneumatic conveyor differs altogether from other machines for transporting materials. It depends on a high-velocity air stream to move material in about the same manner as does the wind. If the velocity is too low, the material drags and builds up. If the velocity is sufficiently high, the material is carried in suspension, causing little erosion in the duct except at the bends and short tangents beyond, where eddies occur. The power requirement and capacity cannot always be predetermined accurately, but experience has provided a background that enables the specialist to estimate quite closely what the results will be with a sample material and proposed layout. If it is not a true sample, unfortunate results may follow. The possibilities are so tempting that sometimes it is specified for a material to which it is not suited. Like the rest of the material-handling family it is by no means a universal conveyor.

The pneumatic conveyor takes far more power per ton per hour moved than any mechanical conveyor. If the material is lumpy and heavy, the efficiency drops sharply. If it is caky or packed, as with bulk cement, it must be loosened up before it can feed into a nozzle. If it is a material which tends to build up a static charge, sulphur for example, there is a possibility of a dust explosion. The good features are that it can solve problems that no mechanical conveyor can attempt; that having no moving parts it eliminates danger to men working around it; and that its "vacuum-cleaner" action provides dustless operation, as when unloading pulverized material from a boxcar.

*Historical.* Among the first to use air for handling various flowable materials was Sturtevant, who in 1866 began experiments directed primarily toward the removal of dust in grinding operations, buffing, etc. The B. F. Sturtevant Company grew out of his work. Sturtevant developed the pneumatic conveyor for the lighter materials, like shavings, sawdust, waste paper, and cotton wool, which are not abrasive and may be passed through the fan. If harmful to the fan blades the material may be separated out of the suction line by a receiver, dropped through an air-lock gate, and again caught in the air stream from the pressure side of the fan; the material by-passes the fan.

J. M. Dodge, in 1901, experimented with a unique application of air to convey slabs from one end of a foundry to the other. He used a double-bottom trough with a perforated partition plate. Each perforation was closed by a light ball loosely held by a retainer. An air pressure was maintained within the double bottom, and when a slab was placed in the trough those balls directly under it at any moment were pressed down so that the air jetting through lifted the slab and floated it along the trough. Only one was built; there are better means

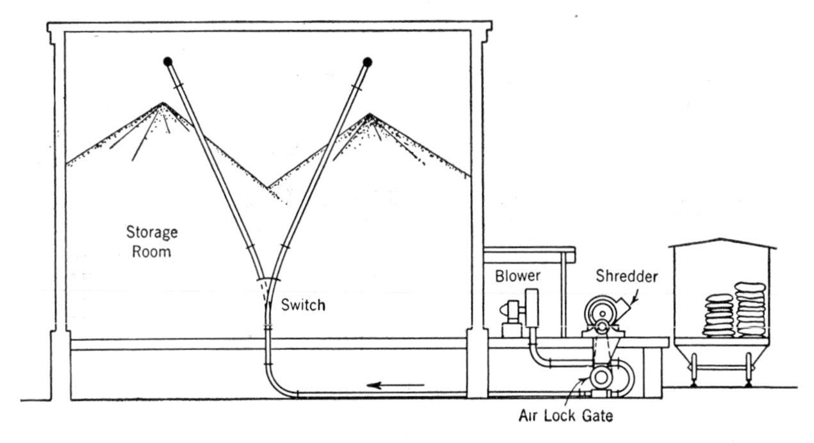


Fig. 9-1. Pressure system for storage of shredded sulphite lap. (Hudson.)

than compressed air for conveying slabs. However, there are circumstances in which the method might have applications today.

*Typical Pneumatic-Conveyor Installations.* The easiest way to visualize the applications of the pneumatic conveyor is to outline actual installations, though these are almost endless in their variety and method.

Figure 9-1 shows a system for moving sulphite lap to storage. Formerly the laps were stacked by manual labor and broken up when needed for the beaters. Now they are fed to a shredder mounted on the platform. The material passes through the air lock to the air stream from the pressure side of the blower and is sprayed to a stock pile up to the ceiling of the storage room. The pneumatic system provides larger storage capacity, faster handling, lower handling costs, and better performance in the beaters.

Figure 9-2 shows a combination pressure and suction system. The flowable material is drawn into the nozzle *A* in the car and enters the centrifugal receiver *B*. It passes downward through the air lock into

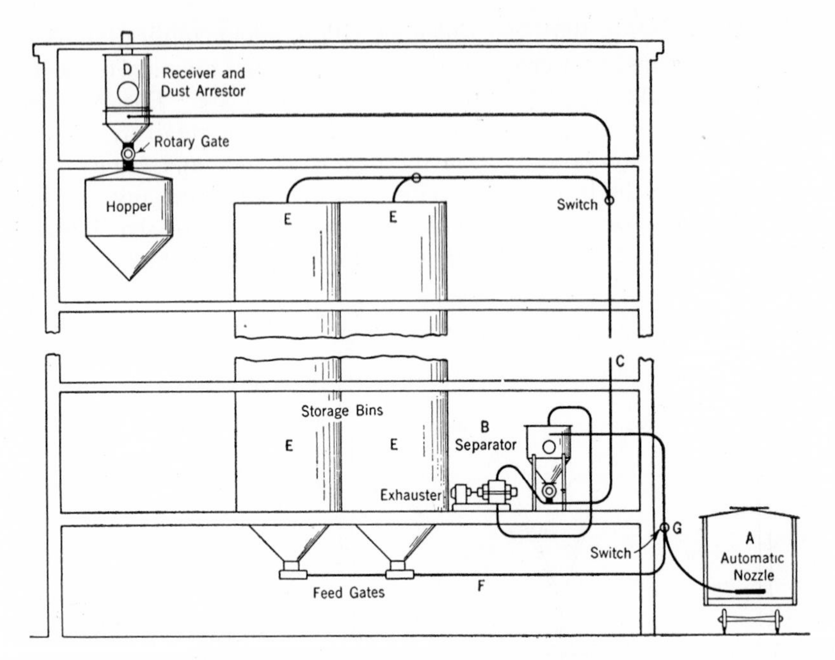


Fig. 9–2. Pneumatic car unloader. Suction system from cars. Pressure system to storage. Suction system for reclaiming.

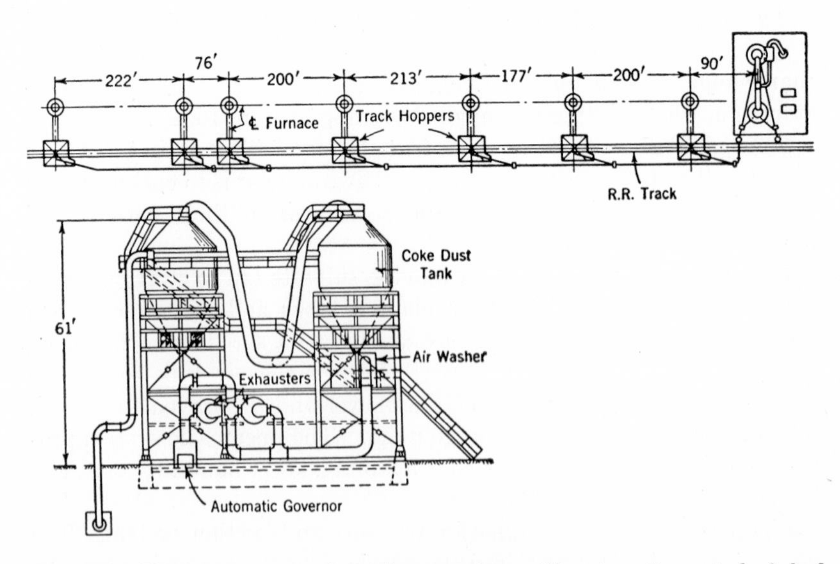


Fig. 9–3. Pneumatic system for coke screenings with automatic control of dual exhausters. (Hudson.)

the pressure line *C* and is blown either into the receiver dust collector *D* above the storage bin or sprayed into reserve storage *E*. When the reserve is required it is drawn through the suction line *F* after adjusting the switch *G*. The advantage of this system for dusty or harmful materials is obvious.

Figure 9-3 shows an installation at a large blast-furnace plant, where the pneumatic system solves the requirements better than any possible combination of mechanical conveyors. Coke screenings passing into the hoppers under the track are to be deposited in either of two overhead storage tanks. The distance from the last hopper to the tanks is 1178 ft. A 10-in. duct lies along the track with branch lines into each hopper. Connection from the riser may be made to either tank by switch. Two centrifugal exhausters maintain a partial vacuum in either tank and produce an air stream in the duct.

The exhausters are of the centrifugal type; that is, they have constant-pressure, variable-volume characteristics. Normally one exhauster operates, but the exhaust is through an automatic governor which functions, when the volume of air passing through it falls below a certain point, to start the second exhauster and connect it in series to the first by opening the blast gate between the two units. This action occurs when the inlet in the fourth hopper from the tanks, or in any hopper beyond the fourth, is fed with material. The result of connecting the two exhausters in series is to double the suction pressure, thereby bringing the air blast up to the required velocity. If operations are shifted to one of the first three hoppers while the exhausters are in tandem, the automatic governor functions in reverse to close the blast gate and stop the further exhauster.

Figure 9-4 illustrates a layout where compressed air is available. Bagged pulverized slate is received in cars and emptied into a duct fitted with a venturi nozzle. The pressure blast conveys the material to the storage tank, from which the air drifts out through a cloth filter. When the slate is needed for the charge of melted asphalt in the mixer at the right, a second venturi blows it to a centrifugal receiver from which it passes through an air lock into the mixer. The exhaust air leads back to the storage tank and up through the filter. Arching of the pulverized slate in the storage tank is broken by the injection of air just above the air lock. The system is completely dustless and practically noiseless.

The pneumatic conveyor works in nicely where grains and similar flowable materials are to be unloaded from open barges and delivered either to cars or to a conveyor on a wharf. Figure 9-5 shows one such installation handling flaxseed, either direct to the plant by a long wharf conveyor or into box cars. The grain passes from the separator through an air-lock gate. The discharge, if to the belt conveyor, is a direct flow, but, if to a car, it is caught by the air blast from the discharge side of the exhauster.

As an illustration of the flexibility of the pneumatic system, Fig. 9-6 shows the layout at a burned lime plant in Pennsylvania. From the kiln the lime feeds to a 6-in. suction line at *A*. If the lime is in condition for bagging, it is drawn through the main pipe line to the blower house where it enters a receiver, passing out through an air-lock

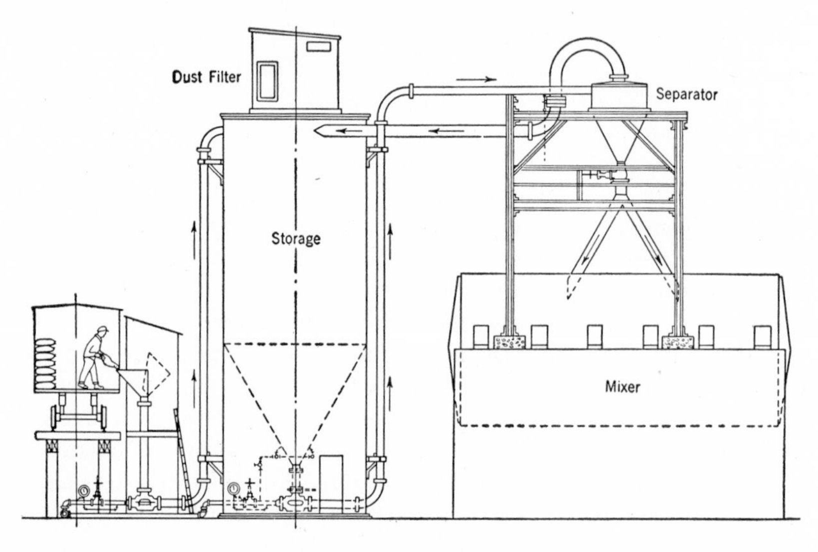


FIG. 9-4. Compressed-air system for handling pulverized slate. (Hudson.)

gate back into the air stream and up to a stocking-type separator in the bagging house. If the lime is to be pulverized, the switches *s*, *s′* are shifted to divert the flow through a separator feeding to a rod mill. The test data are given beneath the illustration. Intervening buildings (not shown) and low cost of power at this locality made the pneumatic system a better proposition than a combination of mechanical conveyors and elevators.

An industrial plant in Pennsylvania is located directly above an anthracite coal vein some 800 ft. below ground level. The coal belongs to the company and was mined under royalty; the small requirements of the plant were filled by sending a truck to the mine shaft about 1½ mi. away, where the mining company loaded it. Eventually the vein was worked out as a mining proposition, and so the coal was no longer available.

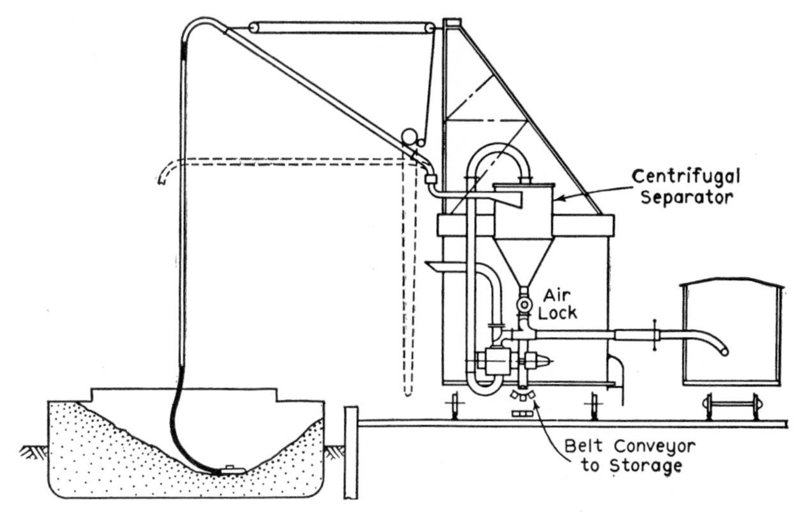


FIG. 9–5. Pneumatic unloader for flaxseed with delivery to plant belt conveyor or to cars for shipment. (Hudson.)

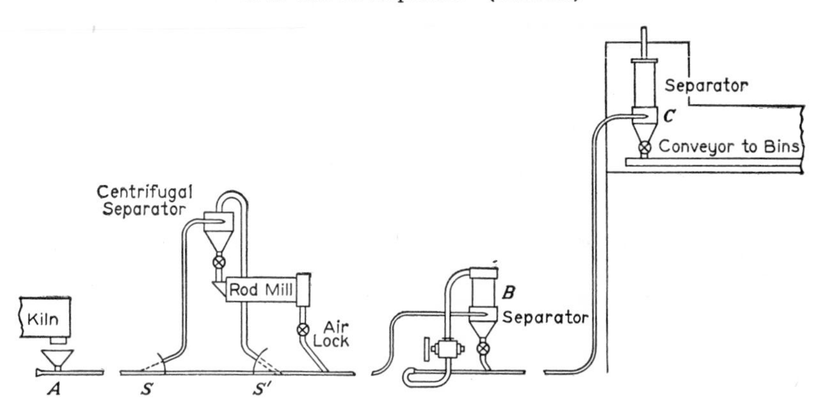


FIG. 9–6. Pneumatic handling of burned lime from kiln to storage. (Hudson.)

Blower, 18 by 20, 9.35 cu. ft. per revolution.
Speed, 345 r.p.m.
Capacity, 3200 cu. ft. gross; 2800 cu. ft. net.
Motor, 100 hp.

Conveying line, 6 in. Capacity, 12 tons per hour.

Movement direct from *A* to *B* and thence to *C*.
Vacuum, 3 lb.
Pressure, 3 lb.
Total, 6 lb.; 96 estimated horsepower, 92 actual horsepower.
Running light.
Vacuum, 1.75 lb.
Pressure, 2.0 lb.
60 hp.

A 12-in. well casing was driven down to the gallery where a chamber was excavated large enough to accommodate a feeder, crusher, and positive blower (Fig. 9-7). The power lines and an 8-in. conveyor

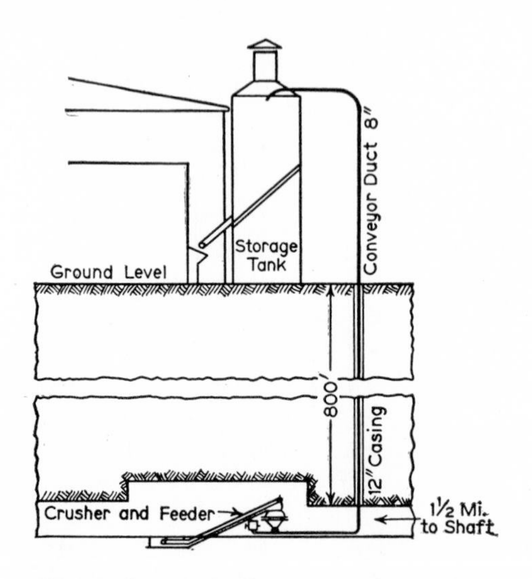


Fig. 9-7. Pneumatic coal lift direct from mine to bin. (Hudson.)

pipe were led down as shown. Once a week two men took care of breaking out the supply of coal and feeding it to the crusher. Where power is cheap the arrangement has interesting possibilities if the material to be lifted has a specific weight not too great.

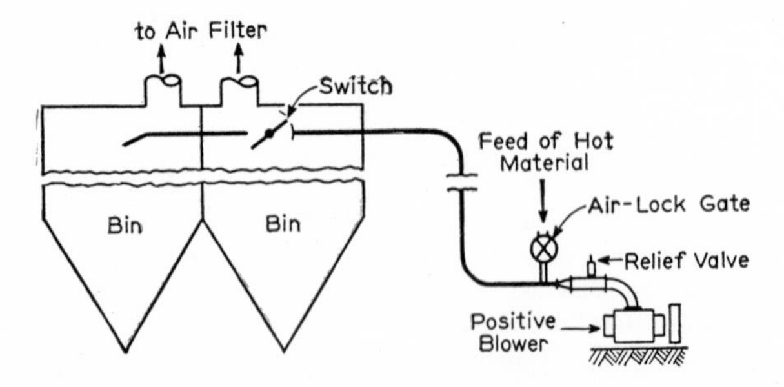


Fig. 9-8. Pressure system with discharge by switch to either bin.

For material at very high temperature, especially if some cooling in transit is desired, the pneumatic conveyor may have advantages as shown in Fig. 9-8. Here the material is fed to the pressure side of the blower through an air-lock gate and blown into two bins, with the discharge point determined by a switch operated from outside. When open, the switch section serves as a deflector.

In American practice the positive blower or the centrifugal fan is used. The principal English manufacturer, Henry Simon, Ltd., uses an inverted double-action air pump. The suction and exhaust ports

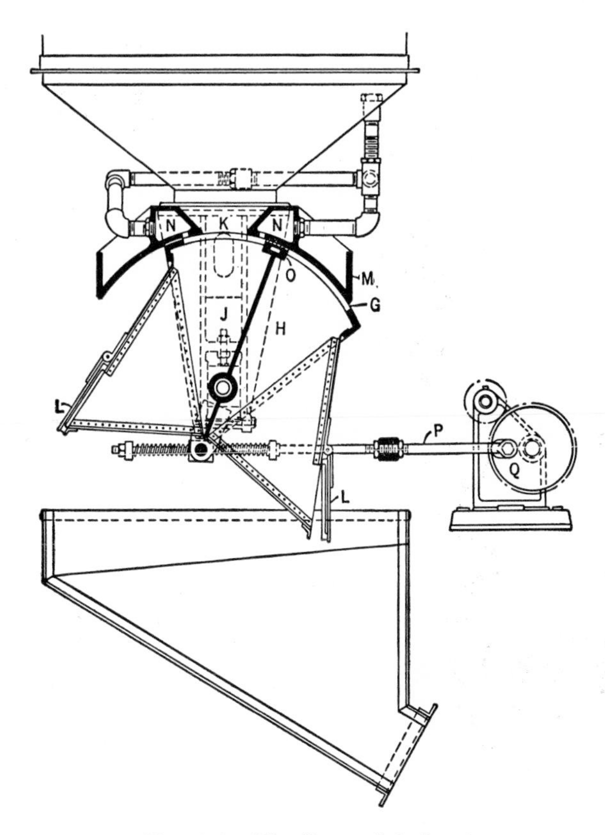


Fig. 9-9. The Simon air-lock gate.

are directly above and below the piston. The cylinder is water jacketed and lubricated with graphite. This slow-speed pump is efficient, pulling 7 to 12 in. of vacuum (mercury), and is not affected by dusty air passing through the cylinder. It is a costly machine.

American practice favors a rotary air-lock gate. The Simon air lock (Fig. 9-9) is a two-compartment oscillating gate with an air-tight joint formed by steel packing, *O*, on the partition plate between the two compartments. The sides are sealed with leather strips, and a hinged door at the lower edge of each compartment is rubber faced.

It is oscillated by a crankshaft and connecting rod protected by helical springs which yield if hard material should jam between the plates. The amplitude of oscillation is such that the material flows out when the gate is tilted to one side or the other.

Fig. 9–10. Four-hose pneumatic system unloading corn. (Fuller.)

Since the compartments are under reduced air pressure which would prevent the opening swing of the trap doors, a port ($G$) is opened at the end of the swing to admit atmospheric air. Auxiliary ports ($N$-$N$) connected with the receiver facilitate the flow of the material to the compartments.

*Car Unloading.* The routine method of unloading grain from box cars when the requirements do not call for a car dumper is by power shovel. A crew averages 24 men with several sets of shovels. One squad breaks down the door bulkheads, and another squad sweeps out after the shovel has cleared the bulk of the load. The lumber from the bulkheads is overhauled and new sections refitted to the cars. Such a crew will average eighty 1500-bu. cars per 8-hr. day, including car shifting time, equivalent to about 630 bu. per man-hr.

Figure 9-10 illustrates the application of a four-hose pneumatic car unloader (Fuller Company) with a free digging capacity of 2000 to 2500 bu. per hr. The car doors remain intact. If we include clean-up and car-shifting time the capacity per man may not be much greater than with power shovels, but there are other considerations. The

Fig. 9-11. Three-way switch of the Fuller system. Board at left diagrams the layout.

installation illustrated is unloading corn for a distillery where modern practice requires strict attention to cleanliness. Bacterial counts and other requirements extend to the handling of incoming grain. These requirements are best fulfilled by the pneumatic unloader. There is an obvious advantage with materials calling for dustless operation.

Figure 9-11 shows the pneumatic switch mechanism leading to the main filter, which may be connected to any one of three branch lines. Just above is a glass section which enables one to see whether the grain is flowing. This is a 4-in. system with a capacity of 600 bu. per hr. with a 30-hp. exhauster, or 1.5 hp. per ton per hour. To the left is a panel board with the push-button controls and a diagram of the layout.

The *continuous-type air filter* of a pneumatic system is a combination receiver and dust collector. The air passes from the receiver compartment upward through cloth filter tubes. Each tube is cut out periodically, shaken free of dust while auxiliary air is passed through in reverse, then cut back into service. The grain passes downward out of the receiver through the usual air-lock gate.

*Feeding Dense Materials.* Materials that are too dense or that will pack so that they will not flow into the usual nozzle must be loosened up and aerated. The pressure system is best when it can be applied, since higher pressure-velocities may be provided and the inertia of the material is overcome at the point where the greatest effort of the air blast is concentrated.

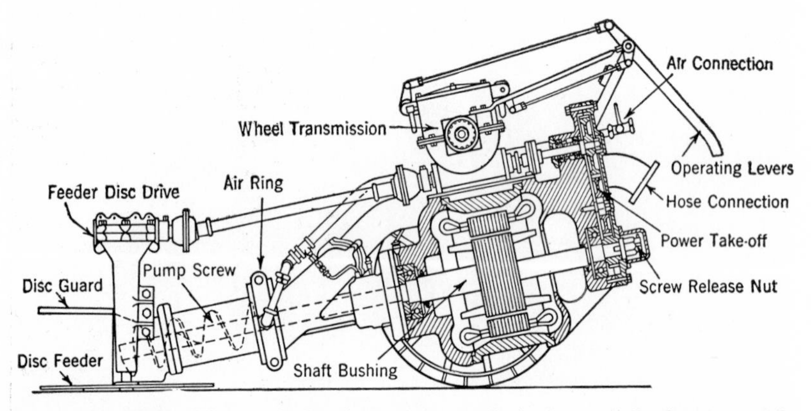


Fig. 9-12. Fuller-Kinyon feeder for cement and similar non-flowing materials.

Figure 9-12 shows the Fuller nozzle for cement and similar material. Beyond the air inlets a perforated disc is rotated slowly to feed the cement to a choke-feed screw driven by a built-in motor. At the discharge end of this screw, auxiliary air jets aerate the cement as it enters the duct. The choke feed prevents backward air flow through the screw. One man controls the operations of the machine from outside the car.

*Pneumatic Ash Conveyors.* In these the air blast may be derived from a motor-driven exhauster, suitably protected from dust; by the suction-pusher action of a steam jet at some intermediate point in the line, usually at the up-turn; or by the suction action of an argand-type steam jet between a receiver and air washer.

Activity in the blower-operated ash conveyor began about 1900. It had a 6- or 8-in. pipe extended up to a storage tank. The exhaust line from the tank (Fig. 9-13) led through a centrifugal dust collector to the inlet side of the exhauster. The exhauster might be a constant-pressure variable-volume high-speed fan, or a constant-volume variable-pressure positive-type blower (Roots, Connersville, etc.). In practice the suction pressure at the exhauster ranges from 1 to 3 lb. per sq. in. to produce a reduction of 5 to 6 oz. below atmospheric pressure at the most distant ash inlet.

FIG. 9–13. Pneumatic ash-handling system.

With an air inflow of 2500 cu. ft. of free air per minute the handling capacity is 300 to 400 lb. of dry ashes per minute, or about as fast as a man can rake them into the duct. The ashes must be dry, or nearly so, or they will pack at the elbows. The air enters at the far end of the duct, with a partial inflow just sufficient to draw in dust and gas at the opened ash feed point. To quench live clinkers and coagulate the dust a water spray is injected adjacent to the entrance to the storage tank. The dust collector protects the exhauster, and the life of the exhauster depends upon its effectiveness.

The ashes move at a velocity of about 50 ft. per sec., and the impact at the elbows and the eddies just beyond have an erosive action. Replaceable wearing backs of manganese steel or white iron are provided at the elbows. Short sections of duct are placed beyond each elbow and may be shifted axially to bring new surfaces to bear.

The motor and blower being costly units, the steam jet became common as the actuating device for pneumatic ash conveyors. Originally the jet fitting was located at the foot of the riser pipe. This emphasized the eddy currents and the erosive effects of the air blast. The nozzle uses considerable steam; a 5/8-in. nozzle with steam at 100-lb. pressure takes the equivalent of about 90 hp. for a handling capacity of 300 lb. of ashes per minute. On the other hand the cost of the nozzle fitting is about 1 per cent of the cost of a blower and motor.

A few of these early systems located the steam nozzle in the air pipe between tank and smoke stack. This loses the advantage of the pressure-velocity beyond the jet and lowers the efficiency, since the air velocity is built up in the duct, drops to zero in the tank, and is again built up in the pipe beyond the tank. The ashes are stored dry instead of dripping wet, if desired, which facilitates their discharge from storage but is dangerous if the ash contains incandescent clinkers. The danger in a system in which the tank is under reduced air pressure is that some free air leaks upward from the discharge gate and with live ashes an explosive condition may exist. The author recalls one installation where the dust collector and air pipe were wrecked, and it was discovered later that when the plant fire-protection system was tested the water pressure was not sufficient to bring water to the overhead spray. In another installation the entire top of the ash tank was blown off because the operator neglected to turn on the spray water and also had found it easier to hoe accumulations of coal drippings into the ash conveyor pipe than to wheel them to the coal elevator.

The steam-jet system of today (Fig. 9-14) locates an argand or annular-type fitting in a venturi section between a receiver and dust collector mounted above the storage tank. This jet assembly is far more efficient than the single orifice jet as a " vacuum producer." The receiver and dust collector are somewhat similar to an ordinary centrifugal-type collector but made with heavy cast-iron sections. At the bottom of the receiver is a flap gate operated by a thruster or similar device. The dust collector or air washer drains to a sewer or elsewhere. The steam throttle is interlocked with the operating mechanism of the gate. Flap gate and throttle are controlled by a time-limit relay set to a 1-min. cycle, so that the operation is intermittent.

After a batch of 200 or 300 lb. of ashes has entered the receiver the relay cuts off the steam flow and opens the gate, and the batch discharges into the storage tank. The relay closes the gate and opens the steam throttle, and the cycle repeats. Ashes are stored dry, but as the tank is at atmospheric pressure without updraft there is no risk from explosion. If it is essential to reduce the dust nuisance in loading out dry ashes, a paddle mixer with water sprays is provided under the discharge gate.

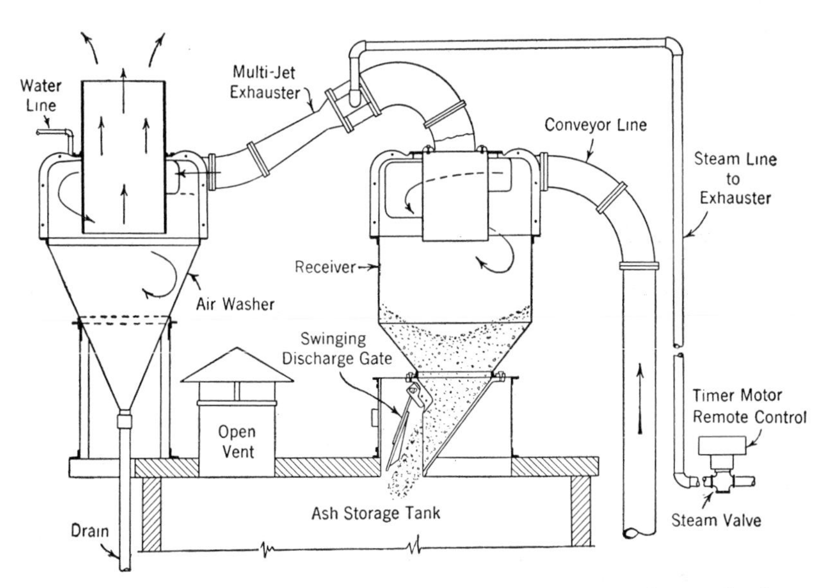


FIG. 9–14. Assembly of the Nu-Veyor. (United Conveyors Corporation.)

A storage tank is not necessary with a steam-jet system. If there is a waste area adjacent to the plant the duct may be led thereto and the ashes sprayed over the ground, but it is advisable to inject water into the duct near the outlet end.

*Pneumatic Handling of Dusts.* The removal of dusts from the rooms where industrial processes are performed is a requirement either by law or by the health regulations. Dust is injurious not only to the health of the workers but also to fine machinery and many types of electrical equipment. Aside from these considerations, floating dust from sugar, paper, flour, starch, sawdust, coal, cork, resins, plastics, and other combustibles is an explosion risk. Pneumatic collection systems usually provide the simplest and most effective means of eliminating this risk.

Some dusts can be handled by a single collecting system with branch ducts to each machine. Sometimes it is better to have an exhaust fan adjacent to each point of collection, either because of the character of the material or because the machines are widely separated and not readily tributary to a single collecting duct. The centrifugal separator functions for some dusts. For others, a cloth filter, air washer, or electric precipitator may be necessary. Many of the industrial dusts may be drawn through the exhaust fan, but some are so abrasive that it is better to locate a suitable separator with air-lock gate between the collecting duct and the exhaust fan. Fortunately

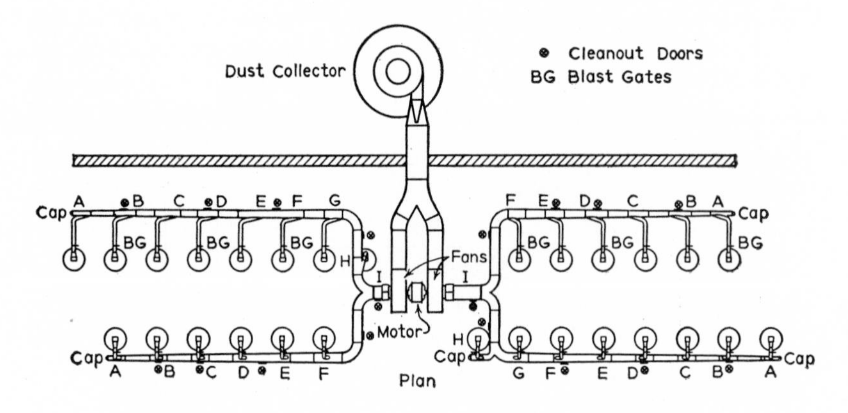


Fig. 9–15. Pneumatic dust-collecting system. (Sturtevant.)

most of the abrasive dusts are those which will flow from a conical-bottom collector through an air lock.

The air velocity should be just sufficient to insure the removal of the material and no more, since the power increases as the cube of the velocity. It varies from 2500 to 5000 ft. per min. The smaller velocities are for the light fine dusts, such as from leather machines, lighter shavings, and sawdust. The higher velocities are for heavy dusts and for fragmentary materials such as bark and wood chips. The suction required at any hood likewise depends on the characteristics of the material and will as a rule be from 2 to 5 in. (water).

To illustrate the engineering of a layout we will follow the procedure of the B. F. Sturtevant Company, specialists in this field.

Figure 9-15 shows a layout where dust is to be removed from 28 machines and delivered to a central collector. The general arrangement in the machine room lends itself to a layout with two collecting branches discharging to a single dust collector, each branch having its own exhauster. Each branch of the exhaust system has fourteen 4-in. pipes. The size of the fan depends on the volume of air required by the exhausting intakes, and that volume, in turn, is dependent on the area of the branch ducts served and the suction required at the hoods. It is usual to select a fan with an inlet equal to or slightly greater than the main suction duct. The total net area of the branches served may be referred to as the " load area " of the system. The inlet area of the fan should be about 25 per cent greater than the total load area. The load area is $14 \times 12.56 = 175.84$ sq. in. The area of the main duct thus is 230 sq. in. or a fan inlet diameter of 17 in.

The main duct varies in diameter, increasing from the dead end toward the fan, as necessitated by the branch pipes entering it. The exact diameter at any point is determined by the following routine: The area of the main duct at any point should be 25 per cent greater than the sum of the areas of the branches which have entered it. The branch pipes are 4 in. in diameter and the area of each when increased by 25 per cent is 15.7 sq. in., thus we have:

| Section of Main Duct at | Total Area of Branches Served + 25%, i.e., Minimum Areas of Duct | Diameter of Duct, even inches |
|---|---|---|
| *A* | 1 × 15.7 = 15.7 | 4 |
| *B* | 2 × 15.7 = 31.4 | 7 |
| *C* | 3 × 15.7 = 47.1 | 8 |
| *D* | 4 × 15.7 = 62.8 | 9 |
| *E* | 5 × 15.7 = 78.5 | 10 |
| *F* | 6 × 15.7 = 94.2 | 11 |
| *G* | 7 × 15.7 = 109.9 | 12 |
| *H* | 8 × 15.7 = 125.6 | 13 |
| *I* | 14 × 15.7 = 219.8 | 17 |

As the system is symmetrical on both sides, the fans will be similar. If the suction required at each hood and the diameter of each connection are known, the volume passing up each branch can be determined from Table 1. The sum of all these volumes gives the total volume required at the fan.

The suction pressure to be maintained at the fan inlet is the total of the suction pressure at the hoods, the loss in the separator, and the losses in the ducts. The first must be chosen from experience or trials. The separator loss in inches of water will approximate

$$\text{Loss} = C \times \left(\frac{V}{1000}\right)^2$$

TABLE 1

CUBIC FEET OF AIR (65° F.) HANDLED PER MINUTE THROUGH AVERAGE COLLECTING HOODS

Based on Coefficient of Orifice of 0.71 with 10% Added for Leakage (Sturtevant)

| Diameter of Connection Pipe Inches | Maintained Suction — Inches Water Gauge | | | | | | |
|---|---|---|---|---|---|---|---|
| | 1 | 1½ | 2 | 2½ | 3 | 4 | 5 |
| 1½ | 38 | 47 | 54 | 61 | 67 | 76 | 86 |
| 2 | 68 | 84 | 97 | 108 | 118 | 136 | 153 |
| 2½ | 107 | 131 | 161 | 168 | 185 | 214 | 238 |
| 3 | 153 | 188 | 217 | 243 | 266 | 306 | 343 |
| 3½ | 209 | 256 | 296 | 330 | 362 | 418 | 466 |
| 4 | 273 | 334 | 386 | 431 | 473 | 546 | 609 |
| 4½ | 345 | 423 | 488 | 546 | 598 | 690 | 775 |
| 5 | 427 | 523 | 605 | 676 | 741 | 854 | 955 |
| 6 | 614 | 751 | 867 | 970 | 1062 | 1228 | 1373 |
| 7 | 835 | 1023 | 1181 | 1322 | 1448 | 1670 | 1870 |

The constant $C$ varies with the type of separator from 0.145 to 0.065.

The losses due to pipe friction are approximated thus:

Velocity in branch furthest from fan =

$$\frac{\text{Cubic feet per minute through branch}}{\text{Area of branch}} = \text{Velocity in feet per minute.}$$

From Table 2 find the loss of pressure in inches of water per 100 ft., F.

$$\text{The loss in branch} = \frac{L}{100 \text{ ft.}} \times F.$$

where $L$ = the length of the branch in feet.

For each elbow add to $L$ a length equal to 10 diameters of the pipe.

For the loss in the main duct the problem is complicated by the increases in diameter at each branch, and so we must figure the loss in each section by the method given. All the losses added together give the total loss due to friction at the intake of the exhaust fan. The loss in the discharge pipe beyond the fan is usually a minor factor unless it is of considerable length.

Having determined the volume and pressure, we select the size of fan and the motor from the manufacturers' tables of standard sizes of constant-pressure-variable-volume blowers.

TABLE 2

PRESSURES IN INCHES OF WATER LOST BY FRICTION OF AIR IN PIPES 100 FT. LONG

(Sturtevant)

| Velocity of Air, feet per minute | Diameter of Pipe | | | | | | | | | | | | | |
|---|---|---|---|---|---|---|---|---|---|---|---|---|---|---|
| | 4-In. | 5-In. | 6-In. | 7-In. | 8-In. | 9-In. | 10-In. | 11-In. | 12-In. | 13-In. | 14-In. | 16-In. | 18-In. | 20-In. |
| 2000 | 1.50 | 1.20 | 1.00 | 0.85 | 0.75 | 0.66 | 0.59 | 0.54 | 0.50 | 0.46 | 0.42 | 0.37 | 0.33 | 0.30 |
| 2200 | 1.81 | 1.45 | 1.21 | 0.92 | 0.90 | 0.80 | 0.72 | 0.66 | 0.60 | 0.55 | 0.51 | 0.45 | 0.40 | 0.36 |
| 2400 | 2.16 | 1.72 | 1.44 | 1.23 | 1.08 | 0.96 | 0.86 | 0.78 | 0.72 | 0.66 | 0.61 | 0.54 | 0.48 | 0.43 |
| 2600 | 2.53 | 2.03 | 1.69 | 1.45 | 1.26 | 1.12 | 1.01 | 0.92 | 0.84 | 0.78 | 0.72 | 0.63 | 0.56 | 0.50 |
| 2800 | 2.94 | 2.35 | 1.96 | 1.68 | 1.47 | 1.30 | 1.17 | 1.07 | 0.98 | 0.90 | 0.84 | 0.73 | 0.65 | 0.58 |
| 3000 | 3.37 | 2.70 | 2.24 | 1.93 | 1.68 | 1.50 | 1.35 | 1.22 | 1.12 | 1.03 | 0.96 | 0.84 | 0.75 | 0.67 |
| 3200 | 3.84 | 3.07 | 2.56 | 2.19 | 1.92 | 1.70 | 1.53 | 1.39 | 1.28 | 1.18 | 1.09 | 0.96 | 0.85 | 0.76 |
| 3400 | 4.34 | 3.47 | 2.89 | 2.47 | 2.16 | 1.92 | 1.73 | 1.57 | 1.44 | 1.33 | 1.23 | 1.11 | 0.96 | 0.86 |
| 3600 | 4.86 | 3.89 | 3.24 | 2.77 | 2.43 | 2.16 | 1.94 | 1.76 | 1.62 | 1.50 | 1.38 | 1.21 | 1.08 | 0.97 |
| 3800 | 5.41 | 4.33 | 3.61 | 3.09 | 2.70 | 2.40 | 2.16 | 1.97 | 1.80 | 1.66 | 1.54 | 1.35 | 1.20 | 1.08 |
| 4000 | 5.99 | 4.80 | 4.00 | 3.43 | 3.00 | 2.66 | 2.40 | 2.18 | 2.00 | 1.84 | 1.71 | 1.50 | 1.33 | 1.20 |
| 4200 | 6.61 | 5.29 | 4.41 | 3.78 | 3.30 | 2.94 | 2.64 | 2.40 | 2.20 | 2.03 | 1.89 | 1.65 | 1.47 | 1.32 |
| 4400 | 7.23 | 5.77 | 4.81 | 4.12 | 3.61 | 3.21 | 2.89 | 2.62 | 2.41 | 2.23 | 2.07 | 1.81 | 1.60 | 1.44 |
| 4800 | 8.64 | 6.91 | 5.75 | 4.93 | 4.32 | 3.84 | 3.45 | 3.14 | 2.88 | 2.65 | 2.46 | 2.16 | 1.92 | 1.73 |
| 5200 | 10.14 | 8.11 | 6.76 | 5.79 | 5.06 | 4.51 | 4.06 | 3.68 | 3.38 | 3.12 | 2.90 | 2.52 | 2.25 | 2.02 |

*The theoretical discussion of pneumatic conveyors* for bulk materials which follows is based upon readings of power, air velocity, air volume, and capacity in a long series of installations made by the author, which then were analyzed by his engineer, Mr. Ivar Knudsen, who developed a simple mathematical routine thereafter used in engineering new installations. The results agreed closely with the formulas thus developed. It is an empirical analysis.

## Theoretical Analysis of Pneumatic Conveyors

The air velocity through the duct of a pneumatic conveyor depends on the pressure head maintained by the blower or exhauster, and, as with a fluid,

$$V = \sqrt{2 \cdot g \cdot h} \qquad (A)$$

where $V$ = velocity in feet per second.

$h$ = weight of a column of air, in pounds, on a base of 1 sq. ft.

$g$ = 32.16.

The weight of air at 60° F. is 0.0764 lb. per cu. ft.; but, as we work with the weight (pressure) in ounces per square inch, let

$p$ = weight of air, in ounces, on a base of 1 sq. in.

$$p = h \times \frac{0.0764 \times 16}{144}$$

or, solving for $h$,

$$h = 118p, \quad \text{approximately}$$

Substituting in ($A$), we have

$$V = 87.5\sqrt{p}$$

or

$$p = \frac{V^2}{7600}$$

Or, more conveniently, we have

$$= \frac{V^2}{10{,}000} \times 1.32, \text{ in ounces per square inch, approximately}$$

An open-ended pipe has about 82 per cent effective area for air inflow rate; therefore the velocity at the end is higher than within the pipe, or

$$p' = \frac{V^2}{10{,}000} \times \frac{1.32}{0.82^2} = \frac{V^2}{10{,}000} \times 2, \quad \text{approximately}$$

Hose intake nozzles have about 60 per cent of the duct area to speed the "pick-up" velocity of the air at the nozzle and

$$p'' = \frac{V^2}{10{,}000} \times 5$$

which is used to determine the air velocity in nozzle and hose.

*Friction Losses in the Conveyor Duct.*

$h$ = loss of head in feet of air at 0.0764 lb. per cu. ft.
$f$ = coefficient of friction, air against internal wall of pipe.
$L$ = length of pipe in feet.
$D$ = diameter of pipe in feet.
$R$ = hydraulic radius, which is $D/4$.

Then

$$h = \frac{f \times L \times V^2}{R \times 2g} = 4f \times \frac{L}{D} \times \frac{V^2}{2g} = f \times \frac{L}{D} \times \frac{V^2}{16} \text{ in pounds per square foot.}$$

For $p$ in ounces per square inch, $L$ as 100 ft., and $d$ as the diameter in inches, substitute in the above as friction loss in ounces per square inch per 100 ft. of length:

$$p = \frac{V^2}{d} \times \frac{16}{25} \times f, \text{ approximately}$$

Kent uses $f = \frac{1}{2}$ per cent or $\frac{50}{10{,}000}$, or $p = \frac{32}{d}$ oz. per sq. in.

Root uses $f = \frac{5}{8}$ per cent or $\frac{62.5}{10{,}000}$, or $p = \frac{40}{d}$ oz. per sq. in.

Unwin uses $f = 0.0028\left(1 + \frac{3.60}{d}\right)$, or $p = \frac{18}{d}\left(1 + \frac{3.60}{d}\right)$ oz. per sq. in.

These are for $V = 100$ ft. per sec. and $L = 100$ ft. For other velocities multiply by $\left(\frac{V'}{100}\right)^2$, and for other lengths multiply by $\frac{L_1}{100}$.

Table 3 shows the pressures arrived at by the different values. We will use Unwin's factors for $f$, which he determined by trials. Orifice losses are in Table 4.

Friction losses in the pipe bends due to centrifugal forces involved by the change in direction of flow are for convenience resolved into equivalent lengths of straight pipe. For practical purposes add six times the diameter of the pipe for each 90° bend; thus for three 90° bends in an 8-in. pipe we add 12 ft. of straight pipe.

TABLE 3

PRESSURE LOSSES IN PIPES, IN OUNCES PER SQUARE INCH, FOR $V = 100$ FT. PER SEC. AND $L = 100$ FT.

| Diameter, $d$ | Kent | Root | Unwin | Volume of air ($Q$) in Cubic Feet per Minute |
|---|---|---|---|---|
| 4 | 8.00 | 10.00 | 8.50 | 520 |
| 5 | 6.40 | 8.00 | 6.25 | 820 |
| 6 | 5.35 | 6.67 | 4.80 | 1170 |
| 7 | 4.57 | 5.72 | 3.95 | 1600 |
| 8 | 4.00 | 5.00 | 3.25 | 2090 |
| 9 | 3.50 | 4.44 | 2.77 | 2650 |
| 10 | 3.20 | 4.00 | 2.43 | 3270 |
| 11 | 2.91 | 3.64 | 2.14 | 3960 |
| 12 | 2.67 | 3.33 | 1.93 | 4710 |
| 13 | 2.45 | 3.07 | 1.76 | 5550 |
| 14 | 2.29 | 2.85 | 1.60 | 6400 |
| 16 | 2.00 | 2.50 | 1.38 | 8400 |
| 18 | 1.78 | 2.22 | 1.20 | 10600 |
| 20 | 1.60 | 2.00 | 1.07 | 13100 |
| 24 | 1.33 | 1.67 | 0.865 | 19000 |

For pressure loss when velocity $= V$ and Length $= L$

$$P_0 = p \times \left(\frac{V}{100}\right)^2 \times \frac{L}{100}$$

TABLE 4

ORIFICE LOSSES IN OUNCES PER SQUARE INCH

$$\text{Velocity-pressure for 100\% orifice efficiency} = \frac{V^2}{10{,}000} \times 1.32$$

| | | Factor | | | Factor |
|---|---|---|---|---|---|
| Intake | 80% | 3.00 | Intake | 63% | 5.00 |
| " | 75% | 3.50 | " | 60% | 5.50 |
| " | 70% | 4.00 | " | 57% | 6.00 |
| " | 67% | 4.50 | " | 50% | 8.00 |

*Two Systems.* There are two systems of conveying by air. One uses a large volume of air at low velocity, low pressure; the other, a small volume of air at high velocity. In " suction " systems the former is more efficient since the conveying medium is denser and has greater carrying capacity than rarefied air; also frictional loss in the pipe and in the exhauster is less. High pressure means greater slip and heat losses in the exhauster. However, certain materials require a high-velocity air stream.

*Quantity of air* depends on the *specific weight* of the material, that is the weight in the solid, and the required handling capacity.

It has been found by trials that a very simple formula gives a close approximation of the volume of air required, namely,

$$Q = W \times T$$

where $Q$ = cubic feet of free air per minute.
$W$ = the *specific* weight of material in pounds per cubic foot.
$T$ = tons handled per hour.

This may be written for cubic feet of air per minute per pound of material as:

$$Q' = \frac{W \times T}{T \times \frac{2000}{60}} \quad \text{or} \quad Q' = \frac{3 \cdot W}{100}$$

The *velocity* of the air stream depends on the average size and weight of the individual particles (small particles will boost along the larger) and must equal the weight for balancing in a vertical riser pipe plus that required to convey the material at a velocity usually about 50 ft. per sec. When material is moved horizontally the air velocity may be less than in a run with bends and risers.

Let $s^2$ = area of average particle in square inches.
$l$ = longest axis (thickness) of same in inches.
$W_1$ = weight in ounces per cubic inch.
$V$ = air velocity in feet per second.
$c$ = efficiency of the blast.

The blast for balancing in a vertical riser $= \frac{V^2}{7600} \times s^2 \times c$, and it equals the weight of the particle, which is $s^2 \times l \times W_1$ in ounces.

But $W_1 = \frac{W \times 16}{1728} = \frac{W}{108}$, where $W$ is the specific weight in pounds per cubic foot. Thus the air velocity for balancing may be written

$$V = 8 \cdot 4 \sqrt{\frac{W \cdot l}{c}}$$

However, this velocity must be increased to move the material at, say, 50 ft. per sec. From a long series of tests on installations the following values for velocity of air in feet per second were determined and adopted with satisfactory results in subsequent installations.

| | | Balancing Velocity | Line Velocity[1] | Hose Velocity[1] |
|---|---|---|---|---|
| Straight horizontal ducts | Dusty materials | $5\sqrt{\frac{w \cdot l}{c}}$ | $10\sqrt{w}$ | $16\sqrt{w}$ |
| | Grains | $6\sqrt{\frac{w \cdot l}{c}}$ | $12\sqrt{w}$ | $20\sqrt{w}$ |
| | Material gritty and of uneven size | $7\frac{1}{2}\sqrt{\frac{w \cdot l}{c}}$ | $15\sqrt{w}$ | $24\sqrt{w}$ |
| Ducts with ells and risers | Dusty materials | $10\sqrt{\frac{w \cdot l}{c}}$ | $12\frac{1}{2}\sqrt{w}$ | $20\sqrt{w}$ |
| | Grains | $12\sqrt{\frac{w \cdot l}{c}}$ | $15\sqrt{w}$ | $24\sqrt{w}$ |
| | Material gritty and of uneven size | $15\sqrt{\frac{w \cdot l}{c}}$ | $18.75\sqrt{w}$ | $30\sqrt{w}$ |

[1]Plus or minus 6 per cent.

*Horsepower.* The horsepower to handle $Q$ cubic feet of free air per minute at $P$ pounds per square inch is

$$HP = \frac{Q \times P \times 144}{33{,}000} \quad \text{or} \quad \frac{Q \times P \times 4.35}{1000} \quad \text{or} \quad \frac{Q \times P}{230}$$

If we assume the mechanical efficiency as 87½ per cent, the

$$\text{Initial } HP = \frac{Q \times P \times 4.35}{0.875 \times 1000} = \frac{Q \times P}{200}$$

We must increase $Q$ to allow for air slip in the exhauster or blower, which varies as $P^2$. Take the average slip as 14 per cent, or a " pneumatic efficiency " of 87.5 per cent.

In the pressure system

$$\text{Motor } HP = \frac{Q \times P}{175}$$

In the suction system

$$\text{Motor } HP = \frac{Q \times P}{175} \times \frac{14.7 + P}{14.7}$$

We may transpose the formula above for initial horsepower to read, for $P$ the total pressure required in system,

$$P = \frac{HP \times 200}{Q} \quad \text{in pounds per square inch}$$

or

$$P = \frac{HP \times 3200}{Q} \text{ in ounces per square inch}$$

This last is a convenient form for calculating pneumatic systems.

We will now show the step-by-step procedure in calculating a pneumatic system, and then we will follow with the application of these steps, taking three different layouts and developing the figures for three different materials, namely, coarse salt, flaxseed, and ground cork.

The layouts of Fig. 9-16 are merely illustrative. It would be unique to use a pneumatic system to convey horizontally a distance of about 2000 ft. at a rate of 40 tons per hour unless no other method were available. A belt conveyor, for instance, would require about 5 per cent of the power for the pneumatic conveyor. In expense, there would be the much higher cost of 4000 ft. of conveyor belt, 600 belt idlers, the supporting structure, a 10-hp. motorized reducer, and the belt housing, as compared with a pipe line and a 200-hp. motor and blower. The comparison becomes more interesting with a very light material such as the pulverized cork.

## PROCEDURE FOR CALCULATING LARGE-VOLUME, LOW-PRESSURE PNEUMATIC SYSTEMS

1. Determine the quantity of air required per pound of material.

$$Q' = \frac{3W}{100} \text{ cu. ft. of air per pound}$$

   Or use $Q = WT$ cubic feet per minute for conveying $T$ tons per hour.
2. Determine from the tables the velocity of the air, taking into consideration the layout of the line (whether straight or with bends).
3. Select the size of pipe which with $Q$ feet of air per minute will provide the velocity just determined.
4. Adjust the air volume and air velocity to suit a standard size of pipe.
5. Determine the air pressure losses, which are

   (*a*) Pressure loss at orifice: $\left(\frac{V^2}{10{,}000}\right) \times 5$ in ounces per square inch.

   (*b*) Pressure loss in hose: $\left(\frac{V_1}{100}\right)^2 \times \frac{35}{100}$ in ounces per square inch.

   ($V_1$ is the velocity in the hose, and 35 is average hose length.)

   (*c*) Pressure loss in line $\left(\frac{V}{100}\right)^2 \times \frac{L}{100} \times$ coefficient (Unwin, Table 3.)

   (*d*) Pressure loss in tank or receiver: 4 oz. per tank (average).

(*e*) Pressure loss in air line between exhauster and separator or between separator and dust collector: 3 oz. (average).

Total air pressure losses thus are $a + b + c + d + e$ in ounces per square inch ($A$).

6. *Material Pressure Losses.* We assume that the velocity of the material is 80 per cent of the velocity of the air stream in which it floats and that this velocity is attained from rest in 1 sec. by the pick-up velocity of the air in the nozzle and hose,

$$V_1 = \text{speed in the nozzle} = 1.60V$$

$$\text{Speed of material at end of hose} = \frac{V_1}{2} = 0.80V$$

Then

(*f*) Pressure loss due to inertia is $\frac{MV_1^2}{2 \times 550} = \frac{TV^2}{100{,}000}$ in horsepower.

(*g*) Pressure loss in hose assumed as ½ of $f = \frac{TV^2}{200{,}000}$ in horsepower.

(*h*) Pressure loss in conveyor line $= \frac{T}{1000}\left(H^* + \frac{L}{5}\right)$ in horsepower.

(*k*) Pressure loss at each 90° elbow $= \frac{TV^2}{200{,}000}$ in horsepower.

(*m*) Total initial horsepower required for material $= f + g + h + k$.

Convert initial horsepower into pressure, $\frac{m \times 3200}{Q}$ in ounces per square inch ($M$).

(*n*) Total pressure loss is $A + M$ in ounces per square inch, or the summation of air-pressure losses in line starting with the orifice pressure and ending with the tank.

Convert $n$ into pounds; total pressure loss is $\frac{(A + M)}{16}$ in pounds per square inch ($P$).

For pressure system

$$HP = \frac{Q \times P}{175}$$

For suction system,

$$HP = \frac{Q \times P}{175} \times \left(\frac{14.7 + P}{14.7}\right)$$

From these two the size of blower is determined.

*Procedure Illustrated.* We now apply the above procedure to several layouts with three materials, carried through in parallel columns.

* H is lift, if any.

1. Hypothetical pressure system per Fig. 9-16*A* with a straight horizontal pipe having a length of 1900 ft. from blower and adjacent air lock to the separator and dust collector at the far end. Capacity 40 tons per hour. The first column uses coarse salt as a typical heavy material. The second assumes flaxseed as a typical medium material. The third assumes ground cork as an extremely light material. The differences in horsepower required are quite striking and illustrate the effect of the characteristics of the material in pneumatic conveying.

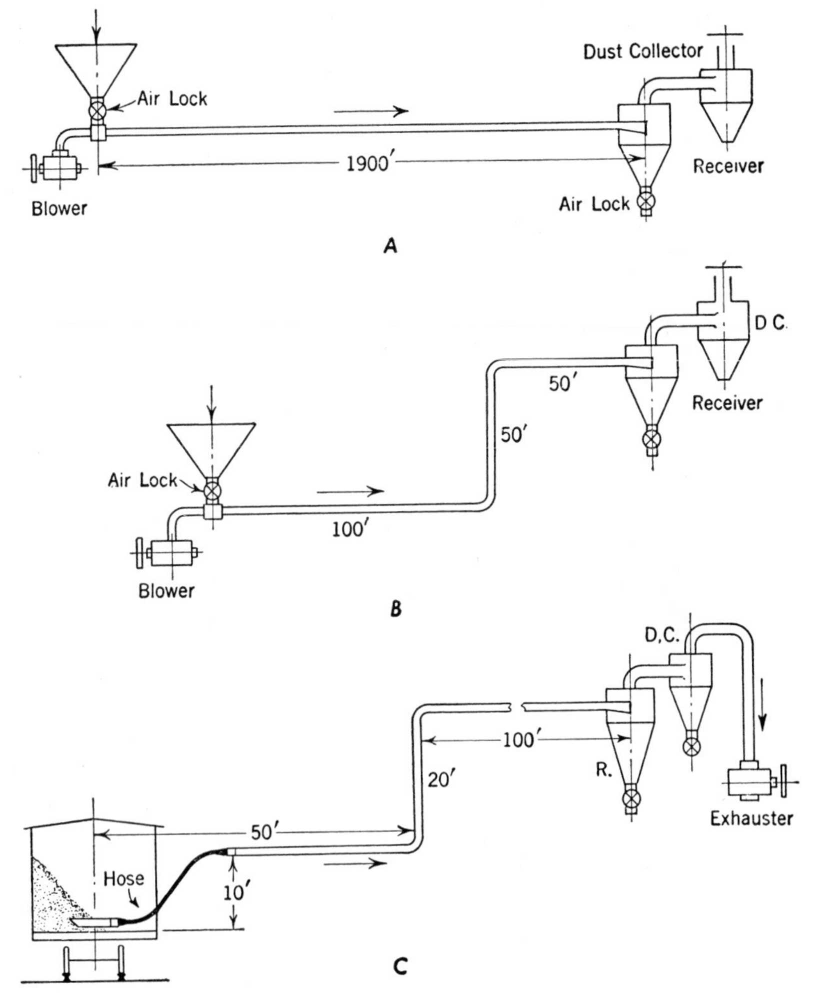


FIG. 9-16. Layouts for theoretical analysis. (*A*) Straight horizontal pressure system. (*B*) Pressure system with horizontal and vertical runs. (*C*) Suction system for unloading from cars.

**1.** Determination of pressure system. Capacity 40 tons per hour. Length 1900 ft. Straight run horizontally. Layout as per Fig. 9–16*A*.

| | Coarse Salt | Flaxseed | Ground Cork |
|---|---|---|---|
| Weight per cubic foot, pounds | 80 | 45 | 5 |
| Specific weight, pounds | 136 | 82 | 37.5 |
| (1) $Q$ in cu. ft. per min.: | $136 \times 40 = 5440$ | $82 \times 40 = 3280$ | $37.5 \times 40 = 1500$ |
| (2) $V$ in ft. per sec.: | $10\sqrt{136} + 6\% = 124$ | $12\sqrt{82} + 6\% = 117$ | $10\sqrt{37.5} - 3\% = 60$ |
| (3) Size of pipe (trial): | 120 ft. per sec. 12-in. pipe gives 5650 cu. ft. per min. | 110 ft. per sec. 10-in. pipe gives 3600 cu. ft. per min. | 60 ft. per sec. 9-in. pipe gives 1600 cu. ft. per min. |
| (4) Continue with values: | $Q = 5650$, $V = 120$ | $Q = 3600$, $V = 110$ | $Q = 1600$, $V = 60$ |
| (5) Air-pressure losses, ounces per square inch: | | | |
| (*a*) | $\left(\frac{120}{100}\right)^2 \times 5 = 7$ oz. | $\left(\frac{110}{100}\right)^2 \times 5 = 6$ oz. | $\left(\frac{60}{100}\right)^2 \times 5 = 2$ oz. |
| (*b*) | 0 oz. | 0 oz. | 0 oz. |
| (*c*) | $\left(\frac{120}{100}\right)^2 \times \frac{1900}{100} \times 1.93 = 53$ oz. | $\left(\frac{110}{100}\right)^2 \times \frac{1900}{100} \times 2.43 = 56$ oz. | (similarly) 19 oz. |
| (*d*) | $4 \times 2 = 8$ oz. | 8 oz. | 8 oz. |
| (*e*) | 3 oz. | 3 oz. | 3 oz. |
| Total, (*a*) + (*b*) + (*c*) + (*d*) + (*e*) = (*A*) oz. per sq. in., | 71 oz. | 73 oz. | 32 oz. |
| (6) Material pressure losses, in terms of horsepower: | | | |
| (*f*) | $40 \times \frac{120^2}{100{,}000} = 6$ hp. | $40 \times \frac{110^2}{100{,}000} = 5$ hp. | $40 \times \frac{60^2}{100{,}000} \times 3^1 = 4.5$ hp. |
| (*g*) | 0 hp. | 0 hp. | 0 hp. |
| (*h*) | $\frac{40}{1000} \times \frac{1900}{5} = 16$ hp. | 16 hp. | 16 hp. |
| (*k*) | 0 hp. | 0 hp. | 0 hp. |
| (*m*) (totals) | 22 hp. | 21 hp. | 20.5 hp. |
| $M$ | $\frac{22 \times 3200}{5650} = 13$ oz. | $\frac{21 \times 3200}{3600} = 19$ oz. | 41 oz. |
| $P$ | $\frac{71 + 13}{16} = 5.25$ lb. | $\frac{73 + 19}{16} = 5.75$ lb. | 4.6 lb. |
| $HP$ | $\frac{5650 \times 5.25}{175} = 170$ hp. | $\frac{3600 \times 5.75}{175} = 120$ hp. | $\frac{1600 \times 4.6}{175} = 42$ hp. |

[1] Fine cork dust assumed to come up to speed in ⅓ the time, hence multiply by 3.

**2.** We now analyze a pressure system for the same materials and the same capacities, with the layout shown in diagram *B*, Fig. 9–16, which includes a riser, or vertical lift, in the line. The duct is 200 ft. long with two ells, or an equivalent length of 212 ft.

| | Coarse Salt | Flaxseed | Ground Cork |
|---|---|---|---|
| Weight per cubic foot, pounds | 80 | 45 | 5 |
| Specific weight, pounds | 136 | 82 | 37.5 |
| (1) $Q$ | 5440 | 3280 | 1500 |
| (2) $V$ | $12\frac{1}{2}\sqrt{136} + 6\% = 154$ ft. per sec. | $15\sqrt{82} + 6\% = 146$ ft. per sec. | $12\frac{1}{2}\sqrt{37.5} - 3\% = 74$ ft. per sec. |
| (3) Pipe size: | 11-in. line at 150 ft. gives 5950 | 9-in. line at 140 ft. gives 3700 | 8-in. line at 76 ft. gives 1600 |
| (4) Continue with values: | $Q = 5950$<br>$V = 150$ | $Q = 3700$<br>$V = 140$ | $Q = 1600$<br>$V = 76$ |
| (5) Air-pressure losses: | | | |
| ($a$) | $\left(\frac{150}{100}\right)^2 \times 5 = 11$ oz. | $\left(\frac{140}{100}\right)^2 \times 5 = 10$ oz. | $\left(\frac{76}{100}\right)^2 \times 5 = 3$ oz. |
| ($b$) | 0 oz. | 0 oz. | 0 oz. |
| ($c$) | $\left(\frac{150}{100}\right)^2 \times \frac{212}{100} \times 2.14 = 10$ oz. | $\left(\frac{140}{100}\right)^2 \times \frac{212}{100} \times 2.77 = 11$ oz. | $\left(\frac{76}{100}\right)^2 \times \frac{212}{100} \times 3.25 = 4$ oz. |
| ($d$) | $4 \times 2 = 8$ oz. | 8 oz. | 8 oz. |
| ($e$) | 3 oz. | 3 oz. | 3 oz. |
| ($A$) = ($a$) + ($b$) + ($c$) + ($d$) + ($e$) | 32 oz. | 32 oz. | 18 oz. |
| (6) Material pressure losses in terms of horsepower: | | | |
| ($f$) | $40 \times \frac{150^2}{100{,}000} = 9$ hp. | $40 \times \frac{140^2}{100{,}000} = 8$ hp. | $40 \times \frac{76^2}{100{,}000} \times 3$[1] $= 7$ hp. |
| ($g$) | 0 hp. | 0 hp. | 0 hp. |
| ($h$) | $\frac{40}{1000}\left(50 + \frac{212}{5}\right) + 4$ hp. | 4 hp. | 4 hp. |
| ($k$) (approx.) | $\frac{40 \times 150^2}{200{,}000} \times 2 = 9$ hp. | $\frac{40 \times 140^2}{200{,}000} \times 2 = 8$ hp. | $\frac{40 \times 76^2}{200{,}000} \times 2 \times 3 = 7$ hp. |
| ($m$) (totals) | 22 hp. | 20 hp. | 18 hp. |
| $M$ | $\frac{22 \times 3200}{5950} = 12$ oz. | $\frac{20 \times 3200}{3700} = 17$ oz. | $\frac{18 \times 3200}{1600} = 36$ oz. |
| $P$ | $\frac{32 + 12}{16} = 2.75$ lb. | $\frac{32 + 17}{16} = 3$ lb. (approx.) | $\frac{18 + 36}{16} = 3.5$ lb. |
| $HP$ | $\frac{5950 \times 2.75}{175} = 94$ hp. | $\frac{3700 \times 3}{175} = 63$ hp. | $\frac{1600 \times 3.5}{175} = 32$ hp. |

[1] Fine cork dust assumed to come up to speed in ⅓ the time, hence multiply by 3.

**3.** Finally we analyze the suction system for the same materials and capacities with the layout shown in diagram $C$, Fig. 9–16.

| | Coarse Salt | Flaxseed | Ground Cork |
|---|---|---|---|
| (1) $Q$ | 5540 | 3280 | 1500 |
| (2) $V$ | $12.5\sqrt{136} + 6\% = 154$ | $15\sqrt{82} + 6\% = 146$ | $12.5\sqrt{37.5} - 3\% = 75$ |
| (3) Pipe size | 11-in. line at 150 ft. gives 5950 cu. ft. | 9-in. line at 140 ft. gives 3700 cu. ft. | 8-in. line at 76 ft. gives 1600 cu. ft. |
| | 9-in. hose[1] at 225 ft. gives same | 7-in. hose at 230 ft. gives same | 6-in. hose at 136 ft. gives same |
| (4) Thus: | $Q = 5950$, $V = 120$, $V_h = 225$ | $Q = 3700$, $V = 140$, $V_h = 230$ | $Q = 1600$, $V = 76$, $V_h = 136$ |
| (5) Air pressure losses, | | | |
| ($a$) | $\left(\frac{225}{100}\right)^2 \times 5 = 25$ oz. | $\left(\frac{230}{100}\right)^2 \times 5 = 26$ oz. | $\left(\frac{136}{100}\right)^2 \times 5 = 10$ oz. |
| ($b$) | $\left(\frac{225}{100}\right)^2 \times \frac{35}{100} \times 2.77 = 5$ oz. | $\left(\frac{230}{100}\right)^2 \times \frac{35}{100} \times 3.95 = 7$ oz. | $\left(\frac{136}{100}\right)^2 \times \frac{35}{100} \times 4.8 = 3$ oz. |
| ($c$) | $\left(\frac{150}{100}\right)^2 \times \frac{190}{100} \times 2.14 = 10$ oz. | $\left(\frac{140}{100}\right)^2 \times \frac{190}{100} \times 2.77 = 11$ oz. | $\left(\frac{76}{100}\right)^2 \times \frac{190}{100} \times 3.25 = 4$ oz. |
| ($d$) | $4 \times 2 = 8$ oz. | $4 \times 2 = 8$ oz. | $4 \times 2 = 8$ oz. |
| ($e$) | 3 oz. | 3 oz. | 3 oz. |
| ($A$) = ($a$) + ($b$) + ($c$) + ($d$) + ($e$) | 51 oz. | 55 oz. | 28 oz. |
| (6) Material pressure losses in terms of horsepower: | | | |
| ($f$) | $40 \times \frac{150^2}{100{,}000} = 9$ hp. | $40 \times \frac{140^2}{100{,}000} = 8$ hp. | $40 \times \frac{76^2}{100{,}000} \times 3 = 7$ hp. |
| ($g$) | $50\% \times f = 5$ hp. | $50\% \times f = 4$ hp. | $50\% \times f = 4$ hp. |
| ($h$) | $\frac{40}{1000}\left(30 + \frac{190}{5}\right) = 3$ hp. | 3 hp. | 3 hp. |
| ($k$) | $f/2 \times 3$, approx. 14 hp. | 12 hp. | 11 hp. |
| ($m$) (totals) | 31 hp. | 27 hp. | 25 hp. |
| ($M$) | $\frac{31 \times 3200}{5950} = 17$ oz. | $\frac{27 \times 3200}{3700} = 23$ oz. | $\frac{25 \times 3200}{1600} = 50$ oz. |
| ($P$) | $\frac{51 + 17}{16} = 4.25$ lb. | $\frac{55 + 23}{16} = 5$ lb. | $\frac{28 + 50}{16} = 5$ lb. |
| $HP$ | $\frac{5950 \times 4.25}{175} \times \left(\frac{14.7 + 4.25}{14.7}\right) = 187$ hp. | $\frac{3700 \times 5}{175} \times \left(\frac{14.7 + 5}{14.7}\right) = 142$ hp. | $\frac{1600 \times 5}{175} \times \left(\frac{14.7 + 5}{14.7}\right) = 62$ hp. |

[1] In practice, twin smaller hose would be used for more convenient handling.

In case 2, page 169, we found that, for coarse salt with 5440 cu. ft. of air required, the power with 11-in. pipe was 94 hp. Let us see what difference results through substituting a 10-in pipe.

$$Q = 5440$$

$$V = 166$$

Air-pressure losses:

$$(a) = \left(\frac{166}{100}\right)^2 \times 5 = \quad 14 \text{ oz.}$$

$$(c) = \left(\frac{166}{100}\right)^2 \times \frac{212}{100} \times 2.43 = 14 \text{ oz.}$$

$$(d) = \quad 8 \text{ oz.}$$

$$(e) = \quad 3 \text{ oz.}$$

$$\text{Total} \quad 39 \text{ oz.}$$

Material losses:

$$(f) = 40 \times \frac{166^2}{100{,}000} = \quad 11 \text{ hp.}$$

$$(h) = \quad 4 \text{ hp.}$$

$$(k) = 40 \times \frac{166^2}{200{,}000} \times 2 = \quad 11 \text{ hp.}$$

$$\text{Total} \quad 26 \text{ hp.}$$

$$M = \frac{26 \times 3200}{5440} = 15 \text{ oz.}$$

$$P = \frac{39 + 15}{16} = 3.4 \text{ lb.}$$

$$HP = \frac{5440 \times 3.4}{175} = 106 \text{ hp.}$$

*Saturation.* It is interesting to compare the volume of the material with the volume of the air required to transport it, or the "saturation," as determined from the formula, page 163; namely:

$$Q = W \cdot T$$

In terms of cubic feet of air per hour, we may write this,

$$Q' = 60W \cdot T \qquad (AA)$$

We handle $\dfrac{T \times 2000}{W}$ cubic feet of material per hour $\qquad (MM)$

Then

$$\frac{AA}{MM} = 60WT \div \frac{T \times 2000}{W} = \frac{3W^2}{100}$$

is the ratio of volume of air to volume of material in the solid.

If the weight of the material in bulk is $W_b$ the ratio of volume of air to volume of material in bulk is

$$\frac{3W^2}{100} \times \frac{W_b}{W} = \frac{3W \times W_b}{100}$$

To illustrate, for coarse salt:

$W_b$ = 80 lb. per cu. ft. (weight in bulk)
$W$ = 136 lb. per cu. ft. (specific weight, or weight in the solid)

Ratio of volume of air to volume of material in the solid is

$$\frac{AA}{MM} = \frac{3 \times 136^2}{100} = 555$$

Ratio of volume of air to volume of material in bulk is

$$\frac{3 \times 136 \times 80}{100} = 326$$

The saturation, as might be expected, is quite different with ground cork. Natural dry cork with 60 per cent voids weighs 15 lb. per cu. ft. "Solid" cork weighs 15/0.40 = 37.5 lb. per cu. ft. = $W$. Ground cork weighs 5 lb. per cu. ft.

$$\frac{AA}{MM} = \frac{3 \times (37.50)^2}{100} = 42 = \text{ratio for the material in the solid}$$

$$\frac{3 \times 37.5 \times 15}{100} = 17 = \text{ratio for natural cork}$$

$$\frac{3 \times 37.5 \times 5}{100} = 5.6 = \text{ratio for ground cork}$$

*Dense Air at Low Velocity vs. Rarefied Air at High Velocity.* Returning to example 1 (Fig. 9-16) with this extremely long line, the air is under considerable pressure at the loading point and correspondingly dense. The velocity is lowest at that point and increases as the air expands along the duct. However, the denser the air the more effective it is as a conveying medium; or dense air at the lower velocity is as effective as the expanded air at higher velocity. Stating it another way, if in the pressure system the material starts to move it will continue to move.

In example 3, it makes little difference, as regards power, on which side of the exhauster we place the dust collector. However, if it is desired to have tandem dust collctors to reduce the dust in the discharge, additional power is measured by the added back pressure (assumed at 4 oz.). Thus:

$$HP = \frac{Q \times 0.25}{175}$$

Thus in the salt system the added power is approximately 9 hp.; in the flaxseed system, approximately 6 hp.; in the ground-cork system, approximately 3 hp.

As mentioned, the layouts assumed were purely illustrative. In the usual industrial applications the power may be much lower. In unloading grain from barges with a short length of duct, special nozzle, direct lift, and high capacity, a minimum of 1 to 2 hp. per ton per hour handled may be attained. (See Fig. 14-12.)

*Power Requirement for Ash-Handling Systems.* In these, the layout starts with a horizontal run along the ash-pit fronts with an inlet at each, and the air velocity must be higher than those arrived at by our analysis. The ashes and clinkers are shoveled into the duct in batches, momentarily choking the flow with each batch, and the duct must clear itself before the next batch enters. This can be noted by listening at the feed point. The roar of the blast drops as each batch is fed and builds up to full strength a few seconds later. Of course, it is possible to choke the conveyor completely, but the operator soon learns by the sound of the air blast to control the rate of feed. In the intermittent system like the Nu-veyor (United Conveyor Corporation) the air blast is cut off at intervals of 60 sec. or so, but the ash intakes are offset (Fig. 9-17) and the air velocity is so high that it is difficult to choke the line unless a succession of heavy clinkers is fed.

**Applications and Limitations.** The performance of a high-velocity air stream is less predictable than the action of any other type of conveyor. Certain materials are unexpectedly abrasive; for example, the shell of flaxseed has an abrasive action approaching that of a sand blast and will cut through a steel pipe elbow in a few days. Oats are readily handled, but turbulence damages the sheath of the grain. Acid phosphate quickly gums up at the elbows and cannot be dislodged. Cottonseed would seem to be an ideal material for the pneumatic conveyor. A difficulty is that it will not flow into a suction nozzle. The fuzz interlocks the mass, and the nozzle simply drills holes into it. Pneumatic unloading of copra from the holds of vessels is feasible and is practiced, but it tends to cause exudation of the essential oil; the oil is deposited on the walls of the receiver, and if it is not returned to the copra the quality is reduced. The centrifugal receiver automatically removes the masses of cockroaches by centrifugal action, but this is of no interest to the stevedore paid by weight of material unloaded. In one of the author's west coast installations he insisted they be put back "where they belonged."

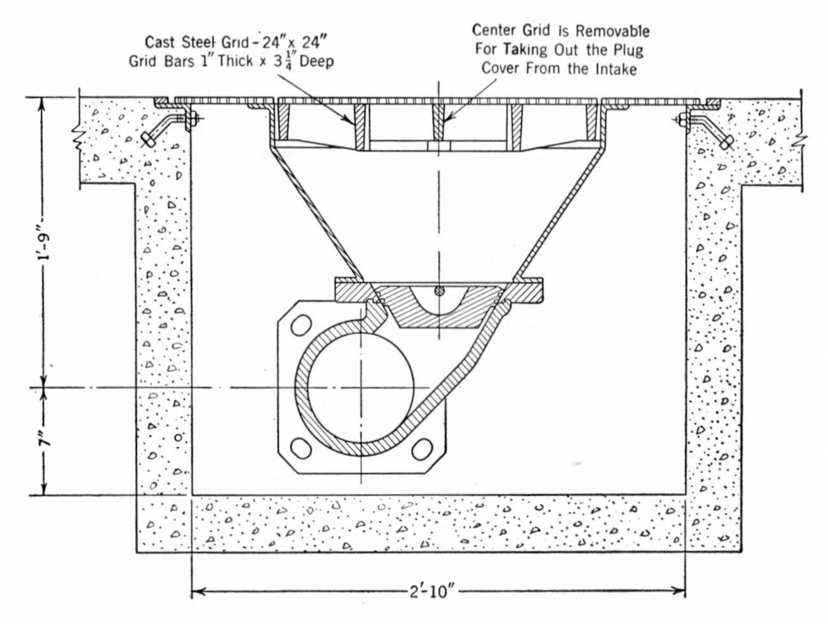


FIG. 9-17. Standard ash intake of the Nu-Veyor.

Possibly the outstanding advantage of the pneumatic conveyor is its flexibility. The duct may be run in almost any course, around bends, under and over obstructions, fulfilling conditions which are impossible for any type of mechanical conveyor. It will handle materials that are corrosive and abrasive, if not too abrasive; it is dustless in operation, and frequently it is the best conveyor to use.

Experience has provided a sound groundwork of empirical formulas for air velocity, volume of air per pound of material, power, etc., and has determined the materials which can and cannot be handled successfully by air. Pneumatic conveyors as now engineered are uniformly successful, with advantages which more than compensate for the very high power requirements.

**Hydraulic Conveyors.** The hydraulic conveyor requires less power than a pneumatic conveyor because the conveying medium is dense. Assume a theoretical condition, a 10-in. horizontal pipe line 200-ft. long and a coal-handling capacity of 40 tons per hour. Without here going through the details of procedure for the determination of power, the volume of coal is 1600 cu. ft. per hr., the total volume of coal and water is 17,600 cu. ft. per hr. or 293 cu. ft. per min. The head loss is 8.8 ft. in 200 ft. and the theoretical horsepower is

$$293 \times 64 \times \frac{8.8}{33{,}000} = 5 \text{ water hp., i.e. 10-hp. motor}$$

The ratio of air to coal in a pneumatic conveyor would be 140 : 1 by volume, and the blower motor would be 25 hp. Incidently, a belt conveyor for the same job would call for 1.0 hp. for the empty belt plus 0.5 hp. for the material, a total of 1.5 hp. or a 3-hp. motor.

Figure 9-18 outlines the loading-out side of an anthracite-coal preparation plant. Coal is chuted over screens to trains of cars on a loading track. Screenings feed down to a sluice stepped at intervals to accommodate booster jets as shown in Fig. 9-19. The mixture of coal and water flows to a sump boot of a continuous bucket elevator with perforated buckets so that the coal is dewatered as it is lifted. The water draining from the sump rejoins the washing water used in the plant.

Since cars are being loaded almost continuously, the booster jets are maintained in operation for a volume and velocity that will take care of any volume of screenings that may be produced. An alternate layout would be tandem screw conveyors. Since water under sufficient pressure was available from the coal-washing operations and eliminates all danger to men operating the loading chutes, the sluice is better. Moreover it is immune to destruction by corrosion.

The hydraulic conveyor is not well adapted to bin storage since the water must be drawn off, leaving the coal in a difficult condition. If the ground slopes easily so that water will drain off *and* if investigation has determined that there will be no legal difficulties resulting from the runoff, a simple movable pipe line provides an inexpensive emergency storage system. One such installation observed during the war, when it was impossible to secure a priority on a conveyor, is shown in Fig. 9-20. The duct was formed of 6-in. leader pipe, supported on wood cross frames, and extends out from the discharge chute of the elevator. With the available water the coal-handling capacity was about half the capacity of the elevator, and so an adjustable by-pass controls the percentage of flow to the duct. The water

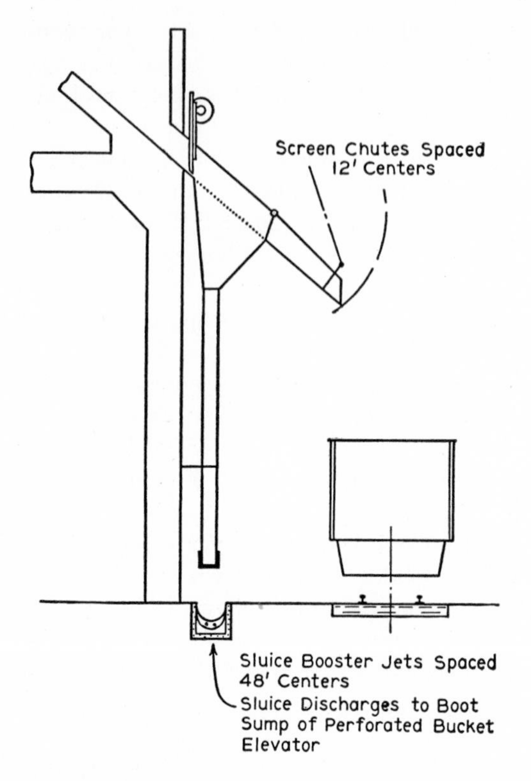


FIG. 9–18. Hydraulic conveyor for anthracite screenings.

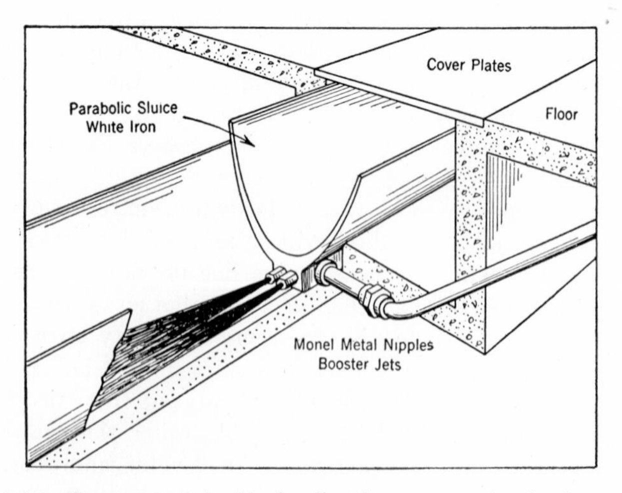


FIG. 9–19. Stepped trough of hydraulic ash conveyor, showing booster jets.

approximates 500 g.p.m., and the handling capacity is about 10 tons per hour, depending on the length and slope of the pipe.

Ashes handling where water in sufficient volume is available frequently has striking advantages, especially when the disposal area is so located that the ashes may be sluiced direct from the ash pits. The investment then is within the reach of the small plant since it involves only an 8- or 10-in. pipe or sluice, with a high-velocity jet and booster jets at intervals along the run. The conveyor is dustless, has no moving parts except the pump, and is safe. Maintenance is low, since the ashes carry along in suspension with little or no abrasive action.

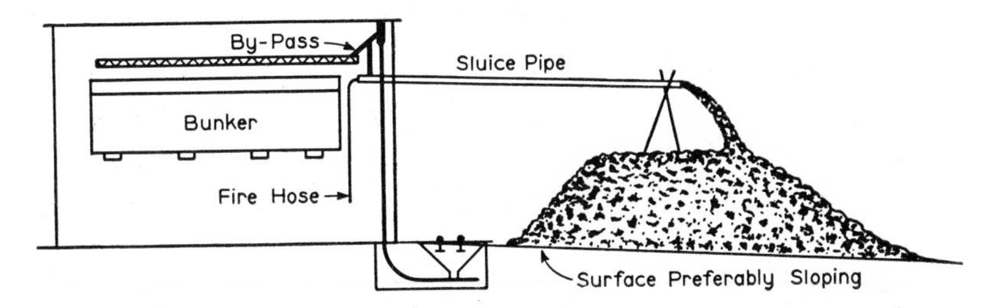


FIG. 9–20. Emergency hydraulic system for reserve coal storage.

For large stations the hydraulic-disposal system as developed by the Allen-Sherman-Hoff Co. has become quite generally accepted. The investment and quantity of water required are large, but the advantages outweigh these objections where the conditions are suitable. One of the A.S.H. arrangements is shown in Fig. 9-21. The ashes may be flushed from the ash pit by a hand-controlled jet, and the mixture flows along with suitable booster jets either to a disposal area or to a pit from which, after dewatering, the ashes are removed by grab bucket or by a special type of pump in which an inflow of clean water protects the parts from erosion. Often the pumps are in duplicate to permit repairs without interruption of operations.

In the following discussion of *pipe-line transportation* we will quote by permission from the excellent paper by Mr. J. R. Thoenen of the U. S. Bureau of Mines, I.C. 6875.

Pipe-line transportation may be designed so that two or more pumps operate in series on a single pipe. The dredge pump in this case is supplemented by one or more pumps in the discharge line. The choice of pumps depends on a number of factors such as (1) the quantity of material to be transported, (2) the presence of enough water as a transporting medium, (3) the length of haul, (4) the height to which the material must be elevated, (5) the physical characteristics of the gravel, (6) the power required, and (7) the cost of in-

FIG. 9–21. Hydraulic ash-disposal system. Ashes are here flushed from the pit by hand-controlled jet to the main sluice trough. (Allen-Sherman-Hoff.)

stallation. The quantity of material determines the size of pump and pipe line. The required capacity may be so large that the cost of power and maintenance is excessive and some other method is better.

The transporting medium is water, and under average conditions the sand and gravel conveyed constitute 10 to 15 per cent by volume of the mixture pumped, the balance being water. Sand and gravel contain voids between particles, the percentage of which varies with the size gradation of the gravel and sand. When the mixture is moved by pumping, these voids are filled with water; hence the actual quantity of water present in a given volume is always greater than the complementary percentage of sand and gravel. If sand and gravel are assumed to average 110 lb. per cu. ft. loose measure and to contain 40 per cent voids the relative quantities of water and gravel for various mixtures are as given in Table 5. After the percentage of solids is once determined the water required as a vehicle can be read from the table. Correction should, of course, be made for variation in weight and void content of the gravel. When gravel is dredged from a running stream there is assurance of enough vehicular water. When it is dredged from a pond in which the subsurface water movement is retarded additional water may be necessary from an independent source. Again, pumps handling material from a sump may require more water than enters the sump with the gravel, although ordinarily the feed to the pump can be made more uniform, resulting in a heavier percentage of solids and requiring less water than in original pumping or sluicing.

The head against which material must be pumped is affected by the length of the pipe line and the height to which the material must be elevated. The length and diameter of the pipe determine the friction head, and the elevation determines the static head.

The physical characteristics of the sand and gravel affect the pumping operation in various ways, all of which, though evident, are difficult to evaluate accurately. Round particles create less internal pipe friction than flat or sharp-edged particles; coarse gravel creates more friction than sand and requires a higher velocity of flow; and increased percentages of solids, either coarse or fine, increase friction and require greater velocity. The direct effect of these characteristics must be determined by trial or from past experience.

The power required is determined by the quantity pumped, the percentage of solids, the total pumping head, and the operating characteristics of the pump. Power is probably the factor of greatest economic importance in the selection of a pump and pipe lines as a means of transportation, as may be illustrated thus:

An operator who is pumping a mixture containing 12 per cent solids against a total head of 25 ft. at a rate of 100 tons of sand and gravel per hour wishes to increase the head to 100 ft. and put the material directly to the top of his washing plant. If the sand and gravel weigh 110 lb. per cu. ft. the required quantity in cubic feet per minute will be

$$\frac{100 \times 2000}{60 \times 110} \text{ or } 30.3 \text{ cu. ft. per min.}$$

From Table 5, 30.3 cu. ft. of sand and gravel at 12 per cent solids will require

$$12 : 92.8 :: 30.3 : x = 234 \text{ cu. ft. of water}$$

Assuming 40 per cent voids and allowing for the water filling the voids the volume of mixture pumped per minute will be

$$30.3 - \frac{40 \times 30.3}{100} + 234 = 252 \text{ cu. ft.}$$

TABLE 5

COMPOSITION OF SAND, GRAVEL, AND WATER MIXTURES
U. S. Bureau of Mines, I.C. 6875

(Sand and gravel assumed to weigh 110 lb. per cu. ft. and contain 40 per cent voids.)

| Sand and Gravel by Volume, per cent | 100 Cu. Ft. of Mixture Will Contain | | | | | 1 Cu. Yd. of Sand[1] and Gravel Will Require Water as Follows: | | | Ratio of Sand and Gravel to Water | | | |
|---|---|---|---|---|---|---|---|---|---|---|---|---|
| | Sand and Gravel | | Water | | | | | | By Volume | | By Weight | |
| | Cubic feet | Pounds | Cubic feet | Pounds | U.S. gallons | Cubic feet | Pounds | U.S. gallons | Sand and Gravel | Water | Sand and Gravel | Water |
| 5 | 5 | 550 | 97.0 | 6,060 | 726 | 524 | 32,750 | 3,920 | 1 | 19.4 | 1 | 11.0 |
| 6 | 6 | 660 | 96.4 | 6,020 | 721 | 434 | 27,120 | 3,245 | 1 | 16.0 | 1 | 9.1 |
| 7 | 7 | 770 | 95.8 | 5,990 | 716 | 370 | 23,120 | 2,770 | 1 | 13.7 | 1 | 7.8 |
| 8 | 8 | 880 | 95.2 | 5,950 | 712 | 321 | 20,070 | 2,400 | 1 | 11.9 | 1 | 6.8 |
| 9 | 9 | 990 | 94.6 | 5,910 | 708 | 284 | 17,750 | 2,125 | 1 | 10.5 | 1 | 6.0 |
| 10 | 10 | 1,100 | 94.0 | 5,875 | 703 | 254 | 15,875 | 1,900 | 1 | 9.4 | 1 | 5.3 |
| 11 | 11 | 1,210 | 93.4 | 5,840 | 698 | 230 | 14,375 | 1,720 | 1 | 8.5 | 1 | 4.8 |
| 12 | 12 | 1,320 | 92.8 | 5,800 | 694 | 209 | 13,050 | 1,563 | 1 | 7.7 | 1 | 4.4 |
| 13 | 13 | 1,430 | 92.2 | 5,760 | 690 | 192 | 12,000 | 1,435 | 1 | 7.1 | 1 | 4.0 |
| 14 | 14 | 1,540 | 91.6 | 5,725 | 685 | 177 | 11,050 | 1,324 | 1 | 6.5 | 1 | 3.7 |
| 15 | 15 | 1,650 | 91.0 | 5,690 | 681 | 164 | 10,250 | 1,226 | 1 | 6.1 | 1 | 3.45 |
| 20 | 20 | 2,200 | 88.0 | 5,500 | 658 | 119 | 7,440 | 890 | 1 | 4.4 | 1 | 2.5 |
| 25 | 25 | 2,750 | 85.0 | 5,310 | 636 | 92 | 5,750 | 688 | 1 | 3.4 | 1 | 1.9 |
| 30 | 30 | 3,300 | 82.0 | 5,120 | 613 | 74 | 4,625 | 554 | 1 | 2.7 | 1 | 1.55 |
| 40 | 40 | 4,400 | 76.0 | 4,750 | 568 | 51 | 3,190 | 381 | 1 | 1.9 | 1 | 1.08 |

[1] One ton of sand and gravel will require approximately two-thirds the tabulated figures.

The weight of the mixture per cubic foot will be

| | |
|---|---|
| 30.3 cu. ft. of gravel at 110 lb. | 3,333 |
| 234 cu. ft. of water at 62.5 lb. | 14,625 |
| Total | 17,958 lb. |

Then

$$\frac{17{,}958}{252} = 71.3 \text{ lb. per cu. ft.}$$

The theoretical or water horsepower required can be computed from the formula

$$HP = \frac{QWH}{33{,}000}$$

in which $HP$ = the theoretical or water horsepower.
$Q$ = cubic feet of mixture handled per minute.
$W$ = weight of mixture per cubic foot.
$H$ = total head in feet.

If there is no increase in the length of the discharge pipe required by the increase in total head, substitution in the formula gives the following power requirements:

$$HP = \frac{252 \times 71.3 \times 25}{33{,}000} = 13.6 \text{ to pump the mixture against a 25-ft. head}$$

$$HP = \frac{252 \times 71.3 \times 100}{33{,}000} = 54.4 \text{ to pump the mixture against a 100-ft. head}$$

The motor rating in each case should be about double these figures. Instead of changing from a 30-hp. pumping unit to a 100-hp. unit it may be cheaper to dewater the pump discharge and use a bucket elevator for the added 75 ft. of elevation.

Assume that the gravel could be transported dry instead of in water:

$$\frac{30.3 \times 110 \times 25}{33{,}000} = 2.5 \text{ hp. to pump gravel only against 25-ft. head}$$

$$\frac{30.3 \times 110 \times 100}{33{,}000} = 10.1 \text{ hp. to pump gravel only against 100-ft. head}$$

That means, 80 per cent of the power is used to move the water.

*Gravel Size.* Transport by pump and pipe line is limited to those gravel deposits which are comparatively free from oversize boulders. Ordinarily, with a deposit containing 10 per cent of boulders larger than ⅔ the diameter of the suction inlet of the pump, this type of transportation cannot be used.

*Length Limits.* The discharge length will depend upon the operating characteristics of the pumps used, the diameter of the pipe, and the characteristics of the material pumped. Where booster pumps are necessary the material should enter the suction of the booster at some positive pressure; that is, the booster should not be called upon to overcome any suction head. If the suction of the booster is put under a vacuum, leakage of air would probably result, causing pulsation in the flow. The amount of pressure required is only that necessary to insure against any vacuum in the booster suction at any time — from 4.3 to 6.0 lb. per sq. in. or 10 to 14 ft. of head.

*Location of Booster Pump.* The booster pump should be so located that the discharge head or pressure is well within the bursting strength of pipe and pump. Sand and gravel moving in long, straight, fairly level pipe lines tend to separate and drag along the floor of the pipe, which may cause the line to fill up gradually and plug. Therefore the booster pump should be placed as near the center of the discharge line as possible, to reagitate the material and prevent plugging. If the dredge pump is stopped and there is no positive head on the suction of the booster, some means of relief must be provided or the line beyond the booster will also plug. The motors should be interlocked or there should be a by-pass valve between the booster and the dredge pump. This valve is placed in a submerged depression in the discharge line with its emergency opening under water. Ordinarily the pressure in the pipe line holds this valve closed. When the pressure is removed by stoppage in the dredge pump or a plug in the line the valve opens and allows the booster pump to pull clear water into its suction and thus clear the line beyond. This does not help if the stoppage occurs in the booster line; hence interlocked motors are essential.

*Conditions for Pump Efficiency.* The power required to operate a pump and pipe-line system varies directly with: (1) the rate of discharge, governed by the diameter of the pipe and the velocity of flow; (2) the weight per cubic foot of the material pumped, governed by the percentage of solids; and (3) the total head against which the pump must operate, governed by the suction head, the friction head, and the static head. The head against which a pump can deliver depends upon the peripheral speed of the impeller, which in turn depends upon the diameter and revolutions per minute of the impeller, or, in short, the characteristics of the pump.

The total head against which a pipe line operates may be constant or may vary from day to day. To illustrate, a pump obtaining material from a sump, supplied from other equipment, and transporting it to a treatment plant will operate under constant head; but delivery from a constantly shifting dredge may or may not be subject to a corresponding change in head, depending on whether the dredge movements lengthen, shorten, or do not change the discharge line. A pump and pipe line subject to frequent change in head should be provided with means for varying the peripheral speed of the pump impeller usually by means of a variable-speed transmission. The efficiency of the pump varies inversely with the ratio of the peripheral speed of the impeller to the velocity equivalent of the total head, and highest efficiency results when the impeller speed approaches the velocity equivalent of the total head.

*Capacity.* The capacity of the pump and pipe-line system depends upon the internal diameter of the pipe, the velocity of flow, and the percentage of solids in the mixture.

The diameter of the discharge line is ordinarily fixed by the discharge diameter of the pump.

The velocity of flow in pumping sand and gravel will seldom be less than 10 ft. or more than 18 ft. per sec. The average is 12 ft. per sec.

The amount of solids in the mixture is largely a function of the skill of the operator and the nature of the gravel. It ranges from 5 to 20 per cent by volume and usually averages 10 to 15 per cent.

Table 6 gives the capacity of pump and pipe-line systems for the average range of velocities and percentages of solids. The figures in the table are based on sand and gravel weighing 100 lb. per cu. ft. loose measure. The capacity corresponding to heavier material will vary in direct proportion; thus for sand and gravel weighing 110 lb. per cu. ft. the figures should be increased 10 per cent.

*Analogy between Water and Air-Pressure Losses.* It is interesting to see if there is a relationship between the pressure losses with water and air in pipe lines.

The loss of head in pumping water containing about 10 per cent sand or gravel has been found by tests to approximate:

1725 g.p.m. through 8-in. pipe – head loss per 100 ft. = 8 ft.
2830 g.p.m. through 10-in. pipe – head loss per 100 ft. = 6.7 ft.
4240 g.p.m. through 12-in. pipe – head loss per 100 ft. = 5.8 ft.

The velocities for the above quantities in feet per second and the above head losses converted to ounces per square inch are:

| | Velocity, feet per second | Head Loss, ounces |
|---|---|---|
| 8-in. pipe | 11. | 56 (*a*) |
| 10-in. pipe | 11.6 | 47 (*b*) |
| 12-in. pipe | 12. | 41 (*c*) |

The hydraulic medium plus material weighs about 72 or 73 lb. per cu. ft. or 950 times the weight of air (0.0764 lb.), and the coefficient of friction is 1.5 that of air.

Let us use Unwin's values in Table 1 for air, multiplying by 950 and 1.5 to see if there is agreement with (*a*), (*b*), and (*c*), above:

$$\text{Head loss in 8-in. pipe} = \left(\frac{11}{100}\right)^2 \times 950 \times 1.5 \times 3.25 = 56 \text{ oz.}$$

$$\text{Head loss in 10-in. pipe} = \left(\frac{11.6}{100}\right)^2 \times 950 \times 1.5 \times 2.43 = 47 \text{ oz.}$$

$$\text{Head loss in 12-in. pipe} = \left(\frac{12}{100}\right)^2 \times 950 \times 1.5 \times 1.93 = 40 \text{ oz.}$$

This indicates that by means of Table 1 for air we can ascertain pressure losses with water by using the 1.5 friction coefficient and the weight multiplier.

TABLE 6

CAPACITY OF PUMP AND PUMP-LINE SYSTEMS IN TONS PER HOUR[1]

U. S. Bureau of Mines, I.C. 6875

| Pipe Diameter, inches | Solids, per cent | Velocity of Flow, feet per second | | | | | | | | |
|---|---|---|---|---|---|---|---|---|---|---|
| | | 10 | 11 | 12 | 13 | 14 | 15 | 16 | 17 | 18 |
| 6 | 5 | 17.7 | 19.5 | 21.2 | 23.0 | 24.7 | 26.5 | 28.4 | 30.0 | 31.8 |
| | 10 | 35.4 | 39.0 | 42.3 | 46.0 | 49.5 | 58.2 | 56.7 | 60.0 | 63.6 |
| | 15 | 53.1 | 58.5 | 63.5 | 69.0 | 74.2 | 79.7 | 85.0 | 90.0 | 95.4 |
| | 20 | 70.8 | 78.0 | 84.7 | 92.0 | 99.0 | 106 | 113 | 120 | 127 |
| 8 | 5 | 31.3 | 34.5 | 37.7 | 40.8 | 43.8 | 46.9 | 50.0 | 53.3 | 56.4 |
| | 10 | 62.7 | 69.0 | 75.4 | 81.6 | 87.6 | 93.9 | 100 | 107 | 113 |
| | 15 | 94.1 | 104 | 113 | 122 | 131 | 141 | 150 | 160 | 169 |
| | 20 | 125 | 138 | 151 | 163 | 175 | 188 | 200 | 213 | 225 |
| 10 | 5 | 49.0 | 54.0 | 58.8 | 63.7 | 58.7 | 73.6 | 78.4 | 83.4 | 88.3 |
| | 10 | 98.0 | 108 | 118 | 127 | 137 | 147 | 157 | 167 | 177 |
| | 15 | 147 | 162 | 176 | 191 | 206 | 221 | 235 | 250 | 265 |
| | 20 | 196 | 216 | 235 | 255 | 275 | 295 | 314 | 333 | 353 |
| 12 | 5 | 70.7 | 77.7 | 84.8 | 91.8 | 98.8 | 106 | 113 | 120 | 127 |
| | 10 | 141 | 155 | 170 | 184 | 198 | 212 | 226 | 240 | 254 |
| | 15 | 212 | 233 | 254 | 276 | 296 | 318 | 339 | 360 | 382 |
| | 20 | 283 | 311 | 339 | 367 | 395 | 424 | 452 | 480 | 509 |
| 14 | 5 | 96.3 | 106 | 115 | 125 | 135 | 144 | 154 | 163 | 173 |
| | 10 | 193 | 212 | 231 | 250 | 269 | 288 | 308 | 327 | 346 |
| | 15 | 289 | 318 | 346 | 375 | 404 | 433 | 462 | 490 | 520 |
| | 20 | 385 | 424 | 462 | 500 | 538 | 577 | 616 | 654 | 693 |
| 16 | 5 | 126 | 138 | 151 | 163 | 176 | 188 | 201 | 214 | 226 |
| | 10 | 251 | 277 | 302 | 327 | 352 | 377 | 402 | 427 | 453 |
| | 15 | 377 | 415 | 453 | 490 | 528 | 565 | 603 | 641 | 679 |
| | 20 | 503 | 553 | 604 | 654 | 704 | 754 | 804 | 855 | 905 |
| 18 | 5 | 159 | 175 | 191 | 207 | 223 | 239 | 255 | 271 | 286 |
| | 10 | 318 | 350 | 382 | 414 | 446 | 478 | 510 | 541 | 573 |
| | 15 | 477 | 525 | 573 | 621 | 669 | 716 | 764 | 812 | 860 |
| | 20 | 637 | 700 | 764 | 828 | 892 | 956 | 1018 | 1082 | 1145 |
| 20 | 5 | 197 | 216 | 236 | 256 | 275 | 295 | 315 | 334 | 354 |
| | 10 | 394 | 433 | 472 | 512 | 551 | 590 | 630 | 669 | 708 |
| | 15 | 590 | 650 | 708 | 768 | 826 | 885 | 945 | 1000 | 1060 |
| | 20 | 787 | 866 | 945 | 1023 | 1100 | 1180 | 1260 | 1338 | 1415 |
| 24 | 5 | 283 | 311 | 339 | 368 | 396 | 424 | 452 | 481 | 509 |
| | 10 | 566 | 622 | 679 | 735 | 782 | 848 | 904 | 962 | 1018 |
| | 15 | 849 | 933 | 1017 | 1100 | 1187 | 1272 | 1356 | 1442 | 1527 |
| | 20 | 1130 | 1244 | 1357 | 1470 | 1583 | 1696 | 1810 | 1923 | 2036 |
| 30 | 5 | 330 | 363 | 397 | 430 | 463 | 496 | 528 | 562 | 594 |
| | 10 | 660 | 727 | 794 | 860 | 925 | 992 | 1057 | 1124 | 1188 |
| | 15 | 990 | 1090 | 1190 | 1290 | 1388 | 1487 | 1585 | 1686 | 1783 |
| | 20 | 1320 | 1453 | 1587 | 1720 | 1850 | 1983 | 2113 | 2248 | 2380 |

[1] In this table sand and gravel is assumed to weigh 100 lb. per cu. ft. For material weighing 110 lb. per cu. ft. increase figures 10 per cent, etc.

# CHAPTER 10

## THE BELT CONVEYOR

The belt conveyor is an endless moving belt for transporting materials horizontally or on an incline up or down. The drive pulley is at the head end or an intermediate point along the return run. A take-up, located preferably just behind the drive pulley, adjusts the tension in the belt. The load is discharged over the head or at any point along the carrying run by a plow scraper or a "tripper." It is the most fascinating of mechanical conveyors to study and analyze because of the savings possible through skillful engineering when the capacity and length are sizable. The engineer should have a thorough knowledge of the technical features, since this conveyor is so widely used; for a more complete discussion than is possible here the reader is referred to Hetzel and Albright's *Belt Conveyors and Belt Elevators* (John Wiley and Sons, 1941).

**Historical.** Conveying by endless belt dates back many years. In 1868, Lyster, an English engineer, described to the British Engineers Society his work on conveying bulk materials by endless belts made of two plies of canvas with a facing of rubber. His first idlers were spool shaped, still seen occasionally in small portable conveyors, but he discarded these for straight-faced wood idlers because the flared ends wore the edges of the belt, as they do today. He experimented with two-roll troughing idlers and no doubt found it impossible to prevent the belt from centering on one roll or the other. He devised and used the three-way tripper and the revolving cleaner brush; in fact, Lyster seems to have invented many of the features of the belt conveyor of today. In this country Webster carried on extended experiments with belt conveyors for handling grains, and for a time the Webster Manufacturing Company was the leader in this field. In the early 1890's Edison, as a result of difficulties with flight conveyors handling ore, built several cotton-belt conveyors with continuous skirt boards along the carrying run to keep the load from rolling off the belt. Thomas Robins, apparently independently of Lyster, followed similar lines of investigation and eliminated the difficulty inherent in the two-pulley troughing idler by adding a horizontal pulley just back of each inclined pair. He followed this with the invention of the three-in-line-unit idler and prevented oil from the bearings from leaking onto the belt by means of hollow roll shafts with grease cups on the outer ends and radial ducts along the shaft, incidentally securing the advantage of exuded grease seals to prevent ingress of dirt into the bearings. Robins also did considerable pioneering in belts. His first belts had two or more plies with rubber covers. Then he reduced the thickness of the under side and increased it on the carrying side to secure longer life. About 1896, no doubt because of the loading methods then in vogue and the common practice of partial loading, he originated the stepped-ply belts in which the plies stepped off toward the center with corresponding increasing thickness of rubber in the central zone.

Belt conveyors were increasingly used about this time, competing with the heavy double-strand flight conveyors then common. Five-pulley troughing idlers were tried and were abandoned when it was found that the additional cost was not accompanied by additional life of belt. The manually propelled tripper was made self-propelled and self-reversing by Humphrey, the convenience of operation being greatly improved thereby. Finally came the two great forward steps: anti-friction bearings with labyrinth grease seals, and vastly improved rubber-belt construction.

**Applications and Limitations.** The belt conveyor may be utilized for handling practically all pulverized, granular, and lumpy materials if the capacity is sufficiently large to warrant the investment and if the path is horizontal or on an upward or downward slope. There are the obvious limitations that the temperature must not be high enough to scorch the belt, that the slope shall not be so steep that the material will slip, and that the center's distance shall be within the body strength of the available belt.

On the choice between the inclined belt conveyor and the vertical bucket elevator opinions differ. In general, the inclined belt, with supporting bridge, sheathing, walkways, and foundations, will cost substantially more than the elevator with self-supporting casing and head frame. The power requirements are about the same, and they are a minor consideration from the standpoint of operation, in which long-range maintenance costs are the important factor. With abrasive material, such as sand, sinter, coke, and crushed stone, a belt conveyor properly designed, properly loaded, and given careful servicing will usually outlast a chain and bucket elevator two or three times because fine abrasive dust works into the chain joints, grinding down the pins and bushings. A belt and bucket elevator handling abrasive materials, if properly loaded, has about half the life of an inclined belt conveyor. With less-abrasive material such as coal, a chain and bucket elevator compares more favorably with an inclined belt conveyor. The maintenance of an elevator is essentially covered by the reversal and replacement of the chain pins and bushings. The maintenance of a belt conveyor involves the eventual, though infrequent, replacement of the belt, but the cost is heavy when it comes. As each machine has certain advantages, the requirements of the general layout dictate the selection. The belt conveyor lends itself nicely to many conditions. For example, it is common practice to provide extensions of a steam plant by additional boilers in line, with the bunker extended correspondingly. An inclined conveyor with an upper horizontal run above the bunker may be extended almost indefinitely and the capacity increased by increase in belt speed.

## ESSENTIALS OF THE BELT CONVEYOR

We shall discuss each of the elements of the conveyor, namely, the belt, the carrying and return idlers, the take-ups, the tripper, the drive, the belt cleaner, and the important postwar developments.

**The Belt.** The so-called rubber belt has been used almost universally, as built up on a cotton duck "carcass" which provides the strength necessary to transmit the pull and give body to the belt so that it can carry the load. Different weights of duck are employed, referred to as 28-, 32-, 36-, 42-, and 48-oz., which are the weights of a section 36 in. long by 42 in. wide. The several plies are bonded together with rubber. The pull in pounds necessary to separate adjacent plies in a strip 1 in. wide is called the "friction." In the standard grades of belt the friction is usually 12 to 16 lb., 16 to 19 lb., or 20 to 24 lb. The cementing action must be sufficient to hold the plies together in service, while retaining the flexibility which permits the belt to round the end pulleys without separating the plies. The friction serves also to waterproof the belt. The bottom and top of a belt are protected by rubber covers. The bottom cover protects the belt from damage by impact against the idlers, prevents impregnation of dirt, and takes, or transmits, the driving traction. The top, or carrying side, is protected by a heavier thickness of high-grade rubber, which resists the impact of the load. The different grades of belt are referred to by the quality or tensile strength of the rubber cover, which may range from 800 to 4000 lb. per sq. in. The tensile strength is an approximate, though not exact, measure of the abrasion-resisting quality of the rubber. Cover thickness varies from 1/16 in. to 1/2 in. or sometimes more.

If the service is to be severe, a "breaker strip" of open-mesh fabric is placed beneath the cover to bind the cover to the carcass more firmly and to provide better resistance to any tearing action to which the cover might be subjected. This union is so effective that it is practically impossible to separate cover from carcass, so that if a tear does occur its extent is limited. The cover must not be less than 3/32 in. thick.

*Cord Belts.* Cord belts follow the evolution in automobile tires, which were built up on closely woven fabric until it was found that spaced threads embedded in rubber would withstand shock better and give longer life. The cord belt of the B. F. Goodrich Company embodies this principle. Plies of longitudinal cords embedded in rubber form the carcass, the transverse cord breaker and rubber armor lying above. On the bottom, one or two plies of 42-oz. duck give transverse strength. Each cord of the carcass is surrounded by a thick cushion of rubber with no cross or transverse threads. The advantages claimed for this construction are greater resistance to impact shocks because of greater percentage of rubber, easier troughing, a lower percentage of elastic stretch because of the parallel cords, permissible increase in the number of plies without excessive transverse stiffness or resistance to troughing. The transverse flexibility is controlled by the two plies of 42-oz. duck at the bottom. It would seem that the belt should have maximum resistance to infiltration of moisture and little danger of mildew when cut or bruised. Cord belts must be vulcanized on the job after erection as belt clips will not hold.

*Steel Wire Cable Belts.* Through research to develop a belt which would permit far greater tension than had been attempted, the Goodyear Tire and Rubber Company devised a construction in which the tension is taken by embedded parallel wire cables.

The cables are multi-stranded high-carbon steel wires as used in airplane controls. They are copper plated, then rubber coated for maximum adhesion to the insulating gum or friction in which they lie in the belt. The belt has two bottom plies of 32-oz. duck and one top ply with breaker strip, then the usual top and bottom rubber covers. Laboratory and field tests by the manufacturers are stated to have shown the flexing life to be better than in the usual construction, and with better adhesion between cables and carcass than was foreseen.

The cable sizes and spacing range from 3/64-in. spaced 20 per inch, up to 5/32-in. spaced 6 per inch. Heavy-duty conveyors usually have head pulleys of 30-in. diameter or more and foot pulleys of 20-in. diameter or more. The ratio of diameter of pulley to diameter of cables is thus well beyond the safe minimum as regards bending stresses (see Chapter 11).

The maximum allowable tensions range from 1000 to 3000 lb. per in. of belt width. These figures are the equivalent of 25 to 60 plies for

42-oz. duck. The importance of this fact rests in the possibility of greatly increasing the length of belt conveyors. Belt wear is caused primarily by impact at the loading point and also is a function of the time cycle. If a belt of 400-ft. centers operates at 400 ft. per min., each section is subjected to load impact once every 2 min. If the conveyor may be lengthened to 1200-ft. centers, each section is subjected to load impact once every 6 min.

Comparative costs must be considered. The wire cable belt may cost three or four times as much as the usual construction, but against this are the elimination of intermediate drive and take-up stations, and increased life.

The initial conveyor with a belt of this type was installed in 1942 at the Morris mine in the Misabi range. It is 30 in. by 1075 ft. centers with a lift of 250 ft. and operates with a tension of 1000 lb. per in. of width. In 1946 it was still in action and giving satisfactory service. Two features of the steel cord belt are: stability in length, the Morris mine belt has elongated only 0.05 of 1 per cent in four years; and that determination of carcass condition can be observed by the fluorscope. The X-ray shadows of each cord may be thrown on a screen for visual inspection.

An effective technique for splicing cord and steel wire belts has been developed. The cord or wire ends are not joined together. The tension of one cord end is transferred to an adjacent group of cords through a thin layer of rubber compound in shear, and further along, it is transferred back to the original cord. Each of the cords in the transfer group is handled similarly in a separate zone, thus all the cord ends are dispersed through a section 6 or 8 ft. in length. This gives a splice stronger than that in plied belts and more durable in bending since all the joints are in one plane.

The rubber belt is commonly used for conveying bulk materials; other belts may be mentioned briefly.

*Stitched canvas belts,* usually impregnated with oil or gum, are applied for the lighter duty of handling packages, mail sacks, small fabricated parts, and similar work. The coefficient of surface friction is low, and with light loads these belts may be slid on a wood or steel deck instead of being supported by idlers.

*Balata belts* are of duck impregnated and cemented with balata gum. These belts will stand up under far more punishment than the stitched canvas belts. They are rather stiff, and so the plies must be few or the belt will not train on the usual three-pulley carrying idler.

*Flat steel* belts, often sliding on hardwood decks, are used sometimes for special conditions. A frequent application is for handling cold foundry sand. The best-known belt of this type was of Swedish steel, the Sandvik belt, a cold-rolled steel strip, 0.03-in. thick in 200-ft. lengths, with the ends cut in a V, lapped 2 in., and riveted. If the discharge is at a point between the terminals, a scraper or plow is provided since the short reverse curves of a tripper would not be advisable. The terminal pulleys must be large in diameter, as the coefficient of friction is low; and the maximum distance between centers is comparatively short.

*High-Temperature Belts.* Rubber belts will withstand temperatures up to about 250° F. This limit is increased to about 300° with synthetic-rubber belts. Woven wire belts are used where higher temperatures are involved, as in annealing, drying, sterilizing, and baking. They are preferably of Monel metal which has an upper limit in continuous service in an oxidizing atmosphere of about 900° F. Monel metal belts resist many chemicals and corrosives, withstand abrasives, and, as the composition is ⅔ nickel and ⅓ copper, they will not rust.

*Synthetic-Rubber Belts.* There cannot be any doubt that synthetic-rubber belts are of growing importance. Coal is sometimes sprayed with oil to retard freezing or to reduce the dust nuisance or windage losses. Oil-sprayed coal has a disastrous effect on rubber belts. The cover rots, and the oil penetrates into the carcass, causing the plies to separate and distort. Observations carried over a period of nearly two years have shown that some synthetic-rubber belts (Neoprene, Chloroprene, etc.) are practically immune to the effects of oil or grease. Synthetic rubber hardens gradually when subjected to high temperatures, but it does not weaken. It will swell slightly when exposed to oils, but far less than rubber. Figure 10-1 shows the result of tests by du Pont in which rubber and Neoprene were immersed in lubricating oil (S.A.E. 30) at 82° F. for 219 days. The tensile strength of the rubber dropped sharply as it swelled during the first 21 days and continued through the remainder of the period, whereas the swelling of the Neoprene was negligible for the first 21 days and only slight thereafter. The total loss in tensile strength was 11 per cent compared with 52 and 68 per cent for rubber. Neoprene, and similar synthetics, will resist degradation by many, though not all, of the industrial chemicals. It is affected by coal-tar solvents, aromatic hydrocarbons, and chlorinated solvents. It will resist dilute sulphuric acid at moderate temperatures but not strong oxidizing agents such as nitric acid. It will not perform satisfactorily wherever a rubber belt fails, but it has certain qualities with far-reaching possibilities.

*Sliding belts,* preferably of cotton, are quite frequently specified where the loading is relatively light, as for packaged merchandise, mail bags, and the like. The decking may be of maple or steel or, possibly in the near future, of aluminum. The friction coefficient is about 25 per cent, as compared with 3 to 4 per cent with small-diameter anti-friction rolls.

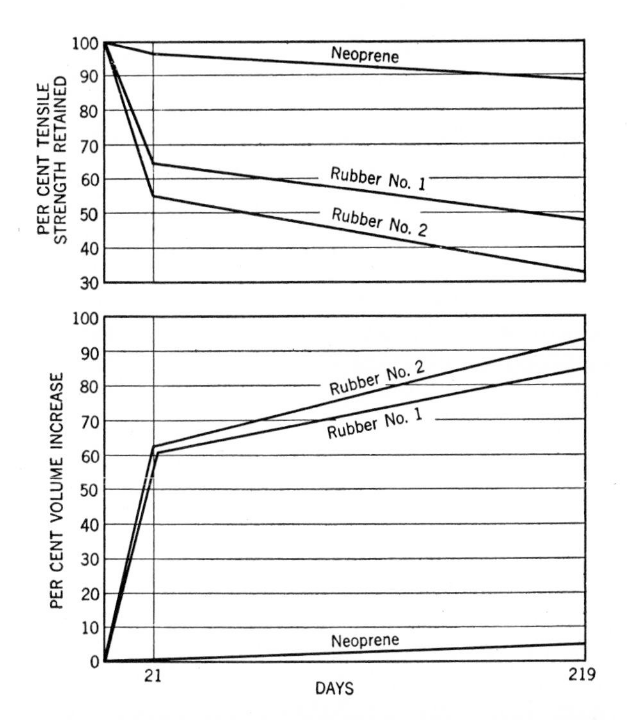


FIG. 10–1. Effect of immersion in S.A.E.-30 lubricating oil at 82° F. on tensile strength and volume of rubber and Neoprene. (du Pont.)

The curves for rubber show rapid swelling for the first 21 days, accompanied by sharp drop in tensile strength. Swelling and loss of strength continue for the remainder of the test period of 219 days.

Neoprene shows a slight swelling and a loss of strength of 11 per cent compared with 52 per cent and 68 per cent for the two rubber samples.

Cotton belts vary in length with changes in temperature, humidity, and length of service much more than do standard rubber-impregnated duck belts; therefore gravity take-ups are advisable, and there should be at least double the travel allowance provided for the latter in conveyors of equal length.

**The Carrying and Return Idlers.** The carrying idlers are almost always of the three-pulley type with the side pair inclined at 20°. The spacing of the idlers, their diameter, and the design of the anti-friction bearings are important factors in the design of a belt conveyor. If the spacing is excessive, the sag from idler to idler causes shock to the belt as it meets the rolls, shortening the life of the belt. Large-diameter rolls reduce the abruptness of the bend as the belt rides the idler. The dust-proof bearings are packed with lubricant by the manufacturer and, if the seals are efficient, require no further attention for a year or two. The most effective seal appears to be a labyrinth of closely spaced annular steel rings mounted alternately on spindle and bearing housing. The supporting frame should be rigid and strong and usually is a pressed or formed shape to which the supporting brackets are riveted. If the brackets have U-slots for the spindle, the rolls may be lifted out without disturbing the adjustment of the bearings. The gap between rolls should be a minimum to avoid creasing the belt. The pockets holding the bearing cups should permit easy removal of the bearing assembly. Of much importance is the way in which the roll heads are secured to the tube, so that heavy shock will not loosen them. The tube should be recessed for the heads, with a pressed fit, and welded after the ends of the tube are rolled over to a slight taper to avoid a cutting edge. The trend is toward pressed or preformed heads of steel instead of malleable iron because the weld is more reliable.

Carrying idlers are made in several weights to suit the duty for which they are intended; they may be described thus:

*Idlers for Light Service.* Three equal-length rolls interchangeable from center to end positions, of 4-in. diameter, are made of finished steel tubing. The end rolls are inclined at 20°, and the rolls are mounted on light steel frames. Grease-sealed labyrinths protect the ball bearings. This type of idler is used for materials of medium weight with fines and small lumps and conveyors under 30 in. in width.

*Idlers for Medium Service.* These are for the medium-capacity conveyors and have 6-in. rolls locked securely to the end discs by spinning and welding. The rolls are interchangeable and have Timkin or Shafer bearings with the inner bearing race or cone having a push fit on the roll shaft and the outer race or cup a press fit into the roll head. The labyrinth seals are removable as a unit. The frames are of steel with the malleable brackets riveted thereto.

*Idlers for heavy service,* as for rock, ore, etc. The rolls are 6 in. in diameter, or they may be 7 in. or larger, made up of heavy steel tubing with pressed steel discs securely set into the recessed tube and welded. In general the medium- and heavy-duty idlers are similar except for heavier construction and heavier supporting frame and brackets.

*Special Idler Types.* Variations from the idlers described above are

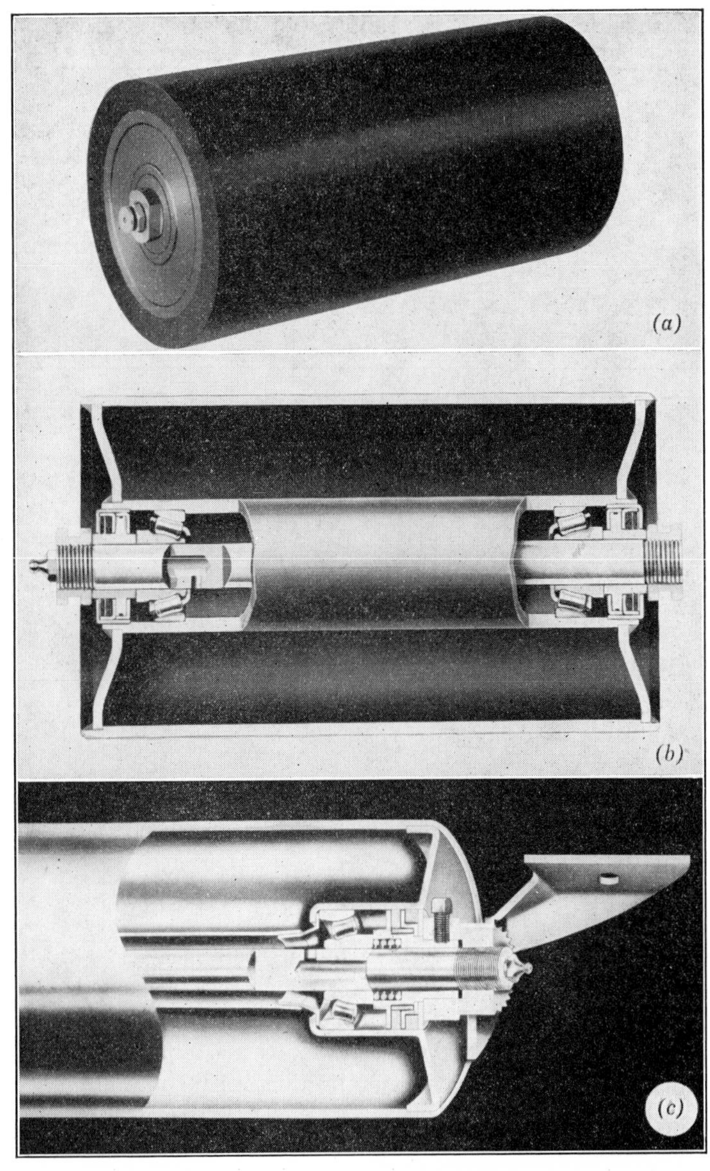


FIG. 10-2. (*A*) Rubber covered roll by Bartlett and Snow Company. (*B*) Cutaway view of Link-Belt roll. (*C*) Cutaway view of Robins Company troughing roll.

used to meet special conditions. For example, if the material is corrosive, or if the equipment is subjected to salt air or acid fumes which would corrode steel tubing, the roll may be made of cast iron.

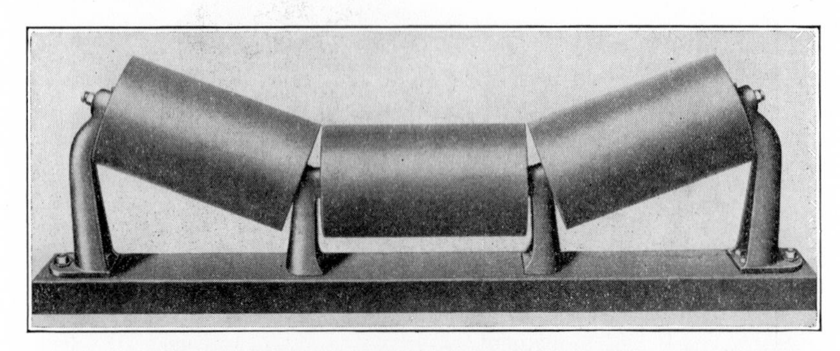

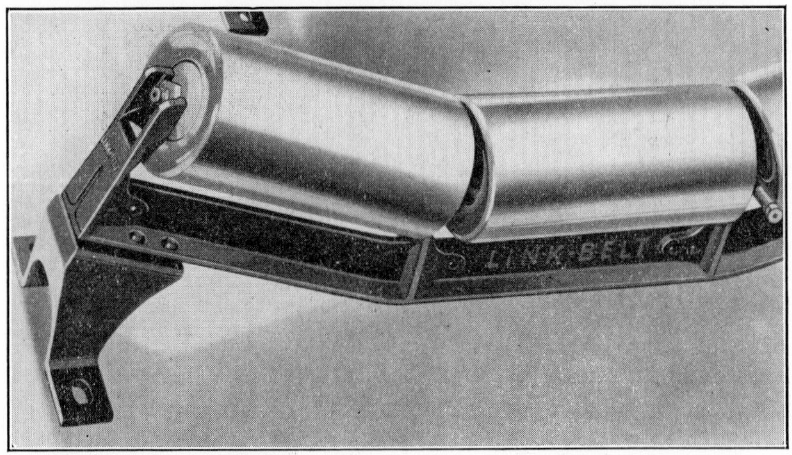


FIG. 10-3. Typical three-pulley troughing idler units. (Top, Robins; bottom, Link-Belt.)

Idlers are standardized by the manufacturers in a series of weights and diameters suited to the duty for which they are rated. In Fig. 10-2, *A* is a Bartlett and Snow rubber-covered idler roll especially adapted to abrasive dust and corrosive materials. *B* is a cutaway view of a Link-Belt roll showing the anti-friction bearing unit and the labyrinth seal. The alemite fitting is attached to the end of the spindle, with the outlet ducts just inside the bearing so that the entire tube is filled with lubricant. *C* is a Robins roll showing the method of setting the end disc into the tube and the seals protecting the Timkin roller bearings.

Figure 10-3 shows assembled idlers by Robins and Link-Belt.

Return idlers are subjected to about the same severity as the carrying idlers, since, although they carry the empty belt, their spacing is doubled. Their bearings and seals should be interchangeable with those of the carrying idlers, and the rolls should be so mounted in their hangers that they can be removed without disturbing the bearing adjustment.

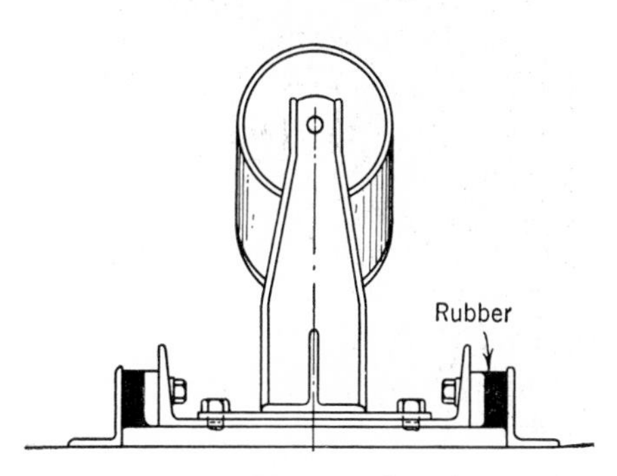


FIG. 10–4. Flexible mounting of troughing roll with rubber in shear.

*Impact Idlers.* Most of the wear on the belt occurs at the loading point. Every effort is made to reduce shock by giving the material a velocity in the direction of the belt movement or by using a screening chute which will let fine material through ahead of the lumps; but if the material is all lumps or is heavy rock or ore, the impact becomes extreme, and if the belt receives the blow as it rests upon an unyielding idler, damage and short life must result. This matter of protecting the belt is more important than would be appreciated offhand. A replacement of a belt often involves an expense of $5000 or more.

Idlers should be closely spaced at the loading point so that material may not wedge under the skirt boards, and they should be of a design which will cushion the shock; thus they may be rubber faced as in Fig. 10-2*A*, or mounted on resilient bases, or bonded to rubber blocks as in Fig. 10-4 — a rubber sandwich, so to speak — or they may be specially designed to relieve heavy shock. Robins uses impact rolls with soft-rubber treads. The Stephens Adamson Company uses impact idlers originated by Goodrich consisting of a row of pneumatic tires mounted on a spindle so that they may either be inflated through nipples to any desired pressure or sealed at atmospheric pressure. Link-Belt uses cushion tires (Fig. 10-5) replaceable by loosening the bolts which bind them in the side plates. The tires are split across the rim to permit this removal. Robins and Link-Belt also use pneumatic tire rolls.

Laboratory tests to determine the relative value of various types of impact rolls in protecting the belt cover against cuts and the carcass from damage gave the following results. The results of impact upon the cover were determined by blows with a sharp edge and upon the carcass by blows with a blunt edge upon a 7-ply belt having a $\frac{3}{16}$-in. top cover and $\frac{1}{16}$-in. bottom cover.

Fig. 10–5. Cushion tire impact rolls (Link-Belt). Worn tires are removed by loosening the bolts which secure the end discs.

| Belt Resting on | Cover Resistance | Carcass Resistance |
|---|---|---|
| 6-in. steel roll | 1. | 1. |
| 6-in. steel roll with 1-in. rubber cover | 9.1 | 1.2 |
| 6-in. steel roll with 2-in. grooved rubber cover | 30. | 4. |
| 6-in. roll with unit rubber tire discs | 28. | 4.4 |
| 14-in. pneumatic tire rolls | 41. | 10. |

The rolls were mounted on a rigid base. If the base had been flexibly mounted, as it should be when heavy loading shocks are involved, the ratios above would change.

Mr. R. S. Carter of the Goodyear Tire & Rubber Company mentions a belt feeder in the Grand Coulee conveyor system which was loaded by power shovel with bank gravel containing boulders as large as 36 in. The life of the feeder belt was two to three months. Pneumatic tire idlers were installed at the loading point, and, after some trials to establish the proper degree of inflation, the belt life was increased to 18 months during which 15 million tons were handled — a remarkable performance.

**The Take-Ups.** Screw take-ups, except for a conveyor with short centers, are not entirely suitable for belt conveyors as they are not self-adjusting for changes in temperature affecting the length of the belt and their range of travel is so small that the belt must be cut and shortened too often. A take-up which may permit slack in the belt may reduce the slack-side tension to a point where slip occurs on the drive pulley, with disastrous results; therefore a weighted or automatic take-up is advantageous. A weighted horizontal take-up has a light wire rope from each bearing of the foot shaft to a shaft parallel thereto on which a drum is mounted to take the wire rope of the take-up weight. This rig tends to hold the foot shaft square with the center line of the belt. A chain drive to a feeder should not lead from such a foot shaft if there is any way to avoid it, as the pull at one end tends to pull the shaft out of square and the chain drive is complicated by the movement of the shaft back or forward. On conveyors of great

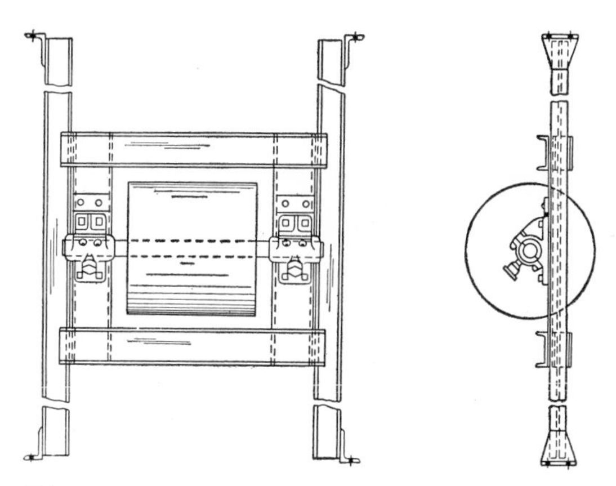

FIG. 10-6. Diagram of take-up pulley, frame, and guides for vertical take-up.

length a vertical automatic take-up is usual. See Fig. 10-6. This consists of a suspended weighted take-up pulley in guides of liberal length and preferably mounted closely back of the drive where its response is immediate when the conveyor is started.

**The Tripper.** Unless the discharge is over the head end, the load is discharged by doubling the belt backward over two snub pulleys so that the inertia of the load carries it clear of the belt to a chute. Trippers may be fixed or movable. If movable, the snub pulleys are mounted on a frame traveling on a runway and arranged for hand or power propulsion. Figure 10-7*A* shows a self-propelled tripper traversed by friction drive against either snub shaft. Figure 10-7*B* shows a motor-propelled tripper with the trolleys overhead.

When it is necessary to pile the discharge well to either side of the conveyor, a high tripper discharging to a transverse reversible belt may be used. The high tripper is so heavy that it should be motor propelled.

When a conveyor is exceptionally long, a troublesome factor is introduced if a self-propelled standard tripper is traversed by traction applied at the front axle. The resultant of the thrust of the belt against the snub pulleys tends to pivot the frame about the rear axle, and the front wheels skid when the tripper should move backward. The correction is a heavy counterweight on the front end, or interconnected axles. Again there may be a tendency to skid the tripper

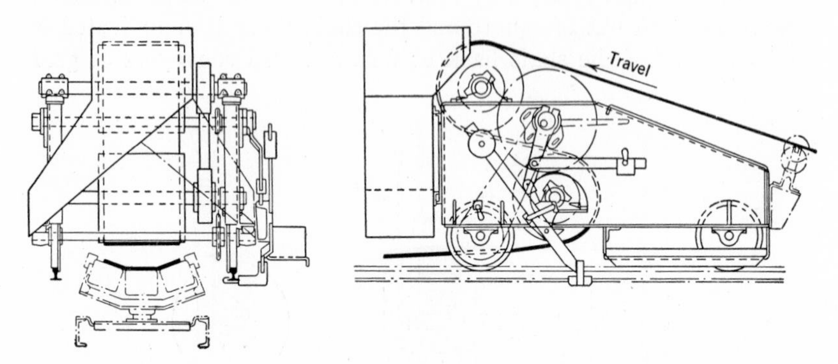


Fig. 10–7A. Automatic self-propelled and self-reversing tripper. Traversed by friction drive against either pulley.

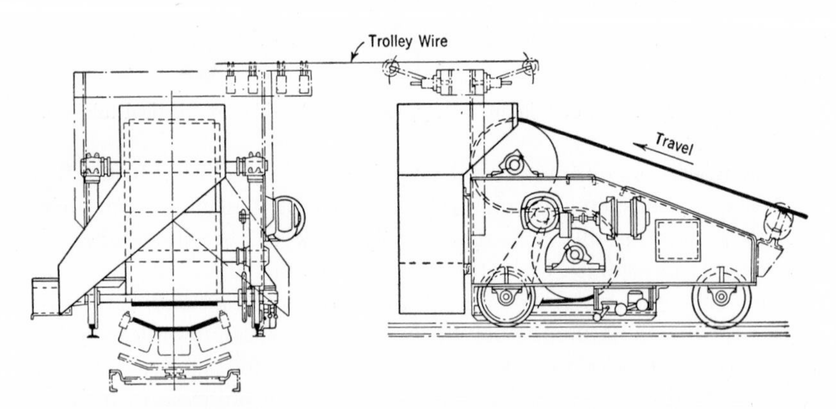


Fig. 10–7B. Automatic tripper, motor-propelled. Small motor is mounted on side of frame. Reversal of travel is by the switches seen alongside the carrying rail.

forward with the belt, especially if the snub pulleys do not have antifriction bearings. Should the bearings bind, the tripper may start forward at belt speed causing a bad wreck. A lever projecting into the path of the frame to actuate an emergency motor stop is some protection.

Effectual cleaning of the face of the lower tripper pulley and the belt between pulleys is important and sometimes difficult. The grease ducts should always be brought out to one side so that the attendant need not reach across the belt when servicing.

Sometimes scrapers (Fig. 10-8) are specified instead of a tripper. They can function on a conveyor with troughed idlers if the belt is

FIG. 10-8. Twenty-inch flat distributing belt for foundry sand with scraper discharge plows. (Link-Belt.)

lifted and passed across a short straight-roll movable platform with a scraper.

Unless other factors enter, a tripper is better than a scraper, except possibly with light non-abrasive materials when the scraper does have some compensation as eliminating two bends in the belt. A steel belt does not take kindly to snubbing over a pair of pulleys, and the scraper is usual. Light materials transported on a flat belt without a tripper are sometimes discharged with difficulty. A diagonal plow functions nicely with wood chips, grass seed, sawdust, peanuts, soybeans, and the like, but materials such as tobacco leaves or stringy paper trimmings as cut from the edges of stacks of magazines, will jam and build up. Paper trimmings may be especially difficult since they take a static charge, sometimes negative, sometimes positive, and tend to adhere to the belt surface.

An adjustable diagonal pipe, crossing just above the belt, with ¼-in. vents spaced 2-in. centers, through which compressed air at 4- to 8-oz. pressure is blown, rolls off leaves, trimmings, etc., gently if the belt speed is not more than 120 ft. per min.

**Shuttle Belts.** Sometimes it is advantageous to feed from one belt to another which may be set at any point suited to the desired point of discharge; that is, the movable belt is mounted on a carriage either manually or power propelled. This is called a "shuttle belt." Often it provides a simple method of distribution along a bunker by the use of a reversing motor controlled by adjustable stops which fix the limits of travel in either direction. A shuttle with about 75-ft. centers will suffice for distribution over a length of about 160 ft. from a loading conveyor midway in its length. A short shuttle is subjected to rough treatment at the loading point owing to the frequency of impact per unit of belt length.

**The Drive.** In the lighter tension range the power may be transmitted to the belt through a flat-face cast-iron or steel pulley. A pulley with crown face should not be used as it would cause uneven stress across the belt. For greater tensions, the pulley is lagged with rubber securely bolted or riveted to the rim, and a snub pulley is provided to increase the arc of contact with the belt. For the heaviest tensions we may have tandem-drive pulleys, geared together and sharing the load, or the dual motor drive in which each pulley is driven by a motor. If the pull per square inch of belt surface is excessive it may be impossible for the rubber to transmit the load to the carcass and the rubber will be stripped off.

The dual motor drive was invented by J. C. Reid and developed by Link-Belt. It is better than two geared pulleys because the belt takes some elongation at each drive point, and, since maximum pull should be at the first pulley, its rim must move slightly faster than the rim of the second pulley. The second pulley is subjected to more or less plastering of dirt from the carrying side of the belt with which it is in contact, and this will upset the speed differential provided by a slightly smaller diameter, causing either slip or an excessive load on the second pulley. Sometimes the wrecking of the second pulley is a mysterious occurrence, but generally it is caused by plastering and the resultant hogging of the load. The dual motor drive automatically adjusts the load on each pulley. The motor driving the first pulley should be a synchronous motor and the other a slip-ring motor. The synchronous motor is started on reduced voltage with time-limit acceleration through an automatic compensator. The timed acceleration assures maximum torque when starting if the synchronous motor is unable to swing its share of the load. The synchronous motor determines the acceleration and then maintains constant speed under all conditions of loading; the slip-ring motor automatically maintains a nearly constant horsepower output and adjusts itself to the speed variation and stretch of the belt, taking only its share of the load under any operating condition unless some circumstance should arise in which it cannot function, such as the presence of ice or water on the belt.

It is of interest to consider the relative cost of a single-pulley single-motor drive and a dual-motor drive. We will assume a 42-in. inclined conveyor, 366-ft. centers, with a lift of 118 ft. for a capacity of 1000 tons per hour. The figures used in the following comparison are those that were current in 1941. Minor items such as the take-ups back of the drive, collars, couplings, and base plates are omitted. If included, they favor the single-motor drive except that the take-up weight is heavier. (See Fig. 10-18 for layout.)

Comparative Cost, Single-Motor and Dual-Motor Drives

| *Single-motor drive* | | *Dual-motor drive* | |
|---|---|---|---|
| Bare head pulley, 54 by 44 in. (2) anti-friction bearings. 6-in. head shaft | $ 630 | Bare head pulley, 54 by 44 in. (2) anti-friction bearings. 6-in. head shaft | $ 630 |
| Snub pulley, 36 by 44 in. 4-in. shaft (2) anti-friction bearings | 255 | Snub pulley, 36 by 44-in. Shaft, 4 in. (2) anti-friction bearings | 255 |
| Duplicate of last item | 255 | Duplicate of last item | 255 |
| Lagged drive pulley, otherwise same as item 1 | 800 | Lagged drive pulley, otherwise same as item 1 | 800 |
| 200-hp. motor, slip ring. Drum controller | 2420 | 125-hp. synchronous motor Starter and exciter, 900 revs. | 2170 |
| Herringbone reducer 200 hp. 900 : 160 r.p.m. R.C. drive to head shaft | 1800 | Herringbone reducer, 125 hp. 9 : 1 and R.C. drive | 1060 |
| Total | $6160 | 2nd drive pulley, lagged, same as above | 800 |
| | | 50-hp. slip-ring motor 900 revs. with drum control | 1000 |
| | | 50-hp. herringbone reducer, 900 : 160, and R.C. drive | 560 |
| | | 20 ft. of additional belt | 190 |
| | | Total | $7720 |

*Vertical Curves* (Fig. 10-9). When a conveyor curves upward from a horizontal to an inclined path, the radius of curvature must be large enough so that the belt will not lift off the carrying idlers at the curve. Robins advises the dimensions shown in Table 1, where $L$ = distance in feet between centers, $l$ = fully loaded section of belt, with the balance of the belt empty, which is the worst condition.

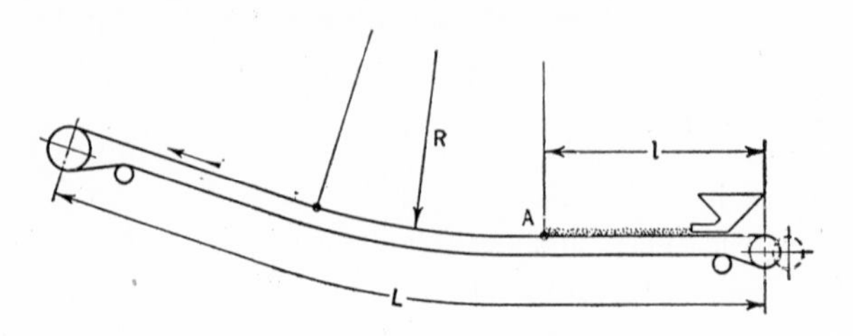


FIG. 10–9. Vertical curves.

TABLE 1

RADII OF VERTICAL CURVES IN BELT CONVEYORS

Assuming that each width of belt is carrying its normal load.

| Belt Width | Length $L$, feet | Length $l$, feet | Radius $R$, feet — Weight per Cubic Foot of Material Handled: 30 lb. to 75 lb. | 75 lb. to 150 lb. |
|---|---|---|---|---|
| Up to 24 in. | Under 200 | Under 100 | 150 | 150 |
| | 200 to 400 | Under 300 | 150 | 200 |
| | 400 to 600 | Under 500 | 200 | 250 |
| 30 in. to 48 in. | Under 200 | Under 100 | 150 | 150 |
| | 200 to 400 | Under 300 | 150 | 200 |
| | 400 to 600 | Under 500 | 250 | 300 |
| | Over 600 | Under 600 | 350 | 350 |
| 54 in. and 60 in. | Under 200 | Under 100 | 150 | 150 |
| | 200 to 400 | Under 300 | 200 | 250 |
| | 400 to 600 | Under 500 | 300 | 350 |
| | Over 600 | Under 600 | 350 | 350 |

**Belt Cleaners.** Cleaning the surface of the belt is essential, especially if the material is damp or sticky, and often is difficult. It is

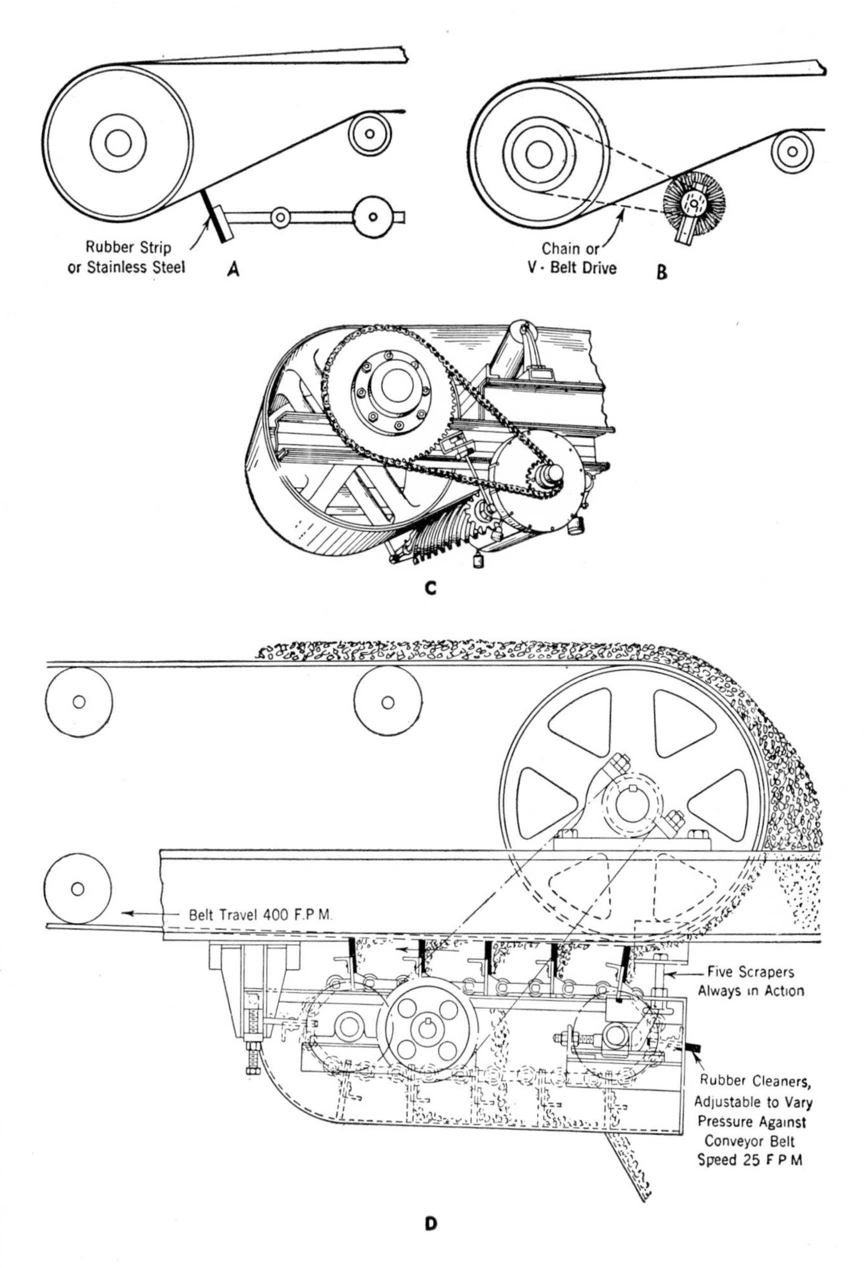


FIG. 10–10. Belt cleaners. (*A*) Counterbalanced scraper. (*B*) Rotary brush. (*C*) Robins rubber helix. (*D*) Hudson cleaner.

of particular importance with dual drives since the dirty side of the belt is in contact with the secondary drive pulley, but in any event such material is carried along over the return idlers on which it builds up and causes the belt to run off center. Briefly, the usual types of cleaners are:

*Scraper.* Figure 10-10*A*. This common form of cleaner is the least effective of the four shown in Fig. 10. It is fairly satisfactory with material readily scraped off but useless with sticky materials such as damp buckwheat anthracite or semi-frozen bituminous slack. A scraper formed of multiple diagonal strips of 18-ga. stainless steel about 1½ by 6 in. and overlapping 1 in. (Stephens Adamson Mfg. Co.) does a very good job on such materials. If the belt ends are connected by metal fasteners these should be set into a recess cut through the cover which then should be patched flush by the application of a repair cement (such as the United States Rubber Company's No. 1951 with accelerator No. 100–E). The intent is, of course, to prevent contact between the fasteners and the cleaner strips.

*The Rotary Brush.* Figure 10-10*B*. This is the usual device with all the manufacturers. It is a high-speed brush with rattan or Bassine bristles projecting radially from a wood cylinder and driven from an adjacent shaft or by a small motor. It has the objection that with sticky material the brush gums up into a solid cylinder, and if sharp fragments become embedded therein the belt may be cut. A better arrangement is to mount strips of metal-backed fiber on discs, with a spiral assembly resembling the rotor of a lawn mower.

The bristles of a rotary brush have a rather short life as they wear to a taper and break off. It is possible that nylon fibers may eventually be used instead of Bassine since nylon is waterproof and does not wear to a taper. Nylon now costs many times as much as other bristles.

One reason for the short life of the rotary brush is the common practice of putting too much pressure against the belt. The drag, or deflection of the bristles in contact with the belt, should not be more than $\frac{3}{16}$ in.

Wet clay, mud, etc., cannot be cleaned from a belt by a rotary brush. Such materials present a difficult problem as they carry back along the return run of the conveyor and build up on the return idlers. Sometimes high-velocity water jets are effective when other methods fail.

Disc return idlers may be used when the belt cannot be completely cleaned. Sometimes they are effective and sometimes not.

Another device is to space "beater pulleys" at intervals along the return run. These resemble a squirrel cage and function well with damp sand.

*Robins Cleaner.* Figure 10-10*C*. This is a rubber helix or elongated spiral pinion, direct-connected to a 600- to 900-r.p.m. motor. It is effective with many rather difficult materials but takes considerable power (7½ hp. for a 48-in. conveyor). The drive may be as shown.

*Hudson Cleaner.* Figure 10-10*D*. Semi-frozen, wet coal-refuse and fine coal are very difficult to remove from an exposed belt, and plaster return idlers as though cemented on. On one such installation, when various cleaners had failed utterly and the situation was serious because five belts were involved and the specifications required complete cleaning, the author devised this cleaner. It is in effect a short-centers, double-strand scraper conveyor with rubber-faced scrapers which operate at 20 to 25 ft. per min. in the direction of belt travel, or the reverse, through a drive from the head shaft. These were still functioning effectively after the follow-up period of three years. Any number of scrapers may be provided in the unit if it is necessary to multiply the effect. This cleaner unfortunately is not adaptable to a tripper. The device must be designed to suit individual conditions. If too few scrapers function simultaneously some material will carry on. Speed and power are low. The scrapings are discharged to the main chute direct or carried thereto by the return run, depending on the direction in which the cleaner is run.

Complete cleaning of the belt is essential if a weightometer is in the line, since any residue is recorded by the weightometer as incoming coal.

## SUPPLEMENTARY FEATURES

Low-head conveyors are required under certain circumstances, as in mines with thin seams. The minimum head might be secured by using carrying and return idlers of extremely small diameter, say 2½ in., which is about the limit to accommodate the anti-friction bearings. Then it is necessary to space the idlers close together to reduce shock. Another device is the Philips ribbed-belt grooved-idler combination (Fig. 10-11), in which the belt is formed with a central ridge along the under side which registers with a groove in the center carrying idler. Since the rib is on top along the return run, it registers with the same idler groove. The terminal pulleys are grooved likewise. The rib is effective in holding the belt central even against the side thrust of heavy concentrated loads placed along one side, and if the belt is forcibly thrust out of line it drifts back before the displaced section reaches the head.

**Magnetic Head Pulleys.** The requirement often made in practice, that pieces of iron shall be removed from material conveyed by the belt, is met by the magnetic head pulley, though it is desirable to have the load spread thinly to reduce the possibility that fragments may be buried in the load beyond the effective pull of the magnet. Since a wider belt may add much to the cost of the conveyor, the alternative of discharging to a short wide belt with magnetic head pulley, in tandem with the long conveyor, should be considered.

Magnetized fragments carry on 3 or 4 ft. along the return run before dropping off, so the belt cleaner must be located beyond the drop-off point. This is awkward if discharge of the load is to a tandem conveyor at an angle.

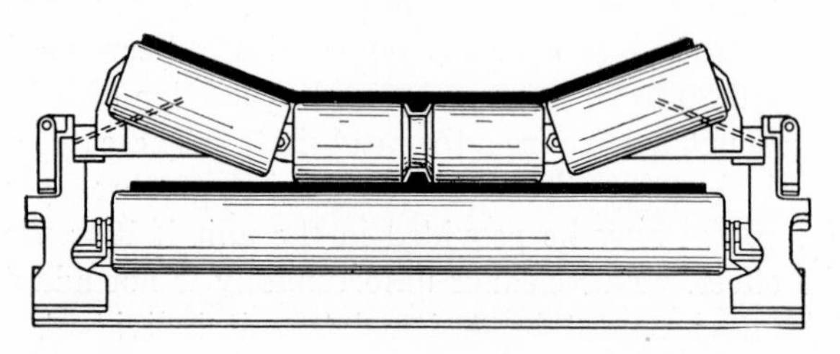

FIG. 10–11. The Philips low-head conveyor. The rib on the under side of the belt registers with the groove in the middle carrying idler in both runs.

**Wind Breaks.** A belt may be lifted off the idlers by high transverse winds. To prevent this a hood is placed over the conveyor, or skirt boards may be placed beyond each side for the entire length. If the prevailing winds are from one direction a wind break along one side may suffice. (See Fig. 14-6.)

**Dust Closures.** The belt conveyor scatters dust at the point of discharge from a tripper. Two methods of prevention have been devised in connection with coal bunkers. The top of the bunker, except for a slot in line with the tripper chute, is covered by a concrete slab forming the floor of the monitor. The Robins Company closes this slot as shown in Fig. 10-12 by a light rubber belt which is led up over the tripper chute and back, thus closing the slot except at the point of discharge. Link-Belt closes the slot by two overlapping light belts which are parted by a plow on each side of the tripper chute. Sometimes the entire gallery above the bunker is closed off to the ceiling of the monitor and a ventilating system exhausts the dusty air.

**Development of the Design.** In the development of a simple conveyor layout and specification, the engineer follows the routine provided by each manufacturer in his data sheets. In the more complex and important projects the engineer will of course call in a specialist for consultation, as an error in judgment may cost thousands of dollars.

To illustrate the method of procedure we will reproduce and use

FIG. 10–12. Dust prevention. Belt seal on tripper slot (Robins). Slot in floor over coal bunker is covered by a thin belt which is passed up and over the tripper chute.

the manufacturer's data and will assume a problem not involving difficult features. First we must determine the width, strength, and type of belt to use, giving consideration to whether the installation is to be permanent or temporary. The belt width is determined by the capacity, the weight of the material, and the size of lumps. The belt thickness, or number of plies, depends on the pull to which the belt will be subjected, and the cover thickness depends on the severity of service.

Assume for our problem a conveyor to handle 2000 tons per 10 hr. of broken coal with mixed fines and lumps up to 6-in. diameter, over a path having a horizontal dimension of 300 ft. and a lift of 90 ft. The coal is delivered to the conveyor by a feeder, and the discharge is over the head. The coal weighs 50 lb. per cu. ft.

The maximum permissible angle, or slope, varies with different materials, and it is well to be conservative as the angle cannot be changed after the conveyor is erected. Table 2 shows the maximum angles generally considered safe for various materials by several manufacturers.

TABLE 2

MAXIMUM SLOPES FOR VARIOUS MATERIALS TRANSPORTED BY BELT CONVEYORS

| Material | Maximum Angle, degrees | Material | Maximum Angle, degrees |
|---|---|---|---|
| Coal, bituminous slack | 20 | Gravel, washed | 12 |
| Coal, mine run | 18 | Grain | 15 |
| Coke, screened | 17 | Ore, crushed | 20 |
| Earth, loose | 20 | Sand, damp | 20 |
| Briquettes | 10 | Sand, dry | 15 |
| Gravel, bank | 18 | Wood chips | 28 |

Our angle of $16\frac{3}{4}°$ is nicely within the 18° maximum for coal. If the angle is too steep the lumps may roll down or bounce off the belt and the impact against the idlers may cause slippage.

As our belt is loaded from a feeder we can assume that the specified capacity of 2000 tons in 10 hr. is the same as 200 tons per hour, and by Table 3 we see that 200 tons of material weighing 50 lb. per cu. ft. can be handled per hour with a 30-in. belt operating at approximately 250 ft. per min., though for a temporary job we might use a 24-in. belt at about 400 ft. per min.

The width of the belt depends also on the maximum size of lumps in the material and whether it has been screened or is a mixture of lumps and fines. The spacing of the idlers depends on the weight of the material, since, if the idlers are so widely spaced that the sag between idlers becomes excessive, power is wasted, the belt wear increases, and if the conveyor is inclined there is slippage of material due to the impact at each carrying idler. Table 4 gives recommended minimum belt widths for lumps and recommendations for idler spacing.

By unsized material is meant that 90 per cent is less than the maximum size and 75 per cent not over $\frac{1}{2}$ in.

From Table 4 we find that the proper idler spacing is 4 ft. 6 in. for the carrying idlers and 10 ft. for the returns. One or two self-aligning idlers would be located along the runs.

## TABLE 3

### Recommendations of the United States Rubber Company

### Carrying Capacities of Troughed Belts

(These are average duties in daily runs, not the possible maximum loads. With a feeder giving continuous full loading the capacities may be exceeded. For grains the capacities will be approximately 85 per cent of the listed capacities.)

| Width of Belt, inches | Tons (2000 lb.) of Material per Hour at 100 Ft. per Min. Belt Speed | | | | | | |
|---|---|---|---|---|---|---|---|
| | Weight of Material, pounds per cubic foot | | | | | | |
| | 30 | 40 | 50 | 75 | 100 | 125 | 150 |
| 12 | 7 | 10 | 12 | 18 | 24 | 30 | 36 |
| 14 | 10 | 14 | 17 | 25 | 34 | 42 | 51 |
| 16 | 13 | 18 | 22 | 33 | 44 | 55 | 66 |
| 18 | 17 | 22 | 28 | 42 | 56 | 70 | 84 |
| 20 | 20 | 27 | 34 | 51 | 68 | 85 | 102 |
| 24 | 30 | 40 | 50 | 75 | 100 | 125 | 150 |
| 30 | 47 | 63 | 79 | 118 | 158 | 198 | 237 |
| 36 | 69 | 91 | 114 | 171 | 228 | 285 | 342 |
| 42 | 97 | 130 | 162 | 243 | 324 | 405 | 486 |
| 48 | 130 | 172 | 215 | 322 | 430 | 538 | 645 |
| 54 | 162 | 215 | 270 | 405 | 540 | 675 | 810 |
| 60 | 207 | 275 | 345 | 517 | 690 | 862 | 1035 |

Tonnage capacity proportional to speed; e.g., at 200 ft. per min., tons per hour = twice table values.

### Maximum Belt Speeds

| Width of Belt, inches | Light or Free-Flowing Materials such as Grain, Dry Sand | Moderately Free-Flowing or Sized Materials such as Sand and Gravel, Fine Stone and Coal | Lump and Moderately Heavy or Abrasive Materials such as Run-of-Mine Soft Coal, Coarse Stone, Crushed Ore | Heavy, Sharp, or very Abrasive Materials such as Run-of-Mine Hard Coal, Hard Ore, Coke |
|---|---|---|---|---|
| 12, 14 | 400 | 250 | ... | ... |
| 16, 18 | 500 | 300 | 250 | ... |
| 20, 24 | 600 | 400 | 350 | 250 |
| 30, 36 | 750 | 500 | 400 | 300 |
| 42, 60 | 850 | 550 | 450 | 350 |

Note: The above recommendations are subject to practical allowances for methods of loading, angle of incline, auxiliary equipment, etc. In special cases where the material is loaded in the direction of belt travel, inclines are small, and discharge is over end, these figures may be substantially exceeded. On the other hand, where inclines are great or where material is subject to breakage (as coke or coal) it may be desirable to establish lower speeds. In general, wide belts can be operated at higher speeds because the material rides better, does not shift as much, and, as a result, causes less wear.

TABLE 4

MINIMUM BELT WIDTHS FOR LUMPS AND IDLER SPACING[1]

| Belt Width Inches | 35-Lb. Material | | | 50-Lb. Material | | | 75-Lb. Material | | | 100-Lb. Material | | | 150-Lb. Material | | | |
|---|---|---|---|---|---|---|---|---|---|---|---|---|---|---|---|---|
| | Idler Spacing | Sized, inches | Unsized inches | Idler Spacing | Sized, inches | Unsized inches | Idler Spacing | Sized, inches | Unsized inches | Idler Spacing | Sized inches | Unsized inches | Idler Spacing | Sized, inches | Unsized inches | Return Idlers feet |
| 14 | 5′ 6″ | 2 | 3 | 5′ 6″ | 2 | 3 | 5′ 0″ | 2 | 3 | 5′ 0″ | 2 | 3 | 4′ 6″ | 2 | 3 | 10 |
| 16 | 5′ 6″ | 2½ | 4 | 5′ 6″ | 2½ | 4 | 5′ 0″ | 2½ | 4 | 5′ 2½″ | 2½ | 4 | 4′ 6″ | 2½ | 4 | 10 |
| 18 | 5′ 6″ | 3 | 5 | 5′ 6″ | 3 | 5 | 5′ 0″ | 3 | 5 | 5′ 0″ | 3 | 5 | 4′ 6″ | 3 | 5 | 10 |
| 24 | 5′ 6″ | 4½ | 8 | 5′ 0″ | 4½ | 8 | 4′ 6″ | 4½ | 8 | 4′ 6″ | 4½ | 8 | 4′ 0″ | 4½ | 8 | 10 |
| 30 | 5′ 0″ | 7 | 12 | 4′ 6″ | 7 | 12 | 4′ 0″ | 7 | 12 | 4′ 0″ | 7 | 12 | 3′ 6″ | 7 | 12 | 10 |
| 36 | 5′ 0″ | 8 | 14 | 5′ 6″ | 8 | 14 | 4′ 0″ | 8 | 14 | 4′ 0″ | 8 | 14 | 3′ 6″ | 8 | 14 | 10 |
| 42 | 4′ 6″ | 10 | 20 | 4′ 6″ | 10 | 20 | 4′ 0″ | 10 | 17 | 4′ 0″ | 10 | 16 | 3′ 6″ | 10 | 15 | 9 |
| 48 | 4′ 6″ | 12 | 24 | 4′ 0″ | 10 | 20 | 3′ 6″ | 10 | 17 | 3′ 6″ | 10 | 16 | 3′ 6″ | 10 | 16 | 9 |
| 60 | 4′ 0″ | 12 | 28 | 4′ 0″ | 12 | 28 | 4′ 0″ | 12 | 28 | 4′ 0″ | 12 | 28 | 4′ 0″ | 12 | 28 | 9 |

[1] Link-Belt Company.

The power required is ascertained from the tables and charts in the catalogues of each manufacturer, for example, Robins Conveyors, Inc., catalogue 82-B; Jeffrey Manufacturing Company, catalogue 87; or Link-Belt Company, catalogue 900. The data from the last named are

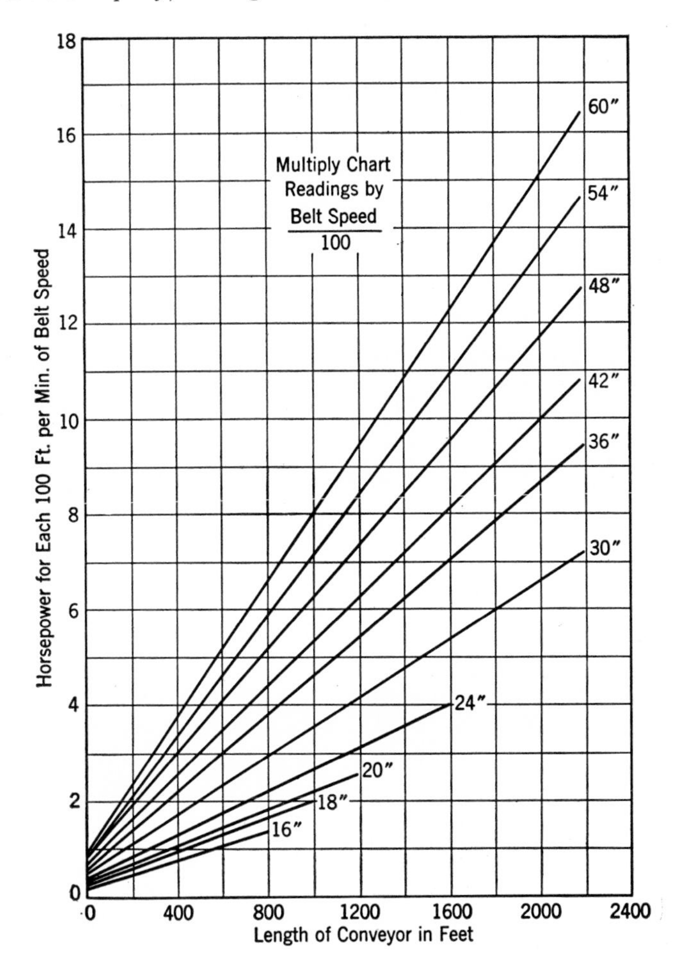


FIG. 10-13. Horsepower to drive empty conveyor.

shown in the charts in Figs. 10-13 and 10-14. The requirement is the total of the power required to move the empty belt, the power required to move the load horizontally, and that required to lift the load, or:

| | |
|---|---|
| For empty belt, 30 in. by 312-ft. centers | 3.50 hp. |
| For moving the load horizontally | 2.80 hp. |
| For lifting the load | 18.00 hp. |
| Total | 24.30 hp. |

It is seen that the power to lift the load exceeds that to move the belt and the load horizontally; therefore we will need an automatic backstop to prevent reversal of the loaded belt should the current fail. If the inclination were less and the third item exceeded only slightly the sum of the other two, the drag of the motor and reduction gearing would suffice.

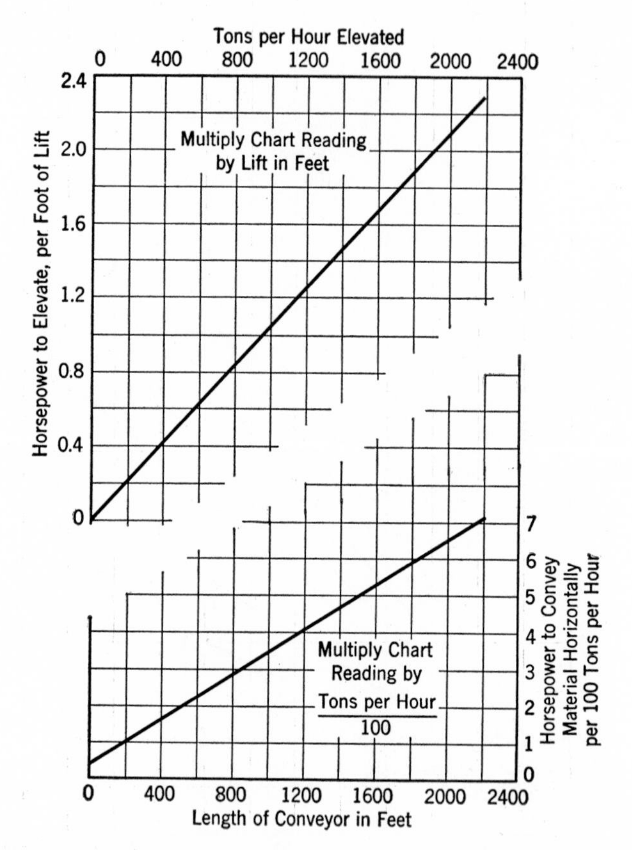


FIG. 10–14. Upper chart, Power to elevate material; lower chart, Power to convey material horizontally.

**The Belt.** By reference to the tables in Link-Belt catalogue 900, we select a 5-ply 36-oz. belt and find that, at the speed of 250 ft. with a 30-in. lagged and snubbed drive, we can transmit 29 hp. It will be noted that the 5-ply belt is listed for " fine coal," etc. If the coal contains a large percentage of lumps we should choose a 6-ply belt.

Two circumstances affecting the drive should be noted: the tabulated values for the power which may be transmitted to the belt are for clean pulley and belt; and, if the drive is exposed or may at times be wet, a substantial allowance should be made.

The load on an inclined belt slips backward slightly owing to the bump at each idler, and an increase of 10 per cent in speed is usual to compensate for this slip if the inclination is near the limit.

The manufacturers describe their grades of belt under trade names or brands, some of which are listed below. The corresponding grades, *a, b, c, d,* agree in general.

TABLE 5

CORRESPONDING GRADES OF CONVEYOR BELTS BY VARIOUS MANUFACTURERS

| | U.S. Rubber | Goodrich | Goodyear | Robins | Link-Belt |
|---|---|---|---|---|---|
| *a* | Matchless | Super Longlife | Stacker | Maltese Cross | Faultless |
| *b* | Giant | Longlife | B | Circle | Lion |
| *c* | Amazon | 2002 | C | Ajax | National |
| *d* | Security | Maxicon | W | Mohawk | Service |

The *a* belts are for the toughest service, ores, rock, jagged lumps, etc. The *b* belts are for tough service a little less severe. The *c* belts are for sand, gravel, coal, with a minimum of heavy jagged lumps. The *d* belts are for light service, wood chips, other non-injurious materials, packages, bags, etc.

*The cover thickness* depends on the severity of service. For less-abrasive materials the cover may be 1/16 in. If there are lumps having some impact effect, the cover should be 1/8 to 1/4 in. For sand, coke, and gravel, the cover should be 3/16 to 1/4 in., sometimes thicker. For crushed stone, ores, and similar material, the cover should be 3/8 in. or thicker.

For the present problem, we select a medium-grade belt either five- or six-ply, 36-oz. carcass, and 3/16-in. cover.

Again from the tables referred to we will find that, for a 30-in. belt with lagged and snubbed head pulley, the minimum slack-side tension ($T_2$) in the problem is 1388 lb. Assuming a vertical automatic take-up, its weight, including the pulley, the frame, and the counterweight, should be twice this figure or 2776 lb.

The table gives the diameter of the head pulley as 30 in., tail pulley as 24 in., snub pulley as 18 in.

**The Drive.** A high-speed motor, which costs less and occupies less space, is preferable to a slow-speed motor, and so there must be speed reduction gearing between motor and head shaft. Typical drive arrangements are shown in Fig. 10-15 with comment.

It is pointed out by the General Electric Company that considerably

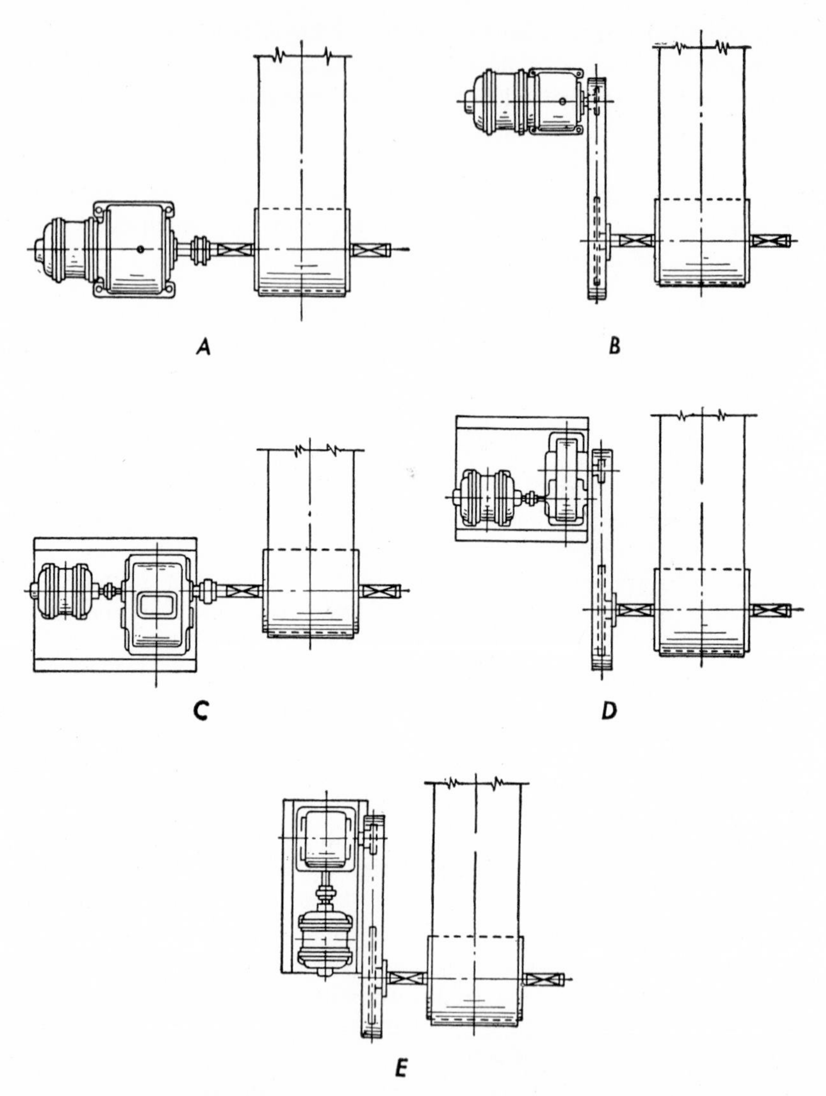


Fig. 10–15. Belt conveyor drive assemblies.

(*A*) Motorized reducer coupled direct to head shaft. Efficiency 95 per cent. Compact but difficult if speed change is desired. (*B*) Motorized reducer with R.C. drive to head shaft. Efficiency practically 95 per cent. Speed change easily made. (*C*) Motor coupled to herringbone reducer which is coupled to head shaft. Efficiency 95 per cent. Same objection as with *A*. (*D*) Motor coupled to herringbone reducer with R.C. drive to head shaft. Efficiency practically 95 per cent. Speed change easily made. (*E*) Motor coupled to worm gear reducer with R.C. drive to head shaft. More convenient as regards footwalk around machinery but has lower efficiency than the others.

higher torque is required to start a belt conveyor than to run it at speed, especially if the conveyor has been standing for some time or is exposed to cold weather, as the grease in the idler bearings becomes congealed. While operating, the conveyor functions at constant speed with infrequent variation in loading from that which corresponds to the speed-torque curve *A*, Fig. 10-16. It is desirable to have a motor with the highest efficiency and power factor such as the General Electric " general-purpose squirrel cage," the characteristics of which are shown in curve *B*. On the other hand it is seen that the starting torque is low just where it should be high, that is, when starting the conveyor.

If we use a larger motor of this type, the motor operates under partial load most of the time with poor efficiency and low power factor, and we subject the drive gearing to possible strain because of rapid acceleration. This is due largely to the low resistance in the rotor winding, usually of solid cast aluminum. If we use an insulated winding in the rotor slots, brought out through collector rings to an adjustable resistance, we can step up the torque gradually. This is the " wound rotor " or slip-ring motor which permits a variation in starting torque from 50 per cent up to maximum by cutting out the resistance in graduated steps. The long belt with embedded wires in the carcass mentioned on page 189 is so driven by a 250-hp. motor with wound rotor. A motor-driven secondary drum switch and resistor connected to the collector rings of the rotor give a smooth acceleration and will not strain the belt when starting. This type of motor and control is costly.

If the squirrel-cage motor has a high-resistance rotor there is considerable slip at full load with poor full-load efficiency. A double squirrel-cage winding in the rotor provides the desired characteristics to better advantage as it has good starting torque and good running characteristics. In this motor the rotor has two sets of bars. The outer set has high resistance, giving high starting torque with low starting current. The inner set of bars is of low resistance. When at rest the rotor is at line frequency and the iron between the windings provides high reactance, forcing the current through the outer high-resistance windings; but at high speed the frequency in the rotor (and thus the reactance) is much lower, and so the low-resistance inner windings carry most of the load current. Curve *D*, Fig. 10-16, shows the result attained. It is a composite of curves *B* and *C*. At low speed *C* predominates, and at high speed *B* predominates. This motor has a simple full-voltage starter and is used frequently on major installations — the " high-torque, low starting current, double squirrel-cage motor." Both open and splash-proof motors are usual as the motor generally has protection against exposure, and if necessary strip heaters alongside or under the motor may be provided to protect it when idle for long periods.

This closes the discussion of the simple problem, and we proceed to the more complex analysis of the belt conveyor theory. The costly item in a belt conveyor is the belt. Although in a belt drive it makes little difference whether the belt is a little wider or thicker than is

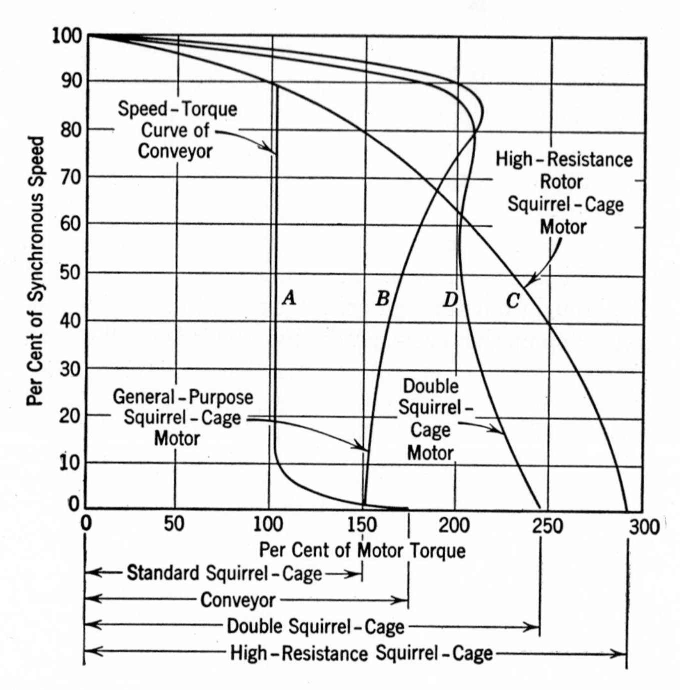


FIG. 10–16. Speed-torque curves of conveyor and motors. (General Electric.)

theoretically necessary, in a belt conveyor of large capacity and length many thousands of dollars depend on the correct selection, the proper method of driving, and other engineering details.

**The Belt as Related to the Method of Driving.** Aside from the rubber cover, the cost of a belt has depended on the number of plies in the carcass and on the pull to which the belt is to be subjected. If the distance we are transporting the material is large, reducing the pull may enable us to use a single conveyor instead of two in tandem. In general, the limits of permissible belt stresses advised by the manufacturers, prior to changes caused by the war, were as listed in Table 6.

Heavier belts have been provided. Figure 10-17 shows a conveyor of 735-ft. centers and a lift of 206 ft., with a 54-in. United States Rubber Co. belt of 48-oz. duck to handle 1000 tons per hour of mine-run coal.

FIG. 10–17. A 54 in. by 735 ft. belt conveyor in action, handling 1000 tons per hour of mine-run coal. The view is at the head end.

TABLE 6

MAXIMUM BELT STRESSES IN POUNDS PER INCH WIDTH PER PLY

| Weight of Duck, oz. | Link-Belt | Goodyear | U. S. Rubber |
|---|---|---|---|
| 28 | 25 | 24 | 24 |
| 32 | 30 | 27 | 27 |
| 36 | 35 | 30 | 30 |
| 42 | 45 | 45 | 40 |

Postwar construction has radically changed the ratings in Table 6 as discussed in pages 236 and 237.

The *effective tension* ($E$) which must be applied to a belt depends on the power required to drive the conveyor and the speed of the belt:

$$E = \frac{HP \times 33{,}000}{\text{Belt speed}}$$

It is the difference between the tight-side tension ($T_1$) and the slack-side tension ($T_2$). Without slack-side tension there could be no effective tension, since we are working with a friction drive, thus:

$$E = T_1 - T_2$$

Let $f$ represent the coefficient of friction between belt and head pulley and $a$ the arc of contact in degrees; then the maximum tension ($T_{max}$) is represented by the formula

$$T_{max} = T_2 \times 10^{0.00758 \cdot f \cdot a}$$

Since the relationship between maximum tension and slack-side tension depends on the coefficient of friction and the arc of contact, the difference between the two determines the effective tension. The coefficient of friction and arc of contact also determine the effectiveness of the head pulley as a driver. The importance of this rests in the fact that it relates directly to the cost of the belt, which depends on the number of plies required.

We can increase the coefficient of friction from 0.25 for rubber on steel to 0.35 for rubber on rubber by lagging the head pulley.* We can increase the arc of contact by snubbing the belt, and we can increase it further by using two interlocked drive pulleys or by dual pulleys driven by separate motors.

For a fixed maximum tension, we can secure a lower slack-side tension $T_2$ (or $T_3$ in a tandem drive) by lagging and snubbing, to increase the capacity of the drive without increasing $T_{max}$. For either a bare pulley or lagged pulley and known arc of contact, the formula for maximum tension may be written

$$T_1 = T_2 \times C$$

where $C$ is the constant $10^{0.00758 \cdot f \cdot a}$ Subtracting $T_2$ from both sides,

$$T_1 - T_2 = T_2(C - 1)$$

Since $E = T_1 - T_2$ we have

$$E = T_2(C - 1)$$

Or slack-side tension

$$T_2 = \frac{1}{C - 1} \times E$$

Maximum tension is

$$T_{max} = T_1 = \frac{C}{C - 1} \times E$$

* The coefficient of static friction is the tangent of the angle at which slip occurs between the faces of two materials in contact. This coefficient as between rubber and rubber varies with the specific gravity, the density, and the make-up of the rubber compound. It varies also if the surfaces are dusty, dirty, greasy, or wet. Clean rubber on rubber has a coefficient of friction of 0.55 to 0.75, but as ideal conditions never exist in practice it is usual to take the figure as 0.35 or 0.36.

Table 7 gives the values for $\frac{C}{C-1} \times E$ and $\frac{1}{C-1} \times E$ for bare and lagged pulleys and various arcs of contact with $f$ taken as 0.25 for a bare pulley and 0.35 for a lagged pulley.

Analyzing the figures in Table 7, we see the advantage of snubbing and lagging the drive pulley and how this is reflected in the cost of the belt which must be used. Thus with a bare pulley and 180° arc of contact and maximum tension ($T_1$) = 3000 lb. we can develop 1621 lb. effective tension:

$$T_1 = 1.85E = 3000 \qquad \text{or} \qquad E = \frac{3000}{1.85} = 1621 \text{ lb.}$$

But if we lag the pulley and snub the belt to 215° arc of contact, the same $T_{max}$ develops 2205 lb. effective tension:

$$T_1 = 1.36E = 3000 \qquad \text{or} \qquad E = \frac{3000}{1.36} = 2205 \text{ lb.}$$

That means that we can transmit more power to the belt without increasing the number of plies, the $T_{max}$, or the related cost of the belt.

*Analysis of the Drive. Dual and Single Drives.* We have seen that with a given $T_{max}$ the power which may be transmitted to the belt depends on the arc of contact and coefficient of friction at the head pulley. The limit with a single pulley is reached when we lag the pulley and snub for maximum arc of contact, but we may increase the arc of contact by using dual pulleys, preferably the dual motor drive as stated on page 200. Although the dual motor drive costs substantially more than the single drive, as we saw by the tabulation on page 201, it may cost less than an additional ply of belt which may be required for a long belt conveyor with high power-requirement.

To bring out more definitely the features of the dual drive we will assume the problem of a 42-in. inclined conveyor for 1000 tons per hour of crushed bauxite weighing 73 lb. per cu. ft. as in Fig. 10-18.

Interpolating in Table 3 we find the speed to be 423 ft. per min. Because of this rather heavy material and steep slope there will be a slight, though imperceptible, slippage of material as the belt rides the idlers, and so we will step up the speed about 10 per cent to 460 ft. per min. As before, from Figs. 10-13 and 10-14,

| | |
|---|---|
| For empty belt | 10 hp. |
| For horizontal movement of material | 14 hp. |
| For lifting the load | 121 hp. |
| Total | 145 hp. |

TABLE 7

CONSTANTS AND TENSION VALUES
(Link-Belt)

| Degree of Belt Contact | Type of Drive | $T_1$ in Standard Drive, Tandem or Dual Motor Drive $\left(\frac{C}{C-1}E\right)$ | | $T_2$ in Standard Drive / $T_3$ in Tandem or Dual Motor Drive $\left(\frac{1}{C-1}E\right)$ | | $\frac{T_1}{T_2}$ in Standard Drive / $\frac{T_1}{T_3}$ in Tandem or Dual Motor Drive | |
|---|---|---|---|---|---|---|---|
| | | Bare Pulley | Lagged Pulley | Bare Pulley | Lagged Pulley | Bare Pulley | Lagged Pulley |
| 180 | Plain | 1.85E | 1.50E | 0.85E | 0.50E | 2.19 | 3.0 |
| 200 | Snubbed | 1.72E | 1.42E | 0.72E | 0.42E | 2.39 | 3.39 |
| 210 | Snubbed | 1.67E | 1.38E | 0.67E | 0.38E | 2.50 | 3.61 |
| 215 | Snubbed | 1.64E | 1.36E | 0.64E | 0.36E | 2.55 | 3.72 |
| 220 | Snubbed | 1.62E | 1.35E | 0.62E | 0.35E | 2.61 | 3.83 |
| 240 | Snubbed | 1.54E | 1.30E | 0.54E | 0.30E | 2.85 | 4.33 |
| 360 | Tandem | 1.26E | 1.13E | 0.26E | 0.13E | 4.80 | 9.02 |
| 380 | Tandem | 1.23E | 1.11E | 0.23E | 0.11E | 5.25 | 10.19 |
| 400 | Tandem | 1.21E | 1.09E | 0.21E | 0.09E | 5.72 | 11.51 |
| 420 | Tandem | 1.19E | 1.08E | 0.19E | 0.08E | 6.25 | 13.00 |
| 450 | Tandem | 1.16E | 1.07E | 0.16E | 0.07E | 7.12 | 15.27 |
| 500 | Tandem | 1.13E | 1.05E | 0.13E | 0.05E | 8.86 | 21.21 |

The required effective pull at the head is

$$\frac{145 \times 33{,}000}{460} = 10{,}400 \text{ lb.} = E$$

The weight per foot of a 42-oz., 42-in., 8-ply belt with ¼- and ⅟16-in. covers is about 18 lb. There should be a pull of about 1500 lb. at the foot wheel to prevent excessive sag between return idlers, and back of the take-up there is a pull due to 145 ft. of belt on an incline, less friction loss of about 100 lb., or

$$145 \times 18 \times \frac{118}{366} - 100 = 741 \text{ lb.}$$

and the resulting tension back of the take-up is

$$T_3 = 1500 + 741 = 2241 \text{ lb.}$$

from which

$$T_1 = 2241 + 10{,}400 = 12{,}641 \text{ lb.}$$

To equalize the tendency to slip on the dual pulleys, $T_1 : T_2 :: T_2 : T_3$, whence

$$T_2 = \sqrt{T_1 \times T_3} = \sqrt{12{,}641 \times 2241} = 5322 \text{ lb.}$$

Thus

$$T_1 = 12{,}641$$

$$T_2 = 5322$$

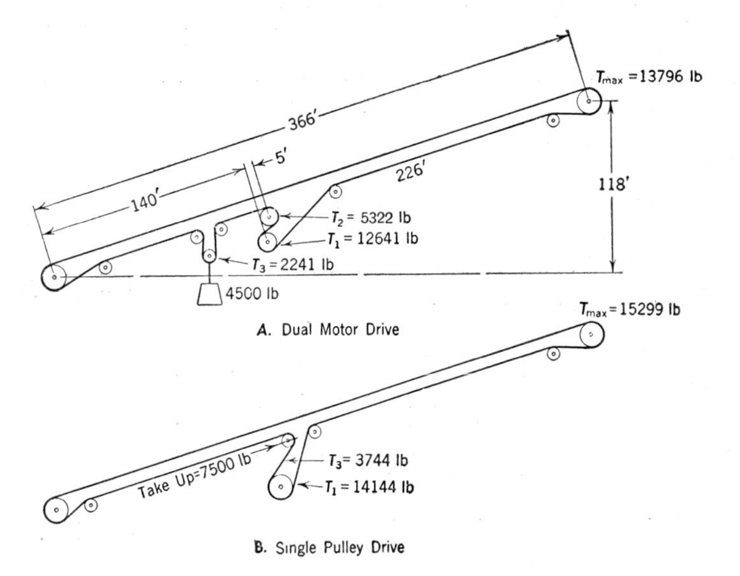


FIG. 10–18. Diagrams of conveyors analyzed, pages 219–223.

The traction on the primary pulley is 7319 lb., and

$$T_2 = 5322$$

$$T_3 = 2241$$

The traction on the secondary pulley is 3081 lb. Therefore the horsepower for the primary pulley is

$$\frac{7319 \times 460}{33{,}000} = 102 \text{ hp.}$$

and the horsepower for the secondary pulley is

$$\frac{3081 \times 460}{33{,}000} = 43 \text{ hp.}$$

We would use standard motor sizes, 125 hp. and 50 hp.

The maximum belt tension, upon which the weight of the belt depends, occurs at the top of the incline; it is $T_1$ plus the net pull of 226 ft. of empty belt back to the primary drive pulley (approximately 1155). Thus

$$T_{max} = 12{,}641 + 1155 = 13{,}796 \text{ lb.}$$

The width of the belt is 42 in. and the number of plies is 8, so that

$$\text{Maximum belt tension per inch of ply} = \frac{13{,}796}{42 \times 8} = 41 \text{ lb.}$$

Of course it is not necessary to abide by this division of the load in the dual drive. The drive effort might be divided equally between the two pulleys, but this means that we do not take advantage of the traction available at the first pulley and throw a heavier load than necessary on the secondary pulley which has the dirty side of the belt in contact with it.

Suppose that instead of the dual drive we assume a single pulley drive at the same location (Fig. 10-18*B*). Then

$$T_3 = 0.36 \times 10{,}400 = 3744 \text{ lb.}$$

$$T_1 = 3744 + 10{,}400 = 14{,}144 \text{ lb.}$$

$$T_{max} = 14{,}144 + 1155 = 15{,}299 \text{ lb.}$$

$$\text{Maximum belt tension per inch of ply} = \frac{15{,}299}{42 \times 8} = 45.5 \text{ lb.}$$

As the limit of tension per inch of ply by Table 6 for 42-oz. duck is 45 lb., a slight increase in our original assumptions would force us to a 9-ply or an 8-ply 48-in. belt with the single pulley drive, while with the dual drive we have a comfortable margin in the 41-lb. tension arrived at.

With the dual drive the $T_{max}$ is the same for any location of the drive, but the weight of the take-up increases as the drive is shifted toward the top of the incline. In the single pulley drive, however, the $T_{max}$ decreases as the drive shifts toward the head end. If it is at the head, the $T_3$ resulting from " sag tension " and return belt on the incline would be 1500 + 750 + 1170 = 3420 lb., which still is less than the required 3750 lb., but there is only 350 lb. to add. The $T_{max}$ is 3750 + 10,400 = 14,150 lb., only 330 lb. more than for the dual drive. If the drives are at the foot end, $T_{max}$ is 16,000 lb. for the single drive and remains unchanged at 13,796 lb. for the dual drive. Whenever the " sag tension " plus the tension due to the pull in the return run is less than the required $T_3$ the most advantageous location of the single drive is at the head.

*Test of Dual Drive.* A test on an actual installation by Mr. W. J. Heacock shows how closely the actual results agree with the theoretical

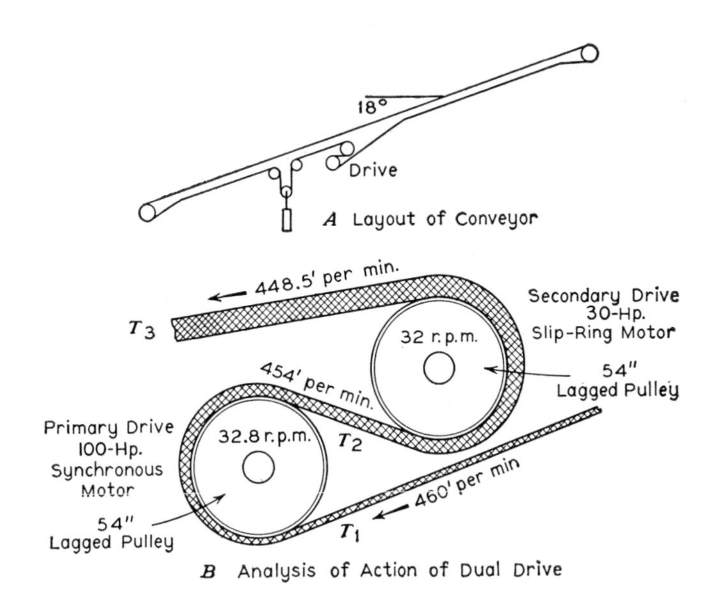


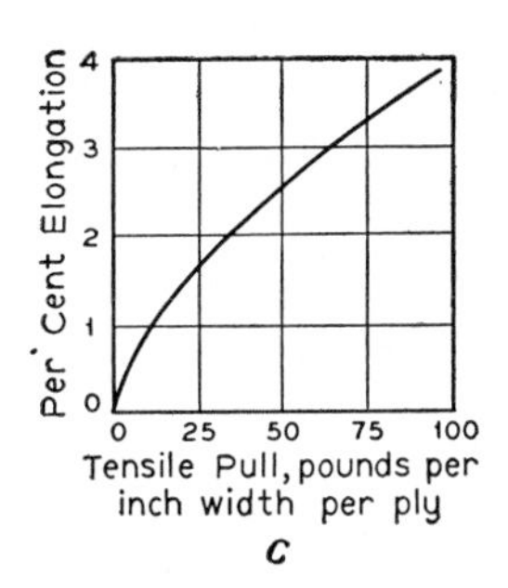


Fig. 10–19.

calculation. The conveyor was an inclined 36-in. belt, 8-ply, 32-oz., 634 ft. between centers, inclined at 18°, designed to handle 750 long tons per hour of iron ore (Fig. 10-19*A*). Actually the load during the test was 895 tons per hour. The dual drive was as shown (Fig. 10-19*B*), with 54-in. lagged drive pulleys. The primary drive was by a 100-hp., 900-r.p.m. synchronous motor, and the secondary drive was by a 30-hp.

slip-ring motor with secondary resistance to give a reduced speed of 802 r.p.m. for the expected pulley speed, determined from the stretch load characteristics (Fig. 10-19*C*) submitted by the belt manufacturer. As noted, the synchronous motor is started on reduced voltage by means of an automatic compensator having time-limit acceleration. The slip-ring motor is provided with a block of permanent resistance in the secondary circuit to assure a fairly constant load on the motor when it is running at full speed. The timed acceleration was used to assure maximum starting torque in the slip-ring motor if the synchronous motor should be unable to handle its part of the starting load (a condition found, however, not to exist), and perhaps a little better starting performance might be obtained with current-limit acceleration for the slip-ring motor.

The calculated requirements were 67.8 hp. for the primary drive, or with 20 per cent reduction loss = 81.5 hp. for the large motor, and with 16.6 + 20 per cent = 20 hp. for the small motor. By Fig. 10-20*A* it may be seen that the large motor delivers 83 hp. and the small motor 21 hp. with full load. The slight excess no doubt is due to the unexpected increase in feed rate.

Figure 10-19*B* is an exaggerated study of what takes place as the belt rounds the drive pulleys. The "thickness" of the belt indicates the tension variations. The belt contracts as it leaves the second pulley, and its speed is less than on the approach side.

With no load on the belt the synchronous motor runs slightly regenerative as shown at *m,* Fig 10-20*A,* and so the output of the slip-ring motor closely approximates the friction, windage, and speed reduction loss (18 hp. less the regenerative drag). As anticipated, the synchronous motor takes all the fluctuations in the load, and the slip-ring motor holds its load within a small range. The curves show the actual output of the two motors starting up with no load on the belt and gradually coming to full load as the ore approaches the head end. Then the feeders are stopped and the belt emptied. There seems to be (at left) a slight slippage in the slip-ring motor drive due to the rapid acceleration of the synchronous motor. This shows only during the accelerating period. The curves make a very interesting study of what happens in a dual motor drive.

Figure 10-20*B* shows the readings when the motor is started with the belt fully loaded and the feed stopped. Here again we see the tendency during the accelerating period toward "hunting" resulting in slight slippage.

The dual drive has been discussed at length because of its importance in conveyors of extremely high belt tensions. In practice one circum-

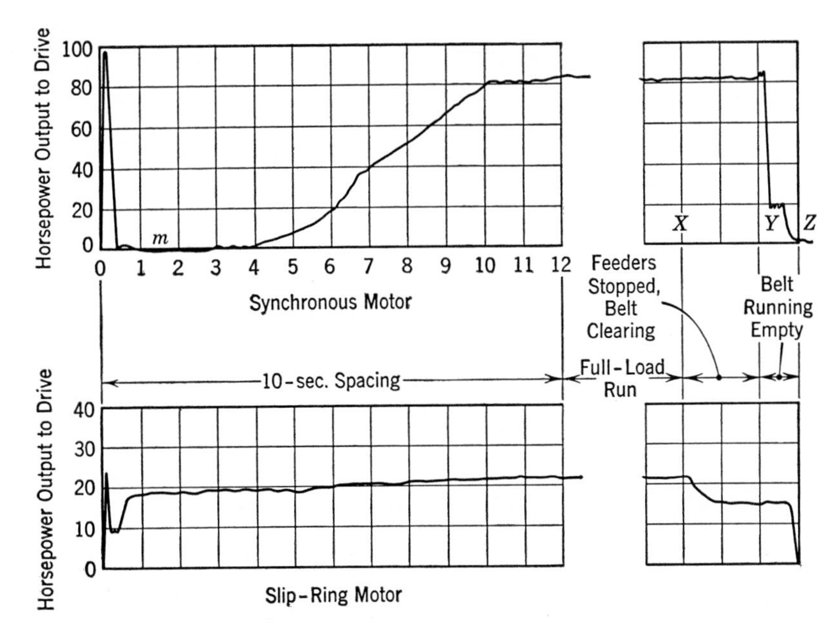


FIG. 10-20*A*. Conveyor started, and when up to speed the feeder is started. Feeder stopped at *X*. Belt empty at *Z*.

stance may enter to upset the theoretical load distribution. The pulley driving against the cover side of the belt may lose much of its traction when the belt is wet or slimy. However, there is a correction so effective that this difficulty is eliminated.

If a pulley is rubber lagged, preferably with the lagging applied by vulcanization rather than by countersunk bolts, and *grooved,* it has the effect of wiping the belt surface dry by squeegee action and substantially reduces slip and creep. This is shown by test in Fig. 10-21. Vertically, the values of per cent of slip and creep were plotted against the horsepower values shown horizontally. It may be noted from the bottom curve *B* that there was no difference in the vertical values, representing per cent of slip and creep at a given horsepower in the values obtained under three conditions, namely grooved wet, grooved dry, and smooth dry. Also the curve is practically a straight line, indicating that the vertical value, representing per cent of creep and slip, is altogether creep, and no slip is occurring.

The upper curve (*A*), shows the action with a bare-face wet pulley. Note that slip began at about 9 hp. where the curve breaks sharply upward. The various *R* values represent the ratio of tight-side tension to slack-side tension. The ratios were purposely run higher than cus-

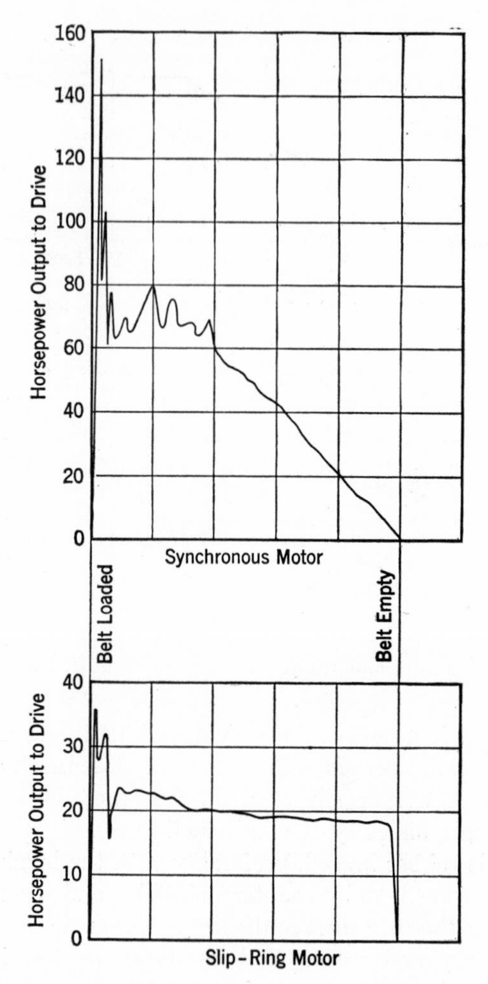


FIG. 10–20*B*. Conveyor started fully loaded, feeder stopped, and run until belt is emptied.

tomary to give a better picture of slip comparison. Slack-side tension could be increased to a point where the slip will be slight, but it would be harmful to belt life. The grooved pulley under wet conditions and with a high ratio of tight- to slack-side tension to encourage slip held its own against creep and slip under dry conditions. The smooth wet pulley slipped badly, and the curve at a comparatively low horsepower ran almost vertical.

The grooved rubber-covered pulley is, of course, not necessary except for belts where the inclination is rather steep and the belt heavily

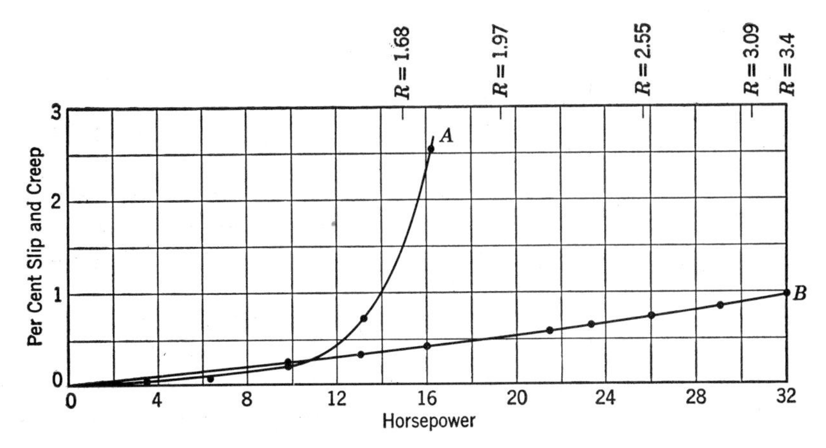


FIG. 10–21. Laboratory tests for slip and creep. (Curve *A*) Bare steel pulley and belt wet. (Curve *B*) Three series of tests with rubber-lagged pulleys gave practically identical slip: smooth lagging, belt dry; grooved lagging, belt dry; and grooved lagging, belt wet. The last shows the advantage of diagonally grooved lagging.

FIG. 10–22. Drive pulley for one of the Shasta Dam belt conveyors, rubber lagged with diagonal grooves.

loaded and operated under bad conditions, especially on downhill belts equipped with tail-pulley brake.

The rubber lagging may be specified as ½ in. thick with ¼ by ¼ in. grooves spaced ½ in. apart and parallel with the shaft or with herringbone grooves as shown in Fig. 10-22 in one of the Shasta Dam conveyor drive pulleys.

**Power Allowance for Tripper.** The power to bend the belt around the two pulleys of a tripper and to turn them is negligible, but if the tripper is self-propelled by power taken from the belt the allowances in Table 8 should be made.

TABLE 8

POWER ALLOWANCE FOR SELF-PROPELLED TRIPPERS WITH PLAIN BEARINGS

If the axle bearings are anti-friction type multiply the tabulated horsepower by 0.85.

| Belt Width, inches | Horsepower |
|---|---|
| 16 | 1. |
| 24 | 1.75 |
| 30 | 2.50 |
| 36 | 3. |
| 42 | 4. |
| 48 | 5. |
| 54 | 6. |
| 60 | 7. |

In addition there is the power required to lift the load to the top pulley, usually about 5 ft., which is

$$\frac{\text{Tons per hour}}{1000} \times 5$$

If a rotary cleaning brush is driven by the tripper allow 2 hp. for the smaller belts, up to 8 hp. for the 60-in. belt.

**Operation and Maintenance.** The belt conveyor has features that make it the best conveyor for many applications, but it is more vulnerable than other conveyors and will not stand misuse or neglect. Mechanical conveyors are protected by shear pins or overload releases. These are of little value in protecting a conveyor belt since the contingencies which damage a belt are not accompanied by heavy overloads. Protection against the most frequent cause of damage — bad alignment — is given by self-aligning idlers (Fig. 10-23). A belt should run centrally if the splice is square, the idlers and terminal pulleys in line, the loading central, and the belt sufficiently flexible to rest on the center carrying idlers. The belt should be trained while running light. If a section runs out of line the idlers causing the trouble will be found just back of the point where deflection begins. If deflection continues after all idlers have been set correctly, as may occur just ahead of or behind a moving tripper, it may be corrected by very slightly tilting the troughing idlers in the direction of belt travel. With belts which run

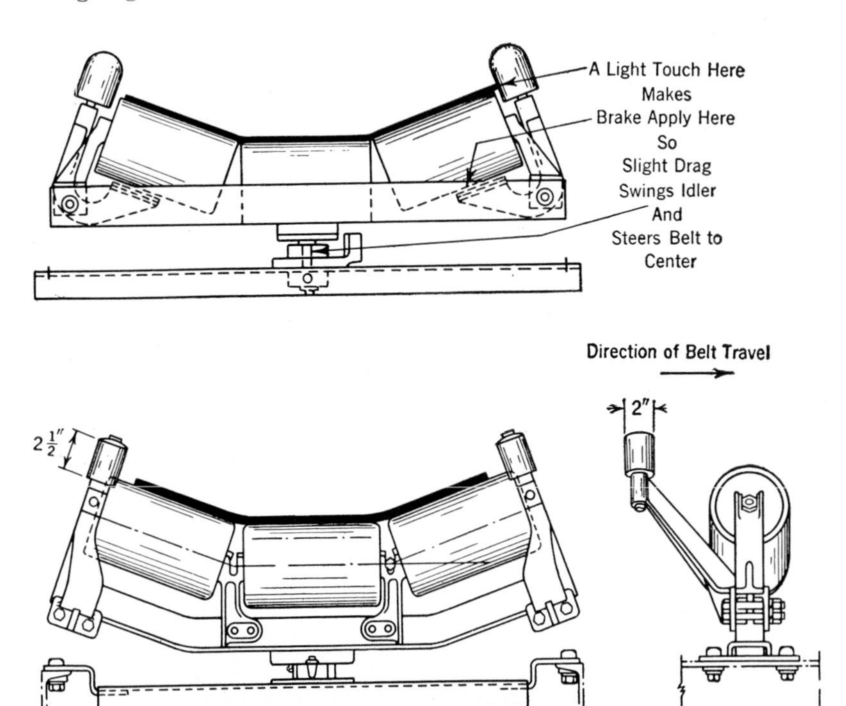


FIG. 10–23. Self-aligning idlers. (Top, Robins; Bottom, Link-Belt.)

in either direction the idler stands sometimes are made with a ridge on the bottom so that they automatically tilt in the direction of motion.

Formerly it was customary to place side-guide idlers along the runs, but if these do function the belt edges suffer. The accepted practice is to place self-aligning idlers every 50 to 100 ft. along the runs. A slight pressure from a side-drifting belt swings the pivoted idler to a position which counteracts the drift. Their functioning, however, is an indication that adjustment is called for; they are not intended to hold the belt central indefinitely. If the conveyor handles large lumps, guards must be placed on the approach side to protect the self-aligning idlers from lumps overhanging the edge.

It is more difficult for the self-aligning idlers to correct trouble along the return run where the rolls may be plastered by dirt. Disc rolls are mentioned on page 204, but they are less desirable with cord belts which have little stiffness when bottom side up. A belt should never be trained by increasing the tension as this puts useless stress in the carcass, increases the driving power, and flattens the troughing, usually augmenting instead of reducing the trouble.

The modern idler requires very little attention, and more damage is caused by too frequent lubrication than by too little. A stuck idler or one in which the end discs have loosened from the tube should be guarded against.

The method of loading is important, particularly with lumpy material. If the impact is severe, immediate easing of this condition is essential. Skirt boards should be set with a widening angle so that fragments cannot lodge beneath them. Loading chutes and hoppers are sometimes made of wood with sheet-steel lining. These liner sheets are dangerous. The author has seen a belt sliced neatly into two belts when a loosened piece slipped down and lodged in the feed chute.

The passage of the belt through the tripper should be noted for side rub. The faces of all pulleys should be kept clean. Power-driven trippers should have emergency cutouts at each end of the run to stop the tripper should the normal stops fail to function. Which ever type of belt cleaner is used it must be kept clear of embedded fragments. Spots, showing cuts, bruises, etc., should be repaired at once; otherwise grit or water will enter, gradually impairing the strength of the carcass.

It is believed by some that conveyor belts are subject to mildew when operating under conditions of sustained humidity. The author has no first-hand knowledge of this. If the purchaser believes that mildew will occur, it is possible to have the belt made with a skim coating of rubber between plies at about 5 per cent increase in cost. Thus for a 30-in., 7-ply, 42-oz. belt the added cost would be about 36 cents per running foot; for a 30-in., 5-ply, 42-oz. belt, about 34 cents per foot (1944).

With an inclined belt handling sloppy material it may be found that the lumps cannot get sufficient grip on the slimy surface of the belt to start upward. This is a dangerous and difficult condition. If possible, surplus water should be drained off ahead of the feed point or the lumps fed ahead of the slimes so that they start along before being deluged.

**Splicing the Belt.** Various types of belt fasteners are made for connecting the ends of a belt. Care must be exercised to cut the ends square, to stretch the belt by clamps and pulling jacks before cutting off the ends, and to butt the ends tightly before the clips are set to prevent a gap. Belt clips are not entirely satisfactory at best. The development of portable vulcanizers has made vulcanizing on the job possible. This method is costly but worth while, as the splices are stronger and smoother and they endure far longer than those with clips. To all intents, the belt so spliced is endless.

The following actual estimate of the cost is given. The job involved five belts at one location, all 36-in., 6-ply, 32-oz. with $\frac{3}{16}$-in. top cover and $\frac{3}{32}$-in. bottom cover. The estimate (1941) was as follows:

| | |
|---|---|
| Splicing material | $ 64 |
| Freight on vulcanizing equipment, both ways | 200 |
| Mechanics' fare both ways | 80 |
| Traveling time, 2 days | 24 |
| Traveling expenses, 16 days | 96 |
| 14 days' labor at $12 | 168 |
| Total | $632 |

The additional belt needed for the splice is 4 ft. for belts up to and including 30 in. and 6 ft. for belts up to 48 in. This is the allowance for stepping back the ends for the overlap of the splice.

**Operating Data.** Tonnages handled and operating costs for belt conveyors of great length are remarkable. One of the earliest at the H. C. Frick Colonial Mines, where coal is transported about 4 miles, using twenty units varying from 320-ft. to 2400-ft. centers, has a handling capacity of 1500 to 1900 tons per hour. The first unit is a 60-in. belt at 350 ft. per min., and the rest are 48-in. at 490 ft. All belts are cleaned by double scrapers. Seven-inch carrying idlers are spaced 3½-ft. centers, and 7-in. return idlers are spaced 10-ft. 8-in. centers. A complete system of mechanical and electrical interlocks protects the system against any ordinary mishap. This installation was started in 1925, and up to January, 1940, it had carried a total of 47,500,000 tons of mine-run coal. The idlers were equipped originally with various types of ball and roller bearings, not the equal of the present-day sealed bearings; about 3 per cent of the bearings had been replaced after 29,000 hours' operation. The last of the original belts was replaced after carrying 39,000,000 tons.

Maintenance costs on industrial installations are difficult to obtain; as the overall costs are not segregated, the "per ton" costs may include those of a feeder, crusher, elevator, etc., in one total.

For one installation with a 30-in. by 300-ft. and a 30-in. by 400-ft. conveyor, both on a flat incline, which handled coal to a steam plant, the maintenance cost totaled approximately $400 for 11 years' operation during which 449,000 tons of crushed coal were handled, or $0.0009 per ton. These figures included the maintenance of an apron feeder ahead of the first belt. The original belts were still in service after eleven years and "in excellent condition." When 1400 ft. of belt is bought, costing about $5.00 per foot, eventually the per ton cost will go to about $0.007 for a tonnage of about one million.

At another steam plant with a single 36-in. by 300-ft. conveyor inclined at 20° handling crushed coal from a loading hopper, without feeder and therefore with severe loading conditions, the records from 1929 to 1936, during which 1,146,000 tons were handled, showed no repairs other than one belt replacement in 1936 at a cost of $2000. This gives a maintenance cost of $0.0017 per ton. Gentler loading and a lower degree of inclination would add much to the life of this belt (Fig. 11-6).

The cost per ton handled depends on the suitability of the belt, the skillful engineering of the layout, the length of the belt, the material handled, and the frequency of damage to the belt. The combinations of these factors make it impossible to predict maintenance costs except by comparison with installations where the conditions appear to be similar. Of course belt life is much less in the average industrial installation than in a long-distance transport set-up like that of Colonial Mines, partly because of more frequent no-load and part-load operation but primarily because of the time cycle or frequency of impact at the loading point with shorter belts. A tripper also is an adverse factor.

The comment of the B. F. Goodrich Company is worth quoting:

> If a belt is worth $3000 and can be made to last ten years instead of two, the saving justifies considerable maintenance expense.
>
> Such a saving is possible on many installations at a very small additional cost in maintenance time and equipment alterations.
>
> This is true because injury and damage are of far greater importance in determining how long a belt will last than the number of tons carried. Some injuries are so serious as to bring a swift ending to the belt's career, even though newly installed.
>
> Since most of these injurious conditions arise after the conveyor is originally installed, and since they are the factors which really determine the life of the belt, any estimate of prospective tonnage or years of service which might be ventured by the designing engineer can be completely upset in many ways.
>
> The operator can understand better how to care for a rubber belt if he bears in mind the following characteristics of the two component parts — cotton fabric and rubber.
>
> The fabric supplies all the structural strength; it does all the work in supporting and pulling the load. The rubber supplies no structural strength.
>
> The cotton, however, is almost worthless to resist abrasive wear, cutting

blows, rot, and corrosion. The rubber with which the cotton is covered and impregnated is 100 times more resistant to all these damaging conditions.

The two in combination — one supplying strength, the other protection — have made possible the modern belt conveyor with all its savings to industry in the economical handling of materials.

Rubber can stand up indefinitely against the abrasive wear and even impact of sharp material so long as the force involved does not distort the rubber beyond the elastic limit. A common rubber band will stand stretching two or three times its length for years, but if you pull it to its elastic limit and keep on pulling it soon will go to pieces. The same thing can happen when you compress the rubber cover cushion of a belt beyond its capacity to yield. The surface is cut or broken and the protective cushion torn away, leaving the cotton exposed to damage.

This kind of injury to rubber belt covers can happen when heavy or sharp lumps drop several feet against the surface, when the edges or cover rub against obstructions and skirt boards, or when pieces of material are caught between belt and pulley. Under such conditions more damage can be done in a few days than in years of normal operation.

**Interesting Prewar Installations.** Subsequent to the Colonial Mines installation, other impressive belt-conveyor systems were engineered as transport by belts became recognized as economical both in first outlay for equipment and in handling costs.

Probably the first attempt to move excavated earth on a large scale was in connection with the removal of Denny hill in the city of Seattle, Washington. The job of the contractor was the removal of 4,500,000 yd. of earth without interfering with street traffic and delivering the material to scows at the water front. A system of three movable and fixed belt conveyors was installed, 920-, 1522-, and 440-ft. centers respectively. After the usual difficulties in a pioneering enterprise the operation was efficient and economical.

The manufacturers furnished conveyors which were specified as having a capacity of 600 yd. per hr., but after they were installed the contractor insisted that this meant 600 yd. bank measurement. Of course the manufacturers meant 600 yd. loose measurement. The increase in volume is between 35 and 50 per cent. The conveyors were speeded up from 400 to 600 ft. per min. and functioned satisfactorily at the higher speed. This sort of misunderstanding occurs not infrequently, and the young engineer should guard against it.

A spectacular set-up, not in tonnage moved but in daring conception and the utilization of up-to-date appliances, is the 1940 installation for Shasta Dam on the Sacramento River near Coram, California, to move the aggregate for 6,000,000 yd. of concrete. There were two sources of sand and gravel, one 28 mi. downstream and the other a tract near Redding, 12 mi. distant. The successful bidder for the job of delivering 7,600,000 tons of gravel and 2,800,000 tons of sand to the contractor for the dam chose the latter. He constructed near Redding a preparation plant and a 9½-mile overland belt-conveyor system to deliver classified aggregates to the storage yard a half mile from the dam site. From this point the dam contractor provided his own belt system to the job. This (Fig. 10-24) is an impressive belt conveyor system. There are twenty-six 36-in. conveyor units with 6-ply belts operating at 555 ft. per min. for a capacity of 1100 tons per hour. Centers range from 850 ft. to 3400 ft. Each conveyor is driven by a 200-hp. motor, except the last unit which has a 75-hp. motor. This and one intermediate unit are on a down grade, and the load drives the motor as a generator.

The loading arrangement provides for successive sizes of gravel or of sand as called for by the dam contractor.

At the loading points between conveyors the receiving conveyor has pneumatic-tire troughing rolls to take the heavy impact, and water sprays to reduce to some extent the dust nuisance. A roadway and telephone line parallel the system. When the installation was first set up, from a central broadcasting system prompt notification of trouble could be given to radio trucks stationed along the line; these trucks could communicate with any drive station or with the main office. Later, wartime conditions forced the abandonment of the two-way radio system. Communication then was entirely by telephone located at each transfer point. Loud horn signals sounded along the entire conveyor line when the call button at any telephone location was pressed.

**Postwar developments** in belt conveyors have been directed toward belt construction of far greater strength to adapt the conveyor for far greater centers length. The over-all handling cost per ton-mile has been found to be substantially less with inclined belt conveyors than with trains of cars on a spiral track, as for bringing ores from mines or pits up to ground level, but this saving depends largely on how long the conveyor may be, since with a long conveyor we reduce not only the frequency of load impact but also other factors of destruction such as the frequency of bending around the terminal and snub pulleys and the scraping action of the belt cleaner.

The author is indebted to Mr. Paul D. Suloff of the Goodyear Tire and Rubber Company for information relating to technical developments of 1946–1947.

Wartime shortages abruptly curtailed the use of natural rubber. The four grades of belts as related to severity of service are listed on

FIG. 10–24. The last three sections of the 9.5-mi. belt conveyor system supplying concrete aggregates to the contractor building Shasta Dam; 36-in. belts at 535 ft. per min.

page 213. The first step eliminated grades *a* and *c*. Finally the rubber content was reduced to a point where none of the prewar grades was permitted (only 5 per cent rubber was allowed), and belts had to be made of a general purpose GRS or, for oil and heat-resistant belts, the more costly GRM (Neoprene). Thereupon the Rubber Manufacturers' Association set up the following standards:

| Grade* | Synthetic | Service | Minimum Tensile and | Elongation Per Cent | Minimum Cover Friction |
|---|---|---|---|---|---|
| 1-N | Neoprene | Abrasive | 1700 | 400 | 14 |
| 1-S | GRS | Abrasive | 1400 | 350 | 12 |
| 2-S | GRS | Low abrasive | 800 | 250 | 10 |

Now the reversal back to rubber has begun, and two increases in rubber content have been allowed at the date this is written. No doubt the use of Neoprene will be continued for heat- and oil-resistant belts, but how far the GRS belts will go is not as yet clear. Much depends on the future costs of GRS and rubber. At present the manufacturers are increasing the use of rubber as fast as increases are permitted.

Along with the use of synthetic rubber as a cover and binder, there is much interest in the possibilities of synthetic fiber as a substitute for natural cotton fiber in duck and cords. Rayon has the advantage of much greater strength and cotton costs are going up while rayon cost is coming down. Even now it is possible to attain a given strength with rayon at less cost than with cotton. One drawback has been the difficulty in getting adhesion to the smooth fibers, but this has been solved. More difficult is the decrease by as much as 40 per cent in rayon strength when watersoaked, as contrasted with cotton which gains slightly. Nylon has even greater possibilities from a strength standpoint. It has excellent aging qualities and resistance to mildew. Elasticity is its drawback. It stretches under tension and grows in length with time and so must be used in combination with cotton duck.

Glass fiber is under investigation. It has great strength and a low coefficient of elongation. Resistance to fungi and chemical deterioration is good. It is costly, and its high modulus of elasticity presents the problem of its resistance to the bending stresses introduced at the terminal pulleys. One interesting 1948 announcement by Hewett-Robins, Inc. is a high-temperature belt with Fiberglas fabric carcass claimed to operate at temperatures up to 350° F. without char or loss of strength and with a substantially longer life than belts with cotton and asbestos carcass.

* In the high-grade prewar belts the minimum tensile strength of the cover stock was 3500–4000 lb., the minimum elongation, 500 per cent, and minimum cover friction (adhesion of cover to carcass) 17 lb.

In working with rayon, glass, and steel, we have materials of high modulus as compared with cotton duck. Duck requires little design attention in belts up to 6 or 8 ply where they round the terminal pulleys, but, with the modulus increased many times, compensating changes in pulley diameter may have to be considered. One answer is the single-layer cord belt with cords of sufficient strength for the tension contemplated.

**Present-Day Strength Factors.** Instead of the stress limits in Table 6 the engineer now has available belts with far greater strength. The B. F. Goodrich Company *cord belt* has longitudinal cords imbedded in the rubber and on the under side one or two plies of 42 oz. duck for transverse strength. These belts now are standardized for 50, 70, and 100 lb. per inch of width per ply (cord layers).

The U. S. Rubber Company belt has the carcass made up of a combination of nylon and specially treated duck fabric with standard ratings of 85, 110, and 150 lb. per inch of width per ply.

The Goodyear Tire and Rubber Company has a wire-cable belt (page 188), rated for 1000 to 3000 lb. per in. of belt width, and a belt with single-layer large-diameter cords, to be specified where such extreme tensions are not involved.

The importance of these developments is illustrated by working through the procedure detailed on pages 208 to 222. We will retain the same centers and lift but increase the requirements to 1500 tons per hour of pebble phosphate, weighing 100 lb. per cu. ft., calling for a 42-in. belt at 460 ft. per min.

The belt pull with single pulley drive is 20,800 lb. or 495 lb. per in. of belt width. This would require an 11-ply 42-oz. duck belt. With the constructions now available we can use a 5-ply 100-lb. cord belt, a 4-ply nylon-duck belt, or the single-layer large-cord belt. The traction necessary can be secured with a single pulley lagged and grooved.

These belts are extremely flexible crosswise and not well suited for belt elevators. The conventional duck belts should be used as listed in Table 7, Chapter 4.

**Factors Contributing to Longer Belt Life.** For convenient reference we group the factors given careful consideration when engineering an installation or supervising its operation, to secure the longest possible belt life.

Since the chief factor in cover wear is at the point where the load hits it and is a function of the frequency and severity of the impact, the length and speed are important. Also the material should be delivered in the direction of belt travel with the least possible vertical drop. A vertical drop is especially destructive if the belt is inclined upward; actually this means delivery of the load in a direction opposite to the direction of belt travel.

The impact must not be directly on a rigid idler, especially with lumpy material.

Skirt boards must be adjusted so that the material will not grind beneath them. If the skirt boards are set too low, it may be that, although there is clearance when the belt is loading, contact occurs when the empty belt lifts somewhat.

If the incline is too steep or if the carrying idlers are too widely spaced, the life of the cover is reduced. A horizontal belt has a longer life than an inclined belt, owing to the imperceptible backward slip of the material accentuated by the "bump" at each idler, especially if the idler spacing is excessive.

The discharge chute is checked. It may appear correctly placed for the full-speed discharge but permits the lumps to drop into the gap between chute and head pulley when the conveyor is started up.

The practice of tilting troughing idlers forward to steer the belt is effective, but it does tend to cause a drag which is harmful to the underside cover. It is better to adjust the idlers laterally when the self-aligning idlers indicate that adjustment is called for.

The degree of belt loading under constant feed is observed, and the speed is adjusted for full loading. Not only are the harmful factors previously noted thereby reduced, but also the entire width of the belt is utilized.

Belt conveyors subject to exposure to extremely cold weather conditions should be run for a half-hour or so without loading so the lubricant in the anti-friction bearings will have a chance to soften up. Low temperatures have little effect on the belt itself, though Neoprene has a higher porosity than either rubber or the Buna-S used during the war and tends to stiffen up. The tension to which a belt may be momentarily subjected is far beyond the rated operating tensions so that there is little if any risk as regards starting pull.

If a horizontal conveyor is exposed to rain or snow it is advantageous to have a reversible drive so that an accumulation of water or snow can be discharged over the tail end instead of into the receiving hopper.

Mr. Suloff has made cold box tests of conveyor compounds and belt samples at temperatures as low as 40° F. below zero, from which he concludes that belts will remain operable at —20°. He found the current rubber belts stiffened much less than synthetic belts. There are belt conveyors operating under subzero conditions, as for example in Alaska where real difficulty is experienced. When the material contains moisture the particles carried to the return idlers immediately freeze solidly to the cold metal and build up. Rubber disc idlers would be better. In one installation in the iron range, handling very wet material, the operators finally had to run steam pipes through the conveyor gallery to keep going late in the fall. Of course free moisture can exist in subzero temperatures only when digging out of the bank below the frost line.

## CHAPTER 11

# AERIAL TRAMWAYS

The practice of transporting materials by means of carriers suspended from overhead cables dates from the early seventeenth century. Rope was first used, until the invention of the steel cable made the system more workable.

FIG. 11-1. Double-track system with four-wheel carriers side by side. Photograph shows method of protecting underpass roads or railroads from material which might fall from the buckets. (Interstate Equipment Company.)

**Types of Aerial Tramways.** Tramways, or cableways, are of four general types:

*Single-cable system,* now obsolete, which had an endless cable from which buckets were suspended.

*Double-cable system,* in which twin fixed cables serve as the runway or track from which spaced buckets are suspended and towed by an endless cable.

*Double-track system,* in which twin track cables are adjusted to parallel catenaries to form a runway for carriers having four grooved wheels and towed by separate endless cable. The carrying and return runs may be side by side or one above the other. Figure 11-1 shows the former arrangement.

*Shuttle system* (Fig. 11-2) in which buckets or cars travel to a discharge point and return, after the manner of a balanced skip hoist. It may be the double-track system or the double-cable system and is nicely adapted to the disposal of waste from a plant to a dump pile if the distance and capacity are not too great. The reverse of the function is the transfer of material from top of a slope to a discharge point at the bottom. Automatic loading is easily provided.

Fig. 11-2. Shuttle system. Frequently used for disposal of refuse from a plant or, as here shown, lowering ore or coal from the crest of a hill to a railroad below. (A. E. Leschen Rope Company.)

**Applications.** Primarily the field of the tramway is for transport of materials over long distances across rough country and heavily wooded routes, preferably along a straight line, though curves are possible. It is free from interference with surface traffic, immune to weather conditions, requires no bridges, cuts, or fills, and with suitable carriers it can transport materials that a belt conveyor cannot handle, such as logs, lumber, sacks, and liquids. The usual speed is 500 to 600 ft. per min.

Most installations are of moderate length, but some have been built 10 miles long, and with tandem systems the length, theoretically at least, is unlimited. The spans may be as long as 5000 ft., but long spans involve costly supporting structures. For convenience in splicing and storage of spares the track cables of either run are unchanged in diameter, regardless of the length of spans.

**Costs.** Investment figures mean little since spacing and weight of towers and weight of terminals vary with each installation. However, operating and maintenance costs are more uniform, and we quote by permission from the analysis by Mr. O. H. Metzger, U. S. Bureau of Mines, I.C. 7095, February, 1940:

> For those tramways which require power, the power costs seldom exceed 0.2 cent per ton-mile, and for some the figure is less than 0.1 cent per ton-mile.
>
> Supervision should cost not more than 0.1 cent per ton-mile for trams of moderate length and capacity. Generally it is less than this.
>
> Labor costs are generally the largest single item involved in operating a tramway. For several metal mine installations in the western United States these range from 5 to 10 cents per ton-mile, but in the coal mining and construction industries in the east labor costs of 2 to 3 cents per ton-mile are reported. The difference can be explained partly by the larger-capacity tramways used in coal mining and construction work, but also by the fact that many of the tramways in these industries are semi-automatic and require a minimum of labor in their operation.
>
> Replacement data are scant. Costs on the Kennicott tramway at Kennicott, Alaska, showed a duty of 1,500,000 to 2,500,000 tons for the track cables and about 115,000 tons for the line sheaves. The large terminal sheaves had a life of about 1,000,000 tons. Usually the wear on the track cables is uniform throughout their length. Table 1 shows the costs for several tramways.

**Capacities and Drives.** Capacity is a simple calculation: If each bucket carrys 40 cu. ft. of material weighing 50 lb. per cu. ft. and the speed is 600 ft. per min. with buckets spaced 300 ft. apart, the tons per hour are

$$\frac{40 \times 50}{2000} \times 2 \times 60 = 120$$

However, the time element enters. There must be an interval for loading the buckets while they are stationary. Loading two per minute is fast work.

Where the discharge level is at a point higher than the loading point, a traction sheave and motor are used to pull the carriers. If the arrangement is the reverse, the motor serves as a brake, pumping current back into the line, except that power is required for starting. In some installations both runs are utilized; for example, coal may be taken to a boiler house and ashes from the plant after the coal has been discharged from the carriers.

Tables 2 and 3 (Interstate Equipment Company) gives the capacities

TABLE 1

MAJOR TRACK CABLE REPLACEMENT COSTS

| Tramway | Situation | Capacity per Hour, tons | Cable, Size in Inches and Type | | | Total Tons Trammed when Replaced | Costs per Ton-Mile, cent | | |
|---|---|---|---|---|---|---|---|---|---|
| | | | Loaded Side | Empty Side | Type | | Loaded Side | Empty Side | Total |
| Sunnyside | Silverton, Colo. | 40 to 50 | 1⅜ | 1⅛ | Locked coil cast steel | 1,500,000 to 2,500,000 | 0.22 to 0.35 | 0.15 to 0.25 | 0.37 to 0.60[1] |
| Silver King | Park City, Utah | 40 | 1¼ | 1 | Flattened strand plow steel | Loaded side, 800,000; empty side 1,200,000 | 0.44 | 0.19 | 0.63[1] |
| Kennicott | Kennicott, Alaska | 21 | 1¼ | 1⅛ | Locked coil cast steel | 1,500,000 to 2,500,000 | 0.23 to 0.38 | 0.19 to 0.32 | 0.42 to 0.70[2] |

[1] Does not include freight costs.
[2] Includes freight costs.

TABLE 2

CARRYING CAPACITIES IN TONS PER HOUR FOR CONTINUOUS TRAMWAYS

| Size of Car, cubic feet | Car Spacing, feet | Line Speed | | | | | | | | | |
|---|---|---|---|---|---|---|---|---|---|---|---|
| | | 400 ft. per min. | | 450 ft. per min. | | 500 ft. per min. | | 550 ft. per min. | | 600 ft. per min. | |
| | | Material | | Material | | Material | | Material | | Material | |
| | | 50 lb. | 86 lb. | 50 lb. | 86 lb. | 50 lb. | 86 lb. | 50 lb. | 86 lb. | 50 lb. | 86 lb. |
| 10 | 250 | 24 | 41 | 27 | 47 | 30 | 52 | 33 | 57 | 36 | 62 |
| | 200 | 30 | 52 | 34 | 59 | 38 | 65 | 41 | 71 | 45 | 78 |
| | 150 | 40 | 69 | 45 | 78 | 50 | 86 | 55 | 95 | 60 | 103 |
| | 100 | 60 | 103 | 68 | 117 | 75 | 129 | 83 | 143 | 90 | 155 |
| 20 | 250 | 48 | 82 | 54 | 93 | 60 | 103 | 66 | 113 | 72 | 124 |
| | 200 | 60 | 103 | 68 | 116 | 75 | 129 | 83 | 143 | 90 | 155 |
| | 150 | 80 | 138 | 90 | 155 | 100 | 172 | 110 | 190 | 120 | 206 |
| | 100 | 120 | 206 | 135 | 232 | 150 | 258 | 165 | 284 | 180 | 310 |
| 40 | 250 | 96 | 165 | 108 | 186 | 120 | 206 | 132 | 227 | 144 | 248 |
| | 200 | 120 | 206 | 136 | 238 | 150 | 258 | 165 | 284 | 180 | 310 |
| | 150 | 160 | 275 | 180 | 310 | 200 | 344 | 220 | 378 | 240 | 412 |
| | 100 | 240 | 412 | 270 | 464 | 300 | 516 | 330 | 566 | 360 | 620 |
| 60 | 250 | 144 | 248 | 162 | 278 | 180 | 310 | 198 | 340 | 216 | 372 |
| | 200 | 180 | 310 | 204 | 348 | 225 | 387 | 248 | 426 | 270 | 464 |
| | 150 | 240 | 412 | 270 | 464 | 300 | 516 | 330 | 567 | 360 | 620 |
| 80 | 250 | 192 | 330 | 216 | 372 | 240 | 412 | 264 | 454 | 288 | 495 |
| | 200 | 240 | 412 | 270 | 464 | 300 | 516 | 330 | 567 | 360 | 620 |
| | 150 | 320 | 550 | 360 | 620 | 400 | 688 | 440 | 732 | 480 | 824 |

TABLE 3

CARRYING CAPACITIES IN TONS PER HOUR FOR TWO-CAR SHUTTLES

| Size of Car, cubic feet | Car Speed, feet per minute | Haulage Distance | | | | | | | | | | | |
|---|---|---|---|---|---|---|---|---|---|---|---|---|---|
| | | 1000 ft. | | 1500 ft. | | 2000 ft. | | 2500 ft. | | 3000 ft. | | 3500 ft. | |
| | | Material | | Material | | Material | | Material | | Material | | Material | |
| | | 50 lb. | 86 lb. | 50 lb. | 86 lb. | 50 lb. | 86 lb. | 50 lb. | 86 lb. | 50 lb. | 86 lb. | 50 lb. | 86 lb. |
| 60 | 1000 | 80 | 138 | 56 | 96 | 42 | 72 | 34 | 58 | 29 | 50 | 25 | 43 |
| | 1200 | 94 | 162 | 66 | 114 | 49 | 84 | 40 | 70 | 34 | 58 | 29 | 50 |
| | 1400 | 106 | 182 | 75 | 129 | 58 | 100 | 46 | 79 | 39 | 67 | 34 | 58 |
| | 1600 | 120 | 206 | 84 | 145 | 66 | 113 | 54 | 92 | 44 | 76 | 39 | 67 |
| 80 | 1000 | 107 | 184 | 74 | 127 | 56 | 96 | 46 | 79 | 38 | 65 | 33 | 57 |
| | 1200 | 125 | 215 | 87 | 150 | 66 | 114 | 54 | 93 | 45 | 77 | 39 | 67 |
| | 1400 | 143 | 246 | 99 | 170 | 77 | 133 | 62 | 107 | 51 | 88 | 44 | 76 |
| | 1600 | 160 | 275 | 111 | 191 | 88 | 152 | 72 | 124 | 60 | 103 | 52 | 90 |
| 100 | 1000 | 133 | 228 | 93 | 160 | 71 | 122 | 57 | 98 | 48 | 83 | 41 | 71 |
| | 1200 | 156 | 268 | 109 | 187 | 83 | 143 | 67 | 115 | 56 | 96 | 48 | 83 |
| | 1400 | 178 | 306 | 124 | 213 | 97 | 166 | 76 | 131 | 64 | 110 | 55 | 95 |
| | 1600 | 200 | 344 | 140 | 240 | 109 | 188 | 89 | 153 | 75 | 129 | 65 | 111 |
| 120 | 1000 | 160 | 275 | 112 | 192 | 84 | 144 | 68 | 117 | 50 | 98 | 50 | 86 |
| | 1200 | 188 | 323 | 131 | 225 | 99 | 170 | 80 | 138 | 68 | 117 | 59 | 102 |
| | 1400 | 214 | 368 | 150 | 258 | 116 | 199 | 91 | 156 | 78 | 134 | 67 | 115 |
| | 1600 | 240 | 412 | 168 | 288 | 136 | 226 | 107 | 184 | 90 | 155 | 78 | 134 |
| 140 | 1000 | 187 | 322 | 129 | 222 | 99 | 170 | 80 | 138 | 67 | 115 | 58 | 100 |
| | 1200 | 219 | 376 | 151 | 260 | 116 | 199 | 94 | 162 | 79 | 136 | 68 | 117 |
| | 1400 | 251 | 431 | 173 | 297 | 135 | 232 | 107 | 184 | 90 | 155 | 78 | 134 |
| | 1600 | 280 | 481 | 196 | 338 | 153 | 263 | 125 | 214 | 105 | 182 | 91 | 156 |
| 160 | 1000 | 214 | 368 | 148 | 254 | 112 | 192 | 92 | 157 | 76 | 131 | 66 | 114 |
| | 1200 | 251 | 431 | 174 | 298 | 133 | 228 | 108 | 187 | 89 | 153 | 78 | 134 |
| | 1400 | 287 | 491 | 198 | 340 | 155 | 266 | 125 | 216 | 104 | 178 | 90 | 155 |
| | 1600 | 320 | 550 | 225 | 388 | 175 | 300 | 143 | 246 | 120 | 206 | 104 | 178 |

in tons per hour for continuous tramways and for two-car shuttles. For single car shuttles use half the capacities shown in Table 3.

**Cables and Sheaves.** Since the readers for whom this book is intended will scarcely be called upon to design a tramway, we will not go into details of design. The reader is referred to the analysis by Mr.

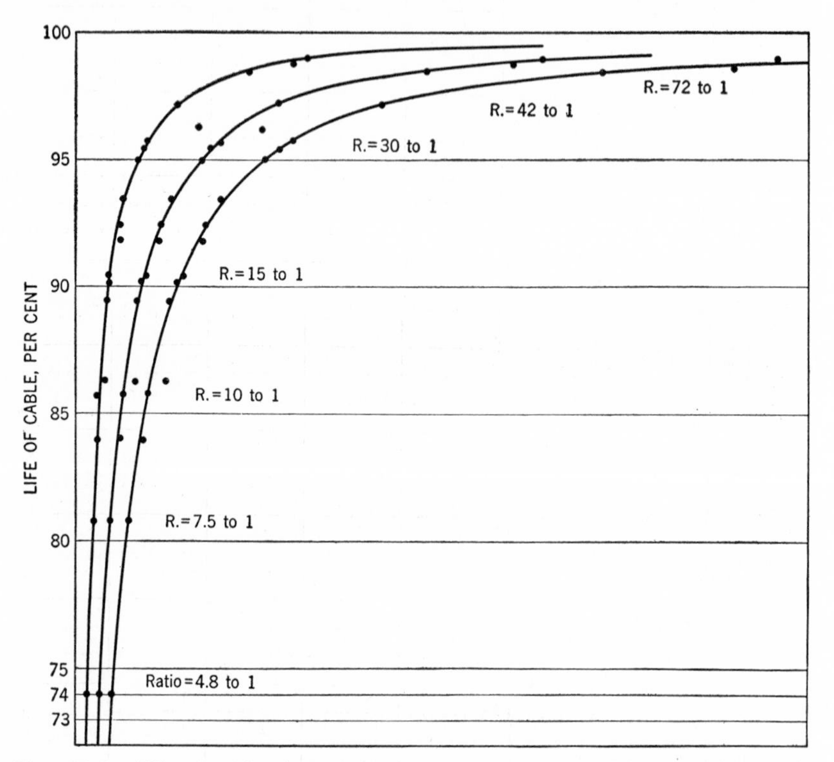


FIG. 11-3. Life of cable with relation to sheave diameter. Life of straight cable represented by 100 per cent.

Metzger referred to above, to U. S. Bureau of Mines, I.C. 6875, by Mr. J. R. Thonen, and to I.C. 6948, September, 1937, by Mr. Metzger. However, the factor of sheave diameters with relation to cable diameters in this or any other type of equipment employing steel cables is important. There is a direct relation between the life of a cable and the diameter of the sheave around which it is bent. Small-diameter bends substantially reduce the life of a cable.

Figure 11-3 shows how the life of a cable increases as the ratio of sheave diameter to cable diameter increases. The three curves are from three different sources, and all are for 6-strand, 19-wire cables. There is a rapid increase in life as the diameters of the small sheaves

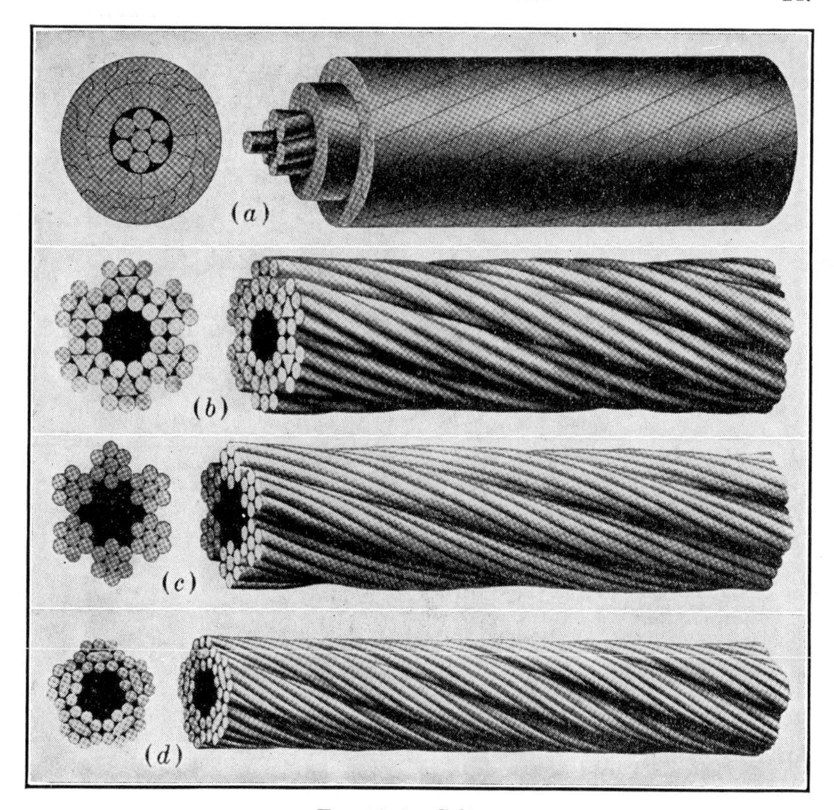


FIG. 11-4. Cables.

(*A*) Locked coil track cable especially adapted for heavy service. The smooth exterior surface assures reduced wear by the trolley wheels. It resists crushing of the cable under the weight of the load. (*B*) Flattened strand track cable. Lower in cost. Outside wires are grouped to minimize surface irregularities. (*C*) Round strand track cable, made lang lay for increased wearing surface. Still lower in cost and adapted for lighter loads. (*D*) Flattened strand traction cable designed for maximum contact surface and wear under the action of sheaves and grips.

increase up to a ratio of about 15 to 1. From there on the improvement is small. The minimum ratio in good practice is 30 : 1, and a good average is 45 : 1. This is for sheaves in the general run of applications, but in mine hoists the ratio is 72 : 1 or greater. Cable maintenance is discussed in Chapter 5 in connection with skip hoists.

Suitable cable construction is another important factor. The A. Leschen and Sons Company recommends the constructions in Fig. 11-4. Both towing and track cables require lubrication for maximum life. Automatic lubrication may be provided for the track cables by a device suspended from one of the trolleys, which travels out along the line.

Fig. 11–5. After crossing the intervening hills the tramway crosses a level plain to the power plant seen in the distance.

Fig. 11–6. Discharge end of the 2½-mile tramway. Steel structure anchors the track cables and houses the traction sheave and take-up and the two 30-ton concrete counterweights. (Hudson.)

**Typical Installation.** As illustrating a typical application of the tramway we describe the essentials of a Leschen-Hudson installation (Figs. 11-5 and 11-6) for the transfer of coal from a captive mine to a steam plant in Pennsylvania. Formerly the coal was shipped from the mine over three railroads on a roundabout route involving heavy freight and transfer charges. The tramway follows a direct route for 2½ mi. from mine to plant over intermediate hills, then down grade and across a level plane. It handles an average of 500 tons per 24 hr., with buckets spaced 500 ft. traveling at 550 ft. per min. Figure 11-5 shows the final level run with the plant in the distance. Figure 11-6, taken before the cables were strung, shows the heavy terminal structure which supports two suspended 30-ton concrete counterweights that maintain the tension in the track and traction cables. The drive is by a 30-hp. motor at the loading station, but as the discharge end is 600 ft. lower than the loading end the motor serves as a brake as soon as a sufficient number of loaded buckets pass the crest of the first hill.

Fig. 11-7. Leschen tramway carrier for extra heavy duty. The four-wheel truck distributes the load on the track cable.

Figure 11-7 shows the Leschen heavy-duty bucket suspended from the track cable, with the lever-operated grip that clutches the towing cable.

**Comment.** Aerial tramways are specified less frequently in recent years because of the developments in large-capacity motor-truck transportation and the alternative of long-range, large-capacity, belt-conveyor systems; but there still arise problems like that described above where the tramway is easily the best solution.

## CHAPTER 12

## STORAGE AND TRANSPORT

Bunker and silo storage are discussed in Chapter 13. Here we discuss stocking out and reclaiming bulk materials and their movement by crane, drag scraper, bulldozer, carryall, motor truck, and tram cars. Storage and transport are usually parts of one problem.

**The Crawler Crane.** Where operations are not too extended the crawler crane, because of flexibility, availability for other duties, and dependability, is widely used for the distribution of material to storage and reclaiming it. The functions of the machine are too well known to require extended discussion. It can move around the property or around the job and handle a wide variety of materials.

Mention should be made of the simplification of control which permits the operator to sit at his work and operate the machine through a bank of finger levers which actuate the clutches hydraulically, thus increasing the day-by-day output by reducing the fatigue of the operator.

When unloading from barge to storage or loading to trucks, cars, or conveyors, the crawler may travel from point to point as the work continues. In breakdown operations (free digging), capacities of 400 tons per hour are not unusual. The Diesel motor has introduced such advantages, both in prime-mover characteristics and in lower operating costs, that the old-type steam-operated crane is seldom seen.

When the crawler is used for unloading cars, flat-bottom cars are best since the bucket cannot reach into the hopper bottoms. The cars should be without cross beams at the top. Where the type of car cannot be controlled a deep track hopper leading off to the side of the track permits the bucket to function either direct from the car or from the pit after the load is dumped. Beyond the radius at which a crawler can operate advantageously, a drag scraper, a bulldozer, or a carryall may be used.

**The Drag Scraper.** This equipment costs much less than a crawler and is therefore available for projects where the investment must be smaller. The drag scraper consists of a haulage engine with two drums rotating in opposite directions, which serve to pull out and return a scraper bucket or scoop attached to cables dead-ended on the drums. The material thus is spread out over an area, usually semi-circular in outline, and reclaimed by reversing the scoop so that it moves outward empty and returns loaded. The principal application is in connection with reserve coal storage. Its flexibility is not as good as that of the crawler crane, and provision must be made for an initial pile from which the scoop may function, and for removal of the coal when it is reclaimed to the focal point. Figure 12-1 shows a typical application. The motor-operated anchorage

Fig. 12–1. Typical semi-circular reserve storage by drag scraper. (Sauerman.)

car or tail tower is shifted as stocking out or reclaiming proceeds, by remote control from the operator's house above the pivot point. The initial pile is formed by the inclined belt conveyor above the head post. The movement of the coal is from the track hopper to the crusher house where, after being crushed, it moves either to the bunkers or to reserve storage. Coal reclaimed from storage is pushed into the track hopper again and may or may not by-pass the crusher.

As a typical cost, Table 1 gives the figures for a Sauerman scraper (Sauerman Brothers) with ¾-yd. scoop having a loaded speed of 300 ft. per min. and return (empty) speed of 400 ft. per min.

This installation has an average capacity of 50 tons per hour, either to storage or reclaiming, over an area with a 100-ft. radius.

TABLE 1

APPROXIMATE COST OF SAUERMAN ¾-YD. INSTALLATION

|  | | |  |
|---|---|---|---|
| Haulage machine, scraper, cables, sheaves, and head post | | | $5,300 |
| Operator's house | | | 1,400 |
| 11 back posts | | | 600 |
| Erection of above items | | | 900 |
| Foundations | | | |
| house and machinery | 13 yd. | | |
| head post | 10 yd. | | |
| outer posts | 67 yd. | | |
| Total 90 yd. concrete at $30 | | | 2,700 |
| | | Total, erected | $10,900 |

**Bulldozer and Carryall.** The extensive ground-storage areas of the large steam plants and steel mills now are quite generally spread by track-type equipment which effectually compacts the mass and prevents air circulation. Although this practice eliminates spontaneous ignition, it introduces the difficulty that the coal is ground up and rained on more or less as more coal comes in, setting up a condition that causes trouble in the bunker and bunker chutes.

The *bulldozer* is strictly a pusher. It does not transport its load, but pushes it ahead, spilling some around the ends and replacing the spillage as it moves forward. It is a track- or caterpillar-type tractor equipped with a blade that can be raised or lowered by a cable or hydraulic mechanism. It is used for short trips, usually not over 200 ft. out or back. The handling capacity ranges from 50 tons per hour on a 200-ft. haul to 135 tons per hour on a 50-ft. haul. A 100-hp. motorized unit will show an operating cost of between $4 and $5 per hour, including labor, depreciation, interest, insurance, fuel and oil, and maintenance.

We will use the designations of the R. G. LeTourneau Company in discussing the following machines.

The *tractor scraper* is a caterpillar- or track-type tractor hitched to a rubber-tired scraper. It loads, transports, and spreads the material evenly in one operating cycle. Usually it is assisted in the loading zone by a pusher tractor to secure larger loads more quickly.

The *Tourneau scraper* (Fig. 12-2) is a self-contained two-wheeled unit connected to a carryall scraper. When empty, 60 per cent of the total weight is on the drive tires. The heaped load capacity of the " Super C " Tourneau scraper is approximately 10 tons of coal. With 100-hp. motor it costs about $10,000 (1946 prices).

The *carryall* is a self-loading self-discharging carrier towed either by a track-type or rubber-tired prime mover. A 100-hp. track-type

FIG. 12-2. Tournapull Super C handling coal on 1300-ft. pulls and on grades up to 18 per cent. Capacity 10 tons per load.

tractor with 10-ton capacity carryall costs about $15,000. The carryall is built in sizes up to 30 cu. yd. capacity.

In Table 2 the letters M, LS, LP, and W are model designations of the LeTourneau carryall scrapers with the capacities noted. The second letters refer to tractors manufactured by the Caterpillar Tractor Company which have the following ratings:

| MODEL | DRAWBAR HORSEPOWER | WEIGHT, POUNDS |
|---|---|---|
| D-6 | 55 | 18,000 |
| D-7 | 80 | 25,000 |
| D-8 | 113 | 35,000 |

As illustrating this method of stocking out and reclaiming reserve coal, Fig. 12-3 outlines a steam generating plant, originally of 50,000-kw. capacity, later expanded to 250,000 kw. with provision for receiving coal by water instead of by rail from self-unloading vessels. The reserve storage was then increased from 50,000 to 150,000 tons.

Incoming coal is piled in a circular ridge by a pivoted belt stacker conveyor and distributed therefrom by two LeTourneau carryall scrapers pulled by caterpillar D8 tractors. Twelve ton loads are picked up in an average of 1 min. The loads are spread in 6-in. layers. One tractor and scraper hauls and stores 100 tons per hour over a 600-ft. haul. Recovery is at about the same rate to the recovery hopper.

In the original plant there was some loss by spontaneous ignition, but, with the current practice of crowning the pile and sealing it by running the tractor and scraper repeatedly over the filled areas, heating has ceased.

TABLE 2

Approximate Tons of Coal Moved per 50-Min. Hour

| | M with D6 | LS with D7 | LP with D8 | W with D8 | Super C Tourneau with LP |
|---|---|---|---|---|---|
| Capacity, heaped | 5.4 tons | 7.45 tons | 10 tons | 15.5 tons | 10 tons |
| Total operating cost per hour[1]<br>One-Way Haul, feet | $3.75 | $4.50 | $5.50 | $7.00 | $6.00 |
| 200 | 70 | 106 | 154 | 230 | Pusher- |
| 300 | 59 | 90 | 131 | 197 | loaded. |
| 400 | 51 | 78 | 115 | 172 | Equipped |
| 500 | 45 | 69 | 101 | 153 | with 150- |
| 600 | 39 | 60 | 89 | 135 | hp. engine |
| 700 | 36 | 54 | 81 | 123 | |
| 800 | 33 | 50 | 74 | 113 | |
| 900 | 30 | 46 | 68 | 104 | |
| 1000 | 28 | 43 | 63 | 97 | 121 |
| 1200 | 24 | 37 | 55 | 84 | 112 |
| 1400 | | 33 | 49 | 75 | 105 |
| 1600 | | 29 | 48 | 67 | 99 |
| 1800 | | | 40 | 61 | 94 |
| 2000 | | | 36 | 57 | 88 |
| 2200 | | | 34 | 52 | 83 |
| 2400 | | | 31 | 48 | 80 |
| 2600 | | | 25 | 45 | 76 |

The above capacities are based on average conditions, better than average conditions will increase the capacities, and vice versa. (Data as of July 1946.)

[1]Operating figures include depreciation, interest, insurance, fuel, oil, operator's wages, parts, and miscellaneous labor.

**Heating of Bituminous Coal.** When coal is piled by dropping from a grab bucket, the larger lumps roll along the flanks while the smaller coal piles up in the central cross section. Air circulates freely through the lump coal, and any tendency to temperature rise is offset by the ventilation effect. The central section is protected against oxidation because the air cannot pass through that mass, but somewhere between these surfaces the air circulation is just right for oxidation and insufficient to carry off the heat as rapidly as it is generated, so that the temperature begins to rise, at first slowly and then rapidly until ignition may occur. The obvious preventive is either to compact the mass by rolling in layers or to seal it with some coating such as emulsified asphalt.

Some bituminous coals have little tendency to heat, and others are quite prone to ignition. At one plant in Indiana where the reserve ground storage was a flat pile only 3 or 4 ft. deep, the author observed that the flanks of the pile were actively burning. This happened to be a state penal institution where labor cost nothing, and evidently severe loss in heating value could be greatly reduced by using this free labor to compact the pile.

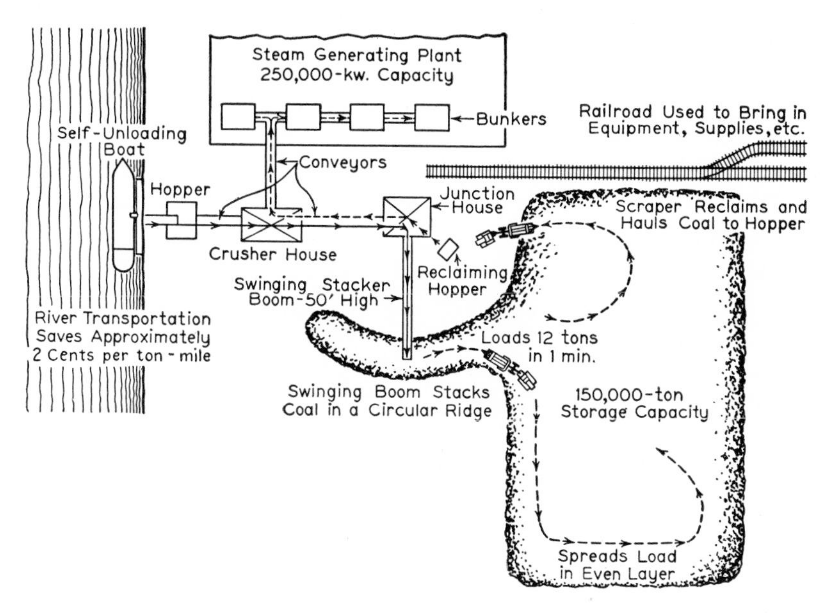


Fig. 12-3. A 150,000-ton coal-storage system with coal spread and reclaimed by 12-ton-capacity tractor scrapers.

Spontaneous heating occurs also in storage bunkers and silos. In bunkers, air enters through the discharge gates and, after heating starts, circulates down the flanks and upward through the central section, building up a temperature rise that may be troublesome if the coal in that section is not removed. In a silo we have the condition referred to in piles formed by a grab bucket. The lumpy coal zone is near the wall, and air circulates upward from the gates. Some will pass through coal whose fineness is right for oxidation. If the temperature increases sufficiently, ignition may occur and explode the gas that has been generated. In one instance the concrete roof of a 300-ton silo was lifted several inches by such an explosion. (The silo referred to is one of those shown in Fig. 13-5.) Even though an explosion may not occur, a clinker may form at the discharge gate. Gates should have close clearance, temperatures should be checked, and if necessary "coal ladders" should be provided to reduce segregation.

At one large middle west plant where coal is delivered by self-unloading vessel, it was spread and piled loosely by a crane. The loss through spontaneous combustion was heavy. Several years ago the procedure was changed, and the coal is now spread by bulldozer and carryall. The carryall is pulled back and forth across horizontal layers of coal so that each layer is smoothed into a stratum 5 or 6 in. deep, and the voids are worked out before the next layer is placed. When the coal pile has reached a depth of 30 ft. or so the top is rounded off as a water-shedding surface. Air circulation is so completely prevented by this process that there has since been no instance of heating.

The performance record of this installation shows, for a tonnage of 388,000 tons:

| | |
|---|---|
| Average, spread and packed per hour | 118 tons |
| Total trips | 39,300 |
| Average trips per hour | 12 |
| Average load | 9.88 tons |
| Average haul | 900 ft. round trip |

When the steam plant calls for it coal is loaded into 70-ton cars by a 60-ft.-radius crawler with 3-ton bucket and hydraulic controls. This machine is stated to maintain a free digging capacity from pile to cars of 400 tons per hour.

The cost of stocking out from dock to pile, including labor, maintenance, charge-off in five years, leveling, and compacting, averages 3 to 4 cents per ton. Rehandling to cars should cost somewhat less except when it is necessary for the bulldozer to break up crusted coal.

*Loss of heating values by weathering* is not severe. Extended research by the Bureau of Mines with New River, Pocohontas, Pittsburgh Gas, and Sheridan Wyoming coals showed that outdoor weathering caused no loss greater than 1.2 per cent the first year or 2.1 per cent in 2 yr. The subbituminous Wyoming coal suffered somewhat greater loss, 2 to 3 per cent the first year and up to 5.5 per cent in five years. In Appalachian coals oxidation starts at about 85° F. and increases in rapidity with temperature increase. With the lower grades the starting temperature is lower. The presence of pyrites is a contributing factor, as is the exposed coal-surface area.

Large-capacity *storage of anthracite coal* is a proposition entirely different from bituminous storage. There is no tendency to heat; in fact the author has seen coal stocked out during a snow storm, still frozen at the core when reloaded the next summer. Prevention of degradation in handling is the major factor with domestic sizes. The

*Dodge System* (Fig. 12-4) does this very cleverly and is generally accepted by the large producers as standard practice.

Each unit of a Dodge coal-storage plant consists of two stocking-out conveyors inclined at 27° and a pivoted reloader with provision for screening out undersize. Figure 12-4 shows a storage plant with a capacity of 500,000 tons in eight conical piles. Each stocking-out conveyor has a capacity of 180 tons per hour, or a total of 14,400 tons per 10-hr. day. Each reloading conveyor has a capacity of 280 tons per hour or a total of 10,000 tons per 10-hr. day.

FIG. 12-4. 500,000 tons capacity anthracite coal storage plant (Dodge System). (Philadelphia and Reading Coal and Iron Company, Abrams, Penn.)

Where possible the serving tracks are straight and on a 1 per cent grade, so the cars will move by gravity. If this cannot be done, a car haul parallels the tracks. The stocking-out conveyor has a steel-ribbon trough bottom which is coiled like a clock spring beneath the lower end of the bow truss and is gradually pulled upward as the pile grows; thus discharge is always closely above the peak and slides gently down along the surface of the cone. Normal capacity is attained when the peak of the pile is at the top of the truss, but in an emergency the capacity may be increased by as much as 30 per cent by chutes. The emergency increase, however, is beyond the reach of the reloader and must be brought to it by bulldozer.

The action of the reloader is gentle. It is a reversible horizontal-runaround conveyor on a pivoted, roller-borne frame so that it has a sweep across the area of the bases of twin piles. With the conveyor in motion the reloader is swung against the toe of the pile (Fig. 12-5), and the coal flows into the open side of the conveyor for several minutes

FIG. 12–5. The Dodge System Reloader. The Reloader is swung in either direction by cables extending beneath the piles and along the reloader frame to drums within the house, actuated by the man standing at the pivot point.

before another bite is necessary. In the event of an avalanche the reloader is backed off until the surge stops. As the great anthracite-storage plants are operated by the producers, their operation is seasonal, stocking out during the slack summer months and reclaiming throughout the winter. Where the climate is severe the system is arranged with a suitable housing, somewhat changing the conveyor layout but retaining the essential feature of handling with minimum breakage.

**Car Shifting.** At storage plants served by a railroad siding or sidings, various methods are employed for moving cars to and from the point of discharge. If the tracks are straight and provide for fifty or more cars, the endless-cable carhaul is good (Fig. 12-6). The cable is carried on rolls between adjacent tracks and is driven at one end

Fig. 12-6. The endless-cable car haul. The cable grip has sufficient traction to pull two or three loaded cars.

of the service track by a double grooved-drum haulage machine. The cable grip which weighs about 15 lb. is attached to 30 ft. of light-steel cable which is hooked into the heavy staple at each end of most hopper-bottom cars. The grip of the towing cable is not strong enough to damage a car. The limit is two or three cars per trip.

A compressed-air locomotive may be favored. This has no furnace, has a one-man crew, and its receiver is recharged at intervals whose frequency depends on the activity of service and the capacity of the receiver. One public-utility plant uses an electric locomotive, remote controlled from a station at the car dumper.

Where the traffic is smaller in volume and extent, a car-puller winch does the job nicely, especially if a straight siding either side of the hopper can be located on a 1 per cent downgrade. An alternative is a small caterpiller tractor.

## COAL STORAGE PROJECT

Figure 12-7 outlines a tract on the Great Lakes where the expansion of a steel plant calls for additional coal storage of 200,000 tons. Coal will be received in a 10,000-ton self-unloading vessel having a discharge rate of 1400 tons per hour. This coal does not heat when stored

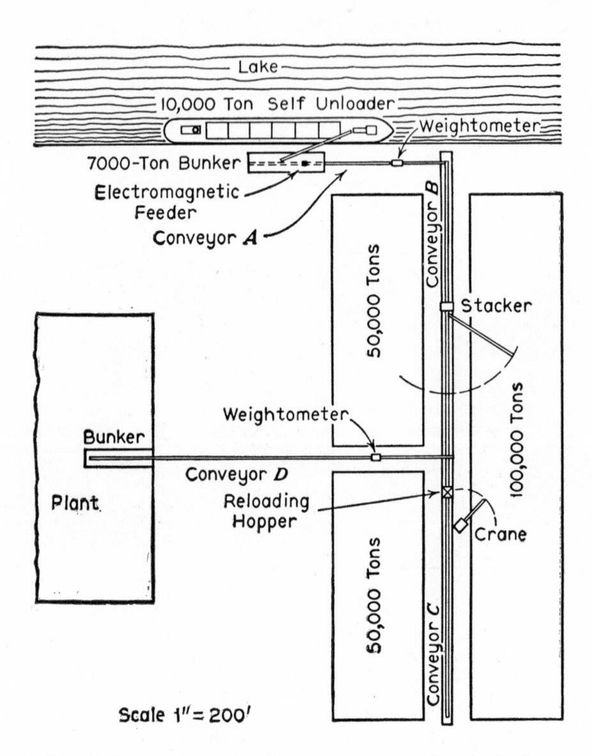


FIG. 12-7. A 200,000-ton reserve coal-storage system for steel plant receiving coal from self-unloading lake-type vessels.

loosely. Deliveries to the plant bunker, either direct or from storage, are to be weighed. As a rule a supplier does not accept as conclusive the readings of automatic scales, but a record of incoming tonnage is desirable as a check on charges.

As the discharge rate of the self-unloader is much greater than is possible for the distribution system except at very great cost, a self-clearing bunker is provided at the wharf. A 36-in. belt conveyor at 450 ft. per min. has a capacity of 500 tons per hour — a reasonable rate of handling both as regards investment and rehandling by crane into and out of storage. It is essential that there shall be no interruption of the unloading of the vessel. Eight hours are required to unload and clean up. At the end of 7 hr. about 9800 tons are delivered to the bin, and 3500 tons have been removed by the conveyors, and so a minimum bunker capacity of 6300 tons is indicated. The bin will be of the suspension type with closely spaced discharge gates and a motor-propelled electromagnetic feeder interlocked so that a gate can be opened only when the feeder is beneath that gate.

The first 36-in. belt conveyor *A* is equipped with a weightometer and discharges to conveyor *B*, bisecting the storage area down to the point where the take-off is made to conveyor *D* serving the plant bunker. The south half of the storage area is covered by the tandem conveyor *C*.

It is advantageous to locate conveyors *B* and *C* in a depressed runway rather than above ground level. We eliminate the danger of the belts being blown off by high winds, the wall of the trench conveniently supports the insulator brackets of the feeder wires, the traveling hoppers can rest on rails directly on the trench walls, and the lift when reclaiming is less.

To distribute from *B* and *C*, we require a traveling stacker with a boom that may be swung to either side to form a pile from which a crane can distribute the coal over the storage areas. We may be able to work out the design so that a single stacker will serve both *B* and *C*. To receive the coal rehandled from storage by the crane we will require a movable hopper which can function with conveyor *B* moving in one direction and conveyor *C* in the reverse direction.

To enable us to use a single reload hopper and stacker, both must be designed to pass the conveyor trippers. To accomplish this we will provide the hopper with a reversible loading chute with direct-gravity flow to the belts. The stacker feeder must be lifted to clear when the stacker must pass a tripper. Self-aligning idlers must be spaced along all the conveyors, and, since *C* is reversible, its self-aligning idler must be of a type that will function with reverse travel, not that shown in the lower cut, Fig. 10-23.

The scheme of operation is as follows. When stocking out to the north half of the storage area, the stacker feeder is set to register with the tripper of *B*. When stocking out to the south half of the area, *B* tripper discharges to belt *C*. The reloader hopper is shifted to the south end of the line. The stacker is brought over and its feeder set to register with tripper *C*. Discharge from *B* to *D* is direct over the head end of *B*. For discharge from *C* to *D*, conveyor *C* is reversed, its tripper is run to the south end, and the hopper is spotted to suit the operation of the crane after the stacker is moved out of the way.

The crane will have a 60-ft. boom and 3-ton bucket for a capacity of 500 tons per hour with average swing of 120° and 30-ft. lift. One or two bulldozers will be helpful for cleaning up and assisting the crane.

The motors should be interlocked to assure starting in proper sequence, and, if one unit should stop, preceding units will stop. A tele-

FIG. 12–8. Coal storage and reclaiming system of the Great Lakes Steel Corporation near Detroit, Mich. Layout developed along the lines discussed in pages 260 to 261. Shown is Conveyor *B*. Diesel operated crane has 3-ton bucket and with 120° swing averages 500 tons per hour. (Link-Belt.)

phone or loud-speaker service covering all points along the line is advisable.

Figure 12-8 is a picture of a 1939 installation similar to the project just analyzed.

**Stackers.** As a means of storing bulk material in piles, as with ore, sand, and gravel, and for in-and-out coal storage in distribution yards, the stacker is commonly used. This may be a pivoted overhead conveyor serving a circular area, or an inclined conveyor, often movable, ranging from the small portable machine with a capacity of a few tons per hour to high-capacity belt-conveyor stackers mounted on caterpillars. The material may be reclaimed by a tunnel conveyor beneath the pile, by a crawler crane or shovel, or by a wagon loader.

Figure 12-9 shows a pivoted stacker for iron ore as used in the Iron Range after navigation closes on the lakes. Ore cars are discharged to a belt conveyor extending from the trestle to a point directly over the pivot of the stacker conveyor which has a swing over an arc of 320°. When the ore is to be shipped out it is rehandled by a crawler shovel to cars on a track encircling the pile.

FIG. 12-9. Iron-ore stacker. Ore is reclaimed to cars by the crawler shovel seen under the conveyor bridge.

**Industrial Cars.** Trestle-mounted electrically operated cars frequently provide a satisfactory method of stocking out sand, gravel, crushed gypsum, and other materials not subject to degradation. A somewhat similar function is the distribution of such materials to long storage bins as shown in Fig. 12-10. This is a drying, storage, and shipping plant for pebble phosphate. As mined, the pebbles contain water which is driven off by passing them through rotary dryers. The pebbles are then lifted in a gravity-discharge elevator and fed through a surge hopper to 5-ton-capacity self-dumping cars. Each car stops when it arrives beneath the hopper, automatically opens and closes the feed gate, and the loaded car starts its round trip, discharging to the bin for which the door trip is set.

**Transport by Truck.** Truck transport from ore pit to surface with pay loads up to 15 tons has been common in the Iron Range since 1936 or 1937. Diesel engines are preferred as having a fuel consumption compared with a gasoline engine in the ratio of 3 to 5.8. The six-wheel truck with single rear axle and two tires on each side is preferred to the ten-wheel truck with double rear axles and four tires, because it gives a smaller turning radius and is claimed to have lower tire and maintenance costs.

The fluid drive has been found advantageous in preventing stalling on overload. Tests with the fluid drive and supercharged Diesels showed gains over the standard Diesels of 24 to 48 per cent on heavy grades.

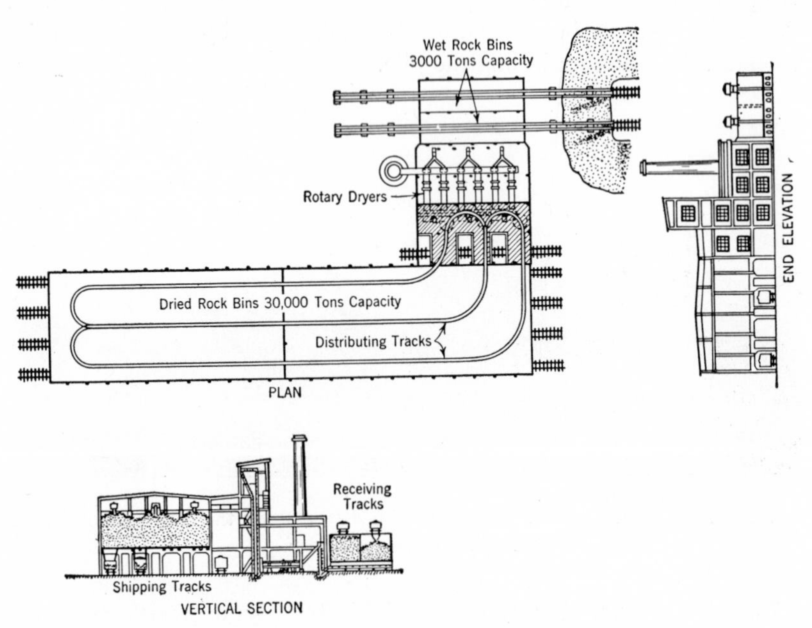


Fig. 12–10. Car system distribution at Florida phosphate plant. (Hudson.)

Supercharging has no advantage on the return trip, but the greater power available on the loaded runs, with resulting higher speeds, increases truck efficiency proportionately to the length of the haul.

Hourly operating costs increase with the age of the truck as shown by the following tabulation:

Hourly Operating Costs with Relation to Age of Truck

| Number of Trucks | Age, years | Cubic Yards Handled | Hours Worked | Operating Cost per Hour | Maintenance Cost per Hour | Tires | Total | Increase over First Year, per cent |
|---|---|---|---|---|---|---|---|---|
| 3 | 1 | 520,000 | 10,500 | $1.18 | $0.20 | $0.32 | $1.70 | .... |
| 3 | 2 | 723,000 | 15,000 | 1.22 | 0.41 | 0.33 | 1.96 | 15.6 |
| 2 | 3 | 631,000 | 15,400 | 1.30 | 0.76 | 0.31 | 2.37 | 40.4 |

The increases are in maintenance, fuel consumption, and oil consumption. Tire life is assumed at 3000 hours. One company charges off the truck in 10,000 hours' operation, which no doubt is extremely conservative.

Truck roads constructed with bulldozers and graders cost about \$3000 per mile, and good road maintenance is important in holding down the cost of trucking. Road maintenance costs, of course, vary widely.

As compared with steam locomotive haulage, the truck has been found to show a 10 per cent reduction in stripping as well as a reduction of 50 per cent in man-hours for ore produced. The small turning radius of the truck, particularly of the six-wheel truck, reduces the percentage of inaccessible ore. Long track benches are eliminated, haulage distances are reduced because of steeper grades, and shovel efficiency is improved by the narrower benches.

At one location in the Iron Range the trucks carry a pay load of 34,000 lb. and are loaded by crawler shovel. These trucks have a 185-hp. Diesel engine with eight forward speeds and are geared for speeds of 3 to 30 m.p.h. on the level, or 10 m.p.h. on an 8 per cent grade. The scoop-shaped body is raised and lowered by hydraulic pressure. The operating figures for these trucks are:

| | |
|---|---|
| Length of round trip, average | 9400 ft. |
| Average lift per trip | 200 ft. |
| Average time to load truck | 50 sec. |
| Average time to dump | 50 sec. |
| Cost per truck-hour, exclusive of depreciation | \$2.35 |
| Tire cost on basis of 3000 hours adds \$4.49 per truck. | |
| Total per truck-hour, including tire costs | \$6.84 |

On a ton-mile basis, the figure is \$0.0643.

The average during the season, including delays, is 12.64 min. per truck per trip. Over 300,000 tons per year are thus transported, and since these costs were recorded reductions have been attained through the purchase of oil in tank-car lots, experience, and improved roads, which have brought the figure close to 5 cents per ton-mile.

The question might be asked, why not use belt conveyors since the cost per ton-mile is substantially less than the above figure. Often there are valid reasons why a belt cannot be used. In the example cited, the properties under lease make it necessary to segregate the ores and rock according to ownerships, and this segregation was not practicable with conveyors.

Some data are available for comparing the cost with electric tramming (railroad) and shaft hoist at three mines with the cost of handling by belt-conveyor system at a fourth mine. The figures may be misleading, however, as the conditions are not exactly the same. The following are costs per ton-mile, excluding depreciation and maintenance. The fact that belt conveyors are superseding other methods wherever they can be utilized is evidence that in this field their operating costs are lower.

COSTS PER TON-MILE: ELECTRIC TRAM AND SHAFT HOIST VS. INCLINED BELT CONVEYOR

Mine 1. Electric tram system and shaft hoist.

| Item | Supplies | Labor | Total |
|---|---|---|---|
| Tramming | $0.0318 | $0.0460 | $0.0778 |
| Hoisting | 0.0235 | 0.0315 | 0.0550 |
| Total | $0.0553 | $0.0775 | $0.1328 |

Mine 2. Same system.

| Item | Supplies | Labor | Total |
|---|---|---|---|
| Tramming | $0.0234 | $0.0512 | $0.0746 |
| Hoisting | 0.0082 | 0.0250 | 0.0332 |
| Total | $0.0316 | $0.0762 | $0.1078 |

Mine 3. Same system.

| Item | Supplies | Labor | Total |
|---|---|---|---|
| Tramming | $0.0176 | $0.0445 | $0.0621 |
| Hoisting | 0.0197 | 0.0155 | 0.0352 |
| Total | $0.0373 | $0.0600 | $0.0973 |

Mine 4. Belt-Conveyor system.

| Item | Supplies | Labor | Total |
|---|---|---|---|
| Hoisting | $0.0235 | $0.0118 | $0.0353 |
| Total | $0.0235 | $0.0118 | $0.0353 |

**Transport at a Strip Mine.** A striking example of truck transport is found at a middle west coal-stripping operation where mining began in 1939. The trucks are semi-trailer type with a pay load of 52 tons; the load is dumped by air-operated gates, two on each side, automatically tripped as the truck crosses slowly over the dump hopper. The six-cylinder 220-hp. engine has five forward speeds, uses gasoline fuel, and is geared to 30 m.p.h. with the truck empty. The rear end of the chassis is mounted on eight 13.5 by 24 in. tires; the front end has eight similar tires, and the motor end has two 12 by 24 in. tires, making eighteen in all.

A 7½-yd. bucket operated by a 40-ft.-radius shovel loads a truck in 3 to 5 min.; under favorable conditions it can load trucks at a rate of 1000 tons per hour, which is a slightly higher figure than the capacity of the coal preparation plant to which delivery is made. Four of these trucks are used at present, each covering about 50 mi. per shift with an average haul of 1 mi. As the haul increases in length, additional trucks may be added to maintain the rate of delivery, or eventually a combination rail-and-truck system can be arranged. The advantage of truck haulage here is that the loading point continually shifts onward and it is a difficult matter to extend a 1000-ton-per-hour belt conveyor repeatedly. Moreover, the coal seam is cracked up by blasting into lumps too large for a conveyor. As compared with a tram system the trucks have far greater flexibility of action.

The trucks deliver to a large dump hopper equipped with a feeder and a 36 by 72 in. crusher which reduces the lumps to 6 in. and smaller

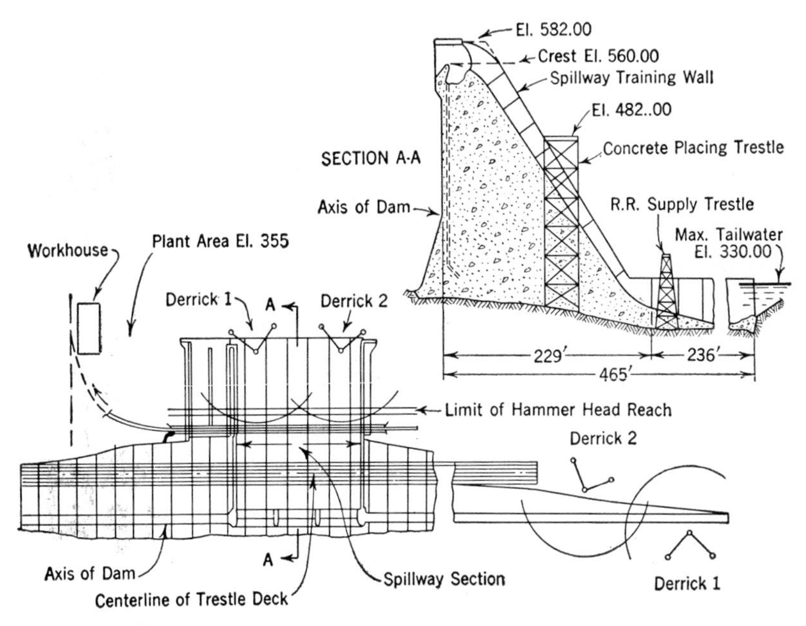


FIG. 12–11. Diagram of concrete-placing equipment for Friant dam.

before the coal passes to a 54-in. belt conveyor leading into the preparation plant.

A few years ago it would have been considered fantastic to attempt to mine and transport coal as described. There is, of course, a limit to the distance to which truck haulage will function efficiently as compared with railroad haulage, and there is a zone in which conveying by belt, where it is possible, will show substantially lower costs than either, not only directly but also in the elimination of roadway maintenance.

**Transport of Concrete — Friant Dam.** As illustrating the careful planning and engineering skill in provision for the transport and placement of concrete, the system devised by the contractors for the $16,000,000 Friant dam on the San Joaquin River, Central Valley project, California, is outstanding.

This dam has a length of 3340 ft., is 325 ft. high, and involved the placing of 2,000,000 yd. of concrete within a time limit of 3¼ yr. from November 1, 1939. The handling equipment was planned for an average placement of 150,000 yd. per mo. or an hourly rate of 125 cu. yd. For this part of the job the contractors constructed two

FIG. 12–12. Concrete-placing equipment used in the construction of Friant dam. Handling capacity planned for placing 125 cu. yd. per hr.

trestles, (Fig. 12-11), on the downstream side of the dam. The nearer one is the concrete placing trestle, 129 ft. from the dam axis. The railroad supply trestle is lower and 120 ft. farther out. The high trestle (Fig. 12-12), required 3800 tons of steel. It had a deck 40 ft. wide on which were mounted two hammerhead cranes and two revolving derricks resting on 38-ft. gauge tracks. The traveling and lifting speeds were 125 and 750 ft. per min., respectively. The total reach of the hammerheads was 314 ft., and each had an estimated concrete-placing capacity of 180 cu. yd. per hr.

The concrete was transported along the trestle in 4-yd. bottom-dump cars towed by Diesel-electric locomotives. At the placing point the buckets were lifted and swung out to either side by the hammerheads or lowered through hatches in the deck.

**Fatigue Factor.** In calculating for a given operating capacity with mechanical equipment such as a crane, bulldozer, truck, or drag scraper, which is dependent on the skill of an operator, it must be kept in mind that the capacity which can be attained in an hour is not the capacity that can be maintained throughout the day. The fatigue of the operator must be taken into account. A conservative rule is to use a 50-min. hour in calculating the day-by-day or running capacity.

# CHAPTER 13

## BINS AND BUNKERS

As distinguished from ground or stockpile storage covered in the previous chapter we here discuss the essentials of storage by bins and bunkers.

For temporary use or for construction work the storage bin should be so constructed that it can be dismantled for use elsewhere. The batcher bins for concrete aggregates are typical. For permanent use the prime essentials are long life and low maintenance costs. The common types of bins and bunkers are:

The *silo,* usually of concrete but occasionally of steel plate.

The *suspension bunker* of steel plate either protected or unprotected.

The *framed bunker* and bin, usually of steel plate with structural-steel bracing and supports.

The silo is the simplest form of storage bin; it is derived from the wood-stave silo of the farmer but is more substantially constructed. For construction work the steel-plate silo with bolted sections provides a container for cement in bulk that has the advantage that it is easily dismounted or erected and packs nicely for shipment. For a permanent structure the concrete silo is preferable. Concrete silos are of three types: concrete stave, concrete block or tile, and poured-concrete or monolithic.

Stave silos are lowest in cost. They are formed of book-shaped precast concrete staves 3 or 4 in. thick and about 36 in. long set up in stepped tiers with outside circumferential turnbuckle rods to hold the staves in position against the outward thrust of the material. This type is preferred by the farmer, but for flowable materials such as coal it is deficient in stability compared with the others. In some cities the building code does not favor it.

Concrete-block and hollow-tile silos cost more than monolithic silos. Block silos are formed with chambered precast concrete blocks and present a rather crude appearance. Hollow-tile silos are of precast chambered tile (Fig. 13-1) erected with reinforcing rods grouted into recesses between the tiers. A burned-tile or glazed-tile silo is a beautiful structure.

The advantage of the hollow-tile silo is that the air spaces retard freezing of the material in storage. A small block or tile silo mounted on a concrete support as shown in Fig. 13-2 provides a neat and economical ash storage bin.

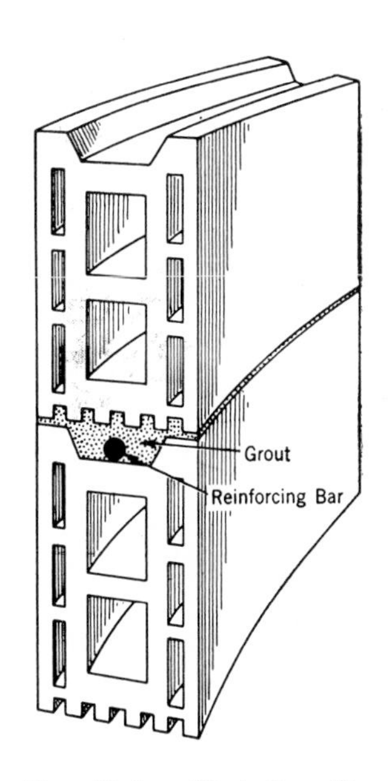


Fig. 13-1. Silo hollow tile.

Fig. 13-2. Concrete block silo mounted on drive-under support.

Hollow tiles are usually 12 by 12 by 6 in. thick and cost about $300 per thousand plus freight. A mason and three helpers can place 150 tile per 8-hr. day.

Monolithic or poured-concrete silos cost less than block or hollow-tile silos except for those of very small capacity. If carefully formed to avoid ridges and form marks and given an outside wash of white cement, they present a pleasing appearance. The smaller silos are as a rule constructed with sectional ring forms about 2 ft. high, which come in sets of three. The first and second rings are filled, then the third. By that time the first ring may be removed and mounted upon the third for pouring the fourth ring; and so on, up to the top.

The ring-form method is slow, and most of the silo builders prefer the slip-form method. With slip forms an entire group of silos may be built simultaneously. The form is moved up slowly and continu-

FIG. 13–3. Four 400-ton elevated silos with 100-ton interspace formed by connecting walls. Monolithic silos for anthracite coal. (Hudson.)

ously by jacks, as the concrete is poured. The rate of lift must be carefully adjusted so that the concrete uncovered below the form ring will not slough — a risky job in freezing weather. The circumferential reinforcing steel is tied in just above the working level.

By spacing multiple silos a foot or two apart, they may be connected by narrow walls to provide a fifth bin for each group of four, usually referred to as the "interspace bin." Figure 13-3 shows a five-compartment group for anthracite coal.

A common application of monolithic silos is for grain storage, sometimes with twenty or more units in twin rows with a belt conveyor along the tops and another in a tunnel beneath.

Since a silo of large diameter has considerable dead storage at the base, the usual limit for coal silos is 30 to 35 ft., and the desired capacity is secured, if necessary, by increased height.

With coal silos excessive height causes heavy pressure near the bottom, degrading and grinding the coal as it is discharged. This crushing action is less with grain because of the characteristic thrust against the wall which prevents a downward thrust proportional to the depth, and so grain silos 100 ft. high or more are not unusual. However, a heavy downward thrust is transmitted to the silo wall that must be considered in designing the footing.

A neat detail in silo construction is to form the elevator casing of concrete as the silo is poured. This actually costs less than a steel-plate casing and is not subject to corrosion.

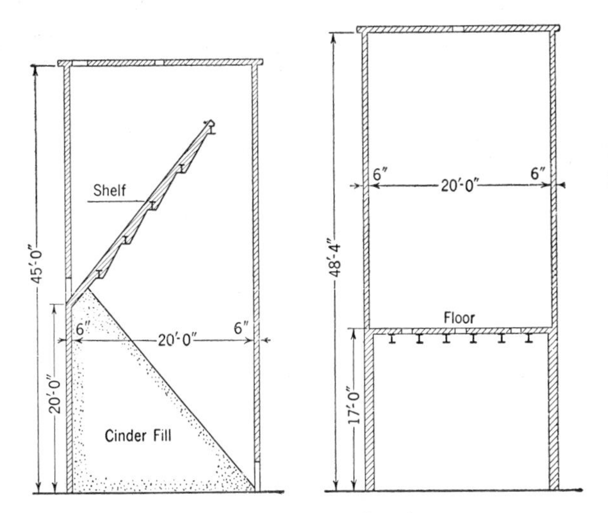


Fig. 13-4. Alternative silos.

**Boiler-House Coal Storage by Silo.** It is usual to have an upper or live-storage compartment from which there is gravity flow to the boiler room, the lower section being the reserve rehandled to the upper compartment by the elevator as needed. The live-storage compartment may be formed by a sloping shelf, preferably on a 50° incline, or by a cone-bottom steel hopper having a diameter about 2 ft. smaller than the inside diameter of the silo. Live storage is so provided readily in monolithic, tile, and block silos, but in stave silos the construction is somewhat risky.

As an alternative to the sloping shelf or storage hopper we may have a flat floor at an elevation which permits the introduction of a horizontal conveyor to the stoker hoppers. Figure 13-4 shows the two arrangements. The silo at the left is 20 ft. in diameter and 45 ft. high with a shelf on a 50° slope. The lower edge of the sloping shelf is high

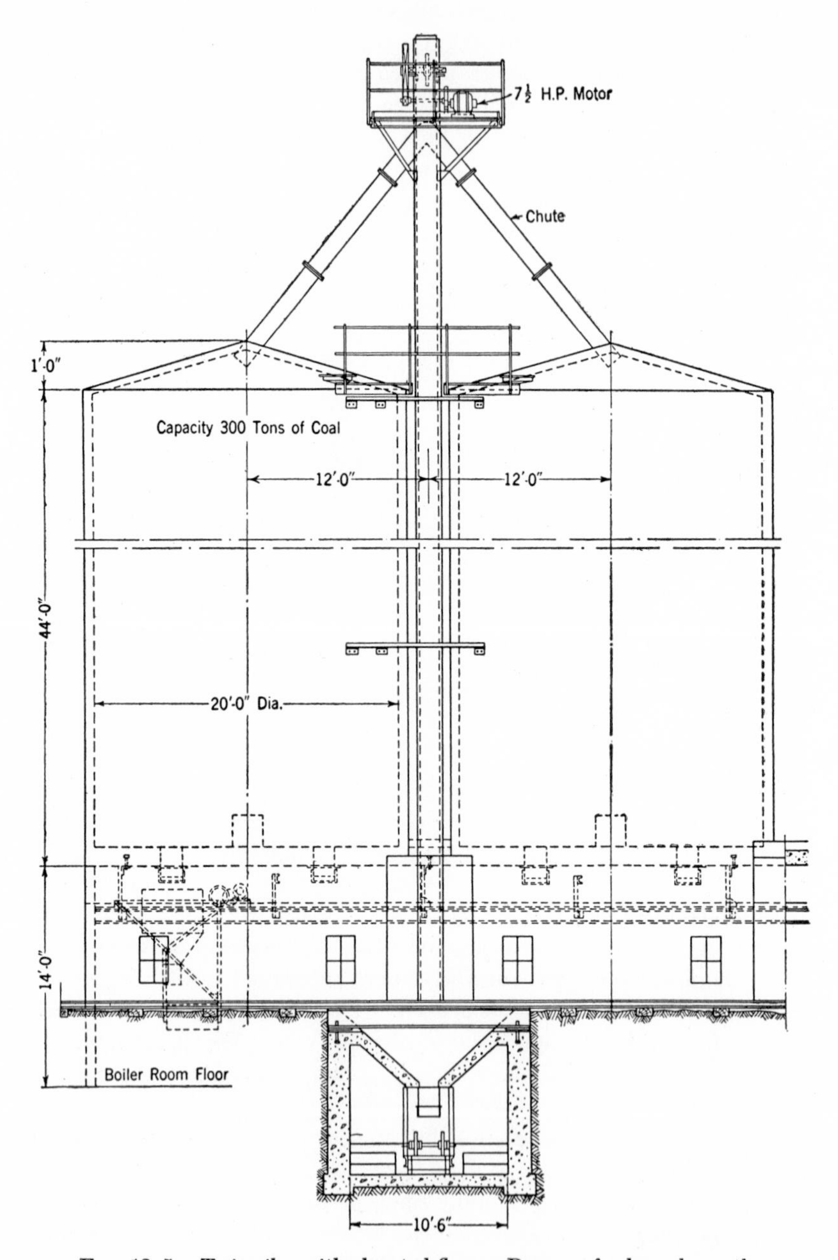


FIG. 13–5. Twin silos with elevated floor. Runway for larry beneath.

enough to chute into the boiler room. The silo at the right has the same diameter and a total height of 48 ft. with a flat floor 17 ft. above ground level, sufficiently high for a screw conveyor into the boiler room.

The cost (1941) of the first was $4300, and of the other, $3615; but if we add the cost of the screw conveyor and extra gates ($800 more than the cost of the chute and one gate), the costs are about the same. The sloping floor provides 57 tons live storage, and coal must be rehandled from the lower section. The elevated floor provides about 150 tons live storage.

Twin silos are used when the capacity is too large for a single unit, or when a single unit calls for a depth which will crush the coal. If the twin silos may be in line with a battery of stokers it is convenient to use the raised-floor type and extend a larry runway beneath both floors. Such a design engineered by the Heine Chimney and Construction Company is shown in Fig. 13-5. Each silo has a capacity of 300 tons, and to minimize dead space each has two discharge gates. Stoker coal is received by a 12 by 12 ft. track hopper with 4-in. grid and flows to an 18-in. apron feeder driven from the elevator foot shaft. The centrifugal-discharge elevator has a capacity of 25 tons per hour at 260 ft. per min., with a 7½-hp. motor. A 2000-lb.-capacity motor-operated weigh larry transfers the coal to the stoker hoppers.

**Silo Design.** This installation may be used to illustrate the routine of silo design. The silos rest on annular concrete rings or footings, 18 in. thick and 5 ft. 6 in. wide, with ¾-in. radially spaced rods 3 in. above the bottom face. Vertical dowels, 2 ft. 11 in. centers, extend up into the supporting wall which is open for a width of 8½ ft. as a passageway for the larry. The substructure extends 16 ft. to the silo floor and is reinforced by ⅝-in. circumferential rods spaced 12-in. centers, as shown in Fig. 13-6. The floor is a flat slab, 20 in. thick, heavily reinforced by a grid of 1-in. rods 3 in. above the bottom face. The silo extends upward with no change in outside diameter but with the wall thickness reduced to 6 in. It is reinforced vertically with ⅝-in. and ½-in. rods on 12-in. centers, to which the circumferential rods are tied. The latter are ⅝ in. on 9-in. centers for about 15 ft., then ½ in. for the next 7½ ft., and ½ in. with 12-in. spacing for the top 19 ft. where a flat-cone roof is doweled to the wall. Throughout, the mix is 1-2-4. Inside ladder rungs should be omitted as inviting accident; men should not go into a coal silo.

The track hopper (Fig. 13-7) must be submitted to the railroad engineers for approval, or the owner may have difficulty in getting cars placed later. In wet soil the concrete wall must be extended above ground level, and the floor should slope to a sump.

Since it is impossible to see whether a silo is filled to capacity, it is desirable to locate a load indicator within the silo close to the full-load

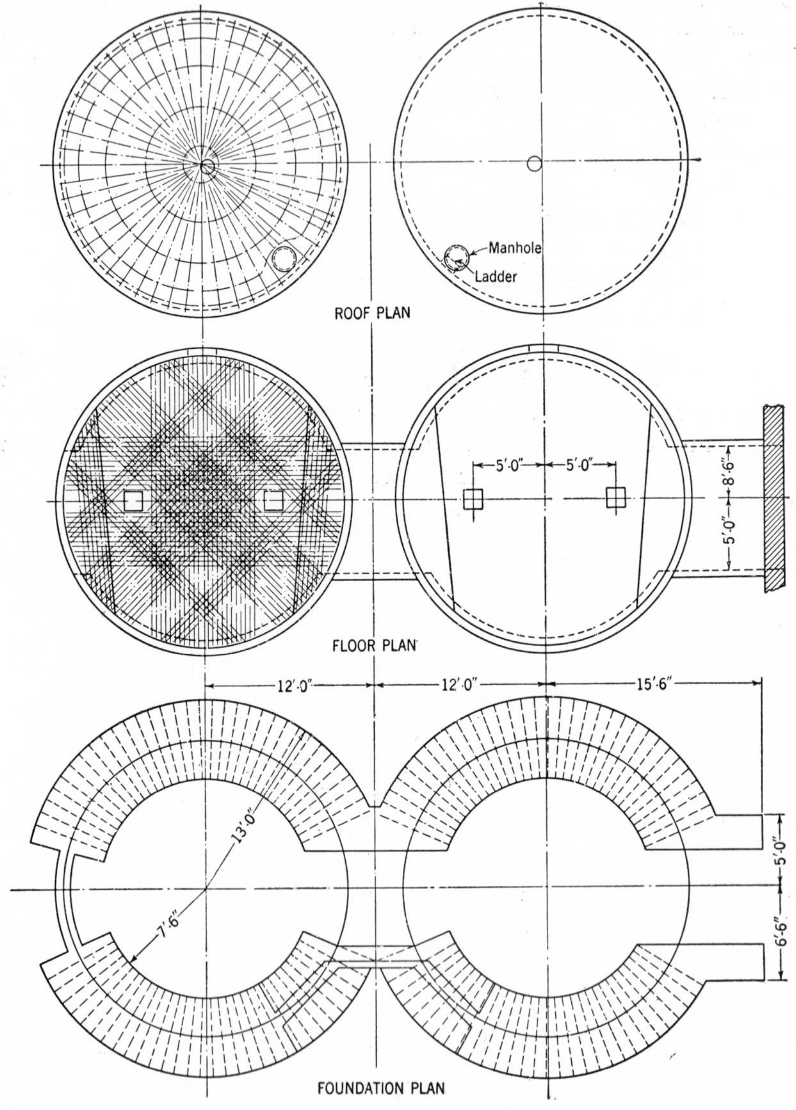


FIG. 13–6. Design details of monolithic silos in Fig. 13–5.

point. One such device is the Bindicator (Bindicator Company). Essentially, this is a flexible diaphragm which, when pushed outward by the thrust of the material, actuates a mercoid switch which either rings a bell or stops the elevator. Figure 13-8 shows the connections. The

Stephens Adamson Manufacturing Company uses a pendulum-like device which is swung aside by the mass and stops the elevator motor. A less desirable indicator is provided by a hole in the side wall of the silo through which the material pours out when it reaches that level.

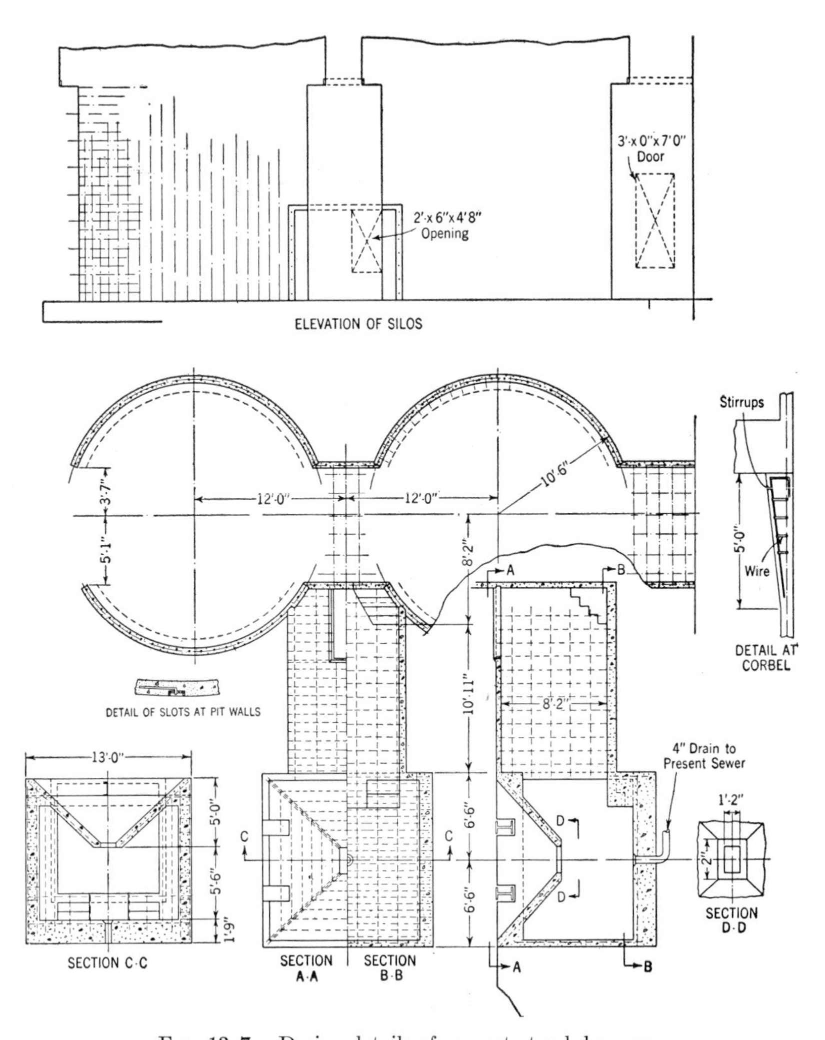


FIG. 13–7. Design details of concrete track hopper.

**Silo Costs.** Since costs vary with labor rates, proximity of materials, and local conditions, the following figures may not be exact, but they are given as a guide for preliminary estimates. For an exact figure the contractor must know all the conditions at the site.

Single-unit silos of monolithic concrete construction, resting on a ring foundation of moderate depth, will cost about $15 to $16 per ton of gross (coal) capacity for capacities around 400 tons. For capacities around 300 tons the cost will be from $18 to $21 per ton. For capacities of less than 300 tons the cost will be above $25. Hollow-tile silos costs about 15 per cent more than monolithic silos, and stave silos about 20 per cent less. A shelf adds substantially to the cost. Frequently

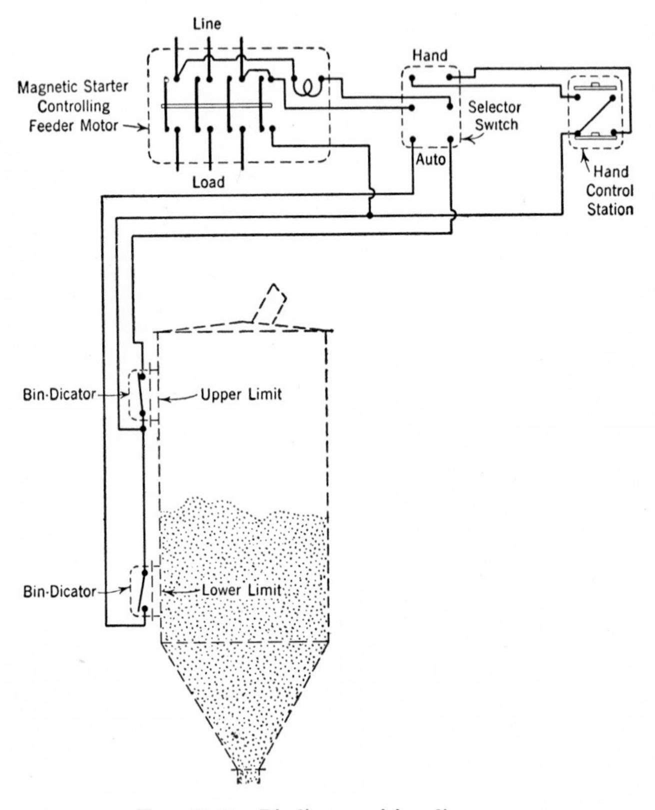


Fig. 13-8. Bindicator wiring diagram.

a sloping floor of concrete resting on a tamped cinder fill is specified. This is not advisable, as the fill always settles and the concrete facing breaks up. It is better and cheaper to tamp the cinder fill and top it off with coal, which soon forms its own slope and is thereafter permanent.

Steel silos cost more than monolithic concrete silos, require painting, and are subject to corrosion by contact with some coals. Coal freezes more readily in a steel silo. Since steel silos may be taken down and shifted from place to place, they are frequently used for storing cement and crushed stone or gravel.

The following is a comparison of the cost of a steel silo with that of a monolithic concrete silo from a 1941 estimate. Each had a diameter of 17 ft. and a wall height of 40 ft. with a sloping shelf for 50 tons of live storage. Gross storage under the shelf was 150 tons. Both were to be erected by union labor at Chicago.

The steel silo as specified by railroad engineers was of rather heavy design, since the coal for which it was intended is at times damp and somewhat corrosive.

The shell was of ¼-in. top plates, ⅜-in. mid-zone plates, 7/16-in. bottom-zone plates, with vertical stiffener angles inside the shell. The shelf was of ½-in. plates carried on I-beams welded to the shell. The roof was of ¼-in. plates. The silo was painted two field coats inside and out. The price was $6800, or $34 per ton of capacity.

The concrete silo had 6-in. walls, concrete shelf on steel I-beams, and a flat concrete roof. The price was $2400 or $12 per ton of capacity (without foundations). Present costs are substantially higher.

The life of the steel-plate silo might reasonably be taken as 20 yr. with occasional repainting. The concrete silo will have a far longer life with practically no up-keep cost.

**Reduction of Degradation — Chutes.** With some materials, such as sized anthracite coal, briquettes, and pellets, it is essential that degradation, or breaking up of the pieces, shall be reduced to a minimum. Some materials are so fragile that degradation cannot be avoided and rescreening and loss are inevitable, but if some rough handling is permissible it is possible to reduce breakage substantially by means of special chutes.

The "coal ladder" (Fig. 13-9), frequently used in anthracite coal pockets, serves to trickle the material downward at reduced velocity. A spiral chute, if properly pitched, retards the flow as the material flows along the outer rim where the path is longest for a given descent. When the material reaches the mass already in the bin the flow is radially inward with reduced impact.

*Chute slope* is difficult to predetermine exactly. Difficulties arise when chutes are either too steep or too flat. The latter condition is the more difficult to overcome. Lining with glass, stainless steel, or Monel metal will often overcome sluggish flow along a chute that is too flat. Where lack of headroom precludes a chute of sufficient slope there is the alternative of a flat vibrating chute. It is not effective with wet material, however.

It is possible to eliminate much of the degradation caused by grinding in the converging flow to the outlet gate. If a square vertical chute from discharge opening to top of bin is provided, with vertically hung trap doors opening inward on all four sides of the chute, the material will flow softly in successive strata off the *top* of the pile instead of from the bottom. With anthracite coal this reduces degradation to a remarkable degree.

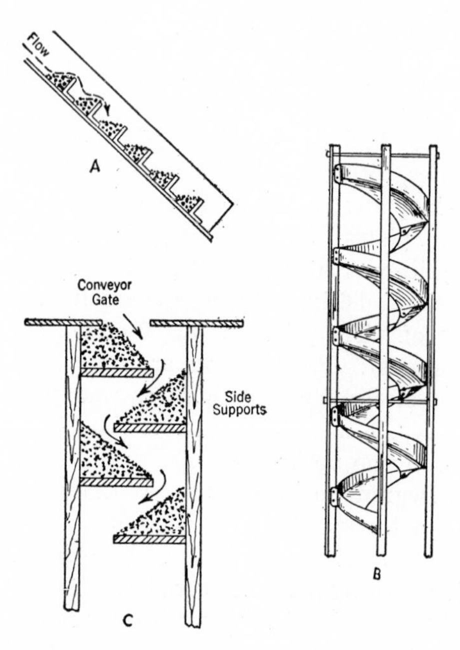


FIG. 13–9. Chutes. (*A*) Baffles retarding the flow along a chute too steep. (*B*) Spiral retarding chute. (*C*) "Coal ladder," a vertical retarding chute.

The coefficient of friction of the material against steel plate is an indication of, though not an exact guide to, the required slope of the chutes. Other factors enter, such as rusting, roughening, and dampening of the material. Bituminous coal usually will continue to flow on steel plate inclined at 38° to 40° when it has an initial velocity, but when it is wet or sticky it will not; a slope of 45° is common practice. However, coal in a long 45° chute can build up considerable velocity with objectionable degradation. Transverse baffles as in Fig. 13-9 may correct this difficulty.

**Coal Silos vs. Bunkers.** Where the winters are severe, difficulties arise in coal stored outside, which is one reason why an inside bunker is preferred in boiler-house design; however, freezing may be prevented by heating coils or by injection of a small amount of live steam at the base and adjacent to the outlets. Fires due to spontaneous combustion are more easily combatted in a bunker than in a silo.

**Bunkers.** The inside overhead bunker has the advantage that the contents are warm and free-flowing, and if spontaneous combustion starts the hot section may be cleared. Overhead bunkers may have steel-framed sides with 45° sloping floor (inverted pyramid), or they may be of the suspension type.

Fig. 13-10. Three-hundred-ton four-compartment aggregate bin and 650-barrel cement bin.

The framed bunker has the good feature that it is nearly self-clearing, but it costs much more than the other because of the stiffening members required in the sides and bottom. Framed bunkers are usual for the largest capacities because the cross-sectional dimensions are beyond those desirable in the flexible suspension type and are framed in with the structure of the building. They should always be protected by a lining of waterproof concrete if material is corrosive.

Framed steel bins are widely used for the storage of sand, stone, and cement in concreting plants, often referred to as batcher hoppers. Figure 13-10 shows a permanent structure with a capacity of 300 tons in four compartments and a separate cement storage of 650-barrel capacity. The fundamental requirements for this type of bin are steep sides — at least 50° to decrease arching; no rivet heads or projections inside the bin, especially near the outlets; and a clear outlet opening without inside flanges.

The large batching plants are equipped with power-operated gates and may have automatic scales. If delivery of materials is by rail, the

Fig. 13–11. The Ferro Inclave suspension coal bunker. Twin outlets lead to each automatic scales. The special corrugated sheets are laid upon the straps. The bunker is shaped by guys attached to the straps to a curve which is that for the bunker fully loaded, then the interior concrete lining is applied.

capacity of each compartment should be more than one carload to reduce demurrage charges on partly cleared cars.

**The suspension bunker** consists of a steel plate from ¼ to ½ in. thick, hung in a catenary between two parallel side girders. In a coal bunker the gates should be closely spaced to reduce dead storage; if this cannot be done it is better to provide a horizontal runaround conveyor beneath closely spaced openings. (Chapter 20). An unprotected steel-plate bunker for bituminous coal may have a life of 10 to 12 yr. or less than a year if the coal is corrosive; therefore it is common practice to protect the steel by a permanent lining of waterproof concrete or by occasional applications of a corrosion-resisting paint. A steel-plate bunker with a concrete lining costs considerably more than an unprotected bunker.

An interesting alternative construction is the "Ferro Inclave bunker" originated by the Brown Hoist Company which has all the advantages of the other but costs much less. It substitutes, for the continuous steel-plate "bag," steel straps spaced about 3-ft. centers

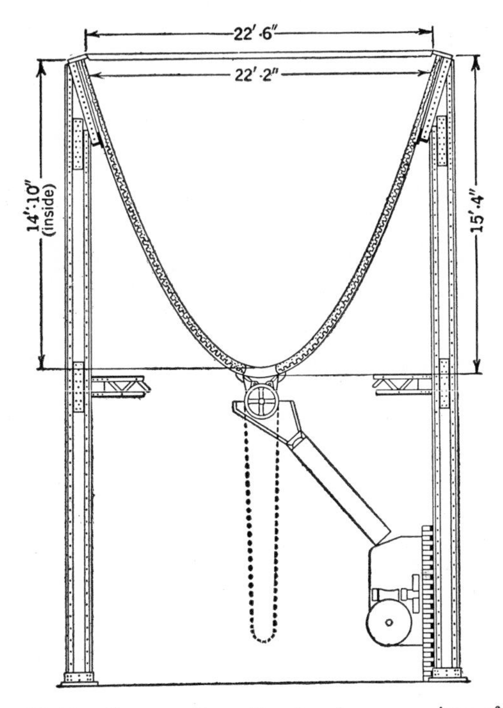


FIG. 13–12. Cross section of bunker for comparison of costs.

(Fig. 13-11) on which are laid light-gauge preformed steel sheets to form the outer reinforcement of the lining. The bag is shaped and held by guys to a curve corresponding to that which the bunker will take when fully loaded. The concrete lining then is applied by the Gunite method to a thickness that varies from 4 or 5 in. at the bottom to 2 or 3 in. at the top where it is continued on wire mesh to the top flanges of the side girders. Formerly the outside face of the Ferro Inclave was plastered with a 1 : 2 lime-cement mixture, but now an anti-corrosion paint is applied at a considerable saving in cost.

The author recently made inquiry about a number of these bunkers he had erected between 1910 and 1915 and was advised that they are in practically the same condition as when erected. Rather oddly, this type costs little more than an unprotected plate bunker because the saving in steel goes far toward offsetting the cost of the lining. We will analyze the comparative costs from an actual estimate.

The bunker is 22½ ft. across the top, with a parabola depth of 15 ft. 4 in. The inside width of the lined bunker (Fig. 13-12) is 22 ft. 2 in. The inside depth is 14 ft. 10 in. The girder spans are 31 ft. 0 in.

The capacity is

$$22.167 \times 14.83 \times 2/3 = 219 \text{ sq. ft. for area of bag}$$

$$\frac{22.167 \times 7.3}{2} = 81 \text{ sq. ft. for surcharge}$$

For coal, the weight of contents is 15,000 lb. per ft. of bunker length. The length of the bunker being 120 ft., the capacity is 900 tons.

The thickness of concrete is 2 in. at the top, increasing to 5 in. at the bottom, or an average of 3½ in. The weight of the concrete per foot of bunker is

$$150 \times 0.291 \times 40 = 1750 \text{ lb.}$$

The weight of the 7 in. by ½ in. straps, spaced 3 ft. 3 in. centers and 35 ft. long, is 135 lb. per ft. of bunker length.

The weight of the side girders is assumed at 500 lb. per ft. of bunker length.

**Ferro Inclave Bunker.** Fabricated steel will be taken at 10 cents per pound, plus drafting at 2 cents, plus erection at 3 cents, or a total of 15 cents per pound. The straps are taken at 12 cents per pound since little drafting or fabrication is involved in them.

*Estimate:*

| | |
|---|---|
| Weight of steel, girders and ends (plate projects below flange) for a bunker length of 120 ft. | 68,000 lb. |
| Straps, 135 by 120 ft. | 16,000 lb. |
| Total | 84,000 lb. |
| Cost | |
| Girders and ends, 68,000 lb. at 15 cents | $10,200 |
| Straps, 16,000 lb. at 12 cents | 1,900 |
| Ferro Inclave sheets | 1,800 |
| Forming the bag and bracing to form | 2,500 |
| Outside painting, scaffolding in place | 500 |
| Inside lining, 5300 sq. ft. | 5,000 |
| Total | $21,900 |
| Cost per ton of capacity, | $24.33 |

*Unlined steel-plate bunker*

| | |
|---|---|
| Weight of steel, girders, and end bracing | 62,000 lb. |
| 3/8-in. bag and ends | 68,000 lb. |
| Total | 130,000 lb. |

Cost

| | |
|---|---|
| 130,000 lb. of steel at 15 cents | $19,500 |
| Painting | 900 |
| Total | $20,400 |

Cost per ton of capacity, $22.67

*Steel-plate bunker, Gunite lined.* (Note: For the areas involved in bunker work Gunite lining costs about $1 per square foot for a thickness of 1½ in., including the mesh reinforcement and circumferential rods.)

Cost

| | |
|---|---|
| Steel, same as in bare steel bunker | $19,500 |
| Painting, outside only | 600 |
| Gunite lining, 5300 sq. ft. | 5,300 |
| Total | $25,400 |

Cost per ton of capacity, $28.22

With the figures taken it is seen that the Ferro Inclave bunker costs more than the unlined plate bunker but substantially less than the protected plate bunker. If the steel can be placed as part of the building structure the pound price can be reduced and the plate bunkers will show lower costs, but usually the Ferro Inclave bunker will cost about midway between the two.

These figures should not be taken as a comparison with silo costs discussed earlier in this chapter as they do not include the bunker cross struts and columns which sometimes are part of the building structure and sometimes not. A medium-capacity bunker of the unlined steel-plate suspension type with columns and struts usually costs between $35 and $40 per ton of capacity.

Because of the cost of Gunite lining, bunkers sometimes are protected by applications of paint. A bitumastic coating, applied cold, costs 4 to 5 cents per square foot of area covered. This is for material only. Labor costs vary widely, as the bunker must be cleaned out for each application. A more effective but more costly protection is bitumastic enamel, which is applied hot to a depth of ¼ in.

**Bin Capacity from Area of Cross Section — Suspension Bunkers.** Figure 13-13 may be used to determine the capacity of a suspension-type coal bunker with concrete lining assumed to have a thickness of 3 in. at the top and 5 or 6 in. at the bottom. The contour of the bag approaches a parabola; actually the bunker should be concreted while being held to a curve having slightly more curvature in the flanks, or approaching the curve that it takes with maximum loading, thus reducing any tendency of the lining to crack under full load.

Referring to Fig. 13-13, assume a bunker with a width across the top of 27 ft. (*B*) and a depth of bag of 20.5 ft. (*C*). The net dimensions inside the concrete lining are 26.5 ft. and 20 ft. Beginning at the 26.5 dimensions for width of bin, follow the vertical line (*D*) to its intersection with line *E*, corresponding to the 20-ft. depth of bag.

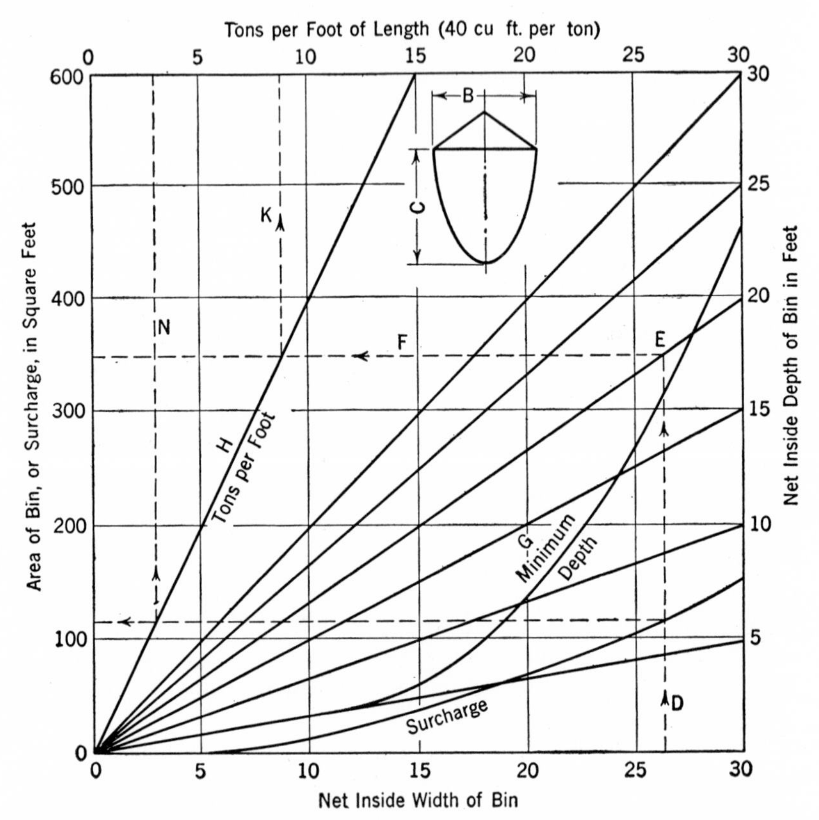


FIG. 13–13. Suspension bunkers: width, depth, and capacity. Free-flowing coal assumed.

Move horizontally to the left, along *F*, and the area of the bin is given by the left-hand figures as 355 sq. ft. without surcharge. The tons per foot of length are given by following vertically the line *K* from the intersection with line *H* and are found to be approximately 9 tons per foot. The surcharge is found by following line *D* to the intersection with the " surcharge curve," then horizontally to the left, and vertically as before. The surcharge per foot is found to be 118 cu. ft. or (line *N*) approximately 3 tons per foot of bunker length. Thus the total capacity is 12 tons per foot of length.

We can reverse the procedure; with a given capacity we can determine the width, and, having determined the width, find the surcharge capacity on that width, and then the depth can be made to suit the balance of capacity required. Usually the surcharge is about 25 per cent of the total, though there may be vertical top sides substantially increasing this percentage.

The intersection of the width and depth must lie on or above the curve *G* if the coal is to flow out until the flanks are cleared. To illustrate: the minimum depth for a width of 25.5 ft. is 18 ft., determined by the intersection of line *D* and curve *G*, then using the figure at the right.

This procedure may be followed for unlined bunkers by eliminating the allowance for thickness of concrete.

**Cylindrical Steel Bins.** Bins of circular section, supported on columns, are used for the storage of various bulk materials. Standardized bins should be used if possible to eliminate design costs. All tank manufacturers have standardized bins with a wide range of capacities. Sometimes it may be advantageous to offset the bottom cone, as when the discharge is to be brought to one side or the other.

**Coal-Bunker Fires.** Air entering through bunker gates is a frequent cause of spontaneous combustion in stored coal. If this condition is found to exist, some method of checking the temperature in the mass is important so that the coal may be withdrawn from the affected area before a large clinker is formed. Experience indicates that there is not only an upward draft from the bunker gates but also a downward circulation along the bunker sides and upward through the center.

One means of protection is a series of pipes near the bottom, through which carbon dioxide may be injected into hot sections. An emergency method is to place Dry Ice upon the top of the coal; the heavy gas filters down through the mass as the Dry Ice slowly evaporates.

**Prevention of Arching.** Many pulverized and granular materials when flowing from a storage bin, bunker, or tank tend to hang up or "arch"— a characteristic which is especially troublesome when materials from a series of containers are to be proportioned into a batch mixer or when coal is fed to a pulverizer in a powdered-fuel layout. Arching is difficult to overcome. One or more electric vibrators attached to the sides of a steel-plate bin will sometimes, but not always, prevent it. If compressed air is available, jetting is effective. Sometimes arching of coal in bunkers is broken up by means of looped chains suspended from above downward to the discharge gates. These are manually operated when the coal hangs up — a tough job.

The author has found that the device of hanging a sheet of 24-gauge stainless steel within the bin, from the top to within a few inches of each outlet, sometimes prevents the formation of arches; if combined with air jetting, it is effective with many materials. The subject is discussed further on pages 429 to 433.

# CHAPTER 14

## UNLOADING WATER-BORNE CARGOES

Equipment for unloading water-borne bulk cargoes covers a wide range because of the various types of carriers. In earlier days bulk cargoes were unloaded by shoveling into tip buckets which then were raised and swung inshore by the vessel's tackle. Then came the mast-and-gaff with grab bucket good for 60 to 80 tons per hour in free

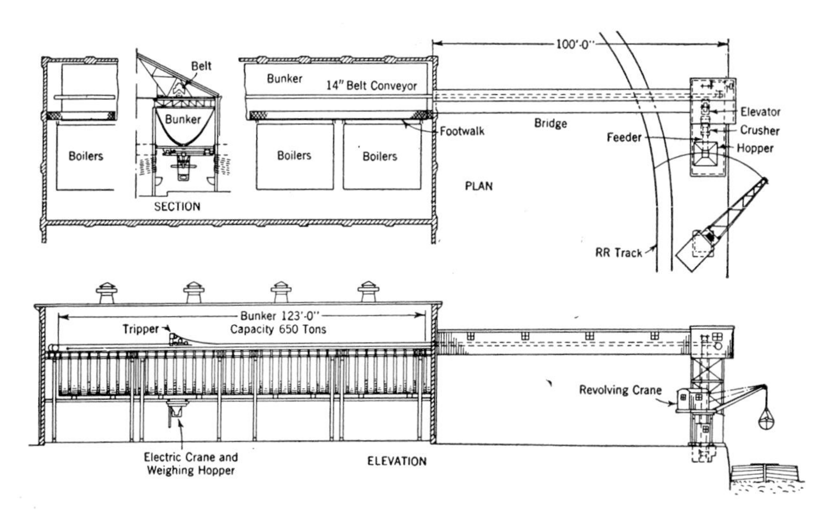


Fig. 14-1. Whirley for unloading from barges. Coal moves through feeder to crusher, bucket elevator, and belt conveyor to suspension bunker. (Hudson.)

digging, and the dock-leg bucket elevator, usually with about the same range of capacity. The former is suitable for various granular and lumpy materials. The latter is primarily for anthracite and the smaller sizes of bituminous coals.

Later came the "whirley," a crane mounted upon a pedestal as shown in Fig. 14-1 in which the bucket discharges to a hopper alongside.

**The Mast-and-gaff** (Fig. 14-2) has long been standard for unloading from open barges. The operating cycle is as follows. With the open bucket resting on the load, hoisting starts with the hoist cable taking the major part of the pull, to dig in and close the bucket. As the lift starts, the boom swings inshore, owing to the difference of pull on the two cables attached to opposite ends of the cross arm. When the bucket is above the receiving hopper, the clutch of the hoist drum is slackened off, and the bucket opens while suspended from the holding cable. By manipulation of the clutches, the bucket, still open, swings back over the barge and drops when both clutches are released. The

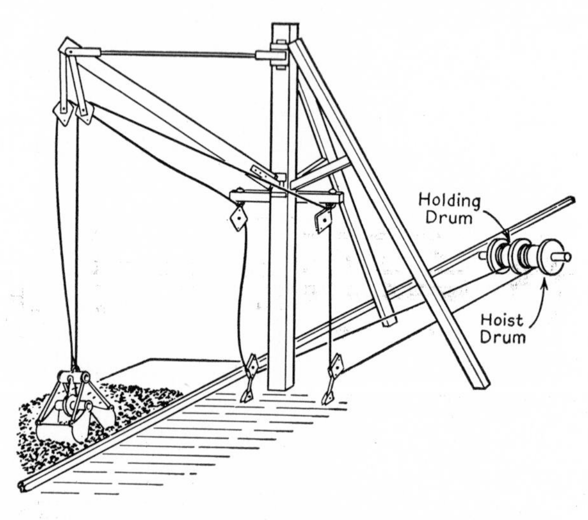


FIG. 14–2. Mast-and-gaff, long standard for unloading bituminous coal, sand, gravel and lumpy materials from open barges when the capacity is about 80 tons per hour.

machine costs only a fraction of the cost of a crane but has the disadvantage that the barge must be moved several times as unloading proceeds to prevent hull strain. It is unsuited for craft with standing rigging.

**The dock-leg elevator** (Fig. 14-3) is used for flowable materials which are not too heavy and not actively abrasive. It is a bucket elevator resembling the gravity-discharge type, but the vertical leg may be swung out or brought within the dock line and may be raised or lowered as unloading proceeds. The boot is a cage, weighted to hold the vertical run of buckets perpendicular and to prevent contact of the buckets with the floor of the barge.

**The whirley** costs more than the mast-and-gaff or the dock-leg elevator but is available for larger unloading capacities. In recent years the advances made in cranes — the application of caterpillar treads, the Diesel engine, and improved methods of control — have led to a wide adoption of the crane for moderately high-speed unloading operations which do not involve repeated raising and lowering of the boom.

The modern application of the high-capacity crane is illustrated by an installation on the Delaware River. The crane is a model K-585

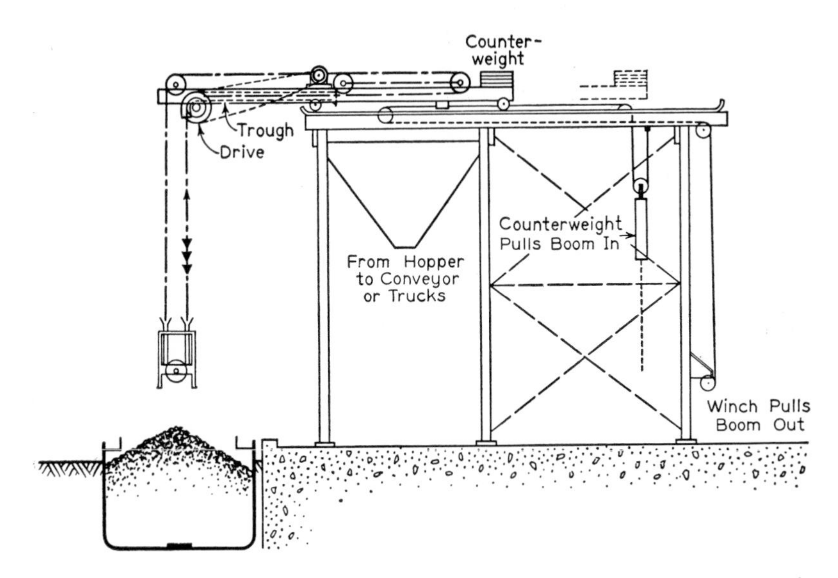


Fig. 14-3. Dock-leg elevator, commonly used at retail coal yards for unloading anthracite coal where a capacity of 60 to 80 tons per hour is sufficient.

Speedomatic (Link-Belt) full revolving, pedestal-mounted, with 60-ft. boom, electrically operated. The lifting capacity at 45-ft. radius is 16,000 lb. The operating speed under full hoist-line load is 260 ft. per min. with the equivalent of 3 r.p.m. swing speed. With an average hoist of 55 ft. and a 90° swing, the theoretical operating cycle is as follows:

| | Operating Time in seconds |
|---|---|
| Close bucket | 7.5 |
| Accelerate hoist | 2.0 |
| Hoist and accelerate swing | 2.0 |
| Continue hoist and swing 54° | 3.0 |
| Complete hoist and decelerate swing, 18° | 7.0 |
| Dump bucket | 3.0 |
| Accelerate return swing, 18° | 2.0 |
| Continue swing, lowering on brake | 3.0 |
| Decelerate swing, complete lowering | 2.0 |
| Total | 31.5 |

The main motor continues in motion and is thrown on the load by the friction clutch, so that it does not have to accelerate itself for each change in the cycle. The control functions through a hydraulic system operated by a 3-hp. motor, with an accumulator for reserve pressure storage. With this hydraulic control the operation is much faster than under the hand lever method and the operator can "feel" or slip the clutches into engagement under load.

The main motor is a type KT General Electric 150-hp. The closing and hoisting cables are ⅞ in. 6 by 19 plow steel. The boom hoist cable is ¾ in.

Weight of empty bucket, 7640 lb.
Rated capacity, 5 cu. yd.
Heaped load, 157 cu. ft.
Water level capacity, 112.4 cu. ft.

The theoretical capacity in free digging is 116 trips per hour, equivalent to 400 tons per hour. However, it is better to rate the operation on a 50-min. hour, which gives about 333 tons per hour.

**Grab Buckets.** The modern grab bucket is a great improvement over the bucket of a few years ago, when the weight of the bucket was two or three times the weight of the coal that it would carry. Buckets now are made with a ratio of 1 : 1; that is, they will carry their weight of coal. They are made of alloy steel, with anti-friction jaw and sleeve bearings, fast closing action, and only 30-ft. wind-up of the cable between the wide-open and the closed positions of the jaws.

**The Steeple Tower.** The steeple tower represents a similar improvement upon the mast-and-gaff and the smaller whirley. The Mead Morrison one-man tower (Hewitt-Robins, Inc.), either steam or electrically operated, came into almost universal use along the Atlantic seaboard. The name "steeple tower" comes from the pointed superstructure. These towers may be fixed or mounted on rails astride a conveyor extending along the wharf.

Figure 14-4 shows a typical barge-unloading installation (Hudson) for transferring coal to a steam plant. The capacity is 150 tons per hour of mine-run coal. From the tower hopper the coal passes to a two-roll crusher which reduces it to stoker size, then to a belt conveyor equipped with a weightometer (Chapter 18), and is discharged to a 3000-ton-capacity Ferro Inclave suspension bunker.

Of interest is the circumstance that in this location (Havana, Cuba) there are occasional tropical storms of extreme severity; the structures are designed for a wind velocity of 125 m.p.h., but the corrugated sheathing is attached with the conventional clips and is swept off with

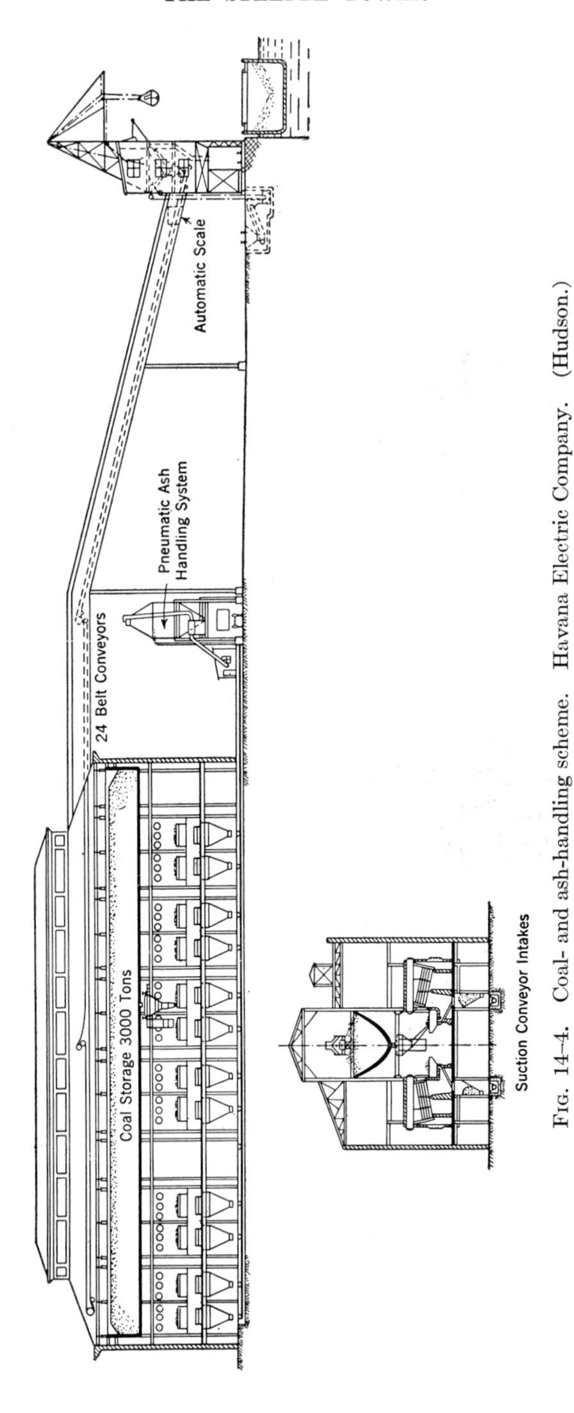


FIG. 14-4. Coal- and ash-handling scheme. Havana Electric Company. (Hudson.)

the first severe gusts to prevent straining the structure to which it is attached.

Referring to the illustration, the reserve coal storage for the plant is some distance away. Reserve coal is brought by cars which discharge to the track hopper back of the tower and is lifted by a slow-speed elevator.

Fig. 14-5. Beneath a traveling steeple tower. (Robins.) Conveyor loaded by belt feeder.

Figure 14-5 shows the arrangement beneath the hopper of a traveling steeple tower. The propelling gear is at the right with automatic clamps to lock the tower in position when it is not traveling. Where hurricanes are possible it is not sufficient to lock the wheels; the tower must be clamped to the rails.

Ordinarily steeple-tower buckets are of 1½- to 3-ton capacity, and unloading capacities range from 150 to 500 tons per hour in free digging. If the tower is not movable, provision is made for shifting the barge by power, preferably by lines attached to bow and stern and leading to motor-driven drums alongside. A skilled operator can make five trips per minute for limited periods with moderate lifts. Some towers have a lift of 100 ft. or more, but though from a layout viewpoint a single lift has advantages there is the disadvantage that mist usually hugs the surface of the water in the morning and the operator cannot see the hatch if he is high up.

*Method of Control.* The electrically operated one-man tower has a two-rope grab bucket. The closing rope closes the bucket or permits it to open; the holding rope holds it as it opens. The two operate in unison from the twin drums of the main hoist machine. A smaller hoist machine operates the trolley from which the bucket is suspended. The ascending loaded bucket moves inshore as the result of the horizontal component of the pull of the two ropes which incline backward to the peak of the tower or steeple. The emptied bucket is pulled outward by the trolley rope. A skilled operator hoists and trolleys simultaneously, starting the bucket inward toward the hopper as soon as it clears the hatch.

Briefly, the cycle of operation is as follows: The operator stands with the master controller of the main hoist motor in his right hand and the controller of the trolley motor in his left. With the bucket open in the cargo the hoist controller is thrown forward, the hoisting rope winds in, closing the bucket jaws into the material. The friction connecting the hoisting drum to its shaft is not sufficient to lift the loaded bucket after it closes, but by then a time-limit relay which controls the friction of the holding drum functions to throw power on the holding rope dead-ended to the yoke above the bucket proper. The two ropes together lift the load, with about two-thirds the pull on the hoisting rope, keeping the bucket closed, and one-third on the holding rope. The bucket rises and moves inward against dynamic braking of the trolley motor, and when the bucket reaches dumping position a foot brake locks the holding drum as the master controller is momentarily reversed, releasing the hoisting rope by a few turns of the drum. The bucket now hangs on the holding rope and therefore swings open. The trolley motor is reversed; the open bucket is pulled outward, descends under the control of dynamic braking in the main motor, and drops into the cargo; then the cycle repeats. All two-rope bucket controls operate on a somewhat similar cycle. If the trolley is to operate beyond the point where the ropes are vertical, the trolley motor pulls the trolley the rest of the way.

**The Bridge Tramway.** With the rapidly growing importance of ore transportation on the Great Lakes and the development of the lake-type cargo vessel with a continuous hold from stem to stern and flat floor, the demand for quick turnaround led to the invention of unloading equipment with capacities far greater than that for unloading oceangoing vessels having isolated hatches. Quick turnaround is of prime importance because the navigation season on the lakes is short and twelve months' supply of ore must be transported in about seven months.

Mr. Alex. Brown, founder of the Brown Hoist Company, one of the remarkable group of pioneers in the material-handling art, invented the graceful bridge tramway. Originally it had two inverted bowstring trusses supported at the ends by towers mounted on trucks. Later straight trusses were adopted with the trolley runway between the lower chords. The trolley unit contains the hoisting and trolleying mechanism and the operator's cabin — the man-trolley, as it is called.

Fig. 14–6. Man-trolley-type Brown hoist bridge. Coal is piled on the wharf by self-unloading vessels, and the bridge rehandles to a stockpile between front and back towers, direct to the belt conveyor through the hopper in the front tower, or from stockpile to belt conveyor.

The front boom can be hinged to swing vertically. The bridge may discharge to cars along a wharf, to a stockpile, or from stockpile to cars. In free digging the bridge has a capacity of 500 tons per hour or more, or if a higher rate of unloading is called for several bridges stand side by side and work the same cargo.

The Link-Belt bridge follows the same general outline but locates the hoist and the operator in the front tower so that the trolley carries only the bucket, permitting a lighter bridge structure.

Figure 14-6 shows a 1941 Brown Hoist bridge forming one unit of the coal-handling and storage system of a midwest utility station. The man-trolley is seen standing between the front tower legs. It is equipped with a 10-yd. bucket.

This bridge has a span of 350 ft. between supports and a front cantilever of 164 ft. Coal is delivered on the wharf by self-unloading vessels, and the job of the tramway is to rehandle this coal from the wharf to a stockpile under the bridge, to a hopper in the front tower which feeds it to a belt conveyor, or from the stockpile to this hopper. Because of prevailing onshore winds the conveyor is protected on that side by a continuous windbreak. The conveyor extends toward the

Fig. 14-7. The Hulett direct unloader. The bucket takes 17 to 20 tons of ore. When rapid unloading is required, three or four Huletts stand side by side. Clearing a 13,000-ton cargo within 4 hr. is not unusual.

right to a Bradford breaker-hammermill from which the crushed coal is taken to the bunkers by an inclined belt conveyor at the extreme right. The capacity from stockpile to conveyor is 400 tons per hour.

Bridge tramways are less common now, as other machines, requiring a lower investment, match their capacity.

**The Hulett Direct Unloader.** George Hulett, another pioneer in fast unloaders for the lake-type vessels, attacked the problem in a different way. After many discouragements the Hulett direct unloader (Fig. 14-7) was perfected. It is now engineered by the Wellman Engineering Company.

This is a remarkable machine, massive in proportions, with a bucket of 17-ton capacity or larger and an unloading rate of 1200 tons per hour in cargo ore, yet so delicately balanced that all unloading functions are controlled by one man stationed in the bucket leg.

The main frame, or gantry, is mounted on rail trucks and spans the tracks for the cars to be loaded. Distribution to cars is through a weighing larry of 45-ton capacity. If no cars are available the larry travels out over a rear cantilever stocking ore behind the rear leg, to be reclaimed by a crane or bridge. The larry loads from a surge hopper at the front of the gantry have a capacity of three bucket loads to provide for temporary delays as when a car is shifted. The larry is controlled by a man stationed in the house in the larry frame. Rails on the fore and aft girders of the gantry frame serve as a runway for the shuttle unit which carries the massive walking beam that is the characteristic feature of the Hulett unloader.

From the front end of the walking beam a stiff-leg bucket is suspended. On the rear end is mounted the operating machinery that controls hoisting, digging, and the forward-and-backward travel of the shuttle. As the section of the walking beam forward of the pivot is heavier than the rear end, the bucket descends by gravity when the brake on the hoist drum is released. Control while lowering is by dynamic braking. From the hoist drum, cables lead around sheaves at the rear end of the shuttle and dead end on the walking beam for lifting and lowering the beam. The bucket-opening and -closing mechanism likewise is located at the rear end of the walking beam with cables leading through it and down the bucket leg to a power drum, directly above the operator, geared to the bucket-closing chains. The bucket is opened by reversing this motor and winding in an opening chain located between the two closing chains. In addition to the vertical movement of the bucket leg there is a rotating movement around a vertical axis which is controlled by cable and sheave segment at the top of the leg. The leg is carried on ball bearings to facilitate this rotation. The rotating movement permits the bucket to revolve through an arc of 90° so that ore beneath the deck beams can be reached.

Figure 14-8 shows a 15-ton bucket in this position cleaning up the last of a cargo. Note the position of the operator in close proximity to his work. The perforated horizontal frame between the bucket leaves is the guide for roller arms attached thereto. When a vessel is to be unloaded the machine is moved to a position opposite the first hatch to be cleared and the bucket is lowered into the ore. The full bucket rises as the walking beam pivots and simultaneously moves backward until the bucket is over the receiving hopper located between the gantry girders. The bucket discharges, and the cycle is repeated. The further movement of the ore is under the control of the larry man. Motor-operated discharge gates permit all or part of the load to be weighed, recorded, and dumped into the larry. The larry traveling mechanism is mounted in its frame with haulage cables dead-ended at the rear end of the runway, which is inclined for return of the larry by gravity.

Power for the unloader is supplied through insulated conductor rails mounted on the wharf deck. For flexibility of control, direct current is used.

FIG. 14-8. Cleaning up with 15-ton Hulett buckets. The operator is seen in the leg just above the bucket, where he controls all unloading operations.

Figure 14-9 shows an unloader of modern type erected in 1940. The principal details are:

Bucket capacity, 17 cu. yd.
Time of round trip, 50 sec.
Travel speed, 75 to 100 ft. per min.
Unloading capacity, 1000 to 1500 tons of ore per hour.

The machine has a rearward-extending belt conveyor which forms a storage pile behind the wharf if cars are not in position for loading.

The power units are as follows:

Bucket-closing motor, 100 hp., series wound.
Walking-beam motor, 450 hp., compound wound, with dynamic control, 36-in. shunt-wound brake, emergency limit switch, and slack cable switches.
Shuttle travel motor, 150 hp., compound wound, with 30-in. shunt-wound brake and limit switch.
Bridge-travel motor, 100 hp., series wound, with 24-in. shunt-wound brake.

Bucket leg rotating motor, 40 hp., series wound, with master controller and limit switch.
Belt conveyor motor, 100 hp., shunt wound.
Gate motors, two, 5 hp.

The walking-beam hoist has a special motor-operated emergency brake with starter pedal in the operator's cabin.

Hulett unloader operating records are impressive. At Ashtabula, Ohio, eight machines of the type under discussion made a record of 70,000 tons in 22 hr. working time. At other ports, four machines working in cargoes up to 13,000 tons have unloaded these cargoes in less than 4 hr.

FIG. 14–9. Hulett unloader with belt conveyor extending rearward to form stock pile when not loading cars. Material in stockpile is reloaded by crawler crane.

The cost of maintenance is low. Unloading costs, including superintendence, labor, repairs, power, and light, are stated to be 2½ to 4½ cents per ton handled. The counterbalanced walking-beam principle lightens the weight to about one-third that of a cable-suspended bucket, should the bucket be rested on the deck of a vessel. Positive guidance of the bucket through the hatch minimizes risk of damage to the vessel, and the operator is close to his work. The extreme reach of the bucket leaves when opened, and the revolving control, permit complete cleanup of the hold with a minimum of manual labor.

**Self-Unloading Vessels.** On the Great Lakes, coal cargoes must often be unloaded at points where shore-mounted high-capacity unloading equipment is not available. The Robins Company and the Stephens Adamson Company developed the self-unloading vessel. This has a belt conveyor, or twin conveyors, along the keelson discharging to a bucket elevator at the bow. Figure 14-10 shows the Robins equipped vessel used for coal transportation by the Dow Chemical Company. Figure 14-11 shows in section a Stephens Adamson equipped vessel. The operation of these self-unloaders is limited to materials which will feed through tunnel gates. They have a handling capacity of 1000 tons per hour or more; thus SS *Crispin Oglebay*

Fig. 14–10. The self-unloading vessel under way. The conveyor boom may be swung out to either side. This is the distinctive lake-type carrier with power plant at the stern, pilot house at the bow, and continuous hatches between.

recently was equipped with twin 48-in. tunnel belts, elevator with buckets 96-in. wide, and 240-ft. boom with 60-in. belt, providing an unloading rate of 2200 tons per hour.

**Pneumatic Unloaders.** Although the pneumatic unloader is not so widely used as abroad, it does serve nicely for unloading grain and other flowable granular materials where the capacity is not too large and power not too costly.

Figure 14-12 shows one such installation by the Fuller Company at Portland, Oregon. The rise and fall of the tide is 30 ft., and so the boom must be rigged to take care of this, in addition to the difference in elevations, as unloading proceeds. The boom may be raised or lowered by a motorized hoist controlled by push button from the deck of the barge. A similar control serves to telescope the leg.

The suction leg terminates in a manifold with six 5-in. flexible hose nozzles giving a combined capacity of 4000 bushels (120 tons) per hour in wheat. This is equivalent to 1.7 hp. per ton per hour, a very good performance for this type of machine. The multiple-nozzle arrangement does not materially affect the unloading rate if one nozzle pulls out of the material. The exhauster is driven by a 200-hp. motor.

A vertical bucket elevator for the same capacity would require about 25 hp. It would have about 20 ft. higher lift because of the chute at

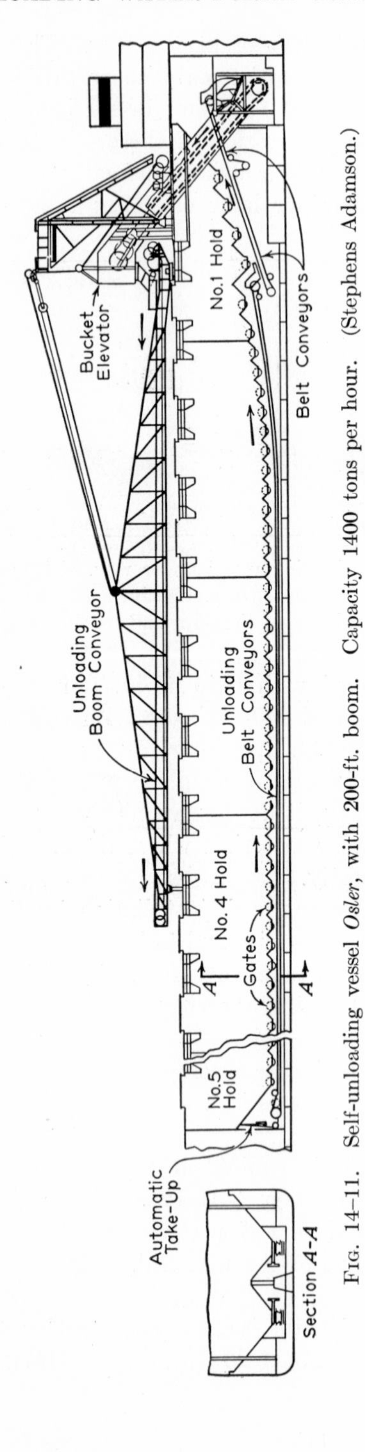


Fig. 14–11. Self-unloading vessel *Osler*, with 200-ft. boom. Capacity 1400 tons per hour. (Stephens Adamson.)

FIG. 14-12. Pneumatic unloader operating in barge of wheat. Capacity 4000 bushels per hour. (Fuller.)

the top. The power saving is offset by the larger crew required when cleaning up, the danger to the men in the hold shoveling into the elevator buckets, and the more frequent barge shifts.

At European grain-unloading ports, pneumatic unloading is quite common with handling capacities running up to several hundred tons per hour. By mounting the unloader on a barge, the cargo may be automatically weighed and discharged to lighters which can be taken to points where the water is too shallow for the ship. Figure 14-13 shows an unloader of this type as manufactured by Henry Simon Co. Ltd.

**Comment.** Subject to special conditions, we might summarize broadly on shore-mounted equipment for unloading bulk materials.

For the smaller capacities, up to 60 or 80 tons per hour from open barges, there is available the mast-and-gaff, the smaller whirley, or if the material is pulverized or granular the pneumatic unloader.

For capacities above 80 tons per hour and up to 300 tons per hour or thereabout, the larger crawler and the steeple tower are suitable.

FIG. 14–13. Floating unloader at English port. (Henry Simon.)

In exceptional cases, for grain, etc., the larger pneumatic unloaders might be chosen although the power requirements might make this selection undesirable. If cargoes are in vessels with standing rigging, that is, with masts and shrouds, the steeple tower with boom hinged to swing vertically and the bridge with similar boom have advantages but cost more than the high-capacity crane.

For the larger capacities and of course with vessels having hatches which are suited to such operations, two crawlers, or the tramway, may be used.

If the required capacity runs to 1000 tons per hour or more, the Hulett unloader is the machine to choose.

The steeple tower has a faster cycle, when handling from boat to a hopper in the tower frame, than the crane. The crane has a faster cycle than the tower when there is a rearward cantilever and material is to be delivered back of the tower. The exception to this statement is a tower having a rearward extending belt conveyor from hopper to above the pile. Because of the horizontal swing of the boom the crane has been at a disadvantage when unloading from vessels with standing rigging; but the hydraulic finger-tip control makes raising and lowering the boom an easier operation than formerly, and a crane costs much less than a steeple tower or tramway. If the crane is mounted on caterpillars it is available for other duties and for work at inshore points while the tower is not.

**Barge Shifters.** For large-capacity shore-mounted loaders and unloaders, a barge shifter is necessary. Under moderate conditions a simple winch, hand-operated or driven from a small motor, may suffice. In the large-scale operations a more powerful and controllable shifter is essential. This is especially so at central loading stations where, as at the Frick mines, some 35,000 tons of coal are loaded daily, and rapid spotting of the barges, complicated by a variable river current, must be assured.

The routine barge shifter is a clutch-and-friction-type hoist costing about $4000. It can be appreciated that it is necessary not only to move the barge into position but also to check its motion smoothly. The weakness of the clutch and brake machine is its waste of power and the difficulty in keeping both towing and trailing lines taut. About 12 years ago Mr. W. J. Heacock invented an improved shifter which eliminated these disadvantages and has proved vastly superior to other types. It costs about twice as much as the friction-clutch type. Its economy rests in regenerative braking, instead of friction braking, to keep the trailing line taut. Moreover, it automatically maintains correct relationship between the pulling and trailing line tensions so that, unless operated manually, both lines cannot at the same time pull at a maximum in opposite directions.

The shifter, nominally rated for a rope pull of 15,000 lb. at 35 ft. per min. is powered and built for an ultimate load of 85,000 lb. which is about twice the strength of the lines. There are no clutches or friction holdback brakes. Two 30-hp. crane-type slip-ring motors operate 36-in. grooved drums through reduction gearing. There is also a torque-motor-operated special gear-shifting unit. The entire machine, except the control panel and master switch, is mounted on a rigid steel base.

The control is by manipulation of the lever of a small master switch.

However, there are two additional master switches, one each for individual control of the two drums when it is desired to move only one at a time. The operator moves his master switch to the first point in the direction in which it is desired to move the barge. On this point the torque motor automatically functions to give the correct relationship between drum speeds for the direction of travel, and both motors are started, pulling in opposite directions with relatively low torque to take up the slack in the lines. When the slack has been taken up, the operator moves the master switch to full running position. The trailing motor still pulls as on the first point, but the towing motor is given sufficient torque to move the barge and pull the trailing motor backward against its torque. The pulling motor quickly accelerates on current-limit control until it reaches full speed at which point a current-limit relay reverses the connections to the trailing motor, which then is slightly above synchronous speed, and it runs as a generator, maintaining a taut trailing line and pumping current back into the current main. When the master switch is moved to off position, the barge is brought to a smooth stop by a solenoid brake.

Movement of the barge in the opposite direction is accomplished in the same manner by throwing the master switch in the opposite direction; then the torque motor automatically shifts the gears to the correct ratio for that direction of travel.

# CHAPTER 15

## CRUSHERS, HAMMERMILLS, AND PULVERIZERS

Crushing and pulverizing are not strictly material-handling operations, but they are so closely related thereto and so frequently an important part of an installation that the subject deserves consideration here. It is possible to select only a few typical machines to illustrate the general principles, following through from coarse crushing to fine grinding and pulverizing. Thus the sequence is:

Jaw crusher
Gyratory crusher
Pick breaker
Roll crushers
Bradford breaker
Ball and rod mills

**Historical.** Jaw and gyratory crushers, formerly used almost entirely for primary crushing, are still used for crushing hard materials. About 1895, Williams invented the hammermill which bears his name. It had immediate success for certain materials but ran into trouble when he attempted to apply it to soft materials such as fertilizers and stockyard refuse. About 1900 the Jeffrey Manufacturing Company began the manufacture of two-roll crushers. About 1905 the Pennsylvania Crusher Company was incorporated. These three, and Gruendler, practically monopolized the field for a time. In 1913 the American Pulverizer Company introduced a European development in which steel rings were substituted for hammers in a hammermill, with the claim that there was a better rebound when a fragment was not shattered at the first impact. The hammermill gradually superseded the jaw and gyratory crushers except for the harder materials.

The two-roll spring-release crusher for primary crushing of coal and similar materials was developed actively, beginning about 1900, and the single-roll crusher a few years later. Their principal application was for coal preparation plants as engineered by Jeffrey and Link-Belt. At that time a crusher was a necessary part of power-plant coal-handling installations, as stoker-size coal was not always obtainable.

The Pennsylvania Crusher Company brought in the slowly rotated perforated cylinder known as the Bradford breaker, in which the coal is lifted by shelves and dropped, the lumps being shattered and the bone, rock, and other refuse culled out.

**Terms Used.** It is customary to express the size of crushed material in terms of the size of the screen through which it will pass; thus "minus 4 in." means that all lumps will pass through a 4-in. screen. The expression "4-in. by 2-in." gives the maximum and minimum

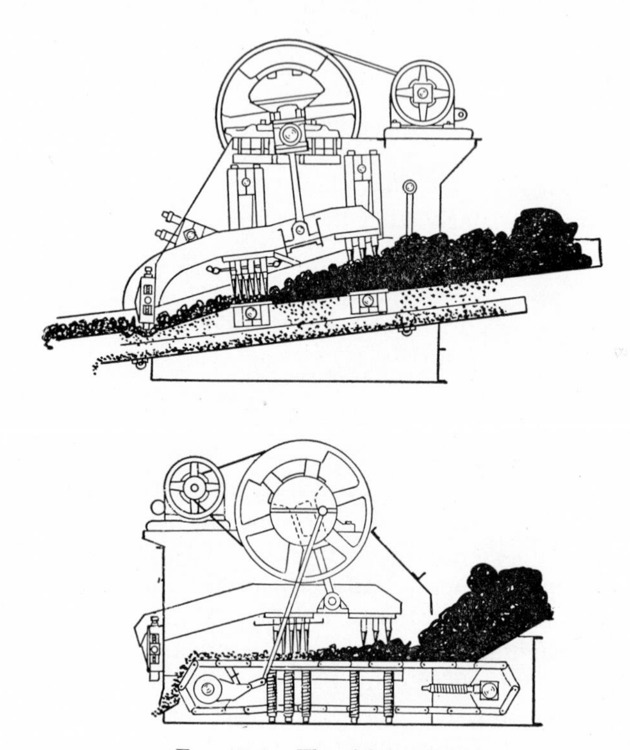

FIG. 15-1. The pick breaker.

sizes. It should always be stated whether the reference is to the size of the lump or to the size of the ring through which it will pass; thus a 1-in. cube is equivalent to the 1½-in. ring size; a 3½-in. cube, to the 5-in. ring size, etc.

The operation of the jaw crusher and the gyratory crusher is too well known to require description. Their application is primarily for rock, ore, and similar hard materials. Of interest is the power requirement as related to the size of product and the tons per hour crushed. In Table 1 these figures are given for the Telsmith jaw crushers (Smith Engineering Company) as typical of this class of machine, and in Table 2 are the figures for the same make of gyratory crushers.

The majority of fragmentation operations are concerned with coal, and for this we have the pick breaker, the roll crushers, and the Bradford breaker.

**The Pick Breaker** (McNally Pittsburgh Company) (Fig. 15-1). The pick breaker acts on a unique principle. It cracks up the lumps by piercing them with a set of picks which project downward from a frame having a vertical reciprocating motion. The feed need not be hand picked since the picks are held in spring mountings which protect them and the feed table, should an unbreakable lump enter. The picks are in two lengths, short at the feed end to split the larger lumps, then longer ones to split the fragments. The reciprocating frame is actuated by an overhead counterweighted shaft with flywheel and V-belt drive to absorb shock. The anvil is similar to an apron-type feeder but is driven by a ratchet which moves the apron forward as the picks rise and holds it stationary as they strike. Sometimes the anvil is a balanced shaker with perforations ahead of both the primary and secondary picks to by-pass the undersize.

Pick breakers are used in coal preparation plants for primary crushing. They require comparatively low power for a given capacity. Table 3 shows the maximum lump, capacity in tons per hour, and motor horsepower.

TABLE 1

SIZES AND CAPACITIES OF TELSMITH JAW CRUSHERS FOR DIFFERENT SIZES OF PRODUCT, AND HORSEPOWER REQUIRED

| Size of crusher (feed opening), in. | 9 by 16 | 9 by 30 | 13 by 24 | 18 by 30 | 24 by 36 |
|---|---|---|---|---|---|
| Horsepower required | 8–15 | 15–25 | 20–30 | 50–60 | 75–100 |
| Capacity, tons per hour, with discharge opening | | | | | |
| ½ in. | 3–4 | | | | |
| ¾ in. | 5–6 | 12–15 | | | |
| 1 in. | 6–8 | 15–18 | | | |
| 1½ in. | 10–12 | 23–28 | 20–25 | | |
| 2 in. | | | 22–27 | | |
| 3 in. | | | 28–35 | 35–45 | |
| 4 in. | | | | | 70–80 |
| 5 in. | | | | | 80–90 |
| 6 in. | | | | | 90–100 |

**Single- and Two-Roll Crushers.** These also are restricted to reasonably soft materials such as coal and are used for crushing from lump to 1½-in. ring size. With special rolls they may reduce to 1 in. or even ¾ in., or with finely fluted rolls to a somewhat smaller size.

TABLE 2

SIZES AND CAPACITIES OF TELSMITH GYRATORY CRUSHERS[1]

| Dimensions of each of two receiving openings, inches | 6½ by 35 | 10 by 51 | 13 by 59 | 16 by 74 | 20 by 88 |
|---|---|---|---|---|---|
| Hourly capacity in tons: | | | | | |
| with 1-in. discharge | 18–20 | | | | |
| with 1¼-in. discharge | 20–23 | | | | |
| with 1½-in. discharge | 23–26 | 38–44 | | | |
| with 2-in. discharge | | 50–57 | 70–80 | | |
| with 2½-in. discharge | | | 80–90 | 120–135 | |
| with 3-in. discharge | | | 90–100 | 135–145 | 200–220 |
| with 4-in. discharge | | | | | 250–280 |
| Horsepower | 15–20 | 25–30 | 40–50 | 60–75 | 75–90 |

[1]Based on stone, weighing loose about 2600 lb. per cu. yd. and having a specific gravity of 2.6. Horsepower varies with size of product, capacity, and hardness of rock.

TABLE 3

PICK BREAKER

Coal: Maximum feed size, 20 by 20 in.

| Width of Breaker, inches | Size of Product, inches: 3 | 4 | 5 | 6 | 7 | 8 | 9 | 10 | 11 | 12 | Horse-power |
|---|---|---|---|---|---|---|---|---|---|---|---|
| | Capacities, tons per hour | | | | | | | | | | |
| 36 | 40 | 50 | 62 | 75 | 86 | 97 | 110 | 121 | 132 | 145 | 10 |
| 48 | 70 | 93 | 116 | 140 | 163 | 186 | 210 | 233 | 256 | 280 | 15 |
| 60 | 100 | 128 | 156 | 185 | 213 | 241 | 270 | 298 | 326 | 355 | 20 |
| 72 | 120 | 153 | 186 | 220 | 253 | 286 | 320 | 353 | 387 | 420 | 30 |

*The single-roll crusher* (Fig. 15-2) consists of a hopper and frame, housing a toothed roll which grips the lumps and crushes them against a stationary breaker plate. It is usual to have a number of long slugger teeth to aid in gripping the larger lumps. These long teeth register with slots in the breaker plate. A good feature of this crusher is the ease with which adjustment may be made while the crusher is running by a simple shift in the position of the breaker plate with reference to the roll.

The heavy frame supports the roll and shaft, the countershaft, and the spring-relieved breaker plate mounted on a pivot shaft. The roll is made of manganese-steel segments bolted to heavy spiders. The breaker plate has a renewable manganese-steel shoe and is held by the adjustable rods. The flywheel or driving gear has a shear pin as a protection against unbreakable lumps. If the crusher is fed by a conveyor with independent motor, there must be provision to stop the feeder automatically if the crusher should stop. Interlocking the motors will not do, as the crusher motor continues to run after the pin shears. This is discussed more in detail in Chapter 19.

FIG. 15–2. Single-roll crusher. Sectional roll bolted to heavy spiders. Ribbed breaker plate with replaceable manganese-steel shoe. Flywheel has shear-pin hub.

FIG. 15–3. Double-roll crusher. Spring release which permits one roll to yield to unbreakable material.

Link-Belt gives the ratings shown in Table 4 for single-roll crushers with hard, medium, and soft coal. The tabulated capacities may be increased somewhat by increasing the speeds. If the undersize is screened out ahead of the crusher a larger crusher is needed.

*The double-roll crusher* (Fig. 15-3) has two interlocked rolls revolving toward each other, usually at the same speed though sometimes at different speeds to secure a tearing action. The rolls may be of solid cast iron or steel, they may be of cast iron with inserted steel teeth, or they may have crushing segments bolted to spiders. One shaft is mounted in spring-relief bearings; the other, or drive shaft, has a heavy flywheel which serves as a driving pulley, preferably by V-belt. Table 5 gives the ratings for this crusher. All manufacturers will furnish similar data on request.

*Adjustable Two-Roll Crushers.* Jeffrey and Link-Belt have developed two-roll crushers which may be adjusted for size of product while running. The Link-Belt crusher is shown in Fig. 15-4. Adjustment while operating is important in coal preparation plants where different prepared sizes are shipped out. Though the coal sent through the crusher is only part of the tipple output, output is curtailed almost immediately when the crusher is stopped.

*Selection and Location.* Large-diameter crushing rolls are required for large lumps. A short stocky machine is better than one with long rolls. A heavy flywheel reduces strain, and a V-belt drive is better than a chain drive because of its flexibility. The crusher should be located where replacements may be made without disturbing adjacent equipment as it takes heavier punishment than other units and repairs are more frequent. One hundred per cent reduction to a stated size should not be called for, as some oversize must be expected. A good requirement is "not over 10 per cent oversize."

*Percentage of Undersize in Roll Crushers.* In producing sized coal it is desired to reduce the percentage of undersize to a minimum. Certain limits prevail, and smaller sizes command a lower price. Opinions differ as to the relative performance of the single-roll and double-roll crusher in this respect. It would seem that the grinding action of a toothed roll against a stationary plate should produce more degradation than two revolving rolls.

Trials by the author with screened 4-in. lump coal, soft, medium, and hard, through a 30 by 24 in. double-roll crusher and a 30 by 24 in. single-roll crusher, after the rolls had been set by trial to give a certain size (stoker size), showed very little difference in undersize percentage. Tests by another engineer, using a 24 by 20 in. single-roll and a 24 by 20 in. double-roll crusher gave the following:

Feed, plus 4 in. Desired product, 1½-in.

Percentage of undersize (1¼ × 0) was 17 per cent for the double-roll; 45 per cent for single-roll.

This is very much in favor of the double-roll crusher.

## TABLE 4

### Capacities of Single-Roll Crushers (Link-Belt) in Tons per Hour

Hard bituminous coal refers to West Virginia Splint, Indiana Block, Illinois, Iowa, Colorado, Wyoming;
Medium bituminous coal refers to West Virginia Thacker, Panther, Banner, Coalburg, Kentucky, Harlan, Ohio Hocking.
Soft bituminous refers to Pocahontas, New River, Connellsville, Pittsburgh No. 7 and No. 8.

| Size of Product[1] | | Size of Crusher, in. | | | | | | | | | | | | | | | | | | | | | | | |
|---|---|---|---|---|---|---|---|---|---|---|---|---|---|---|---|---|---|---|---|---|---|---|---|---|---|
| | | 24 × 24 | | | 24 × 30 | | | 24 × 36 | | | 30 × 24 | | | 30 × 30 | | | 30 × 36 | | | 30 × 42 | | | 30 × 54 | | |
| | | Grade of Coal and Maximum Size of Lumps, in. | | | | | | | | | | | | | | | | | | | | | | | |
| Screen or Ring, in. | Cube, in. | Hard 14 | Med. 16 | Soft 18 | Hard 14 | Med. 16 | Soft 18 | Hard 14 | Med. 16 | Soft 18 | Hard 16 | Med. 18 | Soft 20 | Hard 20 | Med. 22 | Soft 24 | Hard 20 | Med. 22 | Soft 24 | Hard 20 | Med. 22 | Soft 24 | Hard 20 | Med. 22 | Soft 24 |
| 1¼ | ⅞ | 10<br>25 | 20<br>40 | 25<br>50 | 10<br>30 | 25<br>50 | 30<br>60 | 15<br>40 | 30<br>60 | 40<br>75 | 25<br>45 | 35<br>75 | 45<br>105 | 30<br>50 | 45<br>95 | 50<br>135 | 35<br>70 | 55<br>115 | 70<br>165 | 45<br>85 | 65<br>135 | 85<br>190 | 55<br>95 | 80<br>170 | 95<br>240 |
| 1½ | 1 | 15<br>30 | 25<br>50 | 30<br>60 | 15<br>35 | 30<br>60 | 35<br>75 | 20<br>45 | 35<br>75 | 45<br>90 | 30<br>55 | 45<br>90 | 55<br>125 | 35<br>60 | 50<br>110 | 60<br>155 | 40<br>80 | 65<br>130 | 80<br>185 | 50<br>95 | 75<br>155 | 95<br>215 | 65<br>115 | 95<br>200 | 115<br>280 |
| 1⅝ | 1⅛ | 20<br>40 | 30<br>60 | 40<br>75 | 25<br>50 | 35<br>75 | 50<br>95 | 30<br>60 | 45<br>90 | 60<br>110 | 35<br>60 | 50<br>100 | 60<br>140 | 40<br>75 | 60<br>125 | 75<br>175 | 50<br>90 | 75<br>150 | 90<br>210 | 55<br>105 | 85<br>175 | 105<br>245 | 75<br>135 | 110<br>225 | 135<br>315 |
| 2 | 1⅜ | 25<br>50 | 35<br>75 | 50<br>100 | 30<br>65 | 45<br>95 | 65<br>125 | 40<br>75 | 50<br>110 | 75<br>150 | 40<br>70 | 60<br>130 | 70<br>160 | 50<br>100 | 75<br>160 | 100<br>200 | 60<br>120 | 90<br>195 | 120<br>240 | 70<br>140 | 110<br>230 | 140<br>280 | 90<br>170 | 135<br>290 | 170<br>360 |
| 3 | 2 | 30<br>60 | 50<br>95 | 60<br>130 | 35<br>75 | 65<br>120 | 75<br>110 | 45<br>90 | 75<br>145 | 90<br>195 | 45<br>105 | 75<br>150 | 105<br>215 | 60<br>130 | 90<br>195 | 130<br>265 | 70<br>155 | 110<br>225 | 155<br>300 | 85<br>180 | 130<br>270 | 180<br>360 | 105<br>235 | 165<br>345 | 235<br>480 |
| 4 | 2¾ | 35<br>60 | 55<br>105 | 60<br>145 | 45<br>85 | 70<br>130 | 85<br>180 | 50<br>100 | 85<br>160 | 100<br>215 | 55<br>115 | 85<br>175 | 115<br>235 | 65<br>150 | 110<br>220 | 150<br>295 | 80<br>180 | 130<br>265 | 180<br>350 | 95<br>205 | 155<br>310 | 205<br>410 | 120<br>265 | 195<br>395 | 265<br>530 |
| 5 | 3½ | 40<br>70 | 60<br>120 | 70<br>165 | 50<br>90 | 75<br>150 | 90<br>205 | 60<br>105 | 90<br>180 | 105<br>250 | 60<br>130 | 95<br>190 | 130<br>265 | 70<br>165 | 120<br>240 | 165<br>330 | 85<br>200 | 145<br>290 | 200<br>395 | 100<br>235 | 170<br>335 | 235<br>465 | 130<br>295 | 215<br>430 | 295<br>595 |
| 6 | 4 | 45<br>75 | 65<br>130 | 75<br>175 | 55<br>95 | 80<br>165 | 95<br>220 | 65<br>115 | 95<br>195 | 115<br>265 | 65<br>140 | 105<br>205 | 140<br>285 | 75<br>175 | 130<br>255 | 175<br>355 | 90<br>210 | 155<br>305 | 210<br>425 | 110<br>245 | 180<br>355 | 245<br>500 | 140<br>315 | 235<br>460 | 315<br>640 |
| 8 | 5½ | 50<br>95 | 70<br>150 | 95<br>190 | 60<br>120 | 85<br>190 | 120<br>240 | 70<br>145 | 105<br>225 | 145<br>285 | 75<br>155 | 135<br>230 | 155<br>345 | 90<br>190 | 165<br>295 | 190<br>430 | 110<br>235 | 200<br>350 | 235<br>515 | 135<br>275 | 230<br>405 | 275<br>600 | 165<br>345 | 300<br>525 | 345<br>775 |
| Minimum size of motor, hp. | | 10 | | | 10 | | | 15 | | | 15 | | | 20 | | | 25 | | | 25 | | | 30 | | |
| R.p.m. of Roll | | Std. 60 | | Max. 100 | Std. 60 | | Max. 100 | Std. 60 | | Max. 100 | Std. 50 | | Max. 75 | Std. 50 | | Max. 75 | Std. 50 | | Max. 75 | Std. 50 | | Max. 75 | Std. 50 | | Max. 75 |

[1] The " size of product " listed corresponds with the size of round screen or ring opening through which 80 to 90 per cent would pass. Capacities may be increased or decreased as much as 50 per cent by changing the speed of roll, but speeds should not exceed " maximum " specified above. Regardless of capacity, motors should never be smaller than shown as " minimum " in the table.

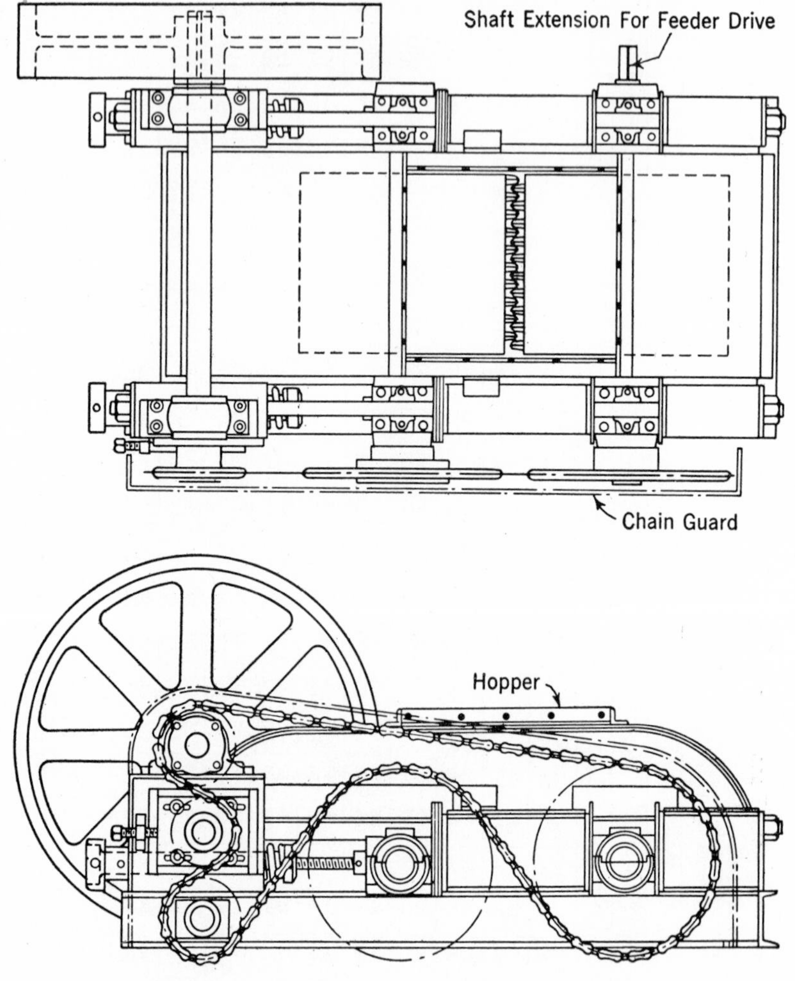


FIG. 15–4. Adjustable two-roll crusher. (Link-Belt.)

Another series of tests in the field with medium-hard bituminous coal gave the following:

Single-roll, 30 by 45 in., 60 r.p.m. Feed 2½ by 1¼ in. Desired product, 1¼ in.

| | | |
|---|---|---|
| Product | Plus 1¼ in. | 9.5% |
| | 1¼ × 5/16 in. | 77.0 |
| | 5/16 × 0 | 13.5 |

Single-roll, 30 by 54 in., 60 r.p.m. Feed 2½ by 1 in. Desired product, 1 in.

| | | |
|---|---|---|
| Product | Plus 1¼ in. | None |
| | 1¼ × 5/16 in. | 92% |
| | 5/16 × 0 | 8 |

Double-roll, 30 by 36 in., 100 r.p.m. Feed 2½ by 1¼ in. Desired product, 1¼ in.

| | | |
|---|---|---|
| Product | Plus 1¼ in. | 2% |
| | 1¼ × 5/16 in. | 78 |
| | 5/16 × 0 | 20 |

These somewhat favor the single-roll; however, the reduction called for was very little, from 2½ in. to 1 or 1¼ in. The single-roll would not have shown up so well if the feed size had been larger.

It would seem that the setting of the rolls and the size and shape of the teeth can easily swing the result one way or the other. The double-roll crusher functions better than the single-roll, which, in spite of slugger teeth, often will dally over a large lump so that succeeding lumps pile up to stall the crusher. Double-rolls quickly pinch through any succession of lumps within the capacity of the machine.

*Cautions Relating to Capacity.* It is difficult for the engineer not a specialist, and in fact for the specialist, to foretell what a given crusher will do with a certain coal. Coals have different degrees of hardness and fracture differently. Again, it should be noted that the tabulated capacities are based on mine-run coals from which none of the smaller sizes has been screened out. If screened lumps are passed through a crusher its capacity is reduced. Consider the 30 by 42 in. crusher, single-roll, in Table 4, listed as having a capacity of 70 to 140 tons per hour for hard bituminous coal with lumps up to 20 in. and a reduction to 2-in. ring size. If we feed this crusher with 70 tons per hour of mine-run coal from which we screen out 33 per cent as undersize, the crusher does work on 46 tons of lumps. If we feed 140 tons per hour of mine-run coal from which we screen out 66 per cent as undersize, the crusher has the same job — to crush 46 tons of lumps.

Often the purchaser will ask for a crusher to handle lumps up to a stated maximum size. The manufacturer will, of course, quote on a crusher which will do that job, which may mean that the crusher specified is larger and more costly than need be. The "maximum lump" may be the exceptional lump. It would involve no great inconvenience if it is broken up by sledge on a grid ahead of the crusher. It is well to ascertain whether there is a distinction between the maximum lump and the rare maximum lump.

*Rubber-Shod Rolls.* In foundry practice it may occur that molding sand, before reconditioning, must be passed through a crusher and then screened. The lumps break up easily in a double-roll crusher, but the job is complicated when metal chills in the sand are to be preserved for use again. If they are of iron they are easily culled out by passing the sand over a magnetic plate or pulley, but if they are non-magnetic they will be damaged by the rolls, especially toothed or corrugated

## TABLE 5

### Capacities of Two-Roll Crushers (Link-Belt) in Tons per Hour

Capacities are based on a feed of mine-run coal from which undersize has not been removed. If smaller sizes have been screened from the feed, the capacity is determined by adding the tons removed to the tons to be crushed.

| Size of Product[1] | | Size of Crusher, in. | | | | | | | | | | | | | | | | | |
|---|---|---|---|---|---|---|---|---|---|---|---|---|---|---|---|---|---|---|---|
| | | 20 × 18 | | | 20 × 24 | | | 26 × 24 | | | 26 × 30 | | | 28 × 24 | | | 28 × 36 | | |
| | | Grade of Coal and Maximum Size of Lumps, in. | | | | | | | | | | | | | | | | | |
| Screen or Ring, in. | Cube, in. | Hard 6 | Med. 8 | Soft 10 | Hard 6 | Med. 8 | Soft 10 | Hard 12 | Med. 14 | Soft 16 | Hard 12 | Med. 14 | Soft 16 | Hard 14 | Med. 16 | Soft 18 | Hard 14 | Med. 16 | Soft 18 |
| 1½ | 1 | 30 | 40 | 50 | 40 | 50 | 60 | 50 | 65 | 80 | 65 | 80 | 100 | 50 | 65 | 80 | 80 | 100 | 120 |
| 1⅝ | 1⅛ | 35 | 45 | 55 | 50 | 60 | 70 | 60 | 75 | 90 | 75 | 95 | 115 | 60 | 75 | 90 | 90 | 110 | 130 |
| 2 | 1⅜ | 40 | 50 | 60 | 50 | 65 | 80 | 70 | 85 | 100 | 90 | 105 | 125 | 70 | 85 | 100 | 100 | 125 | 150 |
| 3 | 2 | 50 | 65 | 80 | 70 | 90 | 110 | 85 | 105 | 125 | 105 | 135 | 160 | 90 | 110 | 130 | 130 | 165 | 200 |
| 4 | 2¾ | 70 | 85 | 100 | 90 | 115 | 140 | 110 | 140 | 170 | 140 | 175 | 215 | 115 | 145 | 175 | 175 | 215 | 260 |
| 5 | 3½ | ... | ... | ... | ... | ... | ... | 140 | 175 | 210 | 175 | 220 | 265 | 145 | 180 | 215 | 215 | 270 | 325 |
| 6 | 4 | ... | ... | ... | ... | ... | ... | ... | ... | ... | ... | ... | ... | 170 | 210 | 250 | 250 | 315 | 380 |
| 8 | 5½ | ... | ... | ... | ... | ... | ... | ... | ... | ... | ... | ... | ... | 210 | 265 | 320 | 320 | 400 | 480 |
| R.p.m. of Roll | | 130 | | | 130 | | | 120 | | | 120 | | | 115 | | | 115 | | |
| Motor hp. | | 7½ | | | 10 | | | 15 | | | 15 | | | 15 | | | 20 | | |

| Size of Product[1] | | Size of Crusher, in. | | | | | | | | | | | | | | | | | | | | |
|---|---|---|---|---|---|---|---|---|---|---|---|---|---|---|---|---|---|---|---|---|---|---|
| | | 30 × 24 | | | 30 × 30 | | | 30 × 36 | | | 30 × 48 | | | 36 × 36 | | | 36 × 48 | | | 36 × 60 | | |
| | | Grade of Coal and Maximum Size of Lumps, in. | | | | | | | | | | | | | | | | | | | | |
| Screen or Ring, in. | Cube, in. | Hard 14 | Med. 16 | Soft 18 | Hard 14 | Med. 16 | Soft 18 | Hard 14 | Med. 16 | Soft 18 | Hard 14 | Med. 16 | Soft 18 | Hard 16 | Med. 18 | Soft 20 | Hard. 16 | Med. 18 | Soft 20 | Hard 16 | Med. 18 | Soft 20 |
| 1½ | 1 | 55 | 70 | 85 | 70 | 90 | 110 | 80 | 105 | 130 | 110 | 140 | 175 | 90 | 110 | 130 | 120 | 150 | 175 | 150 | 185 | 215 |
| 1⅝ | 1⅛ | 65 | 80 | 100 | 80 | 100 | 120 | 100 | 125 | 145 | 130 | 165 | 195 | 100 | 125 | 150 | 135 | 170 | 200 | 165 | 210 | 250 |
| 2 | 1⅜ | 75 | 90 | 110 | 95 | 115 | 135 | 115 | 140 | 160 | 150 | 185 | 215 | 115 | 145 | 175 | 155 | 190 | 230 | 190 | 240 | 290 |
| 3 | 2 | 100 | 120 | 140 | 120 | 150 | 175 | 145 | 180 | 210 | 195 | 235 | 280 | 150 | 185 | 220 | 200 | 250 | 295 | 250 | 310 | 365 |
| 4 | 2¾ | 125 | 155 | 190 | 150 | 195 | 235 | 185 | 235 | 285 | 250 | 315 | 375 | 195 | 240 | 290 | 260 | 320 | 390 | 325 | 400 | 480 |
| 5 | 3½ | 155 | 195 | 230 | 195 | 240 | 290 | 235 | 290 | 350 | 315 | 385 | 465 | 240 | 300 | 360 | 320 | 400 | 480 | 400 | 500 | 600 |
| 6 | 4 | 185 | 225 | 270 | 230 | 280 | 335 | 275 | 340 | 405 | 385 | 450 | 535 | 280 | 350 | 420 | 375 | 470 | 560 | 470 | 580 | 700 |
| 8 | 5½ | 225 | 285 | 345 | 280 | 355 | 430 | 340 | 425 | 515 | 450 | 570 | 690 | 355 | 445 | 535 | 475 | 590 | 715 | 590 | 740 | 890 |
| R.p.m. of roll | | 115 | | | 115 | | | 115 | | | 115 | | | 110 | | | 110 | | | 110 | | |
| Motor hp. | | 15 | | | 20 | | | 20 | | | 25 | | | 30 | | | 40 | | | 50 | | |

[1] The " size of product " listed corresponds with the size of round screen or ring opening through which 80 to 90 per cent would pass.

Capacities given for two-roll crushers are efficient capacities. Greater capacities than listed may be put through the crusher, but if this is done a larger proportion of fines will result.

rolls. A hammermill with the speed adjusted to the fragility of the lumps and with the hammers or rings of replaceable rubber may be used, or a double-roll crusher with the rolls shod with thick rubber cylinders.

**The Bradford breaker** is a combination primary and secondary crusher consisting of a perforated cylinder with lifting shelves attached to the inner circumference. The material is lifted by the shelves as the cylinder slowly rotates, then it drops, and the lumps are fractured by impact. Small pieces pass out through the shell perforations, and material which will not fracture tumbles along and out at the far end. The advantage of the Bradford breaker in a coal-handling scheme is obvious — sulphur balls, rock, tramp metal, planks, and other materials that would cause trouble are removed. The breaker costs two or three times as much as a roll crusher of equal capacity. It does not lend itself to changes in size of product since the entire set of screen plates must be changed, but frequent changes are not required in the field of operation for which the machine is intended.

It is a rugged, slow-speed machine, 25 r.p.m. or less, with low cost of upkeep and a low power requirement. Capacities in the standard sizes range from 50 to 600 tons per hour. The figures for the Pennsylvania Crusher Company breakers are given in Table 6.

**The breaker-hammermill** (Fig. 15-5) is an ingenious variation developed by this company. As its name indicates, it is a combination breaker and hammermill with the mill mounted in the rear end of the breaker cage. The dual action reduces the size of the breaker required for a given capacity since the hammers do part of the work of breaking up lumps and a finer product can be secured than by tumbling alone. If few fines are wanted the mill may be given a slow speed for light hammer action. The construction can best be illustrated by means of a typical specification. It relates to a coal breaker and cleaner with a diameter of 7 ft. and length of 14 ft. The breaker speed is 16 r.p.m.; the hammermill speed is 720 r.p.m.

*Specification:* The capacity of this machine when fed evenly with Indiana or Illinois coal of average structure, hardness, and moisture content, containing lumps not larger than 14 in., is 300 tons per hour with a reduction in size to ¾ in. and under. (Compare this capacity with the corresponding size of breaker in Table 6.) The Bradford cylinder is constructed of two massive steel spiders connected by body-bound bolts with spreader beams of railroad rails, having welded steel end flanges.

The screen plates are ½ in. thick and are secured to the spreader beams by bolts in double shear. Three rows of lifter-deflector shelves

## TABLE 6

### Capacities of Bradford Breakers

The capacities in tons per hour are approximate. The smaller capacities are for hard Pennsylvania "River" coal, or Kentucky Elkhorn; the larger figures are conservative for Pocahontas and similar coals. Standard screen perforations are used.

Capacities are affected by the hardness and structure of the coal, wet or freezing conditions, size and shape of perforations, method of feeding, etc.

| Size of Breaker, feet | Approximate Tons per Hour |
|---|---|
| 6 by 8 | 30–60 |
| 6 by 11 | 40–70 |
| 7 by 8 | 35–65 |
| 7 by 11 | 45–85 |
| 7 by 14 | 55–100 |
| 9 by 11 | 80–150 |
| 9 by 14 | 100–190 |
| 9 by 17 | 120–230 |
| 12 by 11 | 130–240 |
| 12 by 14 | 160–300 |
| 12 by 17 | 190–360 |
| 12 by 19 | 220–420 |
| 12 by 22 | 250–480 |

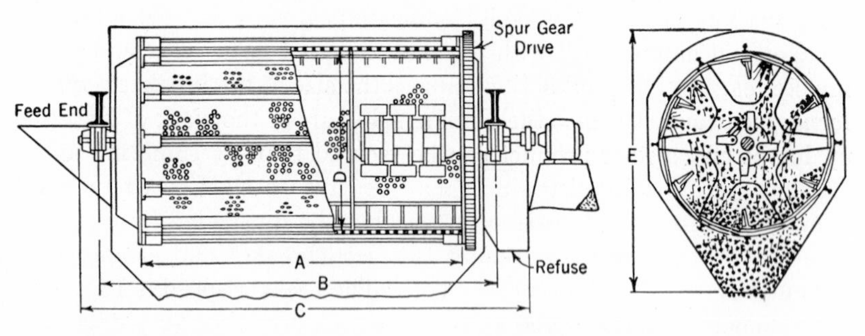


Fig. 15–5. Breaker-hammermill. (Pennsylvania Crusher Company.)

### Approximate Dimensions

| Size | A | B | C | D | E |
|---|---|---|---|---|---|
| 7 × 11 | 11′0″ | 14′ 1⅜″ | 16′11½″ | 6′9″ | 15′0″ |
| 7 × 14 | 13′9″ | 16′10⅜″ | 19′ 8½″ | 6′9″ | 16′6″ |
| 7 × 17 | 16′6″ | 19′ 7⅜″ | 22′ 5½″ | 6′9″ | 18′0″ |
| 9 × 11 | 11′0″ | 14′ 5⅞″ | 17′ 5½″ | 9′0″ | 19′0″ |
| 9 × 14 | 13′9″ | 17′ 2⅞″ | 20′ 2½″ | 9′0″ | 21′0″ |
| 9 × 17 | 16′6″ | 19′11⅞″ | 22′11½″ | 9′0″ | 23′0″ |

are mounted within the breaker to lift the coal and move it through the cylinder.

The hammermill rotor is 30 in. long by 30 in. in diameter, mounted concentrically in the discharge end of the breaker, and carried by the discharge spider, which has an extended hub with two anti-friction bearings forming a quill for the hammermill shaft. The rotor is equipped with three rows of manganese-steel hammers and is direct connected through flexible coupling to a 20-hp. 720-r.p.m. motor.

Two ball-and-socket self-aligning bearings carry the Bradford from supporting girders in the conventional manner. The drive is by a 30-hp., 900-r.p.m. high-starting-torque motor, through a double-reduction herringbone-gear reducer and RC-160 chain in an oil-tight casing.

*Operation:* Coal feeds in at the receiving end. The slack immediately screens out; the lumps are repeatedly lifted by the shelves as the cylinder revolves, and dropped, breaking up by impact against the mass beneath. The fines screen out, and by the time the hammermill rotor is reached only hard lumps remain to be broken by the hammers. All hard lumps larger than the screen perforations, including tramp iron, wire, straw, etc., are ejected by a refuse plow into the refuse chute.

The layout in a recent steam plant is shown in Fig. 15-6. This is a 10 by 17 ft. Bradford hammermill reducing 350 tons per hour of New River mine-run coal to 1¼-in. ring size with 75 per cent of the product ¾ in. and under. The upper conveyor comes in from the rail supply point off to the left. The layout provides for a second conveyor which will come in from colliers off to the right and for a possible duplicate breaker. The breaker supply chutes are arranged so that when the second breaker is installed coal from both supply belts will enter a common hopper from which it can pass to either breaker, be divided between the two breakers, or by-passed direct to the bunker conveyor. From the outlet of the breaker a short conveyor equipped with magnetic head pulley serves to cull out small fragments of tramp iron that may have passed through the perforations. The breaker and hammermill are driven by separate motors, and since it is not essential that the hammermill be running all the time the breaker is in operation, its motor is not incorporated in the interlock series of the coal-handling system. To guard against mechanical failure in the 60-hp. drive of the breaker a photoelectric relay is part of the interlock system. It functions whenever the light interruptions through the breaker screen plate lengthen to a point reached when the breaker speed is one-half normal.

**The Hammermill.** Next in line, for reducing material to ½ in. and under, comes the hammermill. Essentially this is a high-speed machine with some form of slugger hammers attached to a rotor to shatter and grind the material against a bar screen cage. The spacing of the bars determines the size of product, specifically the maximum lump. Usually a trap, or pocket, eventually catches the fragments which cannot be shattered and removes them from circulation. Differing from the roll crusher, the hammermill in addition to its application for coal

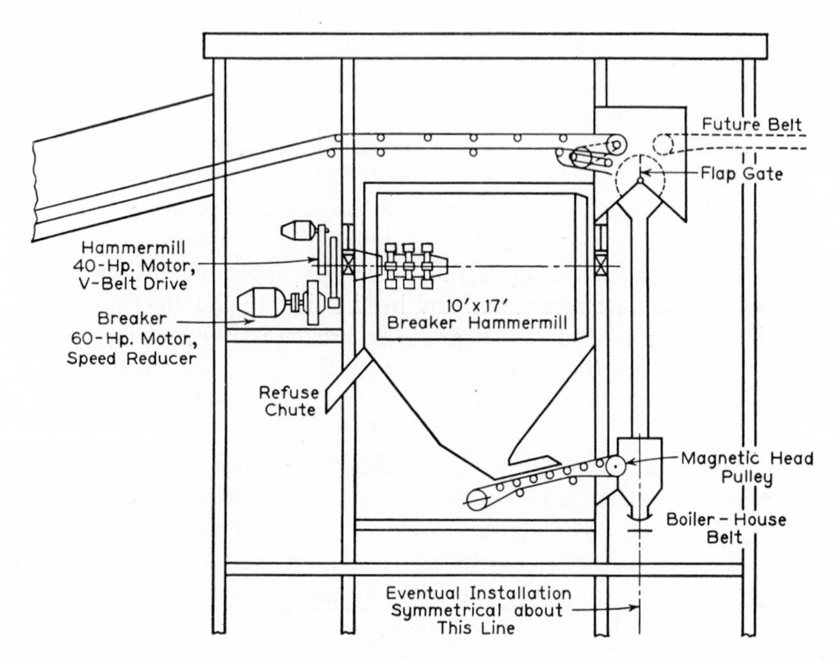


FIG. 15–6. Breaker-hammermill installation with provision for future belt and duplicate breaker hammermill.

may be used for a variety of materials, as in cement plants for limestone or shale, in gypsum plants if the gypsum is dry, in by-product plants for reducing bone scrap, in foundries for reducing brickbats and cores, in glass plants for cullet, and for chemicals, wood refuse, and oyster shells. The fineness of the product depends on the intensity of the blow and may be adjusted by means of a variable-speed drive. Speeds vary from 600 r.p.m. in the large machines to 3000 r.p.m. in the smallest mills. In power-plant work it is usual to couple the mill direct to the motor through flexible coupling.

*Construction Details:* As typical of the hammermills, Fig. 15-7 illustrates the American ring crusher (American Pulverizer Company). It may be direct-connected or may be driven by V-belt. The rotor has an alloy-steel shaft carried in anti-friction bearings, machined and balanced steel discs, and a heavy flywheel. The crushing element consists of a series of manganese-steel rings linked over shafts fitted to the discs. The rings are swung outward as the rotor revolves at high speed, but if a ring encounters a tough unbreakable lump it is thrown back. The anvil, or breaker plate, is a massive manganese-steel casting with a grinding plate at the lower edge. Then comes the grid through which the under size passes. Figure 15-7 shows the mill equipped with a trap and shows also the method of adjusting the grinding plate.

Fig. 15-7. Sectional view of hammermill. Adjustable grinding plate. Trap and cleanout door at lower right. (American Pulverizer Company.)

Table 7 shows the speed, capacity, power requirement, etc., of this mill. The capacities are for coal of medium hardness, structure, and moisture content. For the power plant the trap feature is important as it culls out metal fragments, whether magnetic or not, and either grinds up or traps out hay and fragments of wood which are troublesome if they pass into the fuel pulverizers. Thus the output is in the best condition, as regards fineness and cleaning, for the final pulverizing operation.

**Selection Suggestions for Coal-Crushing Equipment.** Subject to special circumstances, limitations of layout, and other requirements, the selection of crushing equipment may be summarized thus:

For fragmentation of large lumps, a pick breaker or a two-roll crusher with the rolls set well apart may be used.

For large capacity and large lumps, a double-roll crusher or a Bradford breaker is suitable if the product is to be 1 in. or larger. The Bradford breaker is best if hay, wood, or other foreign material must be removed.

For large capacity and large lumps to be crushed to ¾-in. ring size and smaller, a Bradford hammermill, or a hammermill in tandem with a two-roll crusher, may be chosen.

For medium capacity and medium lumps or small lumps to be crushed to 1 in. or ¾ in., a single-roll or double-roll crusher or a hammermill may be selected. For finer crushing as usually desired if the coal is to be pulverized later, a hammermill is best.

TABLE 7

HAMMERMILL: SPEED, CAPACITY, AND HORSEPOWER

| Speed,[1] r.p.m. | Approximate Horsepower[2] | Approximate Capacities[3] | | | | | Size Lump, R.O.M., inches | Approximate Floor Space No Bed Plate | | |
|---|---|---|---|---|---|---|---|---|---|---|
| | | 1½″ | 1¼″ | 1″ | ¾″ | ½″ | | Height | Width | Length |
| 600–720 | 20–25 | 80 | 50–65 | 45–50 | 35–40 | 25–30 | 10 | 4′ 3″ | 5′ 3″ | 6′ 0″ |
| 600–720 | 25–30 | 90 | 70–80 | 60–65 | 50–55 | 40–45 | 12 | 4′ 1″ | 5′ 3″ | 6′ 3″ |
| 600–720 | 30–40 | 150 | 130–140 | 100–120 | 80–100 | 60–70 | 18 | 4′ 1″ | 5′ 3″ | 7′ 0″ |
| 600–720 | 50–60 | 225 | 175–200 | 150–170 | 130–150 | 80–100 | 20 | 4′ 1″ | 5′ 3″ | 7′ 6″ |
| 600–720 | 60–75 | 300 | 225–250 | 200–235 | 175–200 | 125–150 | 24 | 4′ 1″ | 5′ 3″ | 8′ 0″ |
| 600–720 | 75–100 | 350 | 300–325 | 285–325 | 275–300 | 175–200 | 28 | 4′ 1″ | 5′ 3″ | 8′ 6″ |
| 600–720 | 100–125 | 400 | 350–375 | 330–350 | 300–325 | 225–250 | 28 | 4′ 1″ | 5′ 3″ | 9′ 0″ |
| 600–720 | 125–150 | 450 | 390–420 | 360–380 | 325–340 | 250–275 | 28 | 4′ 1″ | 5′ 3″ | 9′ 6″ |
| 600–720 | 150–175 | 500 | 425–450 | 400–425 | 350–375 | 275–300 | 28 | 4′ 1″ | 5′ 3″ | 10′ 0″ |

[1] 600 r.p.m. for 1½-in. and 1¼-in. product; 720 r.p.m. for 1-in. to ½-in. product.
[2] Based on performing these reductions on average bituminous coals.
[3] Capacities vary with size of feed, the hardness, structure, and moisture content of the coal.

**Pulverizers.** Finally we consider the requirement that the material shall be reduced to the finest possible size, or pulverized. Two machines are available, the ball mill and the rod mill. Research and experiment have brought pulverizing more nearly to an exact science than crushing. We cannot cover the subject except in the broader aspects, and the reader interested in a full understanding is referred to the booklets issued by the manufacturers. We will use the data of the Hardinge Company and describe their equipment as typical. The two machines operate on the same principle. In the ball mill a slowly rotated cylinder has a charge of balls which tumble over each other and grind up material introduced at one end until it passes out at the other end. In the rod mill a cylinder, similar except for greater length, contains a charge of rods which roll over each other to grind the material.

THE BALL MILL. Figure 15-8. Capacities range from a few pounds to 40 tons per hour. Table 8 gives some performance records.

The main factors in performance are:

Characteristics of the ore or other material.
Capacity.
Maximum size and screen analysis of feed and size of product.
Percentage of moisture.
Rotating speed.
Characteristics of the lining.
Size of the balls.

Although a hard material is more difficult to grind than a soft material, the degree of hardness does not determine the grinding rate. The harder material may have a greater specific gravity and thus a

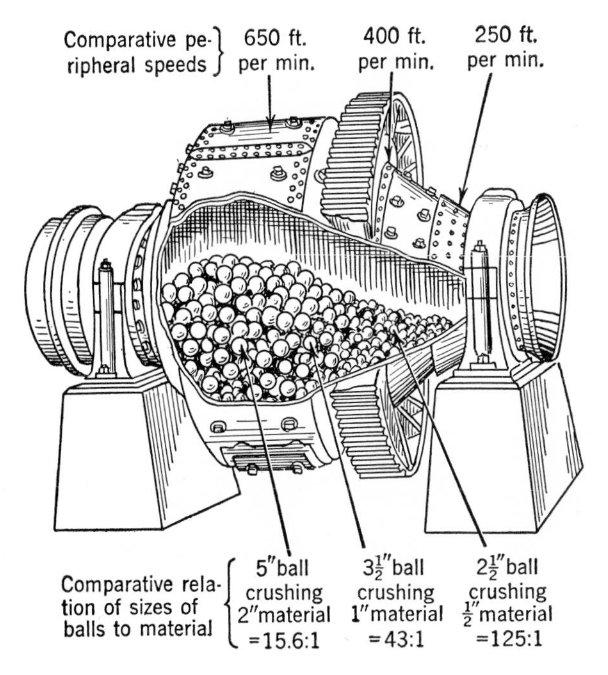


FIG. 15–8. Ball mill. (Hardinge.)

smaller volume for a given weight. Again, the cleavage plane is involved. A brittle material usually has a pronounced cleavage plane and breaks up easily. A tough material is more homogeneous and more difficult to grind. Some materials are both brittle and tough; they crush easily to a given point but resist further reduction. Quartz is hard but crushes easily to 10 or 20 mesh; then further grinding is difficult. Limestone is fairly soft, but primary grinding is difficult, and finer grinding is easier. Actual tests are best to determine the reaction of a material, though an indication is given by breaking up a sample with a small hammer and comparing the results with those of another sample whose characteristics are known.

*Capacity Control.* The capacity of a mill may be modified by changing the rate of feed, the sizes of the pieces in the feed, the fineness of the product, the rotating speed, the water content, and the size and quantity of the grinding media. The feed should contain as little oversize as possible, for oversize affects both the capacity and quality of the output. The rate of feed, to a certain extent, controls both the capacity and quality of output. Reducing the speed of rotation reduces the power required as well as the wear on balls and liner. It reduces capacity also unless the original speed was too high. Changing the ball load changes the capacity. If the size of feed has been reduced, smaller grinding balls will give greater capacity with the same degree of fineness, or the same rate of output with a finer product. Large fragments in the feed must be worn down instead of fractured by the first impact of the heavy balls. Smaller balls mean more balls to the charge, more points of impact, and greater capacity. As pointed out in the discussion of crushers, it is advantageous to screen out the fines ahead of the feed so that the mill is not choked by material already down to size. With increase in rotating speed the mass of balls rises higher before dropping, and so a higher speed may be used for coarser feed. With fine grinding the mulling action with a lower speed is more effective. Experience and trials are necessary to determine the best speed for a given material and product.

At normal speeds, 30 r.p.m. for the small mill or 16 r.p.m. for the largest, the upper layer of balls will cascade; but at higher speeds the balls may be thrown across the cylinder and strike the lining on the opposite side. At low speed the balls slide or roll over each other. A normal speed combines the blow from the falling balls with the attrition which goes on within the mass.

Owing to the cone shape of the Hardinge mill the tendency is to push the finer material onward and hold the coarser material in the larger diameter. Forcing the material through the mill faster produces a granular material. This forcing is done by increasing the rate of feed or by using smaller balls and a greater rotating speed. Increasing the percentage of moisture sometimes increases the granulating effect.

When grinding wet, reducing the percentage of water usually increases the fineness. In dry grinding, bone-dry material grinds with greater efficiency, and the efficiency drops 5 to 10 per cent for every 1 per cent increase in moisture content until a point is reached where packing occurs. Wet grinding means that sufficient water is in the mass to make it flowable, which for average ores is usually 25 to 35 per cent of water by weight for a product of 35 to 48 mesh. However, the figure depends on the material, as the water may run as high as 50 or as low as 15 per cent by weight.

*Construction.* The liner plates are made tough at the core with hard surface and are held in place by manganese-steel wedge bars which project slightly to encourage cascading. For light work the drum is lined with Silox blocks, and the grinding is done with flint pebbles, porcelain balls, or large lumps of the material to be crushed.

Rod Mills. The rod mill, first developed in Germany, has a long barrel and substitutes tumbling rods for the balls. It will produce a more uniform powder than the ball mill and is a good granulator for grinding friable ores and minerals wet. It gives a product with a minimum percentage of fines when the product ranges from 10 to 20 mesh. The efficiency of the rod mill drops more rapidly than that of the ball mill with increasing feed size. It can be operated with less water when grinding wet, and when grinding dry the percentage of water may be higher without causing packing.

*Capacity.* Table 9 gives the essential data for mills from 2-ft. diameter by 4 ft. in length, up to 8 ft. by 16 ft.

TABLE 8

Typical Ball-Mill Performances

| Size of Mill | Ore | Capacity, tons per 24 hr. | Feed | Product (mesh) | Ball Load, pounds | Horse-power |
|---|---|---|---|---|---|---|
| 4½ ft. by 16 in. | Quartz schist | 55 | 1½ in. | 2% + 10<br>30% − 200 | 4,000 | 17 |
| 7 ft. by 36 in. | Quartz schist | 500 | ¾ in. | 10% + 10 | 24,000 | 105 |
| 7 ft. by 48 in. | Silver ore, hard | 500 | 1½ in. | 2% + 10<br>38% − 200 | 34,000[1] | 150 |
| 10 ft. by 72 in. | Copper ore | 856 | 1 in. | 5.7% + 65<br>53.2% − 200 | 78,000[2] | 440 |

[1]Ball wear, 1 lb. per ton of output. Mill speed, 20.5 r.p.m.
[2]Mill speed, 18 r.p.m.

**Closing Comment on Crusher Design.** The crusher has the toughest job in a material-handling sequence; when it " goes out," other operations are halted, and so the working parts must be able to stand unlimited punishment.

In jaw crushers the jaw and cheek plates must be tough abrasion-

TABLE 9

ROD-MILL DATA

| Size of Mill, feet | | Approximate Weight, pounds | | Power | | Capacity | | R.P.M.*i* | |
|---|---|---|---|---|---|---|---|---|---|
| Diameter | Length | Mill and Lining without Rods | Rod Charge | Horsepower to Run | Motor Horsepower | Wet Grinding in Tons per 24 Hr., ¾ in. to 20 mesh | Dry Grinding in Tons per Hour, ¾ in. to 10 mesh | Wet Grinding | Dry Grinding |
| 2 | 4 | 8,000 | 1,500 | 5 | 7½ | 25 | ½ | 40 | 40 |
| 3 | 6 | 21,000 | 5,000 | 18 | 25 | 90 | 2 | 35 | 34 |
| 3 | 8 | 23,000 | 6,700 | 22 | 25 | 110 | 2½ | 35 | 34 |
| 4 | 8 | 34,000 | 12,000 | 38 | 40 | 225 | 5 | 26 | 24 |
| 4 | 10 | 39,000 | 15,000 | 45 | 50 | 275 | 7 | 26 | 24 |
| 5 | 10 | 55,000 | 26,000 | 90 | 100 | 500 | 12 | 21 | 19 |
| 6 | 12 | 76,000 | 50,000 | 150 | 150 | 800 | 18 | 18 | 16 |
| 7 | 14 | 100,000 | 80,000 | 240 | 250 | 1,300 | 25 | 16 | 14 |
| 8 | 16 | 130,000 | 110,000 | 350 | 350 | 1,800 | 35 | 14 | 13 |

resisting material such as manganese steel or the cast nickel-chromium-molybdenum steels with their depth-hardening qualities. Where white iron is indicated a nickel-chromium cast iron such as Ni-Hard (International Nickel Company), a chilled cast iron containing 4½ per cent nickel and 1½ per cent chromium, is tougher, stronger, and when chilled-cast will have a Brinell hardness of 650 to 725, with excellent resistance to impact.

In gyratory crushers the nickel-chromium-molybdenum cast steels stand up well under the severe grinding action. This is important in a crusher where the cutting action is blunted by circumferential wear. The bevel gear and pinion must stand up under heavy shock loads and be wear resistant without brittleness.

Nickel-alloy low-carbon steels have ductility and toughness. The main shaft or spindle is the vital part of a gyratory crusher, and to replace it the machine must be dismantled. Here the SAE-2300 steels are far better than the plain carbon steels because of the toughening effect of the nickel.

Single-roll and double-roll crushers are not subjected to as heavy shock as the jaw and gyratory crushers because they are used for softer materials; but the vital parts, the rolls, should be tough and strong. Manganese steel and the nickel-alloy cast steels give excellent results for roll segments or inserted teeth. Where cast-iron segmental rolls are used, Ni-Hard castings will have 1½ to 2 times the life of ordinary chilled iron.

## CHAPTER 16

# SCREENS AND FEEDERS

Many material-handling installations involve screening operations, and nearly all have feeders to control the rate of flow.

Broadly speaking, screening of materials is by one of three kinds of screen: rotary, vibrating, or shaking.

**The rotary screen** is a slowly rotating, slightly inclined, perforated cylinder in which the material tumbles over itself, the undersize passing through the perforations and the oversize passing out at the end. Because of the tumbling action the rotary screen is well adapted to washing operations as with gravel plants. It has disadvantages with fragile material because tumbling causes degradation. Often the cylinder is divided into longitudinal screening sections, or there may be two or more concentric sections so that several sizes may be produced.

The screen cylinder may be carried on spiders or spokes mounted on the shaft or carried on rollers. Since the axis of the cylinder is inclined, thrust rollers are needed to hold it in position for the driving gears to remain in mesh; in fact, it is not unusual for the cylinder to drift uphill as the result of slight variation in alignment of the rollers, and so thrust rollers at both ends may be advisable.

Theoretically each particle, when it reaches a perforation of sufficient size, will pass out; in practice, however, it does not always do so. The particles in the mass slip over the holes with more or less speed; they are crowded together by other particles, or they side-step; and therefore the particles passing over any given size of opening are smaller than they should be, even though the screen is of considerable length. The operating performance thus varies somewhat from the results with test screens. To those who are called on to produce a particular size of screened gravel under specifications in which the tolerances are rigid this fact is of particular importance. The engineer interested in this phase of the art should read "Recommendations R-163-26-1936, U. S. Dept. of Commerce, Division of Simplified Practice," now generally accepted.

As typical of the heavy rotary screen, Fig. 16-1 shows the Traylor machine. This is a 7 by 24 ft. screen with ½-in. plate sections. The dust section is 86 in. in diameter by 20 ft. long, four sections to the circle of ¼-in. plate. The bolts are on the outside for accessibility. The frame on which the screen will be mounted has 10-in. H-section longitudinal members. At the far end the screen is placed on trunnions on a rigid frame which also carries the worm-wheel speed reducer. The cylinder, or drum, has six strut bars of 8 by 8 in. angles bolted to the ends with 1½-in. radial bolts, and the feed end has a machined flange on

Fig. 16–1. The Traylor heavy-type rotary screen for limestone.

which is shrunk a 6 by 1½ in. tire. The supporting rollers are pressed on 4-in. shafts carried in adjustable dustproof bearings. The bevel driven gear is of cast steel, 54-in. diameter by 6-in. face, 2½-in. pitch, machined on the back face and bolted to the discharge head. The driving pinion is keyed to a worm gear shaft connected through flexible coupling to a 25-hp. slip-ring 900-r.p.m. motor. This outline of the details indicates the massiveness of the heavy-duty rotary screen.

**Vibrating screens** have various means of securing the required movement of the screening surface, and they may be single or multiple deck.

The unbalanced pulley type (Fig. 16-2) is the simplest. It is actuated by a weighted pulley on a shaft mounted on the frame, which causes the frame and the screen to follow the orbit of the center of gravity of the pulley when the pulley is revolved at high speed. Thus the material fed to the inclined screen surface passes through, or over. The frame frequently is carried on curved leaf-springs to reduce transmission of the vibration to the supporting structure.

The positive drive type is quite similar except that the vibrations are produced by an eccentric-machined, fixed-throw, rotary shaft with counterbalance, and are more pronounced.

These screens are used for such materials as borax, gypsum, clay, small coals, sugar, and salt. If used as a de-watering screen, that is, to separate out an excess of water as well as to remove fines, it is made

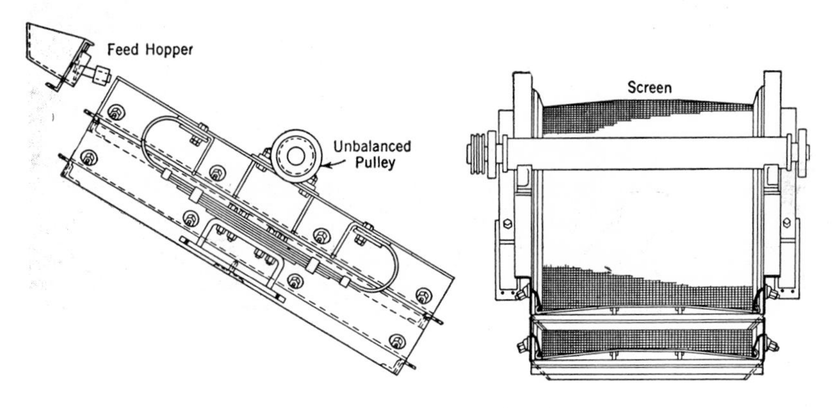


FIG. 16–2. Unbalanced pulley vibrating screen.

of wedge-section wires or " wedgewire," in which a widening gap from top to bottom prevents blinding. The wires are held to proper spacing by cross rods welded to the wires. One objection to wedgewire, even when made of stainless steel, is that the edges of the top of the triangular cross section wear away, increasing the clear space between wires; this has led some engineers to prefer the less costly stainless-steel wire cloth.

Another form of screen with promise consists of longitudinal high-carbon cold-drawn steel wires tightly stretched and without cross wires. The omission of the cross wires is claimed to increase the tonnage life by more than 25 per cent and to be particularly effective for a product between $\frac{1}{8}$ and $\frac{1}{4}$ in.

**Geared Weight Vibrator.** If two unbalanced pulleys are mounted in a housing and geared together to revolve toward each other, a resultant impulse is communicated to the housing in the direction in which the two centers of gravity move in parallel in the same direction, and the impulse is neutralized when the two centers of gravity move in opposite

FIG. 16–3. Allis-Chalmers vibrating screen actuated by geared unbalanced wheels mounted above the screen frame.

FIG. 16–4. The Hendrick balanced whipping action screen. Frame may be set horizontally.

directions. Thus a straight-line vibration may be produced in any direction by adjusting the position of the housing.

Figure 16-3 shows a screen so actuated as made by the Allis-Chalmers Company. The unit is adjustable as to position and mounted above the frame of the screen. This was developed as an alternative to the rotary screen for stone and ore as requiring less headroom and therefore a lower building structure.

**Whip Screen.** It may be advantageous to have a combined pulsating and whipping action as illustrated by the Hendrick Manufacturing Company screen (Fig. 16-4). Here, screening is secured by means of

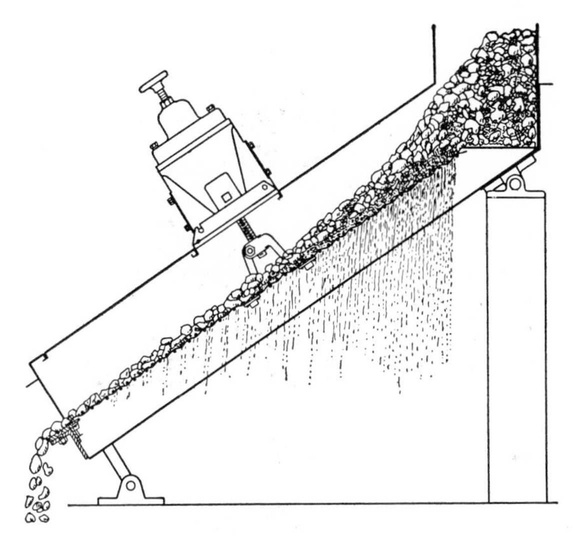

FIG. 16-5. Hummer screen.

short-throw eccentrics connected to opposite ends of a transverse rocker shaft with flexible arms inclined at 25°. One pair is connected to the lower deck and the other pair to the upper deck of a two-deck screen, thus moving the decks in opposite orbits in which the total stroke is that due to the eccentrics plus the whip; since the motions are balanced, little if any reaction is transmitted to the supports. The forward motion tends to lift the material, and the return stroke pulls the screen from under the particles, so that the screen may be set horizontally. The whipping action is sudden, giving a kick at the point in the cycle where it is most effective for screening and minimum blinding.

**Electromagnetic Vibration.** Instead of vibrations by mechanical means a varying magnetic field can be utilized.

Figure 16-5 shows the Hummer screen as made by the W. S. Tyler

Company, in which a high rate of vibration is produced by a solenoid midway in the screen frame, or by tandem solenoids, or by a solenoid at each corner. These vibrators are actuated by an alternating current of low frequency from a small motor-generator set. Figure 16-6 shows the Hummer vibrator in cross section. The movement of material along the screen surface is determined by the intensity of vibration, the angle of inclination, and the tension in the screen cloth. Stratification is induced as the finer particles hug the screen and the coarser particles ride on top.

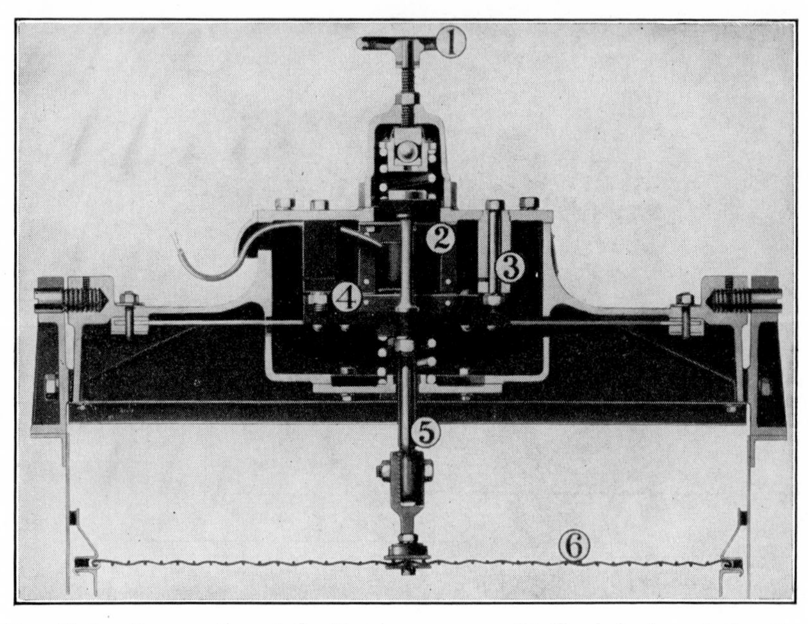


FIG. 16–6. Cross section of the Hummer screen. (1) Handwheel regulating the intensity of vibration. (2) The coil and magnet. (3) The striking block. (4) The armature with post and bracket (5). (6) Taut screen cloth.

Another example of the electromagnetic vibrating screen is the Utah, first developed by the Utah Copper Company for its concentrator plants and now made by the Allis-Chalmers Company. The heavy type has a grizzly which scalps off the fines from the feed to a crusher. The lighter type (Fig. 16-7) is similar except for the screen wire.

The power unit of the Utah screen is a straight-line reciprocating armature mounted between two pole pieces. The current is passed through a tapped transformer with the output voltage determined by a dial switch. The secondary current is passed through a battery of full-wave copper oxide rectifiers, one half of the rectified current ener-

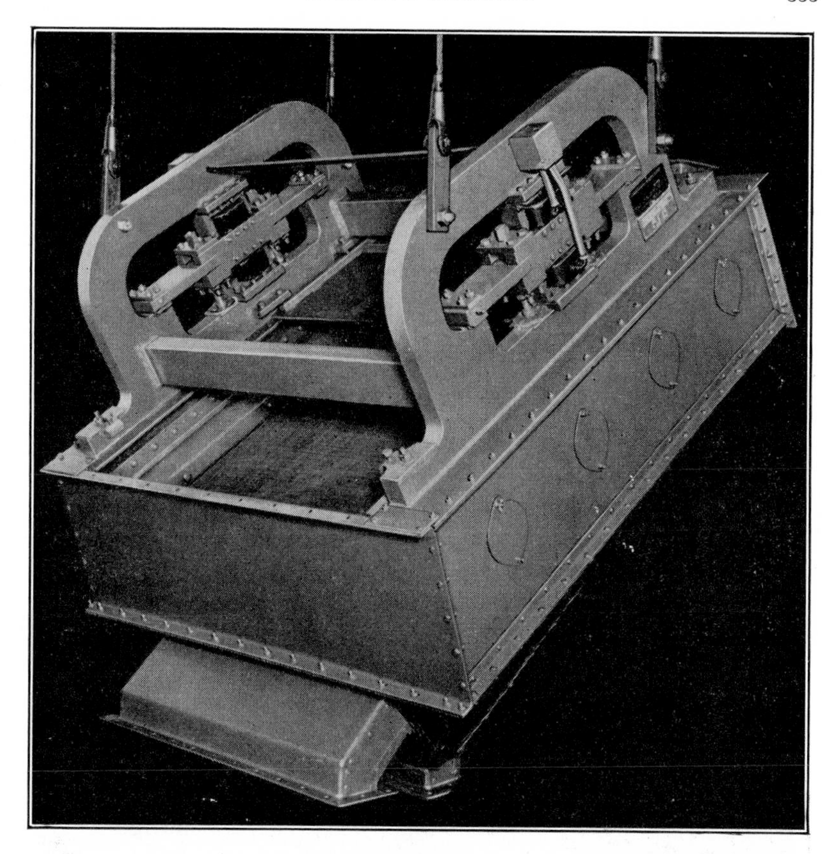

FIG. 16–7. The Allis-Chalmers " Utah " vibrating screen.

gizing each pole piece, and thus the reciprocating armature mounted between the poles is given 3600 vibrations with 60-cycle current or 1500 vibrations with 25-cycle current. The flux density in the pole pieces, which determines the pull on the armature, is controlled by the secondary voltage. The maximum amplitude of vibration is the sum of the two air gaps between the poles and the armature, less clearance. It is possible to have several of these pole pieces in synchronism since any number of armatures on the same alternating cycle will automatically be in step.

**Shaking Screens.** Screens for classifying are commonly of the shaker type in which a succession of screening surfaces are in tandem between two longitudinals suspended from above or mounted on flexible supports. The frame is swung by an eccentric or crankshaft at comparatively slow speed so that the screening action is gentler than with the vibrating screen and is preferable for fragile materials. This type of screen has considerable weight, calling for careful bracing of the supporting structure to prevent transmitted sway.

Figure 16-8 shows a shaker with Hendrick lip screen. This has stepped sections which are quite effective, owing to the long stepped slots, in preventing blinding.

FIG. 16-8. Hendrick shaker screen with stepped screen plates (lip screen).

**Shake-Out Screens.** The vibrating screen is of major importance in another field. In foundry work, after the pouring of the castings, it is necessary to shake out the flasks with their castings, copes, and drags, and to knock out the core sand, and to do this work rapidly without damaging the flasks. The importance of this process is appreciated when it is stated that as many as 650 flasks per hour may come from a continuous pour conveyor to a single shake-out station. These must be cleaned, the castings and scrap separated from the sand, and the sand passed through for reconditioning while the clean castings pass over the end. A vibrating screen of suitably heavy construction has proved best for this job.

As illustrating the time and money saved, the Simplicity Engineering Company refers to one of their large shake-out units in a foundry where castings weighing 14 tons, previously requiring 17 man-hr.

for cleaning, are now so cleaned in 7 min. by one man. The machine is actuated by solid counterbalanced eccentric shafts; that is, the eccentricity which imparts the motion is balanced by an opposed eccentricity between bearings, thus reducing vibration of the supports to a minimum. All bolts holding the frame are in shear, and the grid frame is mounted on rubber pedestals which sometimes are water cooled.

**Screen Mountings.** To prevent transmission of vibration to the structure, and eventual failure of the structure through fatigue, vibrating screens usually are suspended by spiral springs or long steel cables

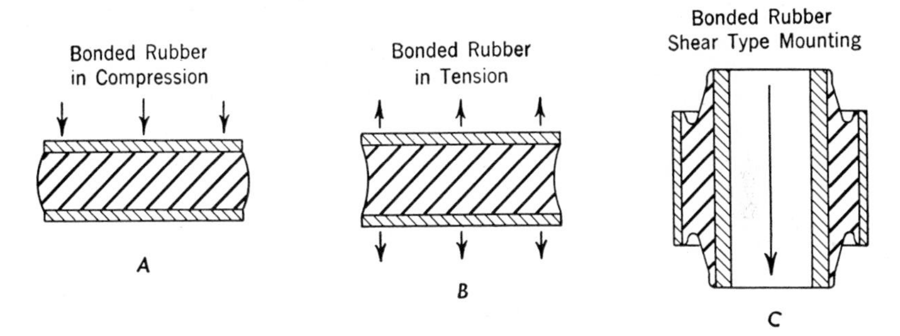


FIG. 16-9. Rubber mountings. (*A*) Compression. (*B*) Tension. (*C*) Shear.

(Fig. 16-3) or are mounted on flexible rubber supports. Contrary to popular belief, rubber is not compressible. It must be free to bulge or flow. The mounting may be the compression sandwich type (Fig. 16-9*A*) but it must be made so yielding in other directions that it may be unstable laterally. It may be as in Fig. 16-9*B* with the rubber in tension and more flexible, but this is risky. It may be as in Fig. 16-9*C* with the rubber in shear and bonded to the parts; then it is still more flexible and is laterally stable.

**Gates and feeders** are discussed together as their functions overlap, and certain types of gates may serve to control the flow, or feed materials. Pulverized material may require a gate or feeder different from those suited to lumpy material.

Figure 16-10 shows in outline various types of gates and feeders. The reciprocating feeder is shown in Fig. 6-4, serving the pivoted bucket carrier. The apron feeder is discussed in Chapter 3. These two have been the routine types for many years. The vibrating feeder has distinct advantages though it costs more. There are no parts subject to wear or requiring lubrication, and the power required is much less. For example, the Utah feeder for 120 tons per hour requires 1.06 hp. A smaller feeder handling 50 tons per hour of ½-in. limestone requires 0.55 hp.

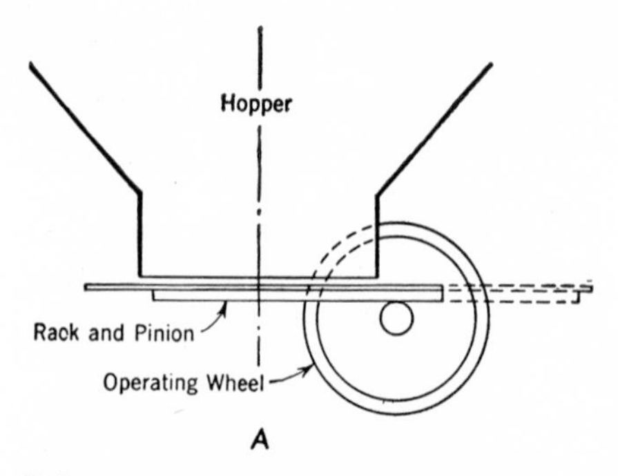


Slide gate. Advantage of low headroom, often saving in height of structure. As fragments may lodge in the gap between gate body and plate when closing, this type of gate may be troublesome at times.

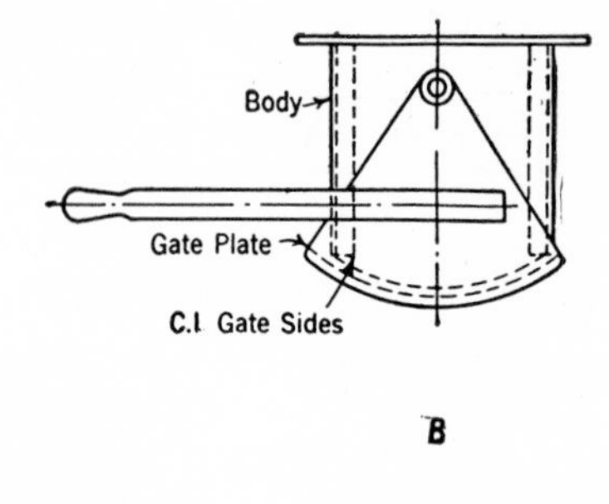


Pivoted gate. A simple, low-cost, rugged bin gate. The pivoted part is heavy to swing by hand but may be counterweighted. Best for openings not greater than 18 in. unless power operated.

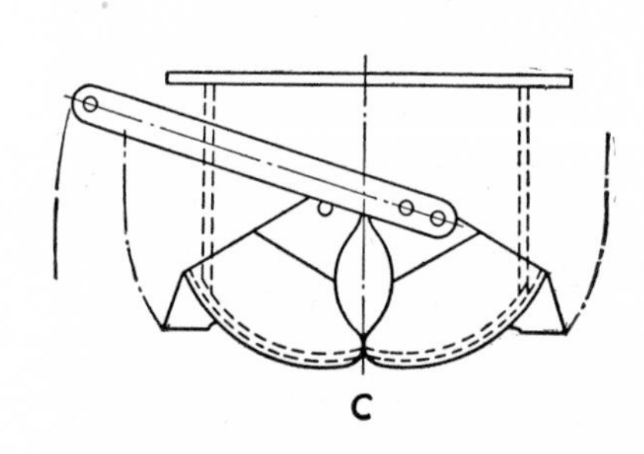


Double-pivoted gate. This is the common form of bunker gate and is preferable to the single-pivoted type. It is suited for larger openings as the two leaves are geared together and swung by a single lever or they may be suitably geared for power operation.

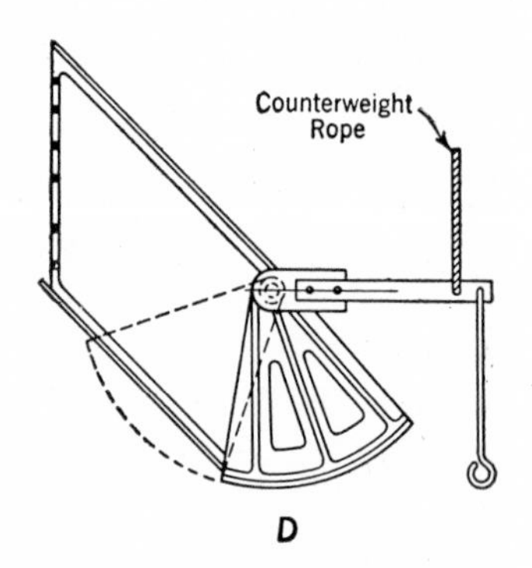


Inclined undercut. Good for lumpy material, as the pivoted plate swings downward to open and the material flows over it. Frequently used on locomotive coaling stations for controlling the flow of mine-run coal.

Fig. 16–10.

Vibrating feeders are well adapted to abrasive and corrosive materials and materials at high temperature, whether pulverized, granular, or lumpy. They are easily enclosed with a dust-tight casing, and the maintenance costs are low. One limitation has been observed, however; if a granular or pulverized material is wet, as with wet sand, the vibrations tend to squeeze out the water, causing the material to build up on the vibrating plate.

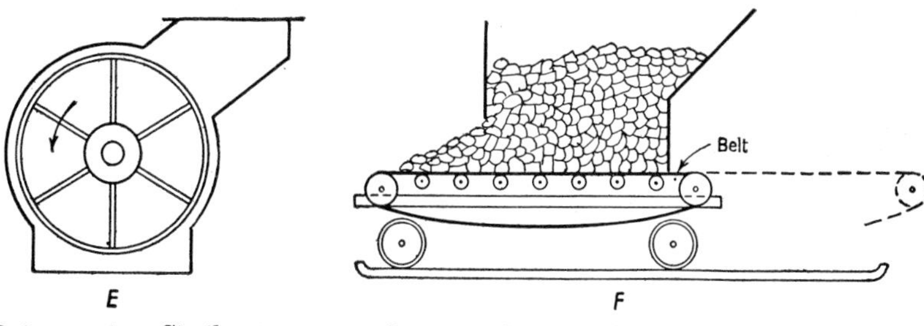


E

Rotary gate. Similar to an overshot water wheel. Suited to pulverized materials. When it is sealed to prevent influx of air, as for the receiver of a pneumatic system, it is referred to as an "air-lock gate."

F

Belt cutoff. Suited to very large openings. Essentially a short-centers belt mounted on a movable carriage, with the material resting on the belt and pouring over the front end if the belt is shifted rearward.

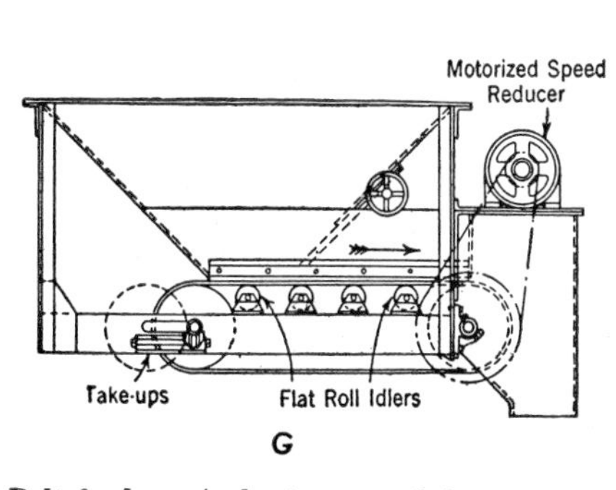


G

Belt feeder. A short-centers belt conveyor with closely spaced idlers. More vulnerable to injury than an apron feeder. If the material is abrasive, belt replacements are frequent.

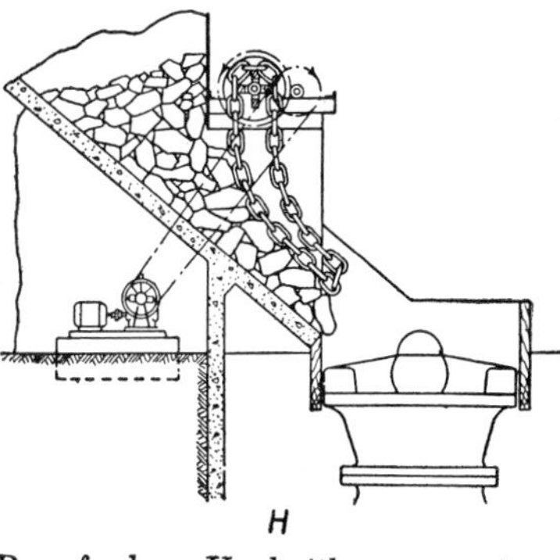

H

Ross feeder. Used either as a gate or as a feeder. The material feeds out when the curtain of endless chains is rotated. Excellent for large lumps, especially coke.

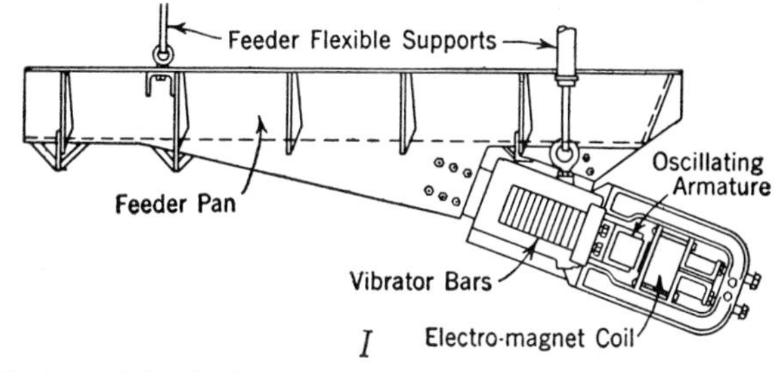


*I*

Vibratory feeders. The feed rate is adjusted by the inclination of the plate or by varying the intensity of vibration. Low cost of upkeep and low power requirement. The cut illustrates the Traylor electromagnetic feeder made by the Jeffrey Manufacturing Company.

FIG. 16–10 (*Continued*).

# CHAPTER 17

## CAR UNLOADING

The method of unloading cars is dependent on the type of car in which the material is carried, the characteristics of the material, and the rate at which the cars must be unloaded. Box cars are awkward, as the material must be taken out through the doorway. Hopper-bottom cars are self-clearing unless the material is wet, frozen, or sticky, and a track hopper of proper size will usually fulfill the requirements unless the unloading rate is extremely high. Wood chips, ballast, sand, etc., may be shipped in gable-bottom cars, the bottom sloping transversely to hinged doors at the sides. These call for a hopper wide enough to take the material as the side doors are opened. Flat-bottom gondolas are troublesome if there are cross braces since the only available method of unloading, except by car dumper, is by a grab bucket. For some materials, cement, soda ash, salt cake, etc., there are special cars loaded through hatches in the roof and discharged through gate openings in the bottom. If the material is fluid the gates are connected by canvas tubes with the conveyor inlets beneath. An electric vibrator (a Syntron or similar device) may be clamped to the car sides to maintain the flow. For the largest unloading capacities a car dumper is used. This may be of the tilting type, or a rotary dumper in which the car is turned bottom side up, discharged, and then returned to the original position.

**Power Shovel.** For box cars, if the material is flowable and the capacity not too great, one of the various types of power shovel is available (Fig. 17-1). The operation is simple and semi-automatic. The operating cable leads from a scoop to a power-operated drum. The drum shaft also winds or unwinds a light counterweight chain. As the drum winds up the cable, the counterweight chain likewise is wound up until it throws out a jaw clutch which releases the drum. The operator in the car pulls back the freed scoop for a new load, then gives a little slack. Immediately the counterweight reverses the drum, which trips a lever re-engaging the clutch. The engaged drum again draws the scoop toward the door under the guidance of the operator. It stops at the door, and the cycle is repeated. Table 1 shows the capacities and power requirements. The capacity depends largely on the skill of the operator.

TABLE 1

Power and Capacities[1] of the Automatic Power Shovel

| Material | Approximate Horsepower | Cubic Feet per Hour |
|---|---|---|
| Grains, cottonseed, linseed, etc. | 5 | 2000 |
| Materials weighing 25 to 45 lb. per cu. ft. pulverized, granular, or with small lumps | 5 | 750–1000 |
| Materials weighing 50 to 100 lb. per cu ft. pulverized, granular, or with small lumps, as pebble-lime or alum | 5 | 600–750 |

[1]These are free digging capacities, not including time lost in cleaning up.

The power shovel is low in first cost and is used widely for a variety of materials which may be scooped up and which are neither too dusty nor too heavy.

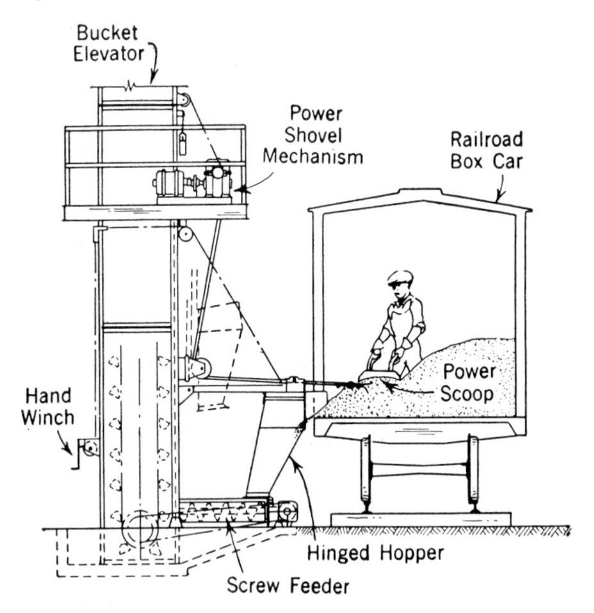


Fig. 17–1. The automatic power shovel.

**The Pneumatic Car Unloader.** Equipped with flexible hose and nozzle, the pneumatic unloader provides the completely dustless operation advantageous with materials that are harmful to breathe. The door bulkheads need not be removed, and the operator stands outside except when cleaning up. The rate of handling can be larger than with the power shovel, but first cost and power cost are much greater. Pneumatic unloaders are discussed at greater length in Chapter **9**.

**Grab Bucket.** In some localities shipments are received in flat-bottom cars, and, unless there are braces across the car, a grab bucket may be used to advantage. A crawler crane with 1½-yd. bucket will unload gondolas at 150 tons per hour, but as time is lost in cleaning

FIG. 17–2. The Shepard telpher with grab bucket.

up and shifting from car to car an average rate of two cars per hour is about all that can be counted on.

Sometimes the unloading is done by a cab-operated telpher, or overhead grab-bucket traveler, as shown in Fig. 17-2, by the Shepard Niles Company. These have a hoisting speed of 60 to 100 ft. per min. and a traveling speed along the runway of 300 ft. per min.

Grab-bucket unloading is sometimes done with hopper-bottom cars by having a deep track hopper extending out beyond the car to one side or the other, into which the material is dropped and from which the bucket digs.

**Car Dumpers.** The tilting dumper and the rotary dumper are the two types usually employed.

*A*

*B*

FIG. 17-3. The tilting car dumper for grains. (Link-Belt.)

The *tilting dumper* (Fig. 17-3) is used for high capacity box car unloading when the material is free flowing, specifically grains. A power-operated ram pushes in the car bulkhead after the car has been clamped on a semi-circular cradle which tilts the car endwise in either direction and is pivoted for lateral tilting. With the car level, the grain starts to flow out into a large track hopper below the cradle. When the flow thins out, the car is tilted first one way, then the other, and finally crosswise. The empty car is levelled and pushed off.

C

Fig. 17-3 (*Continued*).

Under favorable conditions an average unloading rate of nine cars per hour can be maintained by a crew of four men, an operator, sweeper, and two car spotters. At $1 per hour, this represents a labor cost of 45 cents per car. Maintenance cost runs about 3 cents per car.

The tilting dumper is used also for loading into box cars. The bulkheads are nailed in place, the car is tilted endwise, and the grain is chuted in. When one end is filled, the tilt is gradually reversed as the material continues to pour in, to fill the opposite end. Finally, with the car level, the central section is filled, and the car is pushed off the cradle by a ram or by the next car.

*The rotary dumper* will handle any open-top car up to 90-ton capacity or larger and weighing upward of 120 tons loaded. Under normal conditions this machine will unload ten cars per hour continuously with a crew of two or three men. If used with coal which is frozen or adheres to the sides of the car the action is slower.

As typical of the rotary dumpers, we describe the Wellman and Link-Belt machines. Figure 17-4 shows the *Wellman dumper* as the load begins to flow out; Fig. 17-5 shows the arrangement of the operating mechanism.

Referring to Fig. 17-5, multiple clamps hold the car in the cradle while dumping. The clamps are pivoted and counterweighted, and each clamp consists of a steel beam hinged to a sliding hook casting which moves vertically in guides attached to the cradle frame opposite the dumping side. The clamp beam spans the top of the car and is raised or lowered by ropes wound on an operating drum that revolves on the pivot of the counterweight arm. The ropes lead to opposite sides of the drum so that, as the clamp lowers, the lifting rope pays off while the clamping rope winds on. The lifting rope leads from the drum over a sheave in the rear side of the cradle, around a sheave in the hook casting, and is anchored to the top of the guide frame. The clamping ropes lead direct from the clamp to the drum, passing around sheaves in each end of the beam and anchored at the bottom of the dumping side of the cradle. A flat-link chain attached to a spiral cam on the head of the drum functions to revolve the drum in the proper direction to raise the clamp and leads from the cam around a deflecting roller in the cradle. Its end is attached to the counterweight arm. Tension on the chain is produced by swinging the counterweight arm away from the center of the machine by causing the counterweight to travel down an inclined guide on the foundation as the cradle approaches the initial position. The tension is relieved as the cradle starts to revolve toward dumping position, and when this occurs the clamps descend gently by their own weight until they rest on the top of the car. While the cradle rotates, the counterweight arm is connected to the operating drum only through the clamp lifting chain. When the clamp comes to rest the drum ceases to rotate and the chain becomes slack. As the cradle continues to revolve the counterweight leaves the inclined guide and hangs vertically from its pivot until the cradle reaches an angle of about 55°, then a pawl on the counterweight arm engages a cam on the cradle, giving a rigid connection between operating drum and arm. From then on, the counterweight begins to exert a pull on the clamping ropes which increases as the cradle continues to rotate and reaches a maximum when the final dumping position is attained. Limit switches prevent overtravel either in the dumping or returning cycle.

Figure 17-6 is a perspective view of the Link-Belt rotary dumper.

FIG. 17–4. The Wellman rotary car dumper as the load begins to flow out.

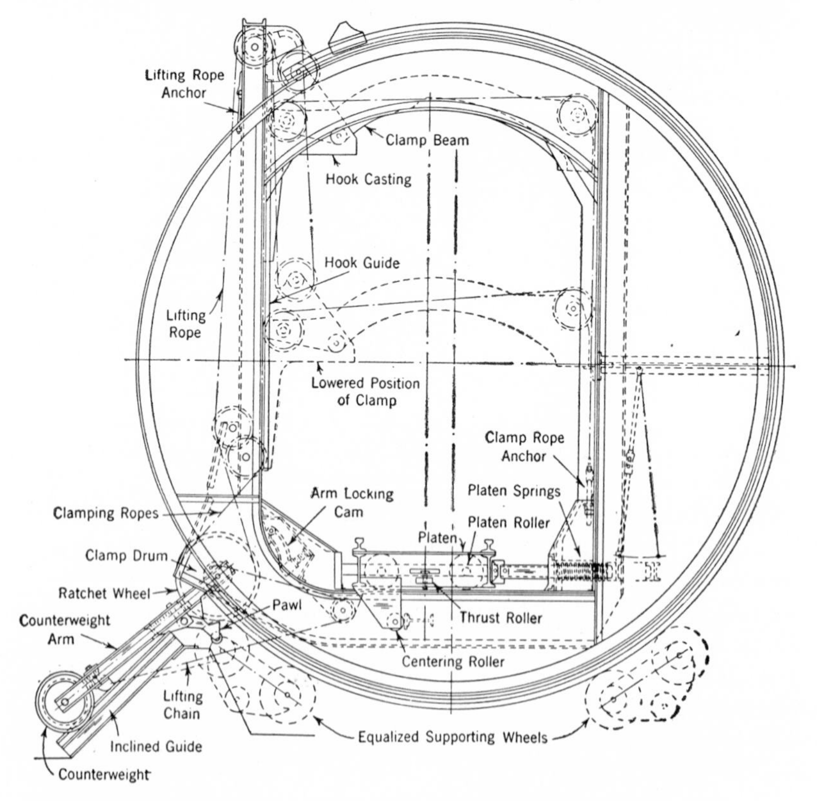


FIG. 17–5. Operating mechanism of the Wellman car dumper.

For rotating the cradle, two 1-in. steel cables are wrapped around the roller rings with the ends attached by spring dead-ends. The drive is by a horizontal countershaft through a herringbone reducer by a 40-hp. crane-type motor with an electrically operated brake which holds the dumper in any position when the current is off. The transfer table,

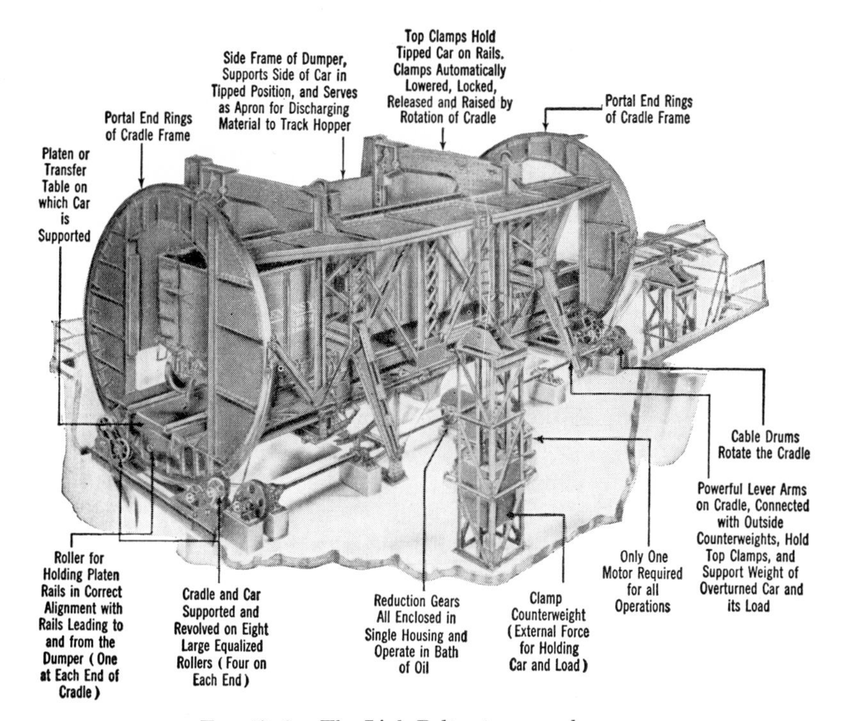


FIG. 17–6. The Link-Belt rotary car dumper.

or platen, is a steel table carrying the car rails and supported on rollers in such manner that it permits a varying lateral movement, depending on the width of the car. In the initial position, centering rollers attached to the arms of the transfer table hold the rails on the dumper in correct alignment with the track by contact with striking plates attached to the foundation. Heavy compression springs in the cradle cushion the cradle as it reaches the initial position and act also to move the car laterally toward the dumping side during the first few degrees of rotation. The transfer table is carried on eight flat-tread rollers which distribute the load in the cradle structure. The side frame is provided with timbers against which the car rests while dumping and which support the car uniformly on its side. These timbers are in two thicknesses, so that the outer layer which is subject to wear is readily replaced when necessary.

There are two sets of gravity-operated top clamps, each functioning independently of the other. They are beam type, spanning the full width of the car and arched to clear any surcharge of the load. Carried in guides in the structure on the dumping side of the cradle, these clamps are lifted by the engagement of the spring bumpers with the fixed stops. In the initial position the pivoted lever which holds the clamp in the upper position is held against a stop. As rotation begins the clamps descend by their own weight but are controlled by the spring bumpers which remain in contact with the fixed stops until the clamps are seated. After a rotation of 30°, sufficient to seat them on the lowest car, the clamps automatically lock and hold the car snugly against the rails. Except the rotation, which is manually determined by the controller, the entire operation is automatic. With the controller in neutral the operator moves the handle forward, and rotation begins. The gravity-operated transfer table moves toward the side support as the counterweight-operated clamps simultaneously descend. With a rotation of 7° the car reaches the side support and the clamps continue to lower until they reach the car. Rotation continues until it has reached 90°, when the motor is automatically stopped. The rotation starts again when the operator moves the handle to the "off" position for resetting; then the handle is again moved forward for the dumper to revolve until the motor automatically stops again at the end of the rotation travel. The car has discharged before the second limit switch is reached, and the operator then moves the controller to "reverse," causing the car to return to normal upright position with the rails held in alignment by an electrically operated brake. Should the operator wish to stop the car at an intermediate point, he can do so by shifting the controller to "neutral" when the dumper stops and is held by the brake.

The dumper just described has a 62-ft. transfer table which can handle open-top cars up to 90-ton capacity and ranging from 6 ft. 11 in. to 11 ft. 7 in. in height and from 9 ft. to 10 ft. 6 in. wide, and it has a continuous capacity of fifteen cars per hour.

*Robins Dumper.* At blast-furnace plants the ore often is received in standard railway cars but is transferred to special cars which serve the plant. Since there may be an advantage in having the railroad and plant tracks at one level, the Hewitt-Robins Co. dumper (Fig. 17-7) is nicely adapted. The car enters on a counterweighted hinged platform and is automatically clamped. The clamps accommodate railway cars of the usual range of heights. In the illustration the main hoist motor in the housing on the top platform drives the two hoisting drums through a speed reducer to swing the car upward and out through an angle of 160°. The machine is stated to have an operating cycle of 1 min. from the time the car starts upward to the time the empty car is returned to its original position.

Car dumpers are costly machines and their use is limited to installations where the highest possible rate of handling is required.

FIG. 17-7. The Robins car dumper.

*Track hoppers* receiving material from bottom-dump cars and car dumpers are of various sizes and capacity. For the average medium rates of unloading the standard size is 12 ft. by 12 ft. in plan. The standardized track hoppers shown in Fig. 17-8 will fulfill the requirements for free-flowing anthracite and bituminous coals, but for the current smaller sizes such as anthracite buckwheat and ½ by 0 bituminous the sides must be much steeper to provide valley angles of at least 50° (see chart, Appendix 2). Grids at track level will cull out oversize pieces, rags, hay, etc., used to protect leakage from bad-order cars and protect the men.

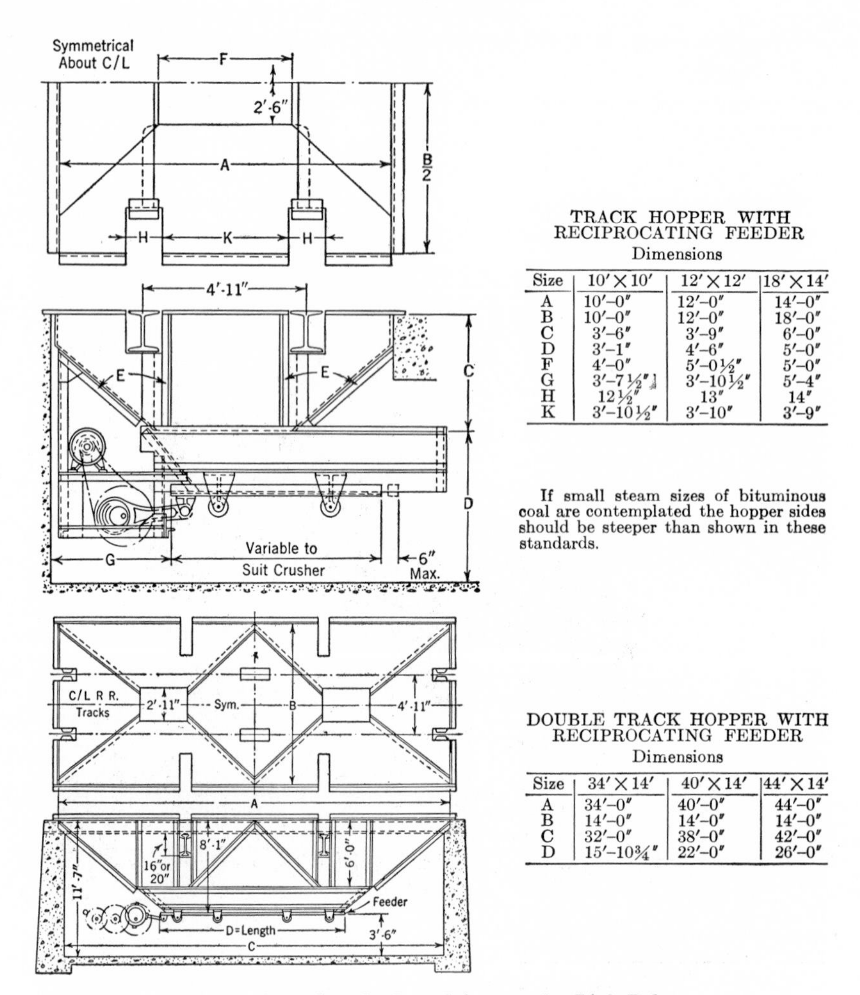


TRACK HOPPER WITH
RECIPROCATING FEEDER

Dimensions

| Size | 10'×10' | 12'×12' | 18'×14' |
|---|---|---|---|
| A | 10'–0" | 12'–0" | 14'–0" |
| B | 10'–0" | 12'–0" | 18'–0" |
| C | 3'–6" | 3'–9" | 6'–0" |
| D | 3'–1" | 4'–6" | 5'–0" |
| F | 4'–0" | 5'–0½" | 5'–0" |
| G | 3'–7½" | 3'–10½" | 5'–4" |
| H | 12½" | 13" | 14" |
| K | 3'–10½" | 3'–10" | 3'–9" |

If small steam sizes of bituminous coal are contemplated the hopper sides should be steeper than shown in these standards.

DOUBLE TRACK HOPPER WITH
RECIPROCATING FEEDER

Dimensions

| Size | 34'×14' | 40'×14' | 44'×14' |
|---|---|---|---|
| A | 34'–0" | 40'–0" | 44'–0" |
| B | 14'–0" | 14'–0" | 14'–0" |
| C | 32'–0" | 38'–0" | 42'–0" |
| D | 15'–10¾" | 22'–0" | 26'–0" |

FIG. 17–8. Standard track hoppers by Link-Belt.

In laying out the track-hopper pit, the floor should be sloped toward a sump of substantial size equipped with a drain or an ejector to avoid the nuisance of a sloppy floor.

*Unloading Rate through Track Hoppers.* The author has no extended data on the rate of handling through track hoppers, but reports on the rate with coal from hopper-bottom cars follow. The first is by observation, the second by the man doing the job. The times should be discounted; men work faster while under observation.

1. With a 12 by 12 ft. hopper, six men unload eight cars of Pennsylvania mine-run coal per hour, or 7½ min. per car, when the coal is free

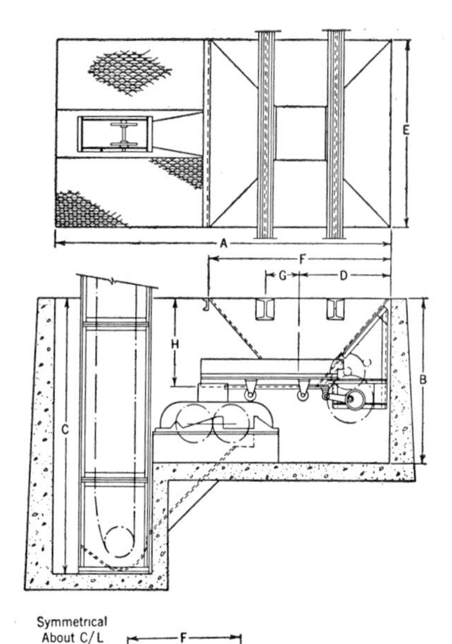


TRACK HOPPER, WITH RECIPROCATING FEEDER, CRUSHER AND ELEVATOR

Dimensions of Hoppers

| Size | 6′-6″ × 9′-0″ | 10′-0″ × 10′-0″ | 12′-0″ × 12′-0″ |
|---|---|---|---|
| A | 15′-8″ | 18′-7″ | 21′-3″ |
| B | 8′-6¾″ | 9′-11″ | 10′-7″ |
| C | 13′-4″ | 15′-9″ | 16′-4″ |
| D | 3′-3″ | 5′-1″ | 6′-1″ |
| E | 9′-0″ | 10′-0″ | 12′-0″ |
| F | 6′-6″ | 10′-0″ | 12′-0″ |
| G | 2′-5½″ | 2′-5½″ | 2′-5½″ |
| H | 4′-7⅛″ | 5′-4⅛″ | 5′-7⅛″ |

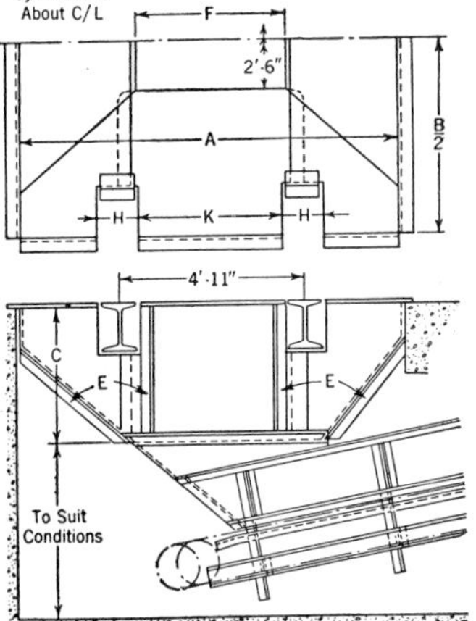


TRACK HOPPER WITH APRON FEEDER

Dimensions

| Size | 9′-0″ × 6′-6″ | 10′ × 10′ | 12′ × 12′ | 18′ × 14′ |
|---|---|---|---|---|
| A | 6′-6″ | 10′-0″ | 12′-0″ | 14′-0″ |
| B | 9′-0″ | 10′-0″ | 12′-0″ | 18′-0″ |
| C | 3′-0″ | 3′-6″ | 3′-9″ | 6′-0″ |
| F | 2′-2″ | 4′-0″ | 5′-0½″ | 5′-0″ |
| H | 11″ | 12½″ | 13″ | 14″ |
| K | 4′-0″ | 3′-10½″ | 3′-10″ | 3′-9″ |

NOTE:—Stiffener angles "E" used only on 18′ × 14′ Hopper.

FIG. 17–8 (*Continued*).

flowing. If it is wet the average time is 15 minutes. With a double track hopper of good depth, six men unload ten cars per hour if the coal is free flowing. If it is sluggish, six men unload two cars per hour if two others thaw the gates before the cars are spotted. Considerable time is lost with cars having defective gates and with large lumps which must be broken by sledge.

2. With four men it is possible to unload four 70-ton cars per hour, either mine run or slack, when the coal is dry and free flowing; 70-ton cars unload more rapidly than 50-ton cars. Mine-run clears more

readily than slack, probably because it is less sluggish when damp. When fine coal is wet it must be barred out, and sometimes several hours are required for a single car. Bad-order cars are frequent (eastern Pennsylvania). Often the gates are bolted fast, and sometimes the hoppers are planked over, causing much lost time.

Since the smaller sizes are now usual for the larger steam plants, unloading rates are slower. Small screenings pack down in the car in transit, and it may take 20 min. or longer to clear them. Mr. G. C. Daniels of the Commonwealth and Southern Company found that it took two men one hour to empty a car of ¼-in. dry coal from a 50-ton car, and when the coal was wet it took three men at least two hours with considerable spading out.

Mr. E. R. Kaiser of Bituminous Coal Research, Inc., collected data from his survey of 43 plants in Ohio, Pennsylvania, New York, and Michigan, relating to coal handling. The following is quoted from his report:

> Thirty plants received coal by rail in hopper-bottom cars. Rotary car dumpers were used at two stations, but the others discharged all or part of each car directly into a track hopper. In the latter cases a clamshell bucket was used at several places to remove coal from cars and place it in storage, but the car was cleaned into the track hopper. With normal weather during transit, coal over 2 in. would flow out of the cars with very little attention after the hopper doors were opened. When the top size was less than 2 in. it was necessary for a man to enter the car to push down part of the coal and finish the unloading with a broom or shovel.
>
> During periods of heavier rainfall the penetration of water into the car of coal varied both with the original moisture content and the amount of rainfall. Coal that was moist when loaded permitted more complete and rapid penetration than drier coal. The top layer of coal tended to shed water to the sides of the car where it would flow downward and drain out.
>
> When the car bottoms were opened under a wet shipment only a portion would flow out. To a lesser degree the same bridging would occur with the drier small coal. A few raps on the car side with a maul broke the arches of coal and caused most of it to flow freely. After free flow had ceased, coal handlers climbed into the car and pushed the rest down the hopper slopes. Almost invariably a man had to enter the car to clean out, except of course where rotary car dumpers were used.
>
> Although the flow of coal was quite different in the smaller sizes than in the larger, the difference in the handling properties was not significant in plant operations where unloading was assigned to helpers as a part-time routine and usually represented only a minor item of attention and cost

Figure 17-9 shows a good layout where a high rate of unloading was called for and the cars were dumped by a rotary dumper at 400 tons per hour. The level full capacity of the track hopper is 8400 cu. ft. Twin reciprocating feeders discharge to a 42-in. belt conveyor at 300 ft. per min.

If, with high capacity, bottom-dump cars discharge direct to the track hopper, the hopper should span two tracks so that operations could continue on one if a slowdown should occur on the other. If the rate is in excess of 150 tons per hour the hopper should have a capacity

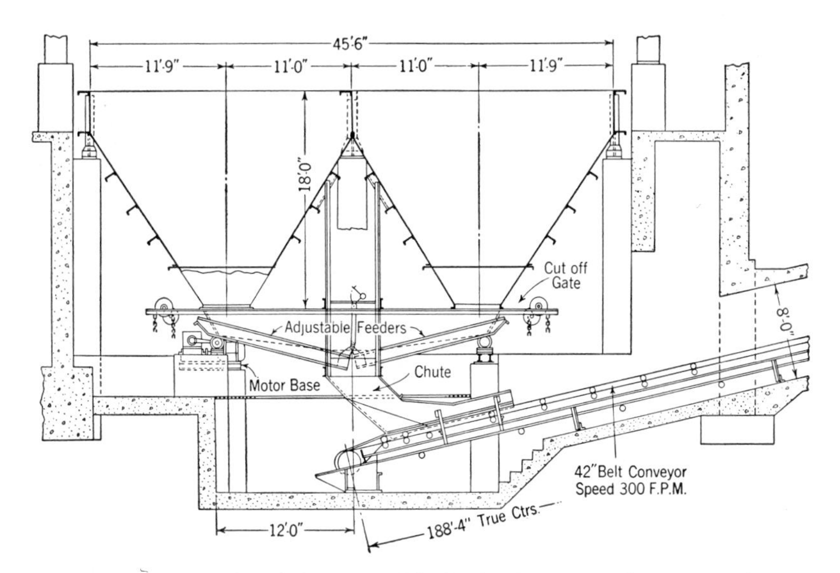


FIG. 17–9. Layout of track hopper and feeder for 400-ton-per-hour rotary dumper. The view is a longitudinal elevation.

of 75 to 100 tons — the larger the better — so that the loads may be dropped without holding up the succeeding car. It is usual to have the cars coupled together in trains to facilitate their movement across the dumping point.

Prompt car movement is facilitated if the track is on a 1 per cent down grade. There may be a car-puller, either the continuous type or a capstan. For the largest stations a car-puller is not altogether satisfactory as it involves risk of injury to the men. As alternative means of moving and spotting cars inside the yard there are the Diesel locomotive, the compressed-air locomotive, and the caterpillar tractor.

*Packed and Frozen Coal.* When gondola cars are loaded with fine wet coal which packs down in transit, or when the coal has frozen en route, unloading is difficult. Several methods of overcoming such difficulty are available.

The Stephens Adamson "accelerator" shown in Fig. 17-10 has a cross frame from which four vertical screws are suspended. The screws are driven by a 15-hp. motor; they may be raised or lowered or reversed in rotation. Control is from a cab at one end of the gantry. A report from one installation is: "By manual labor four men were required for one hour to discharge a 70-ton car of ¼-in. damp slack. With the accelerator the time was reduced to 27 min. with two men — one in the car and the operator."

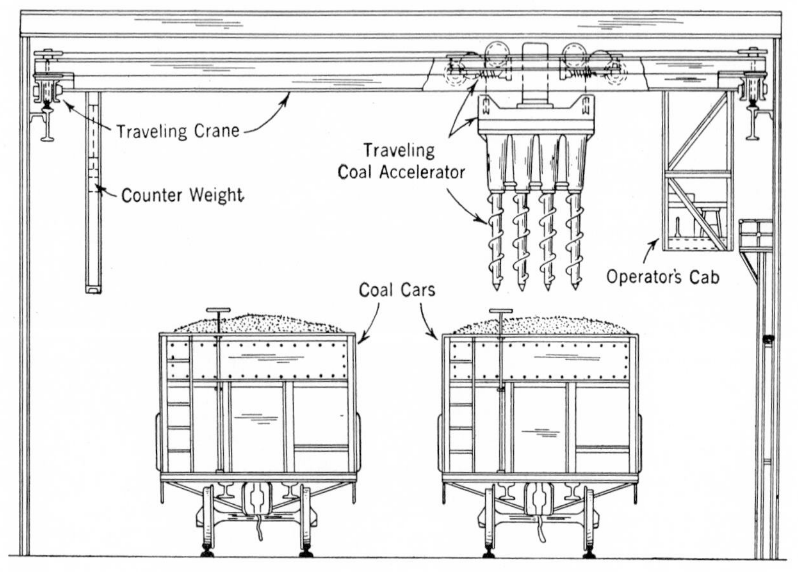


Fig. 17-10. Accelerator for wet or frozen coal. (Stephens Adamson.)

The Link-Belt "displacer" is a heavy spud (Fig. 17-11) which slices off the coal and loosens it to a more flowable condition.

The Robins "shakeout" is a heavy yoke (Fig. 17-12) which is rested on the car sides and agitated by an electric vibrator.

These devices are of great help with sticky or slightly frozen coal. In the northern states shipments frequently are subjected to winter temperatures of 30° below zero, and the solid mass must be thawed out. Where but few cars per week are involved, oil-soaked waste is sometimes burned under the car-hopper doors — until the owners learn about it. Probes of 1-in. steel pipe into which live steam is fed will soften an obstinate carload in a few hours. Infra-red lamps have possibilities.

Good reports have been received from the Hauck radiant-heat thawing device (Fig. 17-13). A firebrick box is placed ahead of the track hopper between ties. Low-pressure venturi burners maintain opposed flame jets in the box, and the heat is radiated upward against the car hoppers. When not needed, the box is covered by a metal plate. The manufacturers claim that a thoroughly frozen load can be thawed in ½ hr. with a fuel consumption of 9 to 12 gal. of oil or the equivalent

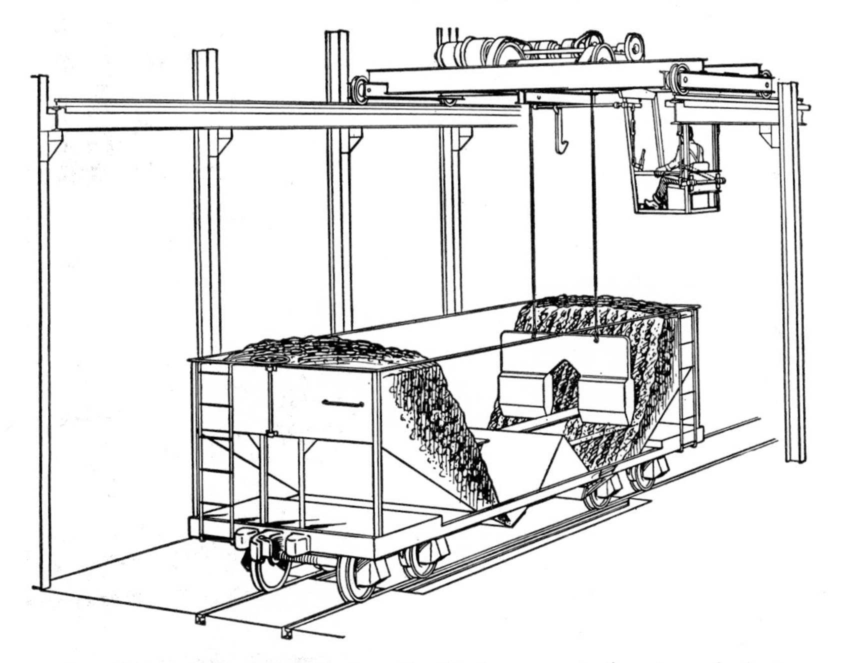

FIG. 17–11. Link-Belt "Displacer." The heavy spud slices down the load.

in gas at a cost of about $1 per car. It may be desirable to have two or more units spaced so that the heat is generated directly beneath each car hopper. The Hauck installation is comparatively low in first cost. Approximate cost (1948) for a single unit where 20 to 25 cu. ft. per min. of air at 60-lb. pressure is available is:

|  | |  |
|---|---|---|
| 2 Venturi high pressure air atomizing oil burners with control valves | | $130 |
| 2 Oil control valves | | 40 |
| 2 Oil filters | | 20 |
| Set of refractory liner tiles | | 60 |
| Oil storage tank | | 200 |
| | Total | $450 |

To this must be added freight, concrete pit, piping and installation

FIG. 17–12. Robins car shakeout. Five-ton vibrating unit specifically designed to expedite discharge from hopper-bottom cars of sluggish materials, such as sticky coal, coke, and ores. (Hewitt-Robins.)

cost which will bring the total cost of a single unit installation to around $1500.

Where the volume and handling rate warrant the investment, a thaw shed may be the only solution, as at water-side barge loading plants where cars in rapid succession are discharged by a high-lift rotating

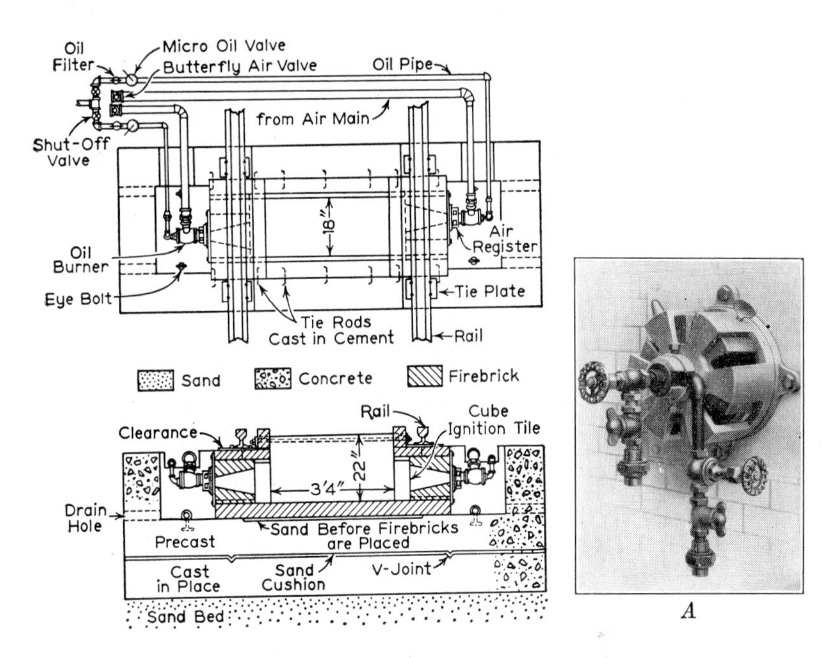


Fig. 17–13. Radiant-heat car-thawing device. Oil-burning installation with Hauck Venturi low-pressure burners mounted in the small combustion chambers. The arrangement is the same with high-pressure oil burners, one of which is pictured in *A*, except that the latter use compressed instead of blower air to supply oxygen for and to intensify combustion. As soon as a coal car has been thawed out it is moved on for dumping, and another takes its place. When not in use, the pits are covered with metal plates.

dumper. A car loaded with frozen coal would cause serious delay, if not damage to the barge, and so complete prethawing is essential. Some means will no doubt be generally adopted for loosening up loads with a wider use of coal of smaller sizes.

**Railroad Clearances** (Fig. 17-14). It is important when laying out a material-handling system involving unloading from, or loading to, cars to ascertain the required clearances. These differ with the type of siding, being less severe for private sidings entering the plant or where locomotives do not pass. Often the requirements are not strictly

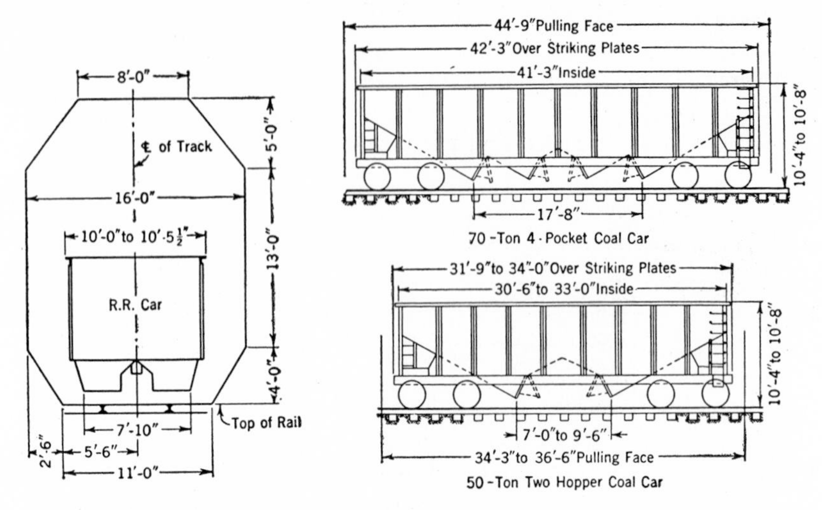


FIG. 17–14. Car dimensions and clearances.

enforced, and a side clearance of 7 ft. or even 6 ft. 6 in. from track center line is common; but much embarrassment may result if the legal requirements are not observed. The owner may be forced to move a structure too close to a siding if the siding cannot be shifted. If a man should be injured an illegal clearance will not help the situation.

## CHAPTER 18

# WEIGHING

Ascertaining the weight of the material at some point in its movement may be by dial or beam scales, weigh larry, weigh meter, or automatic scales. An automatic scale may be: (*a*) a batch weigher which automatically receives and discharges batches of constant weight and registers the number of batches, (*b*) a continuous weigher which integrates the varying weight per lineal foot of the material on a conveyor with the distance the conveyor travels, (*c*) a continuous weigher which holds the stream of material to a constant volume and integrates the weight with the distance traveled, or (*d*) a continuous weigher which holds the stream of material to a constant weight and integrates the weight per lineal foot with the distance traveled.

**The dial or beam scale** is too well known to require description. Except for its application to the weigh larry it is infrequently used in connection with the handling of bulk materials. It does have an important place in connection with cranes and overhead hoists with which loads are raised and transported. Figure 18-1 shows a Kron dial scale (Kron Company) of 30,000-lb. capacity weighing 2000 lb. It is fitted with a printing mechanism which prints the weight on a card. The scale mechanism is released by the push button seen at the left of the frame. The I-beams under the frame serve as rests when the scale is detached from the hook. Any shock to which the mechanism is subjected is absorbed by a dashpot shock absorber. The load cannot possibly fall through failure of the scales, as a stop in the housing supports the levers should they shear and also takes any overload beyond the capacity of the scales. The factor of safety is so large that failure is rare indeed — an important feature when loads are carried overhead. Scales of the dial type are adapted to a wide variety of operations involving heavy unit loads, such as molten metal, steel scrap, sheet steel, and castings, or any material en route from the plant to cars for shipment or from point to point within the plant.

**The Weigh Larry.** Figure 18-2 shows a movable weighing hopper carried on an overhead runway, usually beneath a bunker so that coal from any part is available for any boiler. For loads up to 1500 lb. a larry is easily pushed by hand if equipped with anti-friction bearings. A larry of larger capacity is traversed by endless chain and ragwheel or by a motor. The traversing speed should be slow to avoid damaging the knife edges of the scale beams; 75 ft. per min. is a good maximum. The hopper may be suspended in an ordinary beam or dial scale, with or

Fig. 18–1. The Kron dial scales. A tare beam is provided inside the frame to balance off sling chains, magnet, or other lifting members, thus allowing the net weight of the load to show on the dial.

without card printing device, or there may be an automatic scale which records and totalizes the weight delivered.

It is advantageous to have the bunker-gate operating rod mounted in the larry frame and so arranged that a bunker gate can be opened only when the hopper is in position to receive a load and must be closed before the larry can be moved. When operating, the attendant usually sets the beam weight at some convenient weight, 1000 or 2000 lb., and merely records the number of loadings. Of course it is not difficult to falsify the weights if desired; it is more difficult with an automatic scale.

**Richardson Automatic Scale.** Figure 18-3 shows the mechanism of the Richardson automatic scale (Richardson Scale Company). Essentially this has a rigid steel frame on which is mounted a multiple scale lever system with weight carrier and multiple weights, a motor-driven

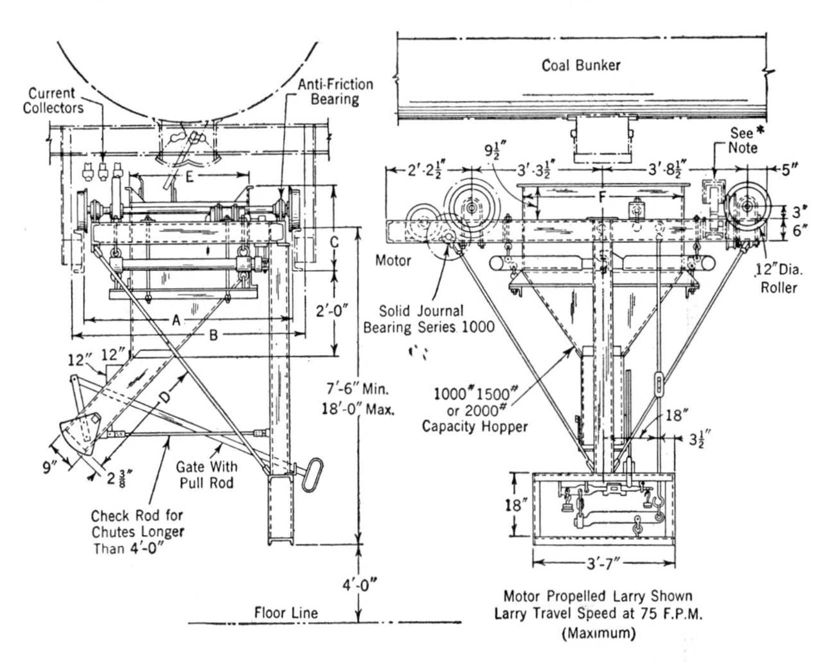


FIG. 18–2. Weigh larry. (*A*) Track gauge. (*B*) Minimum clearance. (*C*) Varies with span of track supports and larry capacity. (*D*) If chute is long, hopper must be counterweighted. $E \times F$ (hopper width and length): 3′–0″ × 4′–0″. Motor, 2 hp.

belt feeder, a weighing hopper, a counter to record the weighing of preset amounts, and the electric controls. The material is conveyed from the supply chute to the weighing hopper by a wide, slow-speed, short-centers belt conveyor. The width of the stream on the belt is determined by skirt plates. The depth of the stream is held uniform by an adjustable regulating slide in the small upper hopper. Scale weights for the quantity to be weighed in each cycle are placed in the weight carrier. The unloaded hopper end of the scale-lever system rises and actuates a mercury switch which closes an electric circuit, starting the motor which drives the belt feeder, and material flows from the feed chute to the weighing hopper. When the proper weight has been delivered the scale beam balances and trips the switch, and the feeder motor stops as the hopper empties through the opening of a solenoid-operated discharge door. The cycle continues unless material backs up; then the discharge door is held open and the cycle stops. Any

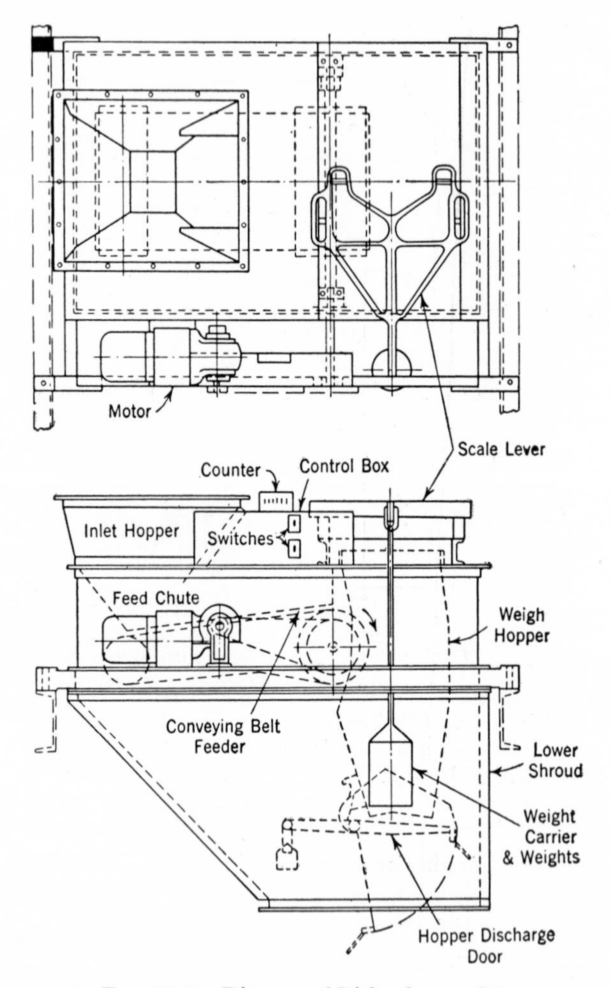


Fig. 18–3. Diagram of Richardson scales.

flowable granular material without lumps larger than 3 in. may be handled in batches from 200 to 1000 lb.

In steam plants there often is an automatic scale above each stoker or pulverizer hopper, and a conveyor brings coal from any section of the bunker to any scale chute which is not filled. The cycle of operations is continuous, and the conveyor, scales, and hoppers may all be enclosed for dustless operation. An accuracy of 0.5 per cent can be relied upon under average conditions.

**Coal Meter.** The simplest automatic weigher — strictly it is a measurer — is the Bailey meter (Bailey Meter Company). This consists (Fig. 18-4) of a small helix free to rotate on its axis within a vertical or nearly vertical chute and impelled by the flow of the mass down

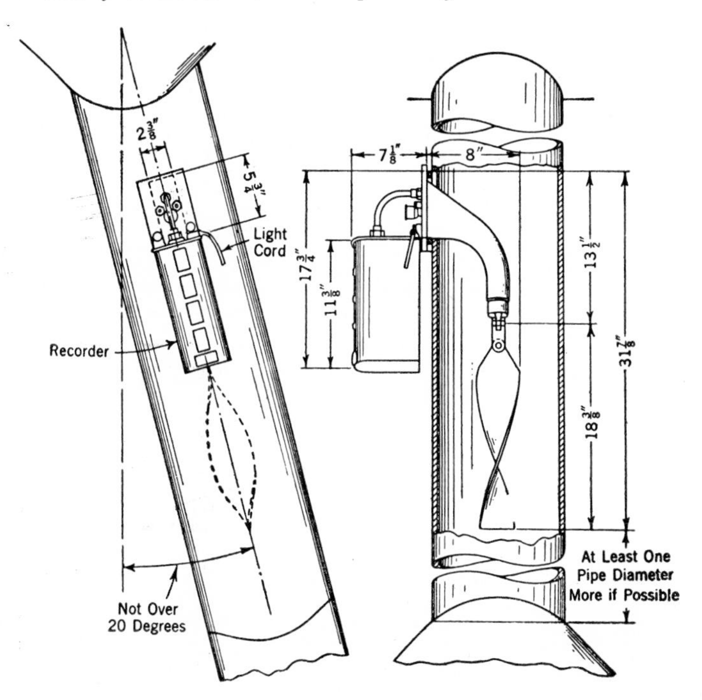


FIG. 18–4. Bailey meter.

the chute. It is geared to a meter which records the number of revolutions. The meter is calibrated to give the readings in pounds. The helix must always be submerged, as the weight record is disturbed if the submergence is interrupted and the incoming material causes the helix to spin. The helix normally makes one revolution in about 30 in. of travel of the column of material. With a stabilized flow an accuracy of about 1½ per cent can be relied upon. It is a simple and effective device where applicable and where extreme accuracy of weighing is not required. The cost is about $300 per unit — much less than for any other type of automatic recorder.

**Continuous weighing** means weighing material as it moves upon a conveyor. The Merrick weightometer (Fig. 18-5) (Merrick Scales

Company) is typical. It suspends a given length of a moving stream of material on a conveyor belt and integrates the continuing weight

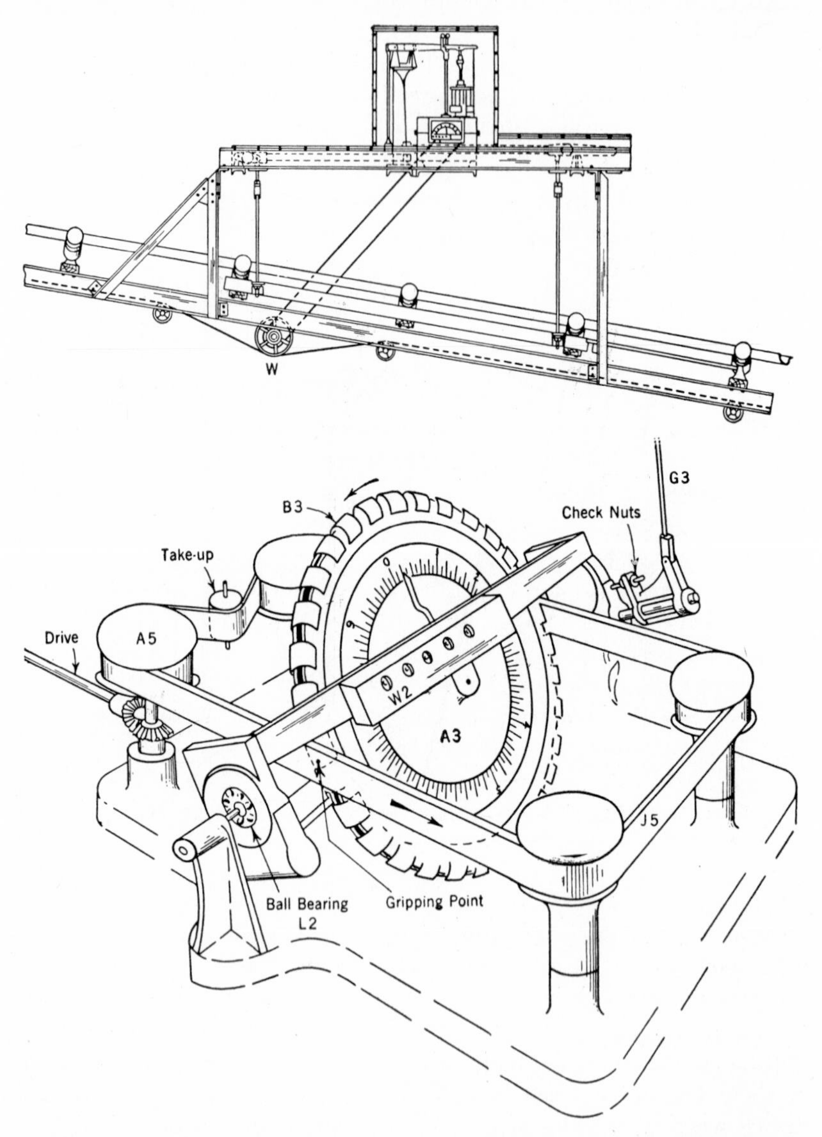


FIG. 18–5. Operating mechanism and assembly of the Merrick weightometer.

with the distance the belt travels. It is accurate to within 0.5 per cent under reasonably uniform conditions. The machine is calibrated and checked by a clever device. A roller chain about 10 ft. longer than the weighing section and of a known weight per foot is laid on the belt and held stationary. When the conveyor is in motion the effect is exactly the same as that of a corresponding load traveling on the conveyor. The weight per foot of the test chain multiplied by the number of feet the belt travels gives the true weight against which the weightometer reading must check. Instead of the scales being suspended, one end may be pivoted and the free end attached to the integrating mechanism. This reduces the required conveyor length to 10 or 12 ft. instead of a minimum of 30 ft.

The weighing and recording mechanism of the Merrick scales is ingenious and remarkably simple. As shown in Fig. 18-5, the weigh beam is connected to a suspended section of the carrying run of the conveyor belt, and the integrating mechanism is driven by an idler pulley pressing against the return run of the belt ($W$). The integrating disc $A3$ has crowned rollers $B3$, carried in recesses around its periphery and free to revolve on shafts tangential to the edge of the disc, but fixed endwise. The disc shaft is carried in ball bearings $L2$ and is free to tilt under the pull of the weigh beam transmitted through $G3$. An endless belt $J5$ is guided around a horizontal enclosing circuit by two idlers and a drive pulley $A5$, and is pressed against the disc rollers at the two opposite contact points by two pressure rollers (not shown). The drive pulley $A5$ being driven from the return run of the conveyor belt, the travel of belt $J5$ is always in a fixed ratio to the travel of the conveyor belt. As long as the rotation of the disc rollers $B3$ is exactly in the plane of the integrator belt movement the disc will not turn. This is the zero load position for an empty conveyor belt. When a conveyor load deflects the scale beam, and therefore tilts the disc, the rollers $B3$ are skewed across the integrator belt and rotate the disc at a speed proportional to the tilt and consequently in proportion to the load on the conveyor belt. The rotation is a measure of the weight of material passing over the suspended section of the conveyor belt, and after calibration the counter $W2$ registers the total weight conveyed.

One application is shown in Fig. 18-6. This is a batching operation where proportioning of four different materials is required. Each weightometer accurately weighs its material, automatically controls the rate of feed, and continuously totalizes the weight delivered. Should a hopper become empty or should the feed stop, all units stop automatically.

Another application is shown in Fig. 18-7, where it was necessary to deliver a certain weight of material to each of three bins. The starting button of bin 1 is pressed, and when the predetermined weight has been delivered to that bin, the feeder conveyor will stop and cannot be restarted until the bin conveyor tripper has been shifted to bin 2 or 3 and the corresponding button pressed.

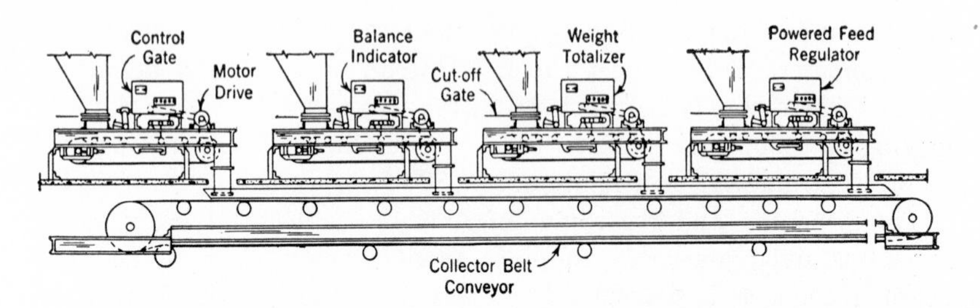


FIG. 18–6. Automatic proportioning of four materials with weightometer.

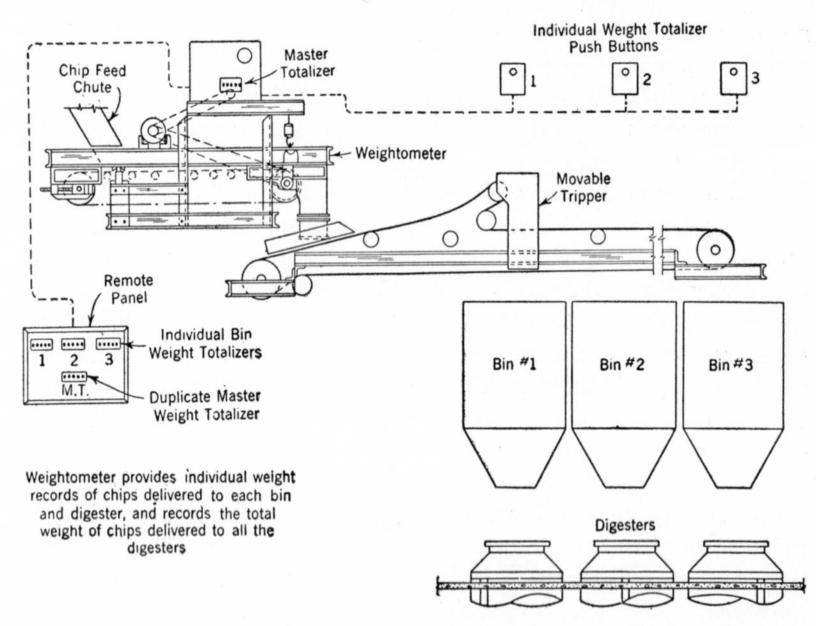


FIG. 18–7. Layout for automatic discharge of predetermined weight of material to each of three bins.

**The Shaffer poidometer** (Shaffer Poidometer Company) feeds material in a uniform stream on a short belt conveyor and registers or records the amount. The weight of material on the belt (Fig. 18-8) actuates a scale beam which, as it rises or falls, lowers or raises a gate which controls the flow from the feed hopper. The effect is to level the stream to a weight per foot determined by the setting of the beam weights and with only such variation in cross section of the ribbon issuing from the hopper gate as results from irregularities, lack of homogeneity, and varying density of the material. An agitator actuated by a crankshaft is used to prevent clogging or bridging of the material. Should the material in the hopper recede below the bottom edge of the control gate, a lever on the gate shaft depresses a push button and stops the motor and the poidometer belt. When the hopper is filled again the motor starts automatically. A meter records the number of feet the belt has traveled, and this figure multiplied by the number of pounds to which the scale beam has been set (pounds per

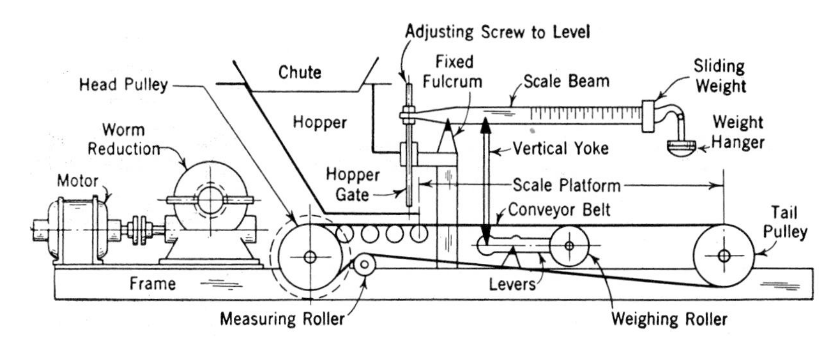


FIG. 18-8. The Shaffer poidometer.

foot of belt) gives the weight of material handled in any given period. The belt must have a constant thickness or weight throughout its length.

The carrying run rests on closely spaced idlers under the hopper. The length of belt from the first of these rolls to the outer terminal pulley constitutes the weighing platform. The roller which actuates the scale beam is at the exact center of the weighing platform and so must react to the weight which is equivalent to the platform length multiplied by the weight per foot of belt as fixed by the scale-beam adjustment. The weight delivered by the poidometer is the weight per foot at which the beam is set, multiplied by the number registered by the meter, which is the number of feet traveled.

An important feature is the non-flooding characteristic. An accuracy of 99.8 per cent is stated to be usual.

**The Hardinge constant-weight feeder-weigher** (Fig. 18-9) (Hardinge Company) operates on a different principle. Coarse or fine material feeds by *weight,* not by volume. The weight is automatically held constant, regardless of variations in specific gravity or segregation.

Essentially the feeder-weigher is an endless belt mounted on a pivoted frame beneath a feed hopper from which the material flows to the belt continuously, but any variation in weight tilts the frame and a lever opens or closes the hopper gate. A constant weight-flow is thus maintained. The rate of feed is set either by an adjustable counterweight on the gate or by a variable-speed drive. The belt maintains a constant rate of discharge by weight, and a revolution counter records the distance it travels.

The machine provides a means of maintaining the feed to a grinding mill or other mechanism which for best efficiency must have a constant feed and has the added advantage that it weighs as well as feeds.

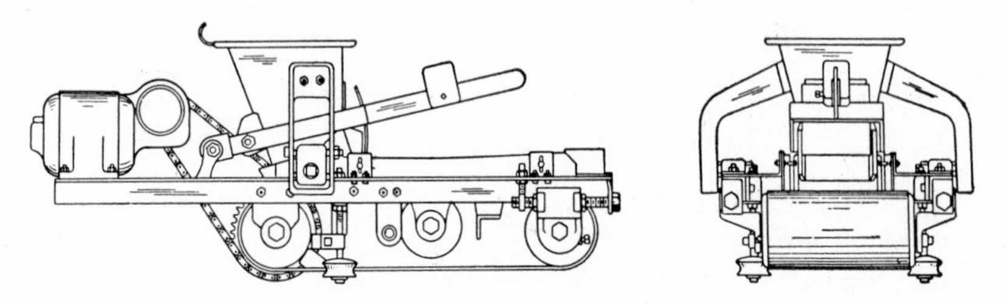

Fig. 18–9. The Hardinge feeder-weigher.

**Comment.** The selection of the type of weighing machine depends on other features of the layout. In handling bulk materials from a bin or bunker the available distance from the bin outlet to an elevator boot may be so short that a Hardinge or Shaffer unit is best adapted. If there is a succession of bin openings in line the weightometer may be best. If the feed may be in weighed blatches, as from a bunker to a stoker hopper, the Richardson will often suit the layout nicely and is readily enclosed for dustless operation.

All types of automatic scales have been developed by their manufacturers to a high degree of perfection, and they perform with remarkable accuracy under reasonably constant conditions. They are frequently installed to check the billed weights of incoming bulk material. As a rule the seller will not accept these readings as against the weights he claims to have delivered, but the automatic recording of the weight passing over a conveyor does give the purchaser protection against systematic overcharge or falsification.

# CHAPTER 19

## CHAINS, DRIVES, DRIVE GROUPS, MOTORS

The engineering of practically all material-handling installations involves a comprehensive knowledge of the proper application of conveyor and drive chains, speed-reduction mechanisms, and electric motors.

Chains may be grouped in two general classes: those used in the conveying element and therefore having a series of standard attachments suitable for flights or buckets, and those used for driving. Some chains may be in both groups, but since the drive chain usually operates at higher speed it must have a shorter pitch than the same chain used in a conveyor.

Drive chains may be called on to operate at such speed that the selection is limited to the short-pitch RC chain or the silent chain running in an oil bath, or it may be desirable to use a V-belt instead of a chain.

The motor must be suited to the conditions under which it will be called on to operate, and the speed-torque characteristics must be suited to the type of conveyor to which it is applied.

Variable speed is a frequent requirement, and high-efficiency speed changers are available to the engineer.

**Chains.** The application of drive chains originated about 1873 when Ewart, observing the difficulties with leather belts on agricultural machinery, invented the detachable metallic belt which still bears his name, the Ewart chain. Soon it was found that, with suitable wings or attachments, the chain had a variety of applications, notably for conveyors and bucket elevators.

Although the original Ewart chain, unchanged except for refinement in detail and quality of metal, still holds an important place, there are other chains with which the engineer must be familiar; accordingly their characteristics and applications are outlined.

The chain drive is a positive power transmission with zero slip. It has three elements: the driver sprocket, the driven sprocket, and the endless chain which transmits power from one to the other. The distance from center to center of adjacent chain pins is the chain pitch and sprocket pitch. The number of teeth in the sprocket, multiplied by the chain pitch in inches, times the r.p.m., and divided by 12 gives the chain speed in feet per minute. The horsepower of the drive is

$$HP = \frac{\text{Chain speed in feet per minute} \times \text{Pull in pounds}}{33{,}000}$$

The chain speed, except for the RC and silent chains which are specifically designed for high-speed work, should not exceed 500 ft. per min.

All chain manufacturers list their chains according to pitch, ultimate strength, and maximum loads. For long life and low maintenance costs it is well to hold the *working load* under $\frac{1}{6}$ the ultimate strength for speeds up to 200 ft. per min., $\frac{1}{10}$ where the speed is between 200 and 300 ft. per min., and less if the speed exceeds 300 ft. per min. For extremely high speed the advice of the manufacturer should be followed.

Many chains have a wide variety of standardized attachments, and special attachments are obtainable if the quantity involved is large. It is better to abide by standard stock sizes and attachments wherever possible in order to prevent delays when replacements are required.

## Applications and Characteristics of Standard Chains

(The designations of the chains described vary with different manufacturers.)

*Figure 19-1A.* Ewart detachable. A malleable-iron, open-joint chain varying in pitch from $\frac{3}{4}$ to 4 in. and with an ultimate strength range of 700 to 17,000 lb., but infrequently specified when the ultimate is more than 7000 lb. In the smaller sizes it is made also in stamped strip steel with corresponding pitch sizes though with a narrower selection of attachments.

Ewart chain is adapted to drives of moderate power if the speed does not exceed 450 ft. per minute. The wide selection of attachments and low cost make it a favorite chain for small-capacity conveyors and elevators. The open joint or " hook " is less desirable than the closed-end link for elevators handling abrasive material, though it does permit pulverized material to work out of the joint.

*Figure 19-1B.* The pintle chain, or 400 class. This has the same standard pitches as the Ewart and fits the same sprockets. Standard sizes range upward to 33,000 lb. ultimate strength, but the applications usually are for less than 11,000 lb. ultimate. The hook is closed, forming a barrel, and the pin is forged steel, so that the pound-for-pound strength is vastly increased. A No. 77 Ewart with 2.3-in. pitch and weight of 1.45 lb. per ft. has an ultimate strength of 3600 lb. The corresponding No. 477 pintle chain weighs 2 lb. per ft. and has an ultimate of 9600 lb. The closed joint gives a better protection to the pin and holds a lubricant better. It has a selection of attachments similar to the Ewart. It is used for drives where the speed does not exceed 500 ft. per min. and for moderate-capacity elevators and conveyors.

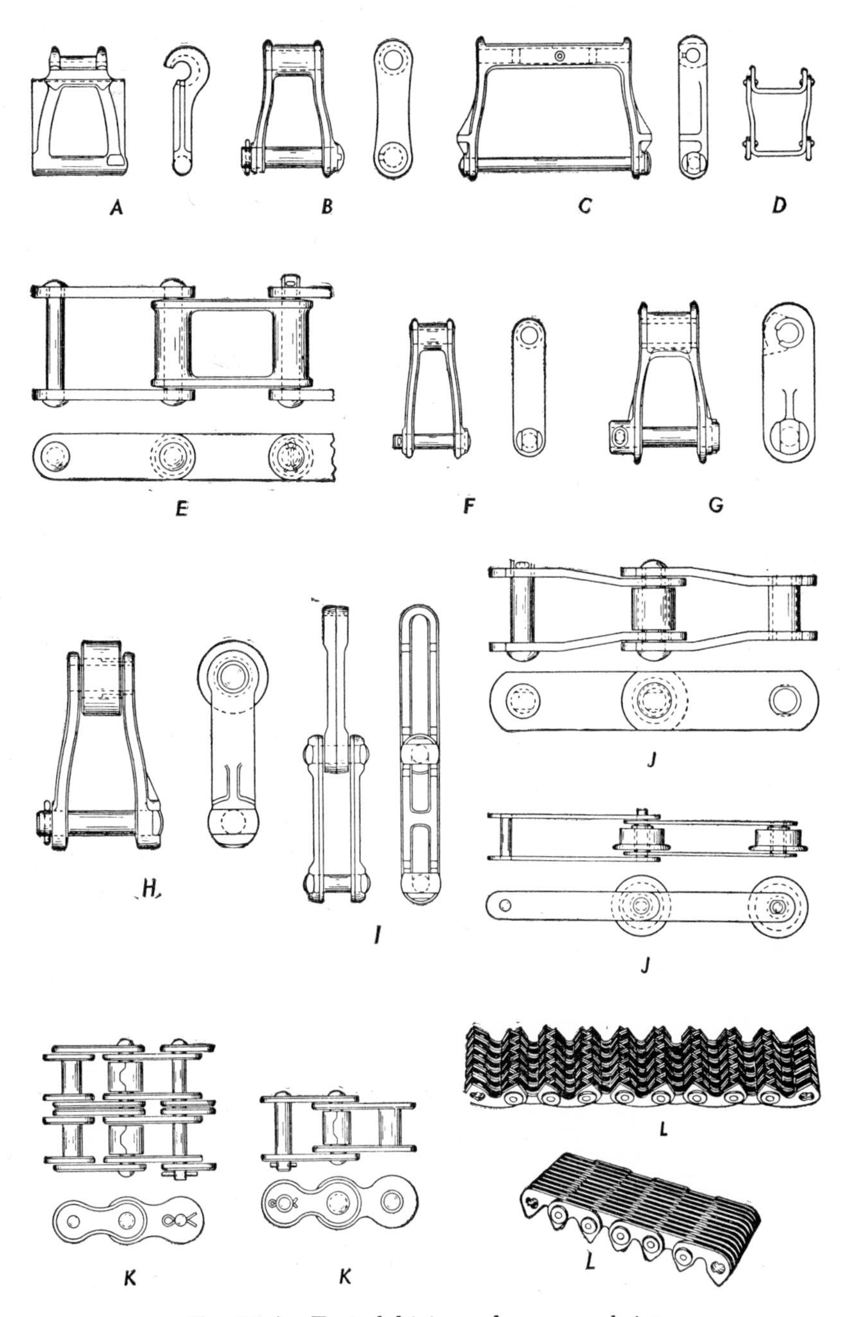


Fig. 19–1. Typical driving and conveyor chains.

*A*. Ewart detachable chain.
*B*. Class 400 or pintle chain.
*C*. H-class chain.
*D*. Refuse chain.
*E*. C-class or combination chain.
*F*. 700-class chain.
*G*. 800-class chain.
*H*. 1100-class chain.
*I*. Rivetless chain.
*J*. SS-class, long and short pitch chains.
*K*. RC-chain.
*L*. Silent chain.

*Figure 19-1C.* The H-class chains are similar to the pintles but have wide links varying from 6½ to 16 in. across, with a range of 20,000 to 40,000 lb. ultimate strength. The faces are flattened, forming a surface on which the chain may slide along a trough. As the pin is locked in the side bars and revolves in a wide barrel the chain has good wearing qualities. The only attachment of interest is the widening of the barrel for increased pusher action. A common use of this chain is in a drag conveyor for ashes, sawdust, refuse, etc. It makes a very simple scraper conveyor.

*Figure 19-1D.* The steel refuse chain, another pusher type, is made of strip steel bent to U-shape links with rivets as pins. It is a low-cost chain made in pitches from 6 to 10 in. for light service.

*Figure 19-1E.* The C-class or combination chain is popular for elevators and conveyors. Malleable-iron block links alternate with steel side bars. It is made in pitches up to 6 in. with ultimate strengths up to 50,000 lb.

It should be noted that when a C-class chain, or one of similar design, with straight side links runs on a sprocket with an even number of teeth, and there is no offset link, the tooth wear is concentrated on alternate teeth of the sprockets. An odd number of teeth or one offset link tends to equalize sprocket wear.

*Figure 19-1F.* The 700-class pintle chain is usually 4.7-in. pitch with 22,000 lb. ultimate strength, or 6-in. pitch with either 22,000 or 30,000 lb. ultimate strength. It is a simple reliable chain for elevators and conveyors where the material is not actively abrasive.

*Figure 19-1G.* The Ley bushed chain or 800 class is similar to the above except that it has renewable hardened-steel bushings which take the wear at the articulations. The usual pitch is 4 in. with 19,000 or 30,000 lb. ultimate strength, or 6 in. with 30,000 or 40,000 lb. ultimate strength. These chains are nicely adapted for ashes, cement, or similar abrasive materials. For exceptionally difficult service the pins are hardened alloy steel and the bushings of manganese steel, which increase the cost about 50 per cent.

*Figure 19-1H.* The 1100-class roller chain is somewhat similar to the 700-class but has rollers at the articulations. It is a rugged chain for conveyors in the middle range of chain stresses.

*Figure 19-1I.* The rivetless chain is probably the most popular for conveyors because it is readily detachable and has enormous strength but is low in cost. The open joint permits pulverized material to work out. Standard sizes are from 3-in. pitch with 18,000 lb. ultimate strength to 9-in. pitch with 160,000 lb. ultimate strength, or 30 per cent higher if heat treated. The chain is often misapplied when ultimate strength only is considered and not the bearing area of the pin. It is of drop-forged steel which has a low galling limit. It is widely used for conveyors subject to heavy shock and severe duty.

*Figure 19-1J.* The SS-class chains are made in short pitches for drives or in long pitches for engineering work. In the engineering chains the pitch ranges from 12 to 30 in. with ultimate strengths of 25,000 to 270,000 lb. The side bars are medium- or high-carbon steel with hardened-steel bushings. The rollers have hardened treads and tough centers. The pins are high-carbon heat-treated steel. The RC chains are better for high-speed drives. This is an excellent chain for elevators and conveyors as the parts subject to wear are replaceable and the chain has a long life. Without rollers as in the SS-111 it gives exceptionally good service in elevators for cement.

*Figure 19-1K.* The RC, or roller chains, are high-quality, short-pitch bushed chains, accurately formed and specially designed for high-speed drives. Standard pitches are 3/8 to 3 in., and the chains come in either single or multiple widths. For corrosive conditions — acids, fumes, steam, etc. — they may be had in stainless steel or bronze. The RC chains are commonly used between the speed reducer and head shaft of elevators and conveyors and for motor truck drives. Speeds are up to 1500 ft. per min.

*Figure 19-1L.* Silent chains are highly efficient, durable, high-speed, and practically noiseless. In effect the silent chain is a geared drive. Of the two best known, the Morse (Morse Chain Company) uses a rocker joint and the Renold (Link-Belt Company) a hardened pin in a renewable hardened bushing. An oil-tight casing is desirable as it permits splash lubrication. A useful life of twenty years is not unusual for a silent chain drive properly lined up and operated.

The silent chain has a wide variety of applications for machinery drives, machine tool drives, etc.

The foregoing covers the range of elevator, conveyor, and power-transmission chains from which the engineer makes his selections.

*Technical Factors in Chain Selections.* Some chains have enormous strength but if selected on the basis of tensile strength only, their life expectancy is not good. Consider the rivetless chains made of drop-forged steel center links coupled to drop-forged side bars in which a drop-forged pin is locked. The No. 698 chain has a listed ultimate strength of 100,000 lb. With a factor of 1/6 it might be assumed as suitable for a working load of 17,000 lb., but the pin has a bearing area in the center link of 1.125 by 1.56 in., and the pressure on the projected area of the pin then would be 9700 lb. per sq. in. The galling limit for forged steel is about 3000 lb. per sq. in. If we work backward, the working limit for this chain is 3000 by 1.75 or about 5200 lb., and it is advisable to keep under that figure.

A chain with alternating square links and side bars (C-class or combination chains), regardless of direction, has a bad action and a good action on alternate teeth; therefore, the sprockets should have an odd number of teeth to distribute tooth wear.

In the packing and canning industries and for some other applications, chains must function in contact with corrosives, either active atmospheric corrosion or corrosion due to organic or inorganic acid solutions, singly or in combination. Malleable iron has a greater resistance to corrosion than steel. Both may be improved by hot dipping or plating with tin. Zinc and cadmium are not permitted by the pure-food laws. Bronze chains are available and will resist most of the organic acids but not nitric acid solutions. Stainless steel (18 and 8) is very good but very expensive. The simple chains with few component parts or interspaces in which corrosion can start are best as a rule.

Sometimes the chains of conveyors are called on to operate under extremely difficult conditions. Temperatures may be high, as in drying or annealing ovens. Cadmium plating cannot be recommended, since the tensile and compressive strength drops off rapidly; in fact the metal melts at 610° F. A nickel cadmium bearing metal containing upwards to 3 per cent nickel has a tensile strength of only 600 lb. per sq. in. at 572° F. as contrasted with 14,000 lb. at room temperature.

For high annealing temperatures the standard heat-resisting alloys should be used, preferably dissimilar alloys, and the chain should be designed with loose joints to permit free movement. Very good results were obtained with one component of 35 per cent chrome and 15 per cent nickel in contact with a component of 15 per cent chrome and 35 per cent nickel. Lubrication is difficult. One of the best high-temperature lubricants is a black grease with a tallow base sold under the trade name of Necrolene. There may be an objection to the use of any lubricating grease because the vaporized lubricant will stain or discolor the material carried on the chain, as, for example, in the long slow-speed cooling conveyors for heavy coils of strip steel at a dull red heat. Oil vapor stains the exposed surfaces.

*Abrasion.* For heavy-duty work there is a decided trend toward the use of midpitch anti-friction rollers. With highly abrasive pulverized material, parts in sliding contact (rollers and bushings) will not stand up. Anti-friction bearings and effective grease seals assure longer service and fewer interruptions in operation, more than offsetting the higher first cost. If the chains operate in an atmosphere of extremely abrasive dust, it may be better to omit greasing and grease seals and use a bearing such as the spiral-wound Hyatt, which has a tendency to clean itself. On one installation for pulverized alumina, including a pivoted bucket carrier with intermediate chain rollers, no lubrication was permitted other than the original packing of the bearings with grease. The assembly is shown in Fig. 19-2. After 6 months operation at 24 hr. per day, the 1-in.-diameter pins showed the diameter reduced to 0.98 in. under the roller bearings and to 0.981 in. under the two felt seals. The grease and dust formed a good grinding compound. Life would be short with plain bearing rollers.

*Galling.* The galling point of a chain is quite as important as ultimate strength. As the chain enters the driving sprocket and (in drives) leaves the driven sprocket, it articulates under pressure, and, if lubrication is impossible or neglected, the surfaces under sliding contact may tear or gall. The distinction between galling and abrasion should be noted. Galling is a tearing, possibly due to atomic seizure, of the surfaces of two metals of the same or similar composition when the contacting surfaces are clean and in direct contact. A slight film of lubricant will eliminate the possibility of galling, thus a coating of 0.0003 in. of cadmium prevents galling under pressures as high as 25,000 lb. per sq. in. of bearing area. Abrasion occurs where a grinding agent is present between two surfaces in motion. Galling can occur only when the surfaces are in direct contact. A lubricant may or may not reduce abrasion. It prevents galling. When small areas of surfaces under pressure-contact have broken through any residual separating matter, destructive action such as seen in Fig. 19-3 may start.

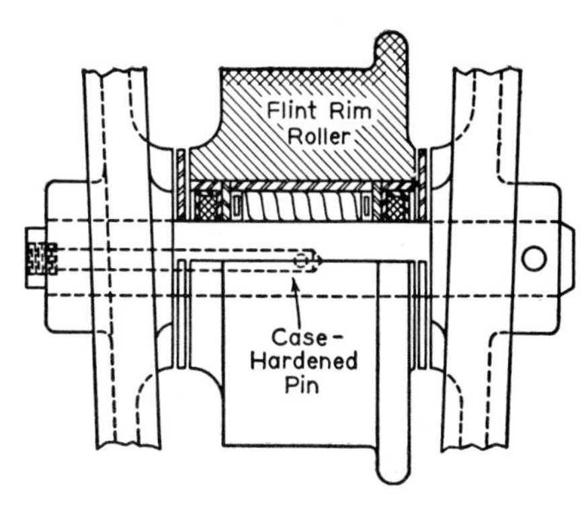


FIG. 19–2. Intermediate chain roller for pivoted bucket carrier. Rollers have Hyatt-wound-type bearings and grease seals.

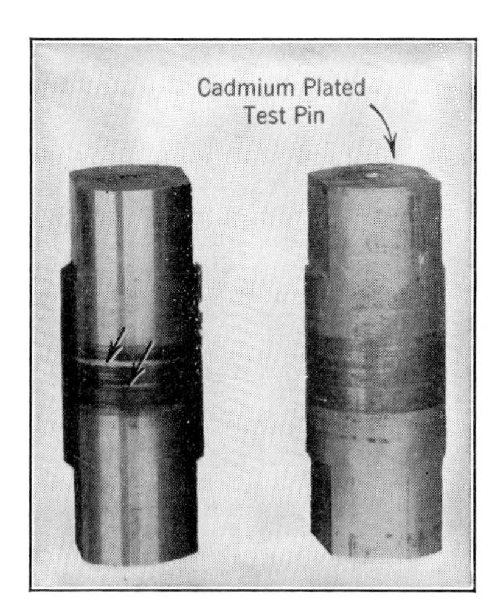


FIG. 19–3. Test pins. Trials at Rock Island, Ill., to determine resistance to galling. Ends of pins are squared to permit rotation under loads. Pin at right shows resistance to galling when cadmium plated to 0.0003-in. depth. Pin at left shows typical galling. (U. S. Engineers Corps.)

In the series of flood control dams, regulation of the flow of water is provided by great pivoted lift gates operated by chains from winches above. Each chain is good for a load of 1,000,000 lb. Since the submerged chains cannot be lubricated, it was essential that the best composition for the pins and side bars should be ascertained. A series of tests were undertaken by the U. S. Engineers, Rock Island, Ill.

The pressure on the test pin was produced by suspending the test bar, holding bars, and test pin between two forks held in the movable and stationary screw shafts of an Olsen testing machine. Test bars and test pin were washed in gasoline, and the pin was rotated back and forth through an angle of 70° under increments of pressure. When the pressure on the pin reached a value of 25,000 lb. per sq. in. or when the torque on the pin was in excess of 1200 ft. lb., the former because the pins used to secure the forks began to bend and the latter because of the difficulty of moving the lever, testing was discontinued.

The chemical compositions of the steels used in the tests are given in Table 1. Table 2 lists the tests made, the hardness of the pins and bars, the loads at which the pins or bars galled, and the torque required to turn the pins under these loads. Usually it was not difficult to determine the load at which galling occurred, and, in general, the harder the pins were, the less was the amount of galling. Figure 19-3 illustrates the galling.

Not only were the nickel chromium steels poor in resistance to galling, but they were also the most difficult to machine. Tables found in the literature list the relative ease of machinability, in decreasing order, as follows X1314, 1045, 4130, 4150, 3140, and 3245.

TABLE 1

CHEMICAL COMPOSITION OF STEELS USED

| SAE Steel | Carbon | Manganese | Sulphur | Phosphorus | Chromium | Molybdenum | Silicon | Nickel | Aluminum |
|---|---|---|---|---|---|---|---|---|---|
| 1045 | 0.42 | 0.68 | 0.023 | 0.019 | | | | | |
| 3245 | 0.48 | 0.42 | 0.005 | 0.019 | 1.20 | | 0.30 | 1.71 | |
| 3140 | 0.40 | 0.59 | 0.027 | 0.021 | 0.65 | | 0.19 | 1.33 | |
| 4130 | 0.30 | 0.47 | 0.0094 | 0.013 | 0.93 | 0.18 | 0.26 | | |
| 4150 | 0.52 | 0.62 | 0.018 | 0.021 | 1.06 | 0.23 | 0.24 | 0.18 | |
| X1314 | 0.10–0.20 | 0.95 | 0.061 | 0.040 | | 0.12 | | | |
| Nitralloy H | 0.24 | 0.46 | | | 1.22 | 0.23 | 0.23 | | 1.03 |

Summarizing these tests we see that none of the alloy-steel combinations successfully withstood pressures greater than 6000 lb. per sq. in. except one (test 18), and on repetition (No. 29) it galled below that pressure. An explanation is that in the first trial the pin was removed for examination several times as the test proceeded, and this later was found to decrease the amount of friction.

Tests 5, 12, 13, and 14 show the lubricating effect of cadmium plating up to pressures of 25,000 lb. per sq. in., the highest attainable, with

TABLE 2

GALLING TESTS BY UNITED STATES ENGINEERS ON CHAIN PINS

| Test No. | Pin SAE No. | Pin Brinell Hardness | Bar SAE No. | Bar Brinell Hardness | Load on Pin per Square Inch | Torque on Pin, foot-pounds | Galled |
|---|---|---|---|---|---|---|---|
| 1 | 3245 | 364 | 3140 | 311 | 1,000 | 50 | Yes |
| 2 | 3245 | 364 | 3140 | 340 | 5,500 | 300 | Yes |
| 3 | 3245 | 364 | 1045 | 192 | 8,000 | 400 | Yes |
| 4 | 3245[1] | 364 | 3140 | 311 | 6,000 | 320[a] | No |
| 5 | 3245[2] | 364 | 3140 | 311 | 25,000 | 660[b] | No |
| 6 | 3245 | 387 | 3140 | 311 | 2,100 | 106 | Yes |
| 7 | 3245 | 444 | 3140 | 352 | 3,000 | 110 | Yes |
| 8 | 3245 | 387 | 3140 | 402 | 2,000 | 140 | Yes |
| 9 | 3245 | 477 | 3140 | 311 | 3,000 | 170 | Yes |
| 10 | 3245 | 477 | 3140 | 364 | 2,500 | 120 | Yes |
| 11 | 3245 | 444 | 3140 | 402 | 2,500 | 130 | Yes |
| 12 | 3245[2] | 477 | 3140 | 311 | 25,000 | 920[c] | No |
| 13 | 3245[2] | 477 | 3140 | 364 | 25,000 | 920[d] | No |
| 14 | 3245[2] | 477 | 3140 | 402 | 25,000 | 990[e] | No |
| 15 | 4150 | 387 | 4130 | 302 | 1,000 | 52 | Yes |
| 16 | 4150 | 387 | 4130 | 364 | 3,000 | 180 | Yes |
| 17 | 4150 | 444 | 4130 | 364 | 2,000 | 120 | Yes |
| 18 | 4150 | 444 | 4130 | 402 | 12,000 | 600 | Yes |
| 19 | 1045 | 187 | 1045 | 196 | 6,000 | 420 | Yes |
| 20 | 1045 | 187 | 1045 | 166 | 5,000 | 280 | Yes |
| 21 | 3245 | 477 | 3140 | 311 | 5,000 | 200[f] | Yes |
| 22 | X1314 | 70-30N | 1045 | 192 | 12,000 | 680[g] | No |
| 23 | X1314 | 70-30N | 4130 | 402 | 20,000 | 1340[h] | No |
| 24 | 3245 | 387 | 3140 | 311 | 2,000 | 110 | Yes |
| 25 | 3245 | 387 | 3140 | 340 | 2,000 | 120 | Yes |
| 26 | Nitralloy H | 80-30N | 4130 | 402 | 17,500 | 1120[j] | No |
| 27 | Nitralloy H | 80-30N | 1045 | 187 | 20,000 | 1050 | No |
| 28 | 3245 | 364 | Bronze | 150 | 18,000 | 1340 | No |
| 29 | 4150 | 444 | 4130 | 402 | 4,000 | 220 | Yes |
| 30 | 3245 | 364 | 1045 | 196 | 7,000 | 400 | Yes |
| 31 | 3245 | 364 | 3140 | 311 | 2,000 | 60 | Yes |

[1]Zinc plate not more than 0.0003
[2]Cadmium plate not more than 0.0003

*a* Plating scratched at 4000 lb. per sq. in.
*b* Cadmium plate of pin scratched slightly at 20,000 lb. but apparently no more at 25,000.
*c* Cadmium plate on pin scratched slightly.
*d* Cadmium plate on pin scratched slightly at 15,000.
*e* Cadmium plate on pin just started to scratch at maximum load.
*f* Cadmium ground from pin of test No. 12 and test repeated using same bar.
*g* Very slight scratching at 12,000.
*h* No gall on pin or bar at maximum load.
*j* Slight scratch at 12,000, which did not increase.

steels which otherwise galled at as low as 1000 lb. per sq. in. Also (test 21), even after the plating had been ground from the pin, it still inhibited galling to a certain extent.

Nitrided or aerocased pins with 1045 steel bars allowed a much higher bearing pressure than alloy-steel pins against alloy-steel bars. A bronze bushing (No. 28) was quite effective in preventing galling up to the limit of the test.

A series of tests by the Link-Belt Company's laboratory gave results confirming the United States Engineers' tests, although made somewhat differently and on pins of 0.250 in. diameter, as contrasted with the 2-in.-diameter pins used in the latter tests.

The cleaned pins were rotated under water at 120 r.p.m., a split bushing being used as the bearing. An ammeter in the circuit of the motor driving the pin, which records the input to the motor, indicates when galling starts. A calibrated lever system indicated the actual bearing pressures. The results are shown in Table 3.

TABLE 3

GALLING TESTS BY LINK-BELT COMPANY LABORATORY

| Bushing | | Pin | | Bearing Load Failure, pounds | Condition of Bearing |
|---|---|---|---|---|---|
| Steel | Brinell | Steel | Brinell | | |
| 3140 | 350 | 3245 | 512 | 11,040 | Very slight galling |
| 1040 | 180 (Not treated) | 1040 | 250 | 7,200 | Pin and bushing galled |
| 3140 | 400 | 3245 | 500 | 13,800 | No galling[1] |
| 1040 | 250 | 1040 | 250 | 9,000 | Pin and bushing galled |
| 3140 | 300 | 3245 (Cadmium plated) | 512 | 18,000 | No galling |
| 1040 | 300 | 3245 (Cadmium plated) | 512 | 14,600 | No galling |

[1] Shear pin in motor drive failed.

As a further test of the effect of cadmium plating, the 1040 bushing at 300 Brinell and 3245 plated pin at 512 Brinell (test 4) was set up and a 14,600-lb. load applied *before* starting the machine. Under these conditions (test 5) the bearing ran for 3½ min. before the load had built up to a point causing shear pin failure, but the surfaces did not gall. Again the same combination was set up, but the bearing was run under 2250 lb. for 30 sec. to seat the bearing; then the load was raised to 14,000 lb. The bearing ran for 7 min. before the shear pin failed.

The tests confirmed the United States Engineers' observations of the value of cadmium plating. In some of the Link-Belt tests, a combination of a Chapmanized-1020 steel pin in an untreated 1020 bushing was tried. Chapmanizing is similar to nitriding in that it produces a high nitrogen case of extreme hardness, about 900 to 1000 Brinell. The bearing was loaded to the limit of the shear pin, about 19,000 lb. bearing pressure, without galling either the hard pin or the very soft bushing, confirming the old principle that for best operating results *one* of the bearing parts must be as hard as possible.

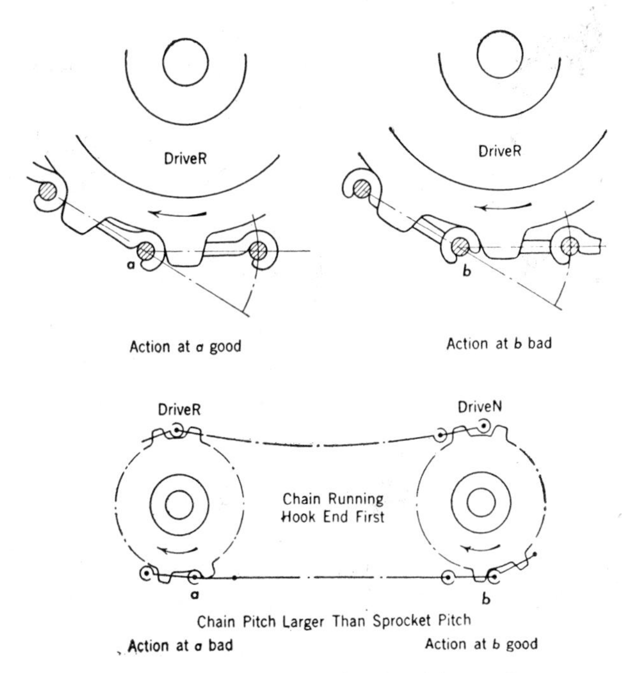


FIG. 19–4. Engagement of chain with sprockets.

*Direction of Motion with Closed-End Pin-Type Chains.* One point often overlooked is that there is a right and wrong way to operate Ewart and closed-end pin-type chains in which the barrel corresponds to the " hook " of the Ewart and the pin to the " bar."

Consider the engagement of the link with the sprocket tooth in the upper diagram (Fig. 19-4). The action may be called good when the bending of the chain around the sprocket is in the articulation as at *a*, without sliding contact between link and tooth; and bad when the link bends around the sprocket with the outside of the hook rubbing the tooth, wearing both tooth and exterior of the hook as at *b*.

Again, in lower Fig. 19-4, there is never more than one tooth in action at one time although the sprockets are ground to pitch. Wear and stretch begin when the chain is put into service so that the chain pitch becomes greater than the sprocket pitch. Under this condition the link entering the drive sprocket does the work. If the chain is run hook end first the barrel rubs momentarily against the tooth but is released as the load shifts to the next tooth. The action is bad as the barrel slips down the tooth, but tooth wear is even, and no hook is

FIG. 19–5. Gates Rubber Company flat V-belt drive. So called because only the small pulley is grooved. Illustration shows motor driving air compressor.

formed. The action at the leaving side is good. At the driven wheel the releasing tooth does all the work. The barrel rests against this tooth and releases as the chain straightens. The action is good. Briefly, there are two good points, one bad point, and one not objectionable point at the entering side of the driven wheel.

If the same analysis is made for a chain running bar end first it will be found that the action is good where the chain enters the driver, not objectionable where it leaves the driver, good where it enters the driven, and very bad where it leaves the driven as the teeth will be worn to a hook and eventually the chain will snag and break.

As the driven wheel is almost invariably larger than the driver, it might be held that since it has more teeth and less chain swivel at each tooth the wear might be equalized by running the chain bar end first. That is so, but on the other hand the small driver sprocket costs much less than the large driven sprocket.

The best all-round performance is gained by running these chains hook end first in drives. In elevators good action is needed at the driver sprocket, and the foot wheel is merely an idler. Therefore these chains are run bar end first. Similarly in flight conveyors, where the foot wheel is usually an idler, the chain bar end is run first.

*V-Belts.* If the speed of a drive is too high for an RC or silent chain, or if the drive is subject to shock, as in a crusher drive, the V-belt may be advantageous (Fig. 19-5). It is elastic and can be run at speeds as high as 5000 ft. per min.

For extremely long centers there is the rope drive, but the use of individual motors has made the rope drive an object of curiosity to the average engineer, though it still has applications.

*Silent Chain and V-Belt Drives.* As silent chains and V-belts are commonly selected for high-speed drives, they will be discussed in detail.

The features claimed for the silent chain drive are:

Complete absence of slip.
98.2 per cent sustained efficiency.
Replacement without dismantling the machines — detachability.
Space economy — small wheel diameters.
Low maintenance cost.
Long life and silent operation.
Freedom from effect by atmospheric changes and varying temperatures.
Steel construction — no deterioration.
Slack tension except tension actually transmitting the load.

Large reduction drives on small centers cost less with smaller pitches. Smaller reductions on long centers are less costly with longer pitches and narrow chains. An even number of pitches avoids the necessity of an offset link at the connection. A take-up is desirable but not absolutely necessary except in vertical drives; then a weighted idler may be used. Casings are obligatory for safety. With oil-tight casings splash lubrication is usual for drives of moderate power. Force-feed lubrication is used with high-speed large-power drives. All drives generate heat, and as operating temperatures may exceed room temperatures by 60° or 70° proper lubrication is essential.

*Routine of Selection of Silent Chains.* To explain the routine involved in the selection of a silent chain drive we will follow the procedure advised by the Link-Belt Company. Table 4 gives the factors or allowances to be made, depending on the type of load and its daily duration.

TABLE 4

SERVICE FACTORS FOR SILENT CHAINS

| Type of Load | Service per Day 10 hr. | Service per Day 24 hr. |
|---|---|---|
| Uniform loads | 1. | 1.25 |
| Moderate shock loads | 1.4 | 1.70 |
| Heavy shock loads | 1.6 | 2.00 |

Table 5 gives the speed ratios and indicates the groups from which the speed change selection should be made, depending on the type of drive.

TABLE 5

SPEED RATIOS

$$\text{Ratio of transmission} = \frac{\text{Revolutions per minute of faster shaft}}{\text{Revolutions per minute of slower shaft}}$$

Selections from the lower group are desirable from the mechanical standpoint. The upper group relates to small reduction drives, where compactness is desired.

| Number of Teeth in DriveN Wheel | Number of Teeth in DriveR Wheel 17 | 19 | 21 | 23 | 25 | 27 | 30 | 33 | 36 | 40 | 45 | 50 | 55 | 60 | 68 | 75 |
|---|---|---|---|---|---|---|---|---|---|---|---|---|---|---|---|---|
| 19 | 1.12 | 1.00 | 0.91 | 0.83 | 0.76 | 0.70 | 0.64 | 0.58 | 0.53 | 0.48 | 0.42 | 0.38 | 0.35 | 0.32 | 0.28 | 0.25 |
| 21 | 1.23 | 1.10 | 1.00 | 0.91 | 0.84 | 0.78 | 0.70 | 0.64 | 0.58 | 0.53 | 0.47 | 0.42 | 0.38 | 0.35 | 0.31 | 0.28 |
| 23 | 1.35 | 1.21 | 1.10 | 1.00 | 0.92 | 0.85 | 0.78 | 0.70 | 0.64 | 0.58 | 0.51 | 0.46 | 0.42 | 0.38 | 0.34 | 0.31 |
| 25 | 1.47 | 1.32 | 1.19 | 1.09 | 1.00 | 0.93 | 0.83 | 0.76 | 0.70 | 0.63 | 0.56 | 0.50 | 0.46 | 0.42 | 0.37 | 0.33 |
| 27 | 1.59 | 1.42 | 1.28 | 1.17 | 1.08 | 1.00 | 0.90 | 0.82 | 0.75 | 0.68 | 0.60 | 0.54 | 0.49 | 0.45 | 0.40 | 0.36 |
| 30 | 1.77 | 1.58 | 1.43 | 1.30 | 1.20 | 1.11 | 1.00 | 0.91 | 0.83 | 0.75 | 0.67 | 0.60 | 0.55 | 0.50 | 0.44 | |
| 33 | 1.94 | 1.74 | 1.57 | 1.43 | 1.32 | 1.22 | 1.10 | 1.00 | 0.92 | 0.83 | 0.73 | 0.66 | 0.60 | 0.55 | | |
| 36 | 2.12 | 1.89 | 1.71 | 1.56 | 1.44 | 1.33 | 1.20 | 1.09 | 1.00 | 0.90 | 0.80 | 0.72 | 0.65 | | | |
| 40 | 2.35 | 2.10 | 1.90 | 1.74 | 1.60 | 1.48 | 1.33 | 1.21 | 1.11 | 1.10 | 0.89 | 0.80 | | | | |
| 45 | 2.65 | 2.37 | 2.14 | 1.96 | 1.80 | 1.67 | 1.50 | 1.36 | 1.25 | 1.13 | 1.00 | | | | | |
| 50 | 2.94 | 2.63 | 2.38 | 2.18 | 2.00 | 1.85 | 1.67 | 1.52 | 1.30 | 1.25 | | | | | | |
| 55 | 3.24 | 2.89 | 2.62 | 2.39 | 2.20 | 2.04 | 1.83 | 1.67 | 1.53 | | | | | | | |
| 60 | 3.53 | 3.16 | 2.86 | 2.61 | 2.40 | 2.22 | 2.00 | 1.82 | | | | | | | | |
| 68 | 4.00 | 3.58 | 3.24 | 2.96 | 2.72 | 2.52 | 2.27 | | | | | | | | | |
| 75 | 4.41 | 3.95 | 3.57 | 3.26 | 3.00 | 2.78 | | | | | | | | | | |
| 84 | 4.94 | 4.42 | 4.00 | 3.65 | 3 36 | | | | | | | | | | | |
| 90 | 5.30 | 4.74 | 4.28 | 3.91 | | | | | | | | | | | | |
| 102 | 6.00 | 5.37 | 4.86 | | | | | | | | | | | | | |

Table 6 indicates the chains and wheels advised for transmitting the horsepowers noted at the left, for various r.p.m.'s and uniform 24-hr. loads.

The manufacturers furnish on request complete tables which give the horsepower ratings per inch of chain width for uniform loads.

**Example.** Select a drive to transmit 17-hp. uniform load, 24 hr. per day. Driver speed, 1160 r.p.m. Driven speed, 400 r.p.m. Distance between centers, 15 in.

The ratio of speeds is 2.90 : 1, and from Table 5 we select a tooth combination of 19 and 55. A normal pitch is ¾ in. The service factor in Table 4 is 1.25, so the horsepower rating is $17 \times 1.25 = 21.25$. From the manufacturers' tables we will find that a ¾-in. chain with a 19-tooth driver at 1160 r.p.m. has a rating of 8.79 hp. per inch of width, so we select a chain 2½ in. wide.

For quiet operation it is desirable to use short-pitch wide chains, larger sprockets, and conservative ratings.

V-Belts. There are several manufacturers of high-quality V-belts. We will use the data published by the Allis-Chalmers Company for illustration.

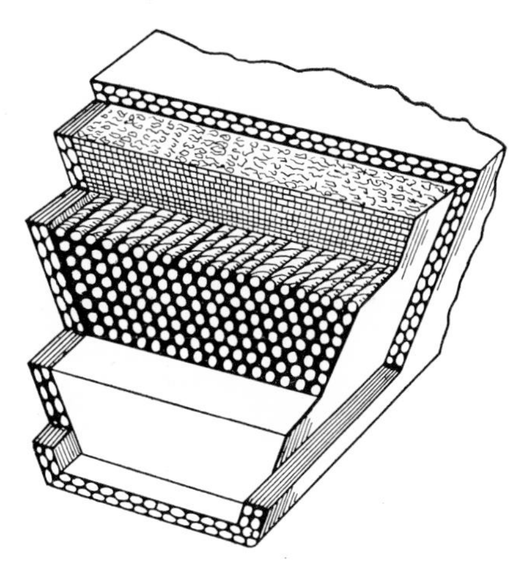

Fig. 19-6. Section of Allis-Chalmers V-belt.

The belt shown in Fig. 19-6 has an outer sheath of two-ply wear-resisting bias-cut cover friction with rubber to protect the carcass. Within the cover is a bias-cut impregnated fabric laid transversely, which provides transverse stiffness. The load is transmitted by a core of prestretched floating cords impregnated and insulated with a cool-flexing gum compound. Next to the core, at the bottom, is a layer of flexing rubber which absorbs the impact and shock of the drive. Long experience by the manufacturers of V-belts has produced a power transmission medium of remarkable life, low temperature rise, and sustained efficiency.

Table 7 gives the normal horsepower ratings for single V-belts by Allis-Chalmers, for speeds from 1000 to 5000 ft. per min., with the sheave sizes noted. It is seen that, for a given belt speed, the larger the pitch diameter of the sheave the higher is the power the belt will transmit.

Belts are made in several trapezoidal cross sections designated as $A, B, C, D,$ and $E$ in Fig. 19-7. The sheave grooves are practically the same size as the belt but cut deeper so that the belt will not bottom. The ratings in Table 7 are for 180° contact with each sheave, and, as in most drives one sheave is larger than the other, there must be a correction factor for arcs of contact less than 180°. These factors are:

TABLE 6

CHAIN AND WHEELS FOR USE WHEN RELATIVELY QUIET OPERATION IS NECESSARY

Based on uniform loads, 10- or 24-hr. service.

| Horse-power | Revolutions per Minute | | | | | | | | | |
|---|---|---|---|---|---|---|---|---|---|---|
| | 1160 R.P.M. | | 860 R.P.M. | | 690 R.P.M. | | 580 R.P.M. | | 450 R.P.M. | |
| | Wheel | Chain | Wheel | Chain | Wheel | Chain | Wheel | Chain | Wheel | Chain |
| | Number of Teeth | Pitch × Width | Number of Teeth | Pitch × Width | Number of Teeth | Pitch × Width | Number of Teeth | Pitch × Width | Number of Teeth | Pitch × Width |
| 3 | 25 | ⅜ × 1 | .. | ........ | .. | ........ | .. | ........ | .. | ........ |
| 4 | 25 | ⅜ × 7¼ | 25 | ½ × 1 | .. | ........ | .. | ........ | .. | ........ |
| 5 | 25 | ⅜ × 1¾ | 25 | ½ × 1¼ | 25 | ½ × 1½ | .. | ........ | .. | ........ |
| 7 | 27 | ⅜ × 2¼ | 25 | ½ × 2 | 25 | ½ × 2½ | .. | ........ | .. | ........ |
| 10 | 27 | ⅜ × 3 | 25 | ½ × 2½ | 25 | ½ × 3 | .. | ........ | .. | ........ |
| 16 | 27 | ½ × 3 | 25 | ½ × 4 | 25 | ⅝ × 3 | .. | ........ | .. | ........ |
| 20 | 27 | ½ × 4 | 27 | ½ × 5 | 25 | ⅝ × 4 | 25 | ¾ × 3 | .. | ........ |
| 26 | 27 | ½ × 5 | 27 | ⅝ × 4 | 25 | ⅝ × 4 | 25 | ¾ × 4 | .. | ........ |
| 33 | .. | ........ | 27 | ⅝ × 5 | 27 | ⅝ × 6 | 25 | ¾ × 5 | .. | ........ |
| 41 | .. | ........ | .. | ........ | 27 | ¾ × 5 | 27 | ¾ × 6 | .. | ........ |
| 56 | .. | ........ | .. | ........ | 27 | ¾ × 7 | 27 | 1 × 5 | .. | ........ |
| 64 | .. | ........ | .. | ........ | .. | ........ | 27 | 1 × 6 | 27 | 1 × 7 |
| 78 | .. | ........ | .. | ........ | .. | ........ | 27 | 1 × 7 | 27 | 1¼ × 6 |
| 95 | .. | ........ | .. | ........ | .. | ........ | .. | ........ | 27 | 1¼ × 7 |
| 110 | .. | ........ | .. | ........ | .. | ........ | .. | ........ | 27 | 1¼ × 8 |
| 135 | .. | ........ | .. | ........ | .. | ........ | .. | ........ | 27 | 1¼ × 10 |

| Arc of Contact, degrees | Correction Factor |
|---|---|
| 180 | 1.00 |
| 160 | 0.95 |
| 140 | 0.89 |
| 120 | 0.83 |
| 100 | 0.74 |
| 80 | 0.64 |

Again, depending on the nature of the load, service factors must be applied. These are shown in Table 8.

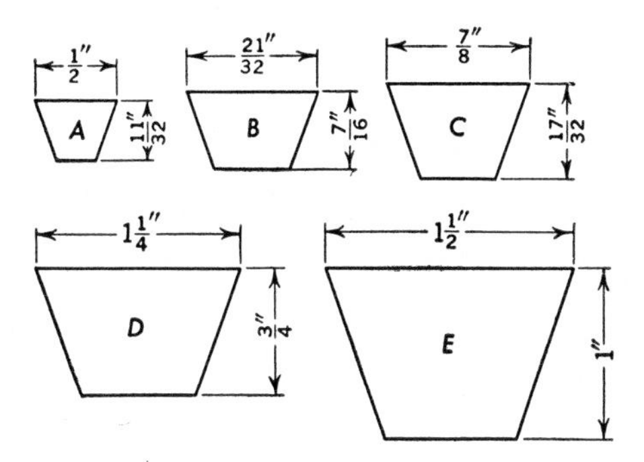


Fig. 19–7. Dimensions of standard V-belts.

**Example.** Select a V-belt for a fan, driven by a 10-hp., normal-torque, line-started squirrel-cage motor. The service factor from Table 8 is 1.6, and a belt rated at 16 hp. is selected.

The features claimed for V-belts are:

High speeds, up to 5000 ft. per min.
Flexibility and shock-absorbing qualities.
Absorption of heavy starting torque and sudden peak loads.
High efficiency, 98 per cent.
Variable speeds without use of separate units.
Practically no slip.
No lubrication.

**Speed Reducers.** The old-style train of spur gears between conveyor head shaft and motor shaft has been eliminated through the introduction of speed-reducer units. The two common types are the herringbone reducer and the motorized reducer.

*The herringbone reducer* (Fig. 19-8) has reached a high degree of perfection. The standard sizes offer ratios of 10 : 1 up to 70 : 1 with single- or double-reduction gearing, or larger ratios with triple-reduction gearing. Since a further reduction of four or five to one is

TABLE 7

NORMAL HORSEPOWER RATING OF SINGLE V-BELTS

| Belt Speed, | A-Section Belts | | | | | | | B-Section Belts | | | | | | C-Section Belts | | | | | |
|---|---|---|---|---|---|---|---|---|---|---|---|---|---|---|---|---|---|---|---|
| | Pitch Diameters, in. | | | | | | | Pitch Diameters, in. | | | | | | Pitch Diameters, in. | | | | | |
| ft. per min. | 2.6 | 3.0 | 3.4 | 3.8 | 4.2 | 4.6 | 5.0[1] | 5.0 | 5.4 | 5.8 | 6.2 | 6.6 | 7.0[1] | 7.0 | 8.0 | 9.0 | 10.0 | 11.0 | 12.0[1] |
| 1000 | 0.5 | 0.7 | 0.8 | 0.9 | 0.9 | 1.0 | 1.0 | 1.3 | 1.4 | 1.5 | 1.6 | 1.7 | 1.8 | 2.0 | 2.5 | 2.8 | 3.1 | 3.4 | 3.6 |
| 1500 | 0.8 | 1.0 | 1.1 | 1.3 | 1.4 | 1.4 | 1.5 | 1.8 | 2.0 | 2.1 | 2.3 | 2.4 | 2.5 | 2.9 | 3.6 | 4.2 | 4.6 | 5.0 | 5.3 |
| 2000 | 1.0 | 1.3 | 1.5 | 1.6 | 1.8 | 1.9 | 2.0 | 2.4 | 2.6 | 2.8 | 2.9 | 3.1 | 3.2 | 3.7 | 4.7 | 5.5 | 6.1 | 6.5 | 7.0 |
| 2500 | 1.1 | 1.5 | 1.7 | 2.0 | 2.1 | 2.3 | 2.4 | 2.8 | 3.1 | 3.3 | 3.5 | 3.7 | 3.9 | 4.5 | 5.7 | 6.6 | 7.3 | 8.0 | 8.5 |
| 3000 | | | 2.0 | 2.2 | 2.4 | 2.6 | 2.7 | 3.2 | 3.5 | 3.8 | 4.0 | 4.3 | 4.5 | 5.0 | 6.5 | 7.6 | 8.5 | 9.2 | 9.8 |
| 3500 | | | | 2.5 | 2.7 | 2.8 | 3.0 | 3.4 | 3.8 | 4.1 | 4.4 | 4.7 | 4.9 | | 7.1 | 8.4 | 9.4 | 10.3 | 11.0 |
| 4000 | | | | | 2.8 | 3.0 | 3.3 | 3.5 | 4.0 | 4.4 | 4.7 | 5.0 | 5.3 | | | 9.0 | 10.2 | 11.2 | 12.0 |
| 4500 | | | | | | 3.2 | 3.4 | 3.5 | 4.0 | 4.4 | 4.8 | 5.1 | 5.4 | | | | 10.7 | 11.8 | 12.7 |
| 5000 | | | | | | | 3.4 | 3.3 | 3.8 | 4.3 | 4.7 | 5.1 | 5.5 | | | | | 12.2 | 13.2 |

| Belt Speed, | D-Section Belts | | | | | | E-Section Belts | | | | | | | | |
|---|---|---|---|---|---|---|---|---|---|---|---|---|---|---|---|
| | Pitch Diameters, in. | | | | | | Pitch Diameters, in. | | | | | | | | |
| ft. per min. | 12 | 13 | 14 | 15 | 16 | 17[1] | 20 | 21 | 22 | 23 | 24 | 25 | 26 | 27 | 28[1] |
| 1000 | 4.5 | 5.1 | 5.6 | 6.1 | 6.5 | 6.8 | 8.0 | 8.5 | 9.0 | 9.4 | 9.8 | 10.2 | 10.5 | 10.9 | 11.1 |
| 1500 | 6.5 | 7.5 | 8.2 | 8.9 | 9.6 | 10.1 | 11.7 | 12.5 | 13.2 | 13.9 | 14.5 | 15.1 | 15.6 | 16.1 | 16.5 |
| 2000 | 8.4 | 9.7 | 10.7 | 11.7 | 12.5 | 13.2 | 15.2 | 16.2 | 17.2 | 18.1 | 18.9 | 19.6 | 20.3 | 21.0 | 21.6 |
| 2500 | 10.1 | 11.6 | 12.9 | 14.1 | 15.1 | 16.0 | 18.3 | 19.6 | 20.8 | 21.9 | 22.7 | 23.0 | 23.9 | 24.7 | 26.3 |
| 3000 | 11.4 | 13.3 | 14.9 | 16.3 | 17.5 | 18.6 | 20.9 | 22.7 | 24.0 | 25.3 | 26.5 | 27.6 | 28.6 | 29.6 | 30.5 |
| 3500 | 12.4 | 14.6 | 16.5 | 18.1 | 19.5 | 20.7 | 23.0 | 24.9 | 26.6 | 28.1 | 29.5 | 30.8 | 32.0 | 33.1 | 34.2 |
| 4000 | | 15.5 | 17.6 | 19.4 | 21.0 | 22.5 | 24.5 | 26.6 | 28.5 | 30.3 | 31.9 | 33.4 | 34.7 | 36.0 | 37.2 |
| 4500 | | | | 20.3 | 22.1 | 23.5 | | | | 31.7 | 33.5 | 35.2 | 36.7 | 38.2 | 39.5 |
| 5000 | | | | | 22.6 | 24.4 | | | | | | 36.2 | 37.9 | 39.5 | 40.9 |

[1]And larger

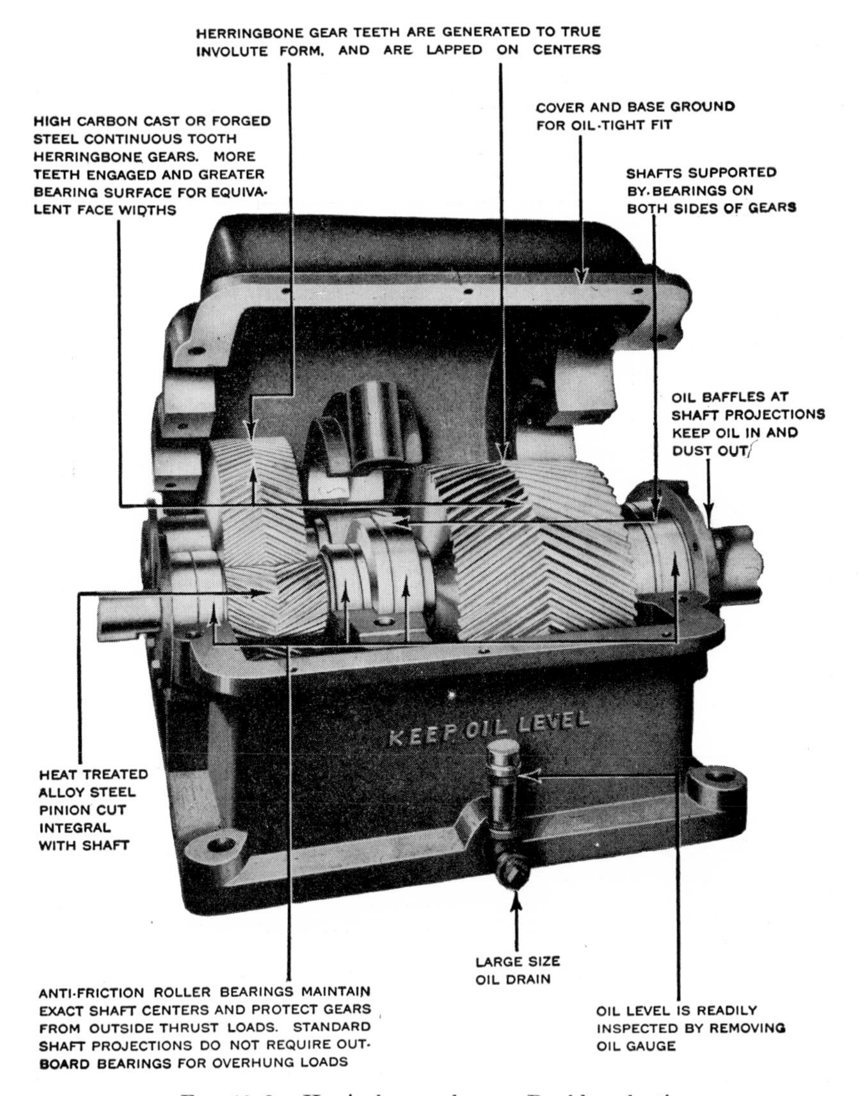


Fig. 19–8. Herringbone reducer. Double reduction.

available in a chain drive either side of the reducer a triple reduction is seldom required.

The gears are high-carbon forged or cast steel. Pinions are chrome-molybdenum steel, heat treated. Heavy anti-friction bearings are used throughout. The housing forms a reservoir in which the gears are bathed in oil and is so designed that the heat generated at full load will not cause undue rise in temperature.

TABLE 8

SERVICE FACTORS FOR V-BELTS

| Applications | Electric Motors | | | | | | | | | | Engines | | |
|---|---|---|---|---|---|---|---|---|---|---|---|---|---|
| | A-C. | | | | | | | | D-C. | | Gas and Diesel | | |
| | Squirrel Cage | | | | Synchronous | | Single Phase | | | | | | |
| | Normal Torque Line Start | Normal Torque Compensator Start | High Torque | Wound Rotor (Slip Ring) | Normal Torque | High Torque | Repulsion and Split Phase | Capacitor | Shunt Wound | Compound Wound | 4 or More Cyl. Above 700 r.p.m. | Steam | Line Shafts and Clutch Starting |
| Agitators — paddle propeller | 1.2 | 1.0 | 1.4 | 1.2 | ... | ... | ... | ... | ... | ... | ... | ... | ... |
| Bakery machinery | 1.2 | ... | ... | ... | ... | ... | 1.2 | 1.0 | ... | ... | ... | ... | ... |
| Brick and clay machinery | 1.5 | 1.3 | 1.8 | 1.5 | ... | ... | ... | ... | 1.4 | ... | ... | ... | 2.0 |
| Compressors | 1.4 | 1.4 | ... | 1.5 | 1.5 | ... | 1.2 | 1.2 | 1.2 | ... | 1.2 | ... | ... |
| Conveyors | ... | 1.6 | 1.8 | ... | ... | ... | ... | ... | 1.6 | ... | ... | ... | 1.8 |
| Crushing machinery | ... | 1.4 | 1.6 | 1.4 | 1.4 | 1.6 | ... | ... | ... | 1.6 | 1.6 | ... | 1.6 |
| Fans and blowers | 1.6 | 1.6 | 2.0 | 2.0 | 2.0 | 2.0 | ... | ... | 1.4 | ... | 1.6 | 1.5 | 1.5 |
| Flour-feed cereal mill machinery | 1.4 | 1.4 | 1.6 | 1.4 | 1.4 | ... | ... | ... | ... | ... | 1.8 | ... | ... |
| Generators and exciters | 1.2 | ... | ... | ... | ... | ... | ... | ... | 1.2 | ... | 2.0 | 1.4 | 1.4 |
| Laundry machinery | 1.2 | ... | ... | ... | ... | ... | ... | ... | ... | 1.2 | ... | ... | ... |
| Line shafts | 1.4 | 1.4 | ... | 1.4 | 1.4 | 2.0 | 1.4 | 1.4 | 1.4 | 1.4 | 1.6 | 1.6 | 1.6 |
| Machine tools | 1.2 | ... | ... | 1.4 | ... | ... | 1.2 | 1.2 | 1.2 | 1.2 | ... | ... | ... |
| Mills | ... | 1.6 | 1.6 | 1.4 | ... | ... | ... | ... | ... | 1.4 | ... | ... | 1.6 |
| Oil-feed machinery | 1.2 | 1.2 | 1.4 | ... | ... | ... | ... | ... | 1.4 | 1.4 | 1.4 | 1.4 | 1.6 |
| Paper machinery | 1.5 | 1.4 | 1.8 | 1.5 | 1.6 | 1.8 | ... | ... | 1.5 | 1.5 | ... | ... | 1.8 |
| Printing machinery | 1.2 | 1.2 | ... | 1.2 | ... | ... | ... | ... | 1.2 | 1.2 | ... | ... | ... |
| Pumps | 1.4 | 1.4 | 1.4 | 1.6 | 1.6 | 1.8 | 1.2 | 1.2 | 1.2 | ... | 2.0 | 2.0 | ... |
| Rubber plant machinery | 1.4 | 1.4 | 1.4 | 1.4 | ... | 1.8 | ... | ... | ... | ... | ... | 2.0 | ... |
| Screens | 1.2 | 1.2 | 1.4 | ... | ... | ... | ... | ... | ... | ... | ... | ... | ... |
| Textile machinery | 1.6 | ... | 1.8 | ... | ... | ... | ... | ... | ... | ... | ... | ... | ... |

*The motorized reducer* is a motor with the reduction gearing and housing mounted directly on the motor frame. The gear assembly should be removable without disturbing the alignment. The gears are helical-cut of heat-treated alloy steel. Lubrication is automatic from a reservoir in the base of the housing. Standard assemblies provide for vertical, inverted, or horizontal positions, and single, double, or triple reductions. The worm-geared reducers may have reductions as high as 6000 : 1.

When the final speeds are very low the motorized reducer should be selected on torque requirements rather than on horsepower output. When the horsepower output is very low with large reduction ratio, ¼ to ½ hp. is needed to drive the reducer without any load. Sometimes such a reducer will require about the same power under no load as with load, giving a misleading efficiency rating. The American Gear Manufacturers Association recommends, as the efficiency rating, 100 minus one-half the ratio. Thus for a worm-gear ratio of 50 : 1, divide by 2, giving 25, and subtract from 100, giving a theoretical efficiency of 75 per cent.

Worm-gear efficiency decreases with increasing reduction; thus from tests the percentages in Table 9 have been determined.

For fractional horsepowers there are small die-cast single-reduction worm gears costing from $30 to $60. Their efficiency is lower than those above.

In selecting a speed reducer, consideration must be given to the contemplated service. The horsepower tables are ratings for uniform

TABLE 9

EFFICIENCIES OF SINGLE-REDUCTION WORM GEARS WITH ANTI-FRICTION BEARINGS

| | R.P.M. of Worm Shaft | | | |
|---|---|---|---|---|
| Ratio | 100 | 450 | 1150 | 1750 |
| 7 : 1 | 87.7% | 92.2% | 94.6% | 95% |
| 25 : 1 | 77.0 | 88.2 | 88.4 | 89.3 |
| 60 : 1 | 60.7 | 69.6 | 77.9 | 79.9 |
| 80 : 1 | 53.2 | 63.5 | 73.0 | 75.5 |

loads, and if the drive is subject to moderate shock the required horsepower must be multiplied by a power factor of 1.25 to 1.50 in selecting a reducer. If the drive is subjected to heavy shock as in reciprocating feeders, drag scrapers, skip hoists, and crushers, the factor is 1.5 to 2. Multiple-cylinder gas engines, because of pulsating torque, call for still higher power factor.

Where there is a chain drive between reducer and head shaft the chain loading should be moderate with large sprockets, but with due regard to chain speed. Crushers and hammermills are subjected to repeated shock, and the elastic multiple V-belt is preferable to a chain. Vibrating screens also should have V-belt drives as the whip is harmful to a chain and to the screen shaft.

**Drive Groups.** In Chapter 10 various drives for belt conveyors are diagrammed. For other conveyors and elevators the drive groups are similar, though for the screw conveyor the output shaft of the reducer frequently is connected through flexible coupling direct to the spindle of the helix.

Let us work through a typical drive for a loop-type 17-in. Redler elevator, of 120-ft. centers to handle 100 tons per hour of stoker coal:

| | |
|---|---|
| Elevator speed | 60 ft. per min. |
| Diameter of head sprocket | 16 in. |
| R.p.m. of head shaft | 14.4 |
| Motor estimated at 35 hp. by Tables 3 and 4, Chapter 8 | |

We have on hand a 40-hp. 1200-r.p.m. motor. The elevator head shaft is 10 ft. above a concrete floor where the motor and reducer may be mounted conveniently.

Between motor and reducer we may use a silent chain or a V-belt. The V-belt has some preference here as the speed is high and a possible change in speed is inexpensive. As a single-reduction unit costs less than a double-reduction one we will use a reduction of 2 : 1 in the V-belt and a standard reducer unit having a 9.77 : 1 ratio. The reducer output speed is $600 \times (1/9.77)$ or 61.4 r.p.m. A roller chain drive with 4 : 1 reduction to the head shaft gives us 15.4 r.p.m. but as the full-load speed of the motor is 1160 r.p.m. we have an operating speed of

$$\frac{1160}{1200} \times 15.4$$

which is close to the desired 14.4 r.p.m.

For the V-belt drive with 10-in. and 20-in. sheaves, a speed of 3400 ft. per min., and the factor for arc of contact shown on page 383 we select a C-section 7-strand belt. For the RC drive, using stock sizes, we select a double-width chain of 2-in. pitch (Link-Belt, RC-D-160) with 15-tooth driver sprocket giving a chain speed of 154 ft. per min. The reduction is 4 : 1, so the driven sprocket is 60 tooth. The allowable pull on the overhung shaft of the reducer should be checked with the manufacturer. Both the V-belt and the RC drive should be enclosed in a mesh wire guard.

Figure 19-9 shows the drive of a rotary kiln. The 5-hp. motor drives through a triple-reduction herringbone gear reducer with an outboard bearing on the slow-speed shaft. A double roller chain connects with the countershaft of the kiln.

Figure 19-10 shows two belt conveyor drives. In *A* a flexible coupling connects the head shaft to a 30 : 1 herringbone reducer which is connected through flexible coupling to the motor. Motor and reducer are mounted on a rigid concrete base. In *B* the motor and reducer are mounted on a steel base, and a chain drive connects the reducer with the head shaft; this layout has the advantage that a moderate change in speed is easily made.

FIG. 19–9. A 5-hp. drive through triple-reduction herringbone reducer and double roller chain drive to countershaft of rotary kiln.

High-speed motors have better operating characteristics than slow-speed motors, cost less, occupy less space, and are more convenient to handle. The reducer should be selected with a margin of power. The motor will deliver an overload with no effect other than a rise of temperature, and when the load is reduced the temperature will drop with no damage if the insulation is not injured, but an overloaded gear drive suffers abnormal stresses, wear, and possibly permanent damage. Rigid mounting is essential to a satisfactory drive. A flexible coupling is not a universal joint.

*Protection of the Drive.* The drive must have sufficient reserve power to pull through possible overloads, as in starting up, but there must be protection against sudden jamming of the element. Continuous-flow elevators usually have shear-pin protection. Figure 19-11

FIG. 19–10. (*A*) A 15-hp. drive through 30:1 reduction gear and flexible coupling to 36-in. belt conveyor. (*B*) Motor connected through herringbone reducer and enclosed roller chain drive to head shaft of belt conveyor.

shows an assembly by Link-Belt. A drive hub keyed to the head shaft receives the tip of the pin held radially in a lug cast on the side of the chain sprocket. If overload shears the pin it is lined up with the slot and driven in again. A desirable feature is that an oversize pin cannot be inserted. Unfortunately it is not completely foolproof as a pin of tool steel — having three times the shear strength of soft steel — might be inserted.

If two conveyors are in series and each is protected by a shear pin, electrical interlocking of the motors may not be effective since the first motor continues to rotate after its pin lets go. Sometimes all that is necessary is to provide an overflow outlet between the two units, but often this cannot be done. It is not, however, difficult to arrange a detail which will cause the holder of the released shear pin to actuate a stop button.

Overload protection is effective with crushers and all types of mechanical conveyors except the belt conveyor. Damage to a conveyor belt is not usually accompanied by heavy overload.

FIG. 19–11. Shear-pin assembly protecting chain drive and motorized reducer.

Heavy-duty elevators and steeply inclined conveyors are always protected against reversal should the current fail or the overload release function, but it is quite possible that an automatic brake may be necessary in a conveyor having a flat slope or no slope. In a specific case a 300-ft. centers conveyor on a 10 per cent incline for 500 tons per hour of coal suffered repeated chain failures, although the twin rivetless-type chains had an ultimate strength far in excess of the working load.

Investigation showed that, when the conveyor was stopped under load, the head shaft reversed nearly a turn, owing to the "elasticity" in the chains. The rivetless chains are unique in being collapsible, adjacent links can be pushed together. Thus the reversal produced a slack in the few feet of chain adjacent to the head sprockets, and, when the motor was restarted, this slack was snapped out, causing extremely heavy shock. A solenoid brake eliminated the trouble.

In a retarding conveyor in which power is pumped back into the line when operating at load, the current flow passes from positive, when starting, through zero, and then in the reverse direction. This does

FIG. 19–12. Booster drive applied to car-type mold conveyor. This is a variable-speed drive to permit the speed adjustments necessary for different classes of foundry output. The booster eliminates drive wheel at the end of the run. (Link-Belt.)

not, however, affect the functioning of a solenoid brake, since the voltage across the line remains unchanged.

One point in the engineering of the drive may be overlooked. Assume an elevator calling for a 20-hp. motor, discharging to an overhead conveyor requiring 5 hp. We find that we can conveniently couple the two and drive from a 25-hp. motor. With an overload release adjusted to let go at a current surge corresponding to about 50 per cent overload, full protection might be assumed, but it may happen that near the end of a run a fragment may jam the conveyor when the elevator is nearly emptied. The release will not let go until the conveyor has been subjected to nearly seven times the strain for which it is designed.

**The Booster Drive.** In large-capacity conveyors of extreme length the chains articulate under very heavy pressure, and the long-pitch chains, owing to chordal action at the drive sprockets, set up a pulsating action in the element which increases toward the foot end. The booster drive (Fig. 19-12) corrects this difficulty. It consists of a short motor-driven section, located preferably just ahead of the head sprockets, with lugs engaging and driving the conveyor chains. The

FIG. 19-13. Electrofluid drive with integral helical reduction gear unit.

head sprockets thus become merely idlers, and, since chain wear is caused almost entirely by articulation under load, chain life is vastly increased and maintenance cost is minimized. By duplicate boosters along the carrying run, a conveyor of any length becomes possible, at least theoretically. Unfortunately the booster drive is not practical for belt conveyors.

**Hydraulic-Clutch Drive.** Under certain conditions it may be essential to protect the motor, speed reducer, and drive chain against sudden shock and high stresses, such as might occur with a crusher, carpuller, or brick press, while eliminating the necessity of resetting the circuit breaker and clearing out the machine. One unit adapted recently by the Link-Belt Company is shown in Fig. 19-13. It is a fluid coupling integral with the motor frame. This permits the motor to gain speed under low torque, reducing the demand for starting current and utilizing the pull-out torque for starting. Should the driven machine become stalled, the coupling will pull the maximum torque capacity of the motor, thereby drawing sufficient current to cause a thermal-overload protective device to function after a few seconds.

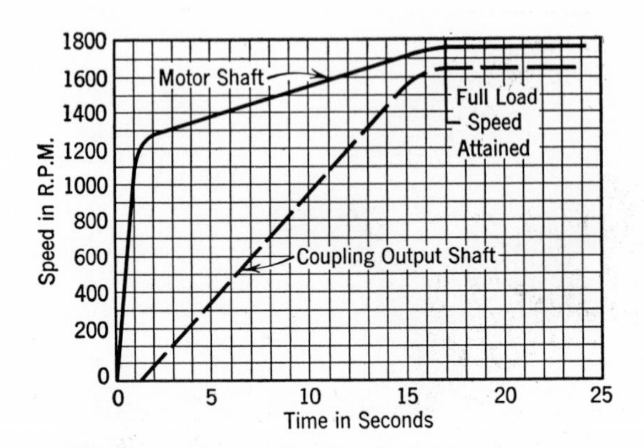


FIG. 19–14. Acceleration of motor- and output-shaft connected through hydraulic clutch to heavy inertia load.

Figure 19-14 shows the acceleration of the motor and of the output shaft with a heavy inertia load. The motor attains about 70 per cent full-load speed before the coupling functions to engage the load, and it continues to accelerate as the load is picked up. The difference between the motor and coupled output speeds shows the hydraulic slip. Figure 19-15 shows the relationship between output torque, current, and speed, with the fluid coupling connected to a squirrel-cage motor. Nearly maximum torque starts the load, while the starting current falls almost immediately to reasonable limits. The curve " motor output torque " shows the effect when a motor is direct connected to the driven machine.

**Variable-Speed Drives.** In a wide variety of industrial applications it is essential to have variable-speed control, as in assembly lines, stokers, and rotary dryers. With the usual alternating-current motor the speed-changing device is located between the motor and the machine it drives, and preferably where the r.p.m. will be high enough so that the torque for a given horsepower permits a unit not too costly. The mechanical speed changers, with the exception of the Morse, function on the same principle. The diameter of the driver pulley or sprocket is increased or decreased as the diameter of the driven pulley or sprocket is decreased or increased, and thus the speed of the driven shaft may be varied throughout the range of the machine. The features of a few well-known speed changers are outlined.

*The Reeves* (Reeves Pulley Company) has been developed through years of experience from the original open machine to the modern

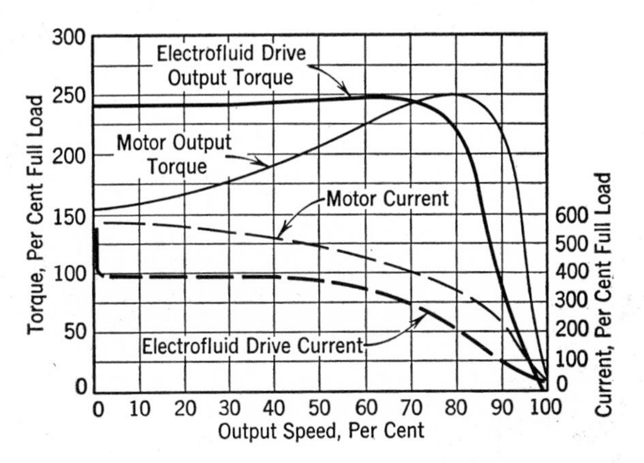


FIG. 19–15. Relationship between output torque, current, and speed with fluid coupling and squirrel-cage motor.

efficient enclosed speed changer with protected anti-friction bearings (Fig. 19-16).

Two opposed cone-faced pulleys on each of two shafts are link connected so that one pair separates as the other closes. Power is transmitted by a single wide-face V-belt. This transmission belt is made with endless heavy cable cords, flexible but practically without stretch and balanced for equal distribution of the load. It is clamped between two rows of beveled-end hardwood blocks accurately ground to fit the V of the discs and tipped with special leather facings to secure a maximum coefficient of friction. The belt is easily installed or removed through recesses in the side of the frame without disturbing the operating parts. A ball bearing is placed between each disc and its speed-changing lever to absorb lateral thrust. An automatic semi-locking device prevents self-rotation of either the belt-tension-adjusting screw or the speed-adjusting screw. Lubrication is not required. Remote control may be provided by hydraulic connections or electrically.

The horsepower of the driven machinery, the maximum speed, and the starting and peak loads (if any) must be known. Usually the transmission is required to operate at constant torque; i. e., the horsepower of the driven machine decreases exactly in proportion to the decrease in speed. Some machines, however, require the same horsepower at minimum speed as at maximum speed, or a constant horsepower throughout the range of speeds; then the capacity of the transmission at its minimum speed is taken. When the horsepower and

FIG. 19–16. Reeves variable-speed drive.

range of speeds are determined, the suitable transmission can be found from the tables issued by the manufacturers.

If the transmission is to be driven by a motor its capacity should equal that of the motor.

*The P.I.V.* (Link-Belt Company). Figure 19-17 shows this speed changer which was introduced to the United States some twenty years ago. P.I.V. means "positive, infinitely variable." It is unique in being a positively geared transmission without slip. Power is transmitted by a chain of ingenious design in which the links carry packs of hardened-steel laminations free to shift laterally. One pair of radially cut conical gears is mounted on the driving shaft and a similar pair on the driven shaft. The teeth of the opposing gears are staggered so that the laminations or chain packs are shifted by the tips of the teeth on one side into mesh between teeth on the opposite side. As the driving gears are brought together, the driven gears separate; the chain remains

Fig. 19–17. P. I. V. Variable-speed transmission. (Link-Belt.)

in mesh, and the output speed increases. Reversing the movement of the opposed gears decreases the speed of the output shaft. The unit is enclosed in a dust-proof casing or housing with splash-lubricated anti-friction bearings. Motorized reducers may be mounted integral with the housing.

There are five standard sizes, from 1 to 15 hp., with speed ratio changes up to 6 : 1 arranged for either hand or remote control. The maximum speed of the driving shaft ranges from 860 r.p.m. in the smaller sizes up to 580 r.p.m. in the largest. For extremely slow speeds the output shaft may drive through a worm gear. Horizontal units may be installed vertically with the control end on top, and vertical units may be installed horizontally.

Figure 19-18 shows the application of the P.I.V. to a variable-speed screw conveyor. The drive assembly is mounted on a rigid steel baseplate, and connection to the worm-gear is through a flexible coupling to facilitate dismantling.

FIG. 19–18. Compact screw-conveyor drive providing for changes in speed.

FIG. 19–19. Vari-Pitch variable-speed transmission. (Allis-Chalmers.)

*The Vari-Pitch speed changer* (Allis-Chalmers Company) operates on the same principle of varying the diameters of the driving and driven elements but uses multiple V-belts (Fig. 19-19). These can operate at very high speeds. The driver shaft may be connected directly to a 1750-r.p.m. motor as the shafts are mounted in anti-friction bearings with the rotating parts accurately balanced. The belts are endless

FIG. 19-20. Morse variable-speed transmission. (Morse Chain Company.)

and have a life comparable with a fixed-centers V-belt drive. Ratios are from 1 : 1 to 3 : 1 with standard sizes up to 75 hp. Belt replacements are easily made, and an idler maintains correct belt tension.

*The Morse variable-speed unit* (Morse Chain Company) is intended for transmissions not above 2 h.p. The general construction is shown by the cutaway view (Fig. 19-20). The principle is different from the others and is rather difficult to describe. In effect the action resembles a planetary transmission in which the planetaries function successively instead of simultaneously, transmitting a variable speed depending on the position of a floating ring to which they are anchored by the linkage. The input shaft is integral with a shrouded or double-flanged eccentric cam. The linkage is operated by rollers and a connecting pin which rides on the eccentric cam. The cam moves the rollers radially outward and inward, and, through the linkage and three indexing clutch pinions which engage the large output gear integral with the output shaft, the power is transmitted. For each revolution of the cam the clutch pinion is forced to make one driving stroke and one return free-wheeling stroke. During the power stroke the pinion drives the output gear and shaft; during the return stroke it idles or runs free in mesh. Each pinion functions in turn. The ratio between the output gear and the drive pinions is 2 : 1. For each revolution of the eccentric cam shaft or input shaft, three pinions successively engage and drive the output shaft. Infinitely variable adjustment is furnished through the adjusting screw or worm shaft which controls the position of the floating ring, since the position of this ring, to which the linkages are anchored, determines the arc of the power stroke. In other words, the shifting of this ring varies the angle through which the indexing clutch functions, so that the position of the adjusting ring determines the speed variation. These units have application in the slow-speed, low-power range. They are silent and low in cost.

The maximum speed of the input shaft is 250 r.p.m., but lower speed is desirable.

The input torque varies with the input horsepower. Assuming 180 r.p.m. input speed, the input torque will vary from approximately 3 to 45 ft-lb., depending on the speed of the output shaft, which will have 200-ft.-lb. torque.

*Electrical Speed Changers.* The electrical speed changers, of which we will describe two, differ basically from the mechanical speed changers. The *Ajusto Spede* unit of the Louis Allis Company transmits power through an eddy-current clutch in which there is no mechanical contact between the driving and driven members (Figs. 19-21 and 19-22).

A direct current which energizes the field pole is furnished by a rectifier and creates intense flux concentration at the clutch field pole faces, producing a constant torque between driver and driven shafts. It is claimed that regulation is provided with about the same accuracy of control as with mechanical speed changers and of course with a far wider range of speed. The rotor of the alternating-current motor is mounted on a quill which in turn is supported on two anti-friction bearings on the shaft. The clutch armature is rigidly attached to the end of the quill and forms the constant-speed driving member of the clutch. Concentric with the armature, and separated by an air gap, is the field part of the clutch receiving its direct-current excitation through two collector rings. The complete field assembly is keyed to the through shaft for connection to the load.

FIG. 19–21. Ajusto-Spede speed changer. Clutch armature and field.

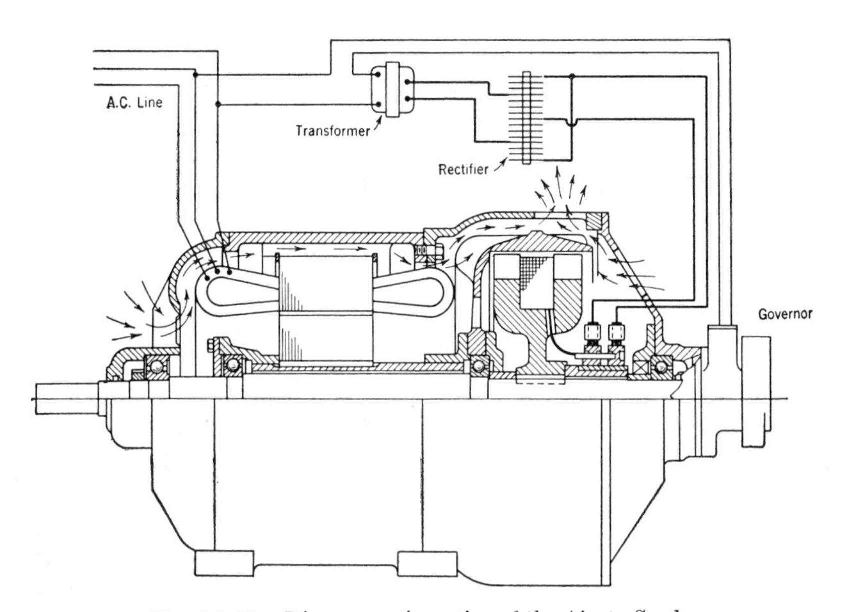


FIG. 19–22. Diagrammatic section of the Ajusto-Spede.

The magnetic fields produced by the eddy currents in the clutch armature react with the flux in the field to produce a torque tending to pull the two members into step; by varying the excitation any desired slip is produced. If the excitaton is maintained constant, the torque increases as the slip increases. By varying the excitation, the clutch slip at loads within its rating may be adjusted and will be maintained. The eddy-current clutch when fully excited is capable of developing two to four times the normal full-load torque of the motor. The starting torque of the clutch, attained by increasing the clutch excitation while the motor is running at full speed, is quite equal to the pull-out torque of the motor (200 to 250 per cent of normal full-load torque). A governor automatically controls the clutch excitation source to maintain the speed substantially constant under varying load conditions.

The *Thy-Mo-Trol* drive of the General Electric Company, through the use of electronic-tube rectifiers, makes possible the wide speed range of a direct-current motor from an alternate-current source. The Thy-Mo-Trol drive (Fig. 19-23) has four elements, the d-c motor, the electronic panel, the power transformer and the control station. A speed range up to 20 to 1 is easily obtainable by varying the voltages applied to the motor armature and up to 100 to 1 by varying also the field strength. The entire range of speed is secured by manipulating one potentiometer dial handle just below the start and stop button. The dial is preset for the desired speed, and when the start button is pressed the motor accelerates to that speed quickly, because the armature current is held at maximum safe value, and the motor always starts with full field voltage. If the preset speed is in the weak field range of the motor, the field voltage is automatically reduced as soon as the accelerating current begins to drop. The electronic limiting circuits prevent the motor current from rising above the preset value, regardless of the load on the motor. If, however, overload continues, a thermal overload relay takes the motor off the line. If the load stalls the motor, the armature current will still be limited to the preset value. The speed can be changed at any time by shifting the dial handle.

When the stop button is pressed, the armature is automatically disconnected from the line and connected across a line resistor, and dynamic braking brings the motor to a smooth stop. The tubes are as readily changed as in a radio set and are conservatively rated for a life expectancy of 3 or 4 yr. under average conditions. At present the Thy-Mo-Trol control is available for drives ranging from the fractional horsepowers to 25 hp.

The possibilities of the electric speed changer in its application to material-handling equipment, specifically for crushers when starting with fragments between the rolls, for automatic skip hoists, and for dual-drive belt conveyors, are very interesting indeed.

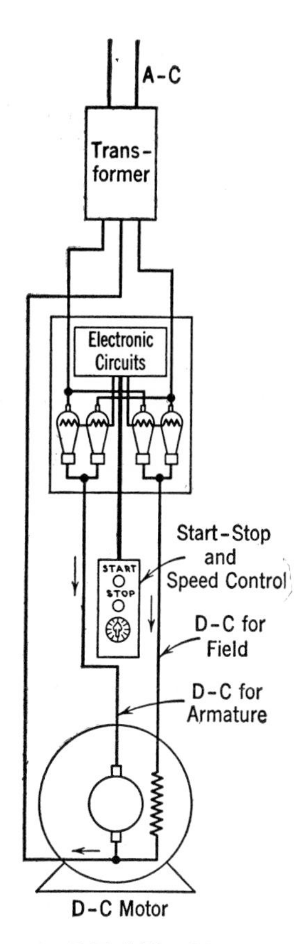


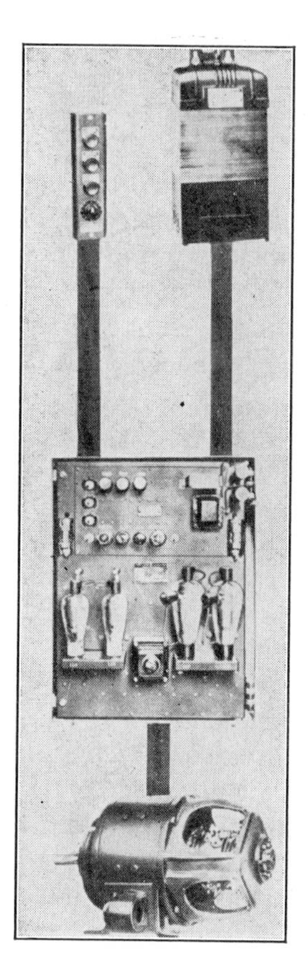

Fig. 19–23. G-E "Thy-Mo-Trol" drive. Schematic diagram and view showing essential components.

**Motors.** The various types of motors have definite characteristics which adapt them to the requirements of the job to be done and the conditions under which the motor must operate. If the surroundings are clean, without dust, dirt, or fragments of material, their structure serves only as a suitable support for the assembly, field coils, bearings, etc., and the windings merely need proper insulation to stand the voltage stresses and to have a reasonable safety factor. Ideal conditions are rare. Conveyors operate under conditions which vary from fair to very bad, and their motors must have additional mechanical and electrical protection. Progressively suited to conditions there are:

*Open General-Purpose Motors.* Until recently most open motors conformed to the meaning of "open" and offered little protection. The insulating materials and varnishes were able to withstand moisture, oil, etc., to a less extent than do the general-purpose motors of today. Improved materials and processes and better mechanical protection have made general-purpose motors suitable under conditions where special-purpose motors were previously considered necessary.

*Splash-proof motors* simply carry the protection to a greater degree. Well-protected ventilated openings and special treatment of windings make the splash-proof motor available where the air is moist, with occasional splashing. They may be used in breweries, dairies, etc., and may be mounted in the open if the climatic conditions are not too severe.

*Totally enclosed motors* are completely enclosed in a cast-iron housing, and no ventilating air enters the motor. Heat from motor losses is dissipated entirely by radiation. Totally enclosed (non-ventilated) motors are generally made with well-sealed joints and good running seals where the shaft enters the frame. This motor is used for extremely dusty conditions, where the air contains fumes, or for outdoor service in any weather — wherever maximum protection is essential. Ball bearings are preferable as the lubricant is better protected against contamination.

*Totally enclosed fan-cooled motors* are fully enclosed yet fan cooled. The motor proper is totally enclosed, but around the inner case is an outer shell. A fan external to the inner casing, but protected by the outer casing, blows air through the interspace and dissipates the heat more rapidly from the inner motor case. Joints and seals of the inner casings are similar to those in the totally enclosed motors. The air passages between the shells seldom clog as the velocity of the air driven by the fan is sufficient to blow dirt through. These motors in sizes larger than 1½ hp. actually are less costly than the enclosed non-ventilated type because the dimensions must be very rapidly increased in the larger sizes if the heat loss is to be entirely dissipated by radiation.

*Explosion-proof motors* are special forms of the two previous types. Basically they do not differ, but special attention is given to seals and strength of parts. There are two common types. The Class 2, Group G, National Electrical Code, is for hazardous dust locations. It has metal-to-metal joints and shaft seals so that grain dust cannot enter (grain dust may be explosive). Class 1, Group D, is for atmospheres containing explosive vapors and fumes, such as gasoline vapors. As it is impossible to prevent some air from filtering into the motor through the seals, the motor is made so strong that if an explosion does occur the flame cannot penetrate to the outside and cause an external explosion. As conveying machinery is often installed under conditions inviting explosions these motors have a specific place in the art.

MOTORS OPERATING ON DIRECT CURRENT. *Series motors* have the field windings in series with the armature windings. They are adapted for high torque and rapid variations in torque, as in railroad locomotives.

*Shunt motors* have the field winding in parallel with the armature winding but it takes only a small proportion of the current. They are essentially constant-speed motors with a drop of 10 or 12 per cent between the speed at no load and full load. They are used on some conveyors, centrifugal pumps, line shafts, etc., where the inertia of the load is low and fairly constant. Speed variation is by field control.

*Compound-wound motors* have both series and shunt field windings. They are used where relatively high starting torque is required and where rapid variations in torque are contemplated, as in hoists, some conveyor installations, and crushers.

MOTORS OPERATING ON ALTERNATING CURRENT. In describing these we will consider the General Electric motors as illustrative.

*Squirrel-cage motors* have the rotor conductors buried in the laminations and short-circuited by rings at the ends. They are essentially constant-speed machines (Fig. 19-24*A*) with better than 150 per cent starting torque on full voltage and better than 250 per cent momentary pull-out torque. They have a 5 per cent slip between no-load and full-load speeds. Power factor and efficiency are good. They are used with moderate margins of starting torque because of high starting current — 600 to 700 per cent.

*Double-squirrel-cage motors* have 240 per cent starting torque (Fig. 19-24*B*) with 400 per cent starting current. Efficiency and power factor are slightly lower. Maximum running torque is 200 per cent with 5 per cent slip. They are suited to crushers, conveyors, and other units having heavy inertia in starting. The speed-torque characteristics lie between those of the normal starting torque of the type K motor and the high-starting-torque, high-slip-type KR motor. Controls are simpler than for the single-squirrel-cage motor.

*The high resistance rotor motor* is for cranes, skips, hoists, etc., and high-inertia loads. Maximum torque (Fig. 19-24*C*) occurs at about 10 per cent speed. The power factor at starting is high. The high rotor resistance gives high slip at full load and a wide range of speeds with changing loads.

*Slip-ring motors* have a wound rotor with the conductors brought out to slip rings to permit the insertion of resistance to increase the starting torque and decrease the starting current and also to secure a 50 per cent reduction in normal speed under full-load torque. They are suited to all types of crushers, conveyors, screens, etc.

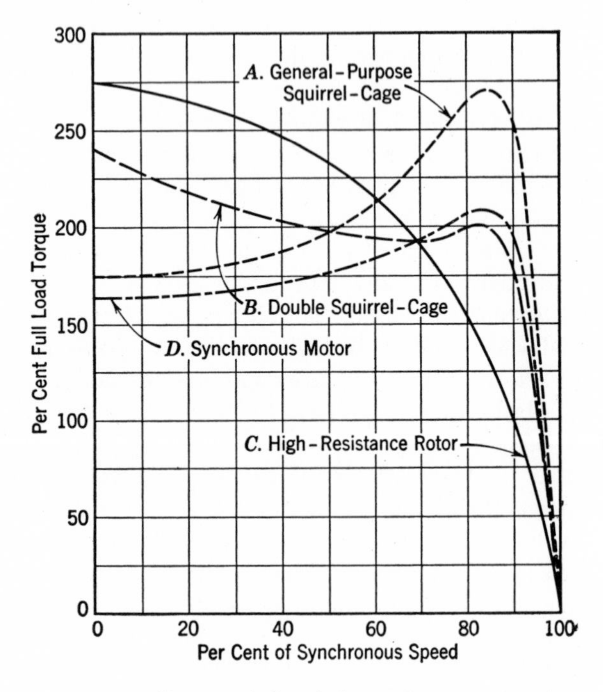


FIG. 19–24. Characteristics of alternating-current motors.

*Synchronous motors* are used where correction of power factor is desired (Fig. 19-24*D*); they are suited to constant loads such as driving generators, fans, and centrifugal pumps. They are made with starting torque up to 250 per cent.

**Motor Protection and Control.** Motors are protected against sustained overload by cutouts having a thermal relay which functions slowly to prevent interruptions because of momentary peaks. Undervoltage protection opens the circuit if the line voltage is much reduced, and the motor will not start if the voltage rises again until the control is reset.

Push-button automatic control assures proper starting acceleration. It may also provide for starting a series of machines in proper sequence, as the bunker conveyor, then the elevator, then the feeder and crusher, and for shutting down preceding units if one stops. Hand controls are usually interlocked to secure starting in proper sequence.

*Automatic Backstops.* In any conveyor or elevator which can reverse if the power is interrupted or the overload release functions, a locking mechanism should be provided. A solenoid brake may be used. This brake is held " off " by the current and applied if the current fails or if the voltage falls to a point at which the motor stalls. A vertical continuous-flow-type elevator may not require a backstop as the material filling the duct serves to check reversal of the element.

A differential brake may be considered better than a solenoid under some conditions. It functions only if the conveyor reverses.

The back-stop should be of extremely rugged construction with a wide margin of safety, and where possible it should be mounted on the higher-speed countershaft rather than on the head shaft. However, the arrangement of the drive group may require that it be mounted on the head shaft.

On long inclined apron conveyors or double-strand flight conveyors the back-stop sometimes consists of pawls distributed along both the carrying and return runs and resting on the chains. Should the chain break, the pawl drops into a link and prevents reversal. The pawls should be set out of step, or located so that they do not synchronize; otherwise the conveyor could get a start of a foot or two before being checked.

The reversal of a long inclined loaded conveyor may be a very serious matter. For example, with a slope conveyor leading from within a coal mine the coal would be jammed and scattered at the foot end, clouds of dust would be formed, a spark might be struck and an explosion result. This has occurred, with serious loss of life. The uncontrolled reversal of a high elevator probably would jam the load in the boot, rip off a succession of buckets, and damage or strain the chain or belt.

## CHAPTER 20

# POWER-PLANT COAL AND ASH HANDLING

Power-plant coal-handling equipment is of major importance since it comprises about 30 per cent of all the engineering problems of material-handling engineers. The subject has already been discussed in the analyses of various conveyors, crushers, car-unloading methods, bunkers, and so on; we here discuss some aspects of the problem, costs, and trends, and illustrate a few recent and earlier installations having features of interest. In the smaller steam plants, mechanical handling can show little return on the investment, but other considerations such as quick release of cars, labor easing, and less dust nuisance may outweigh this fact. In the absence of unloading equipment a local contractor will often take care of shoveling out the cars as delivered, for a fee of $20 to $25 each. Manual unloading is slow work, especially with hopper bottoms, and each car with two shovelers ties up the siding for a day or longer. The cost is about 40 cents per ton, unless the coal must also be wheeled; then the cost may be 60 cents per ton or more. A simple unloader with a capacity of 30 tons per hour costs about $3000, including foundation, and a plant laborer as a part-time duty will clear a car in 2 to 3 hr.

For 25 cars per year the *total* cost of unloading then might be considered as:

| | | |
|---|---|---|
| Labor | $50 | |
| Power and maintenance | 50 | |
| Interest and charge-off | 320 | |
| Total | $420 | or 34 cents per ton |

For 1 car per week this total cost comes to about 20 cents per ton; and for 2 cars per week about 14 cents per ton, but certainly a plant using two cars per week needs not only mechanical handling but also provision for a reserve storage, involving a much larger investment.

**Handling Costs.** Some costs of handling coal have been noted previously. It should be said that those costs are not total costs. Total cost is much higher; in fact, it is disconcerting to find that the cost per ton from cars to bunker is much less in the small plant using a few thousand tons per year than in the great steam plants using many times as much. This is because in the small plant two or three men attend to the job as part of their regular duties, whereas in the larger ones there is a regular squad which when not unloading coal is engaged in cleaning up, maintenance work, etc., all charged to coal handling. The author is indebted to the late James A. Powell, formerly chief engineer of the Associated Gas and Electric Company, and to Mr. Geo. C. Daniels, of the Commonwealth and Southern Company, for interesting data on coal-handling costs with large tonnages.

In Table 1, nine stations (public utility) varying from 14,250 to 74,500 kw. are listed by Mr. Powell. The annual labor cost is based on an average wage of $1500 per year per man. All these stations receive coal by rail.

TABLE 1

Labor Costs at Plants Using 40,000 to 172,000 Tons per Year

| Station | Kilowatt Capacity | Tons per Year | No. of Handlers | Annual Cost | Labor Cost per Ton, cents |
|---|---|---|---|---|---|
| A | 14,250 | 39,900 | 2 | $ 3,000 | 7.7 |
| B | 31,000 | 88,600 | 3 | 4,500 | 5.0 |
| C | 20,000 | 71,500 | 3 | 4,500 | 6.0 |
| D | 23,500 | 55,800 | 4 | 6,000 | 25.5 |
| E | 72,500 | 118,365 | 6 | 9,000 | 8.05 |
| F | 74,500 | 86,500 | 7 | 10,500 | 12.20 |
| G | 53,000 | 43,700 | 8 | 12,000 | 28.0 |
| H | 55,000 | 154,500 | 9 | 13,500 | 8.7 |
| I | 65,000 | 172,000 | 14 | 21,000 | 12.2 |
| | | | | Average | 12.6 cents |

A reasonable breakdown of fixed charges would be: taxes and insurance, 2 per cent; depreciation, 7 per cent; interest, 5 per cent; maintenance, 2 per cent; total, 16 per cent. The total cost of the coal-handling installation at station H was approximately $150,000, and with the above allowance the total annual cost per ton would be:

| | Cents |
|---|---|
| Labor | 8.7 |
| Fixed charges | 15.5 |
| Total cost | 24.2 |

Mr. Daniels' data given in Table 2 are for the most part in connection with larger stations, four of which receive coal by water (the first by self-unloading vessels) and the rest by rail. He takes the fixed charge at an arbitrary 12 per cent of the investment, which makes a large item for waterside stations having the large-capacity unloading equipment necessary to avoid demurrage charges. The average fixed charge is 27.2 cents per ton. Average total charge 37.6 cents per ton.

The utilities usually charge to operating cost the cost of coal, the cost of handling it, and maintenance. Depreciation, taxes, and insurance are charged against gross income.

In the modern plant the coal-handling cost is only a fraction of the total production cost per kilowatt-hour output, but the coal-handling installation is nevertheless important, especially as regards reliability. Illustrating the costs in a pulverized-coal-burning station of excellent efficiency, where the coal handling installation cost approximately $150,000, the ascertained labor cost was 8.7 cents per ton, to which is added the routine 2 per cent for taxes and insurance, 7 per cent for depreciation, 5 per cent for interest, and 2 per cent for maintenance, giving 24.2 cents per ton as the total annual cost for coal handling. The operating figures are:

| | |
|---|---|
| Net kilowatt output | 350,400,000 |
| Fuel cost | $769,400 |
| Fuel cost per kilowatt-hour | 0.220 cents |
| Labor and supplies | $74,200 |
| Cost per kilowatt-hour output | 0.0121 cents |
| Maintenance | $117,600 |
| Cost per kilowatt-hour output | 0.033 cents |
| Coal cost per ton | $4.90 |
| Pounds of coal per kilowatt-hour | 0.896 lb. |
| Total coal consumed | 157,046 tons |
| Total annual charge for handling coal | $38,000 |
| Total production cost | $961,300 |
| Cost per kilowatt-hour output | 0.274 cents |

The total cost for coal handling, $38,000, is 4 per cent of the total production cost, $961,300.

**Trends.** Perhaps the most notable trend in steam-plant coal-handling design is the emphasis now placed on dustless operation. Every effort is made to secure clean operation. When possible the reserve ground storage is located well away from the plant.

There is a more general use of continuous-flow conveyors in the small and medium plants as their possibilities become better known. They have slow speed, are fully enclosed, simple in layout, and often reduce the number of units required. Their cost as a rule is less than the cost of a bucket elevator with feeder and distributing conveyor.

For larger capacities the bucket elevator is quite usual. However, with the present-day expanded use of smaller coal, frequently damp and sticky, there may be considerable difficulty from material building up in the buckets, and the preference may be for an inclined belt conveyor or, if the incline is too steep, a suspended flight conveyor.

TABLE 2

MAINTENANCE AND OPERATING COSTS OF HANDLING COAL AT PLANTS USING FROM 40,000 TO 547,000 TONS PER YEAR

| Coal Delivered by Water, Rail or Truck | Year Installed | Capacity to Bunkers, tons per hour | Cost of Installation Including Docks, Tracks, Pits, Cranes, Conveyors, etc. | Years Represented by Data | Tons per Year | Maintenance Cost, cents per ton | Operating Labor, cents per ton | Total Operating Costs, cents per ton | Fixed Charges, cents per ton | Total Fixed and Operating Costs, cents per ton | Description of System |
|---|---|---|---|---|---|---|---|---|---|---|---|
| W | 1939 | 400 | $691,000 | 1940 | 124,000 | 1.3 | 5.0 | 6.3 | 67.0 | 73.3 | Coal delivered on dock by self-unloading lake boats, gantry crane to storage or to belt conveyors to plant. (Fig. 14–6) |
| W | 1925 | 350 | 1,220,000 | 1937–39 | 382,046 | 5.3 | 7.6 | 12.9 | 38.1 | 51.0 | Gantry crane from lake boats to storage, or by car and belt conveyor to plant. Auxiliary drag line storage. |
| W | 1926 | 250 | 655,000 | 1938–40 | 547,574 | 4.2 | 4.0 | 8.2 | 14.4 | 22.6 | Clamshell from river barges to belt conveyors to plant or to Lidgerwood storage. |
| W | 1928 | 125 | 978,000 | 1935–40 | 175,879 | 4.8 | 6.6 | 11.4 | 66.8 | 78.2 | Clamshell from ocean steamers or barges to belt conveyors, to plant or to drag line storage. |
| R | 1939 | 200 | 360,000 | 1940 | 196,000 | 0.7 | 6.1 | 6.8 | 22.0 | 28.8 | Cars discharge by gravity into pit, to belt conveyors, to plant or to drag line storage. |
| R & T | 1939 | 125 | 160,000 | 1940 | 122,924 | 4.5 | 6.4 | 10.9 | 15.8 | 26.7 | From cars by gravity to pit, to belt and bucket elevator, to drag line storage, or to plant by belt. |
| R | 1936 | 100 | 212,000 | 1940 | 79,360 | 1.9 | 7.5 | 9.4 | 32.0 | 41.4 | From cars by gravity to pit, to belt and bucket elevator, to drag line storage, or to plant by belt. |
| R | 1913 | 75 | 66,000 | 1936–38 | 109,000 | 2.4 | 5.3 | 7.7 | 7.3 | 15.0 | Stationary tower with clamshell bucket from cars to distributing belt. Locomotive crane for storage. |
| R | 1925 | 75 | 112,000 | 1936–38 | 217,588 | 2.1 | 4.4 | 6.5 | 6.3 | 12.8 | Locomotive crane with bucket unloads cars to pit, to chain and bucket elevator, to scraper conveyor. Locomotive crane for storage. |
| R | 1927 | 60 | 160,000 | 1938–40 | 62,606 | 6.1 | 9.8 | 15.9 | 30.7 | 46.6 | Cars discharge by gravity into pit, to belt and bucket elevator, to scraper conveyor. Locomotive crane for storage. |
| R | 1928 | 60 | 164,000 | 1937–39 | 43,860 | 4.9 | 10.1 | 15.0 | 45.6 | 60.6 | Cars discharge by gravity into pit, to belt and bucket elevator, to scraper conveyor. Bridge crane for storage. |
| R | 1926 | 50 | 97,000 | 1937–39 | 54,636 | 4.8 | 8.1 | 12.9 | 21.5 | 34.4 | Cars discharge by gravity into pit, to belt and bucket elevator, to scraper conveyor. Bridge crane for storage. |
| R | 1920 | 40 | 20,000 | 1939–40 | 40,077 | 3.4 | 6.7 | 10.1 | 6.0 | 16.1 | Cars discharge by gravity to shallow pit, to inclined scraper conveyor, to bunkers. Storage by portable conveyor. |
| R | 1937 | 150 | 185,000 | 1940 | 275,376 | ... | ... | 10.6 | 8.1 | 18.7 | Cars dumped into pit, to skip hoists, to belt distributors. Storage by locomotive crane and bulldozer. |
| | | | | | Average | 3.6 | 6.7 | 10.3 | 27.2 | 37.6 | |

**Instructive Installations.** Some installations having features of interest are illustrated.

Figure 20-1 shows the application of continuous-flow units at an Indiana plant. Coal is discharged from a track hopper to an L-type elevator with a short cross screw above the silo. This combination is often less costly than an elevator sufficiently high to chute to the silo, with supports, machinery platform, ladder, etc. From the silo the coal passes to a short L-type elevator and then to a screw conveyor across

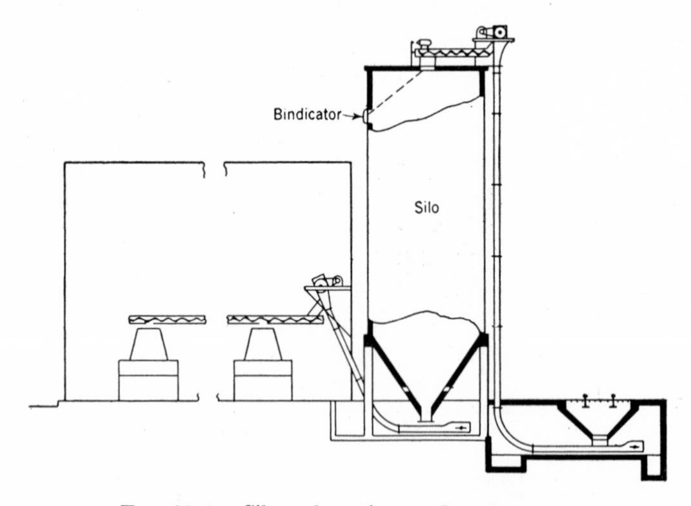


FIG. 20-1. Silo and continuous-flow elevators.

the stoker hoppers. These two units may be automatic in operation, starting when the coal is low in the hoppers and stopping when the hoppers are filled to capacity. One difficulty is that if the stoker demand is not uniformly distributed some coal at times will be left in the screw and piled on the floor beyond the last stoker. The flat top of the silo provides a working platform for repairs and servicing, and is preferable to the cone top.

Figure 20-2, location, Kentucky. The steel cover of the suspension bunker forms part of the roof of the building and supports an overhead screw conveyor with footwalk. The plant is used for tests and research by engineering students and has both stokers and pulverizers. This explains the use of both direct chutes and a weigh larry.

Figure 20-3, location, Ohio. Coal-handling equipment by Link-Belt. Coal is fed to an inclined flight conveyor which discharges either to a belt conveyor or to an initial pile for distribution by drag scraper to a reserve ground storage of about 12,000 tons over a semi-circular area.

Reclaimed coal is delivered back to the track hopper. The coal may pass through or around the crusher, and it is automatically weighed

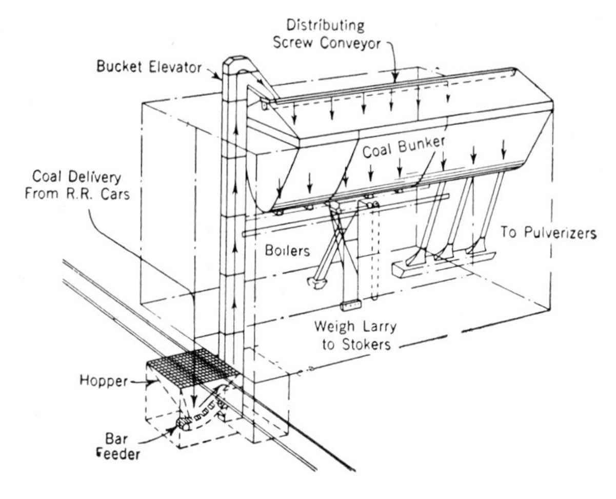


FIG. 20-2. Coal-handling layout at a university heating plant.

as it travels to the boiler-house bunker. Distribution is by a flight conveyor designed for subsequent extension toward the left as boilers are added. Handling capacity, 50 tons per hour.

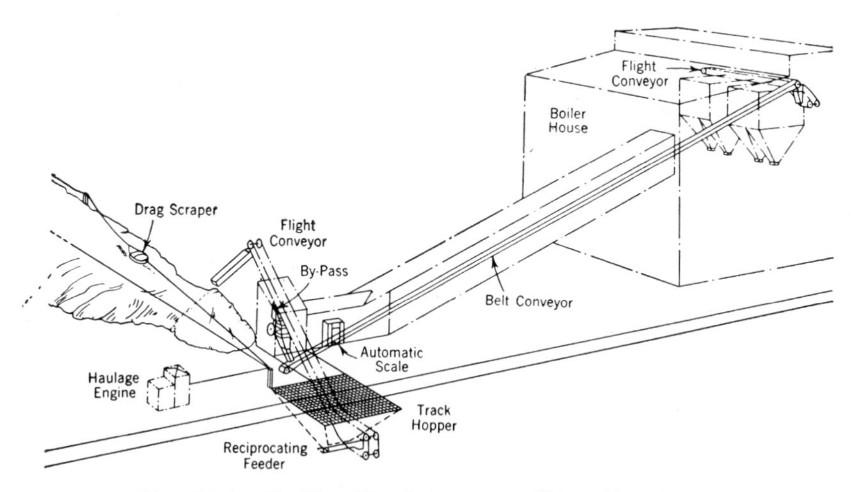


FIG. 20-3. Coal-handling layout at an Ohio utility plant.

If the bunker could have been in line with the belt conveyor, this would have eliminated the flight conveyor.

Figure 20-4, location, New Jersey. This shows a pneumatic coal-

and ash-handling installation (Hudson). A 75-hp. centrifugal exhauster connects through a dust collector to either a 30-ton ash bin or a 75-ton coal bin. The 8-in. ash conveyor duct extends along the ash pits and has a capacity of 400 lb. per min. The 10-in. coal conveyor duct receives coal after it has passed through a feeder and crusher at the rate of 25 tons per hour. Distribution to the stokers is by a 2-ton motor-driven larry in the frame of which the operator rides.

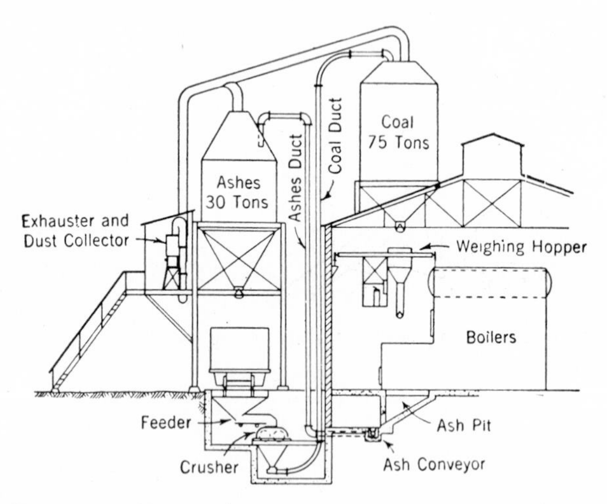


Fig. 20-4. Pneumatic coal- and ash-handling installation.

Figure 20-5. A U.S. Navy Yard installation (Hudson) designed to meet unusual circumstances. In addition to serving this plant it carries a reserve storage for a plant in another part of the yard. Coal from cars feeds through a track hopper and apron feeder to a 36-in. inclined belt conveyor which discharges directly above the pivot point of the bridge, where the coal may pass downward through a crusher, within the pedestal which supports the bridge pivot, to duplicate belt conveyors extending up and across the bunker. The reserve storage pile is formed by diverting the discharge to a belt conveyor mounted on the bridge. By pivoting the bridge a circular pile of 15,000 tons may be formed. It is reclaimed, by a man-trolley grab bucket traveling between the lower chords of the bridge, to cars in a track encircling the pile. Reloaded coal as a rule moves to the adjoining plant, but if bunker coal is needed the cars may discharge to the track hopper. In an emergency, should the apron feeder or the first inclined belt conveyor be disabled, the grab may transfer coal from pile to the crusher for delivery direct to the bunker.

A pivoted bridge can readily provide a large reserve storage; thus doubling the span would provide a storage of 80,000 tons.

Figure 20-6 shows a Pennsylvania installation using a gravity-discharge elevator.

Mine-run coal is taken from the track hopper by an apron feeder to a hammermill. A magnetic pulley is provided, since this plant

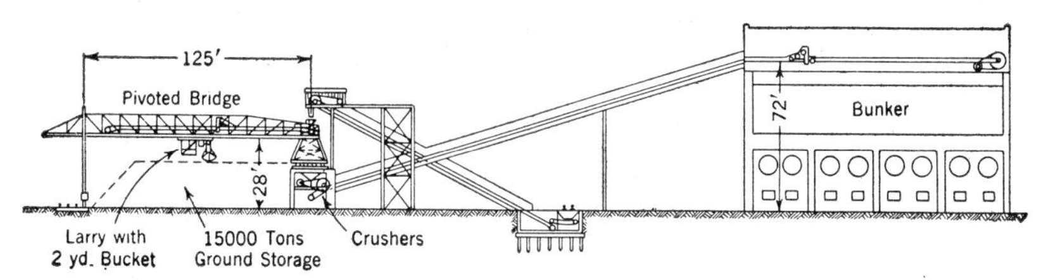


FIG. 20–5. Pivoted bridge and belt conveyors. Coal rehandled by the bridge bucket is returned to track hopper or shifted to an adjoining plant. Coal handling and storage at U.S. Navy yard. (Hudson.)

burns coal after it has been pulverized, and it is essential that any fragments of iron which may have escaped entrapment by the hammermill shall be removed before the coal reaches the pulverizers. Wide chutes lead from the bunker to two Richardson automatic scales which deliver weighed batches to the unit pulverizers.

We might use this to illustrate the several possible arrangements for average conditions.

Instead of the belt conveyor from the crusher to the elevator, an L-type continuous-flow conveyor-elevator could be used. This would discharge to a screw conveyor above the bunker. The magnetic separator then would be located overhead between the two.

The belt conveyor and magnetic pulley might remain as shown, but with a loop-type continuous-flow elevator and overhead screw conveyor substituted for the gravity-discharge elevator.

Although the wide chutes between bunker and automatic scales theoretically reduce to a minimum the dead storage in the bunker, in practice coal has a tendency to hang up or arch in a tapered chute. Also there is the disadvantage that, if one boiler is out, the coal in that section of the bunker is not available for the other boiler or boilers. A runaround conveyor in a horizontal plane would be better, not only in this respect, but also because the runaround conveyor requires about 2 ft. headroom as contrasted with about 8 ft. for the wide chutes. Thus

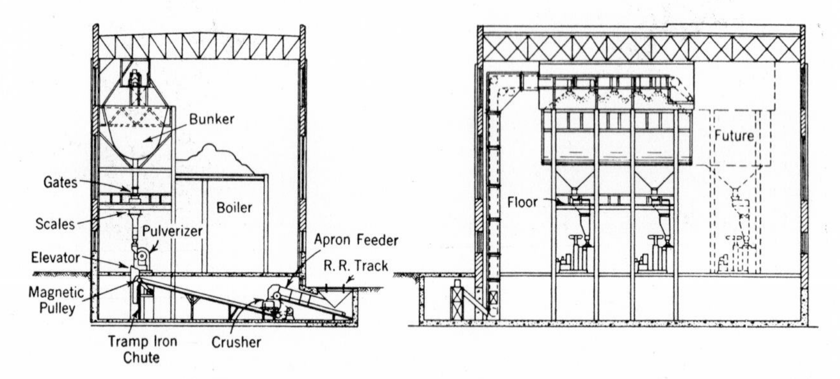


Fig. 20-6. Layout for pulverized-coal-burning plant, with automatic weighing of coal burned.

the suspension bunker could be made with 6 ft. more depth, giving larger capacity, better discharge along steeper flanks, and less dead storage.

In a plant where the coal passes direct from the pulverizers to the combustion chambers, interruption of the flow of coal from the bunker, even though temporary, is to be avoided. The horizontal runaround conveyor reduces, if it does not eliminate, this possibility. Should the conveyor stall the coal may quickly be by-passed from bunker direct to scales.

A "future boiler" is indicated. With the horizontal runaround conveyor it would not then be necessary to extend the bunker, but only the conveyor.

Figure 20-7*A* shows the coal- and ash-handling layout for a southern industrial plant as specified by the architects. It includes a gravity-discharge elevator and apron feeder for coal and a steam-pneumatic system for ashes. The framed steel bunker has two outlets, automatic scales, and conically flared stoker chutes.

Figure 20-7*B* shows the accepted alternate. This has a vertical-runaround pivoted bucket carrier for coal and ashes, a suspended-

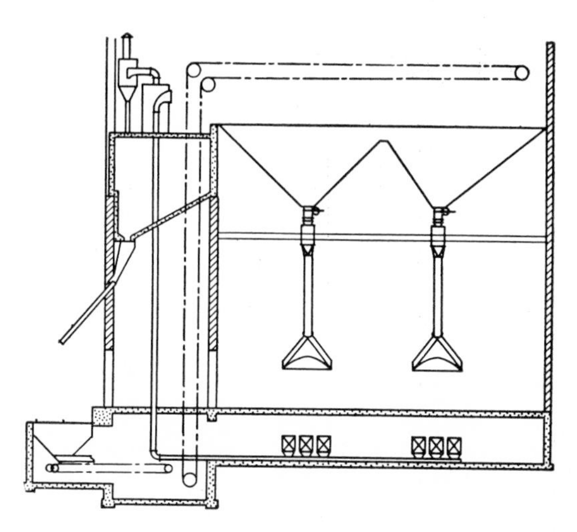

Fig. 20–7*A*. Boiler-house coal- and ash-handling installation as originally contemplated with gravity-discharge elevator and pneumatic ash conveyor.

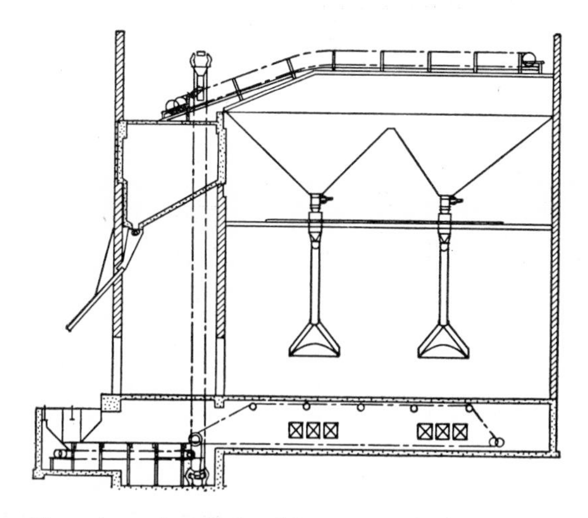

Fig. 20–7*B*. Alternate as installed, with runaround pivoted bucket elevator for coal and ashes. Suspended-flight conveyor above coal bunker. Drag-chain ash conveyor with automatic quenching sprays.

flight roller chain conveyor above the bunker, and a drag chain ash conveyor with automatic sprays near the head end to provide any desired degree of wetting down. Utilizing the pivoted bucket carrier

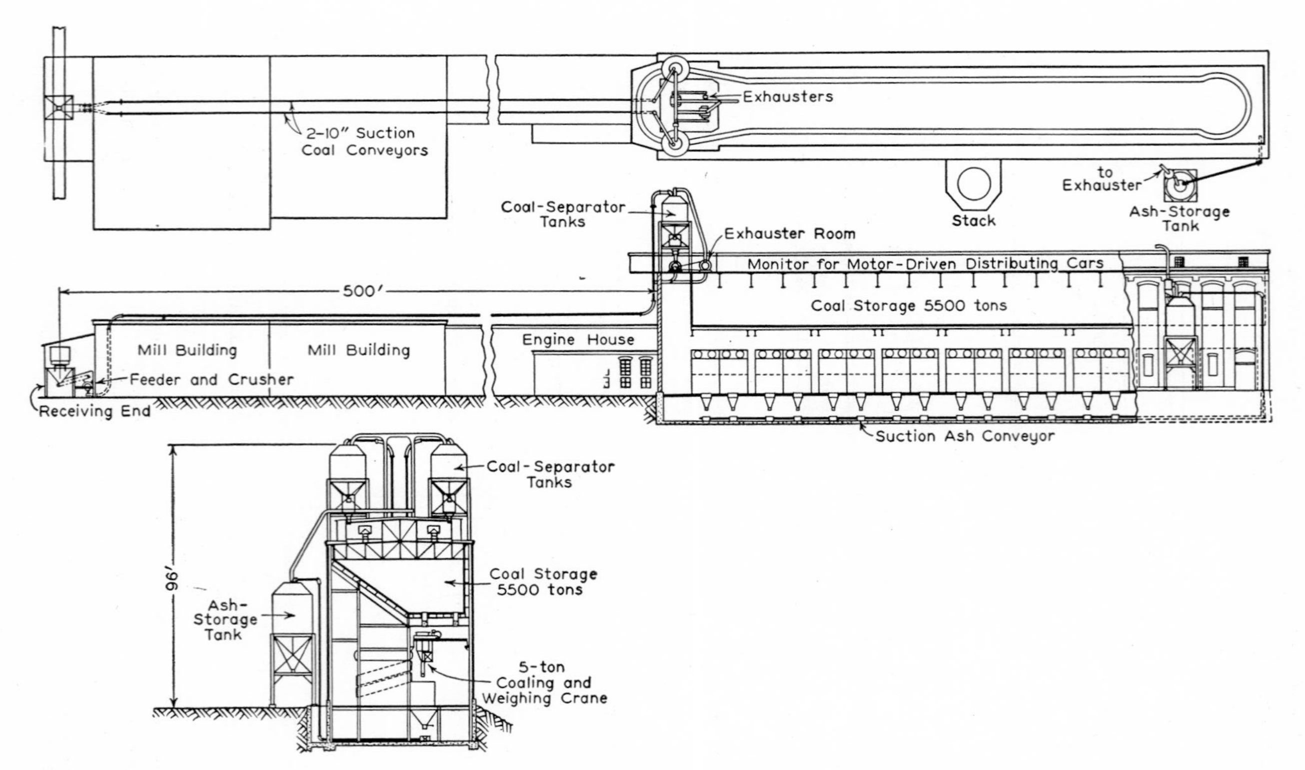


FIG. 20–8. Boiler house (Hudson) at a Massachusetts cotton mill. Both coal and ashes handled by pneumatic conveyors.

for the dual duty provided a saving of approximately $6000. Maintenance costs should be low, as illustrated by the costs listed on page 70. The bunker design could be improved. The valley angles are too flat.

Figure 20-8 shows an installation for a New England cotton mill, whose specifications required that both coal and ashes be handled by pneumatic conveyors. Coal cars are dumped at a point 500 ft. from the boiler house. Twin 10-in. conveyor ducts lead above the roof of intervening buildings, then up and across to the receiver tanks. Distribution to the bunker is by automatic electric trolley cars. The coal-handling capacity of the conveyors was 50 tons per hour.

The pneumatic ash-handling system is very good, but otherwise this is a misapplication of the pneumatic conveyor. It would be better to specify a bucket elevator and inclined belt conveyor, though the initial cost would be much greater. That layout would be complicated somewhat by the unusual width of the 5500-ton-capacity bunker. If the belt is on the monitor floor, the tripper will not fill the bunker to capacity, neither do the automatic cars for that matter. In this instance the structure had not been started, so the monitor could have been designed with sufficient height to provide full bunker loading.

The objection to the pneumatic conveyor is the excessive power requirement per ton of coal moved. The elevator-conveyor system has the same capacity with about 20 per cent of the power. A more serious objection is that dust clouds rise as the trolley cars load and discharge, and it is hazardous to pass a sparking trolley through such atmosphere. This installation dates from about 1916 when the advocates of the pneumatic conveyor were prone to reach out into dangerous territory.

Figure 20-9, a 1947 plant designed by Schmidt, Garden & Erikson, shows the application of the horizontal runaround conveyor for distribution. Ordinarily coal is chuted direct from the bunker to the automatic scale hopper at each boiler. One section of the bunker is reserved for the rather infrequent utilization of coke breeze. The coke breeze feeds to a 9-in. side-pull Redler operating at 52 ft. per min. for a capacity of 18 tons per hour, and discharges to any scale hopper. Automatic interlocks stop the machine when all hoppers are full.

Since coke breeze is abrasive, it is essential that the floor and side faces of the conveyor duct shall be exceptionally hard. The chain does not come in contact with the material (Fig. 8-12).

Figure 20-10 is a general view of a 120,000-kw. waterside public-utility plant designed by its engineering staff and constructed during

FIG. 20-9. A horizontal runaround conveyor for distribution from bunker to any scale hopper. (Photograph, Hedrich-Blessing, Ltd.)

1942-1944. Provision is made for eventual doubling of the capacity. The coal-handling equipment is by Robins.

Coal is unloaded from company-owned barges by a stationary Mead-Morrison-type tower with a 4-ton bucket, giving a capacity of 550 tons per hour based on a 22-sec. operating cycle (the heaped load capacity of a bucket exceeds its rated capacity). A surge hopper in the tower maintains the flow during barge shifts. Figure 20-11 is a flow diagram of incoming coal. From the tower it passes over a feeder to a 12 by 17 Bradford breaker hammermill to cull out foreign matter

FIG. 20–10. Consolidated Gas Electric Light and Power Company, Baltimore, Md. A 120,000 kw. waterside station erected 1942–1944. Coal-handling equipment by Robins.

and give a reduction to 1½ by 0 in. and then to belt conveyor *A* with weightometer recording the incoming tonnage. Discharge from conveyor *A* passes either to initial reserve storage via conveyor *C* to be stocked out and reclaimed by carryall assisted by bulldozers or to a

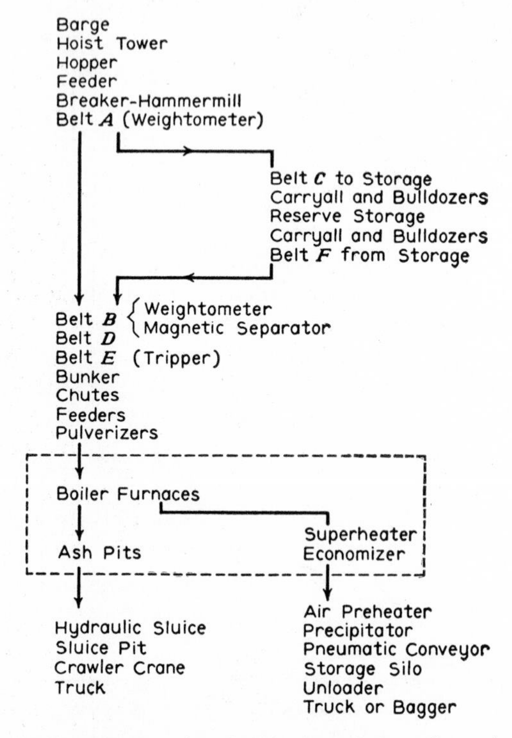


FIG. 20–11. Flow diagram of coal and ashes of plant shown in Fig. 20–10.

long inclined conveyor *B* with magnetic-head pulley and a weightometer recording the tonnage sent to the bunkers. The coal passes to conveyor *D* and is distributed to the two 900-ton-capacity bunkers by conveyor *E*. Conveyors *A* and *B* are 36 in., operating at 375 ft. per min., corresponding to 425 tons per hour. These 36-in. conveyors will be duplicated when necessary. Conveyor *C* is 36 in. and operates at 750 ft. per min. to throw the coal onto the initial pile for storage. Conveyors *D* and *E* are 48 in. operating at 190 ft. per min., corresponding to 425 tons per hour but with provision for a speed of 375 ft. per min. when needed. Coal from storage is delivered to conveyor *F* which delivers to conveyor *B*. Bunker coal is chuted to Babcock and Wilcox unit pulverizers, three per boiler, each with a capacity of 12.1 tons per hour, providing reserve capacity for wet or low-grindability coal.

The motors are interlocked for sequence control, with a four-position switch providing for the four possible flow routes. Should any unit stop, preceding units automatically stop. The location of starting switches is such that the conveyor system can be started only by walking the length of the system in the opposite direction to the coal flow. On each unit, actual movement of the belt closes a centrifugal switch permitting the starting of the preceding unit. Emergency stop buttons are located at convenient points along the line.

Should a second Mead-Morrison tower be installed the 48-in. belts will be speeded up and the 36-in. belt duplicated.

*Ash Handling.* With the exception of such slag as builds up on the furnace walls, the ash is in dry powdery form. Fusion in the pits is prevented by a water-spray curtain. Furnace-bottom ash is flushed from the pits and sluiced by an Allen-Sherman-Hoff hydraulic system to a yard sump where it is loaded to trucks by grab bucket. Fly ash is removed from the flue gases by electrostatic precipitators (Cottrell system) which consist essentially of a series of charged wires suspended between vertical concrete plates forming lanes for gas travel. The particles pick up a charge from the wires carrying a potential higher than 50,000 volts and are attracted to the electrically grounded plates from which they fall into the hoppers beneath. A pneumatic conveyor transports the fly ash to the silo seen within the tower at the top of the incline. The fly ash flows by gravity from the silo to a rotating cylinder, where sufficient water is mixed in to permit disposal to open trucks or later, possibly, to barges.

This is an up-to-date generating station operating at 900-lb. gauge pressure and attaining an efficiency of 0.85 lb. of coal per kilowatt-hour, slightly better than the 0.896 lb. per kw-hr. noted for the station whose costs are charted on page 410.

Of incidental interest are the open framed conveyor bridges with the conveyors protected by U-covers, eliminating the hazard in closed galleries in which dust can collect and which might create a chimney effect in case of fire.

## ENGINEERING A STEAM-PLANT COAL- AND ASH-HANDLING INSTALLATION

To illustrate the routine procedure in developing the general layout of a coal- and ash-handling installation, assume a property between a small river and a railroad main line (Fig. 20-12) where a station is to be erected with an initial installation of two 10,000-hp. boilers with V-type dry-bottom water-cooled pulverized-coal-fired furnaces. (A stand-by boiler might be provided.)

The designer of the station gives us the following information for our guidance. Coal usually will be mine-run, delivered in hopper-bottom cars, frequently in trains of 5 to 20, and the operators desire to check the coal weight only as delivered to the bunker. A substantial reserve coal storage is essential, though the coal when piled has been found subject to spontaneous ignition. No demand has been found for the ashes, and so disposal on the property is suggested. One end of the site is available for ashes and reserve coal storage.

First to be decided is the coal-handling capacity. Consumption will depend on the output curve but will scarcely exceed 10 tons per hour

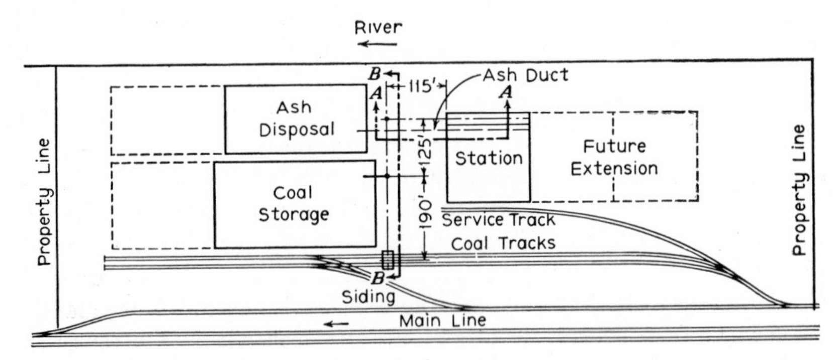


Fig. 20–12. Layout used for analysis. Site lies between railroad main line and a small river.

average throughout the day. To handle this in an 8-hr. day shift means a handling capacity of 40 or 50 tons per hour, but since deliveries will be in trainload lots we need a much higher handling rate. Evidently a belt-conveyor system will be suitable, and, since the coal is mine-run, at least a 30-in. belt will be required to take care of lumps up to 12 in. The capacity available with a 30-in. belt is 300 tons per hour at 380 ft. per min., which will enable us to unload a train of five 50-ton cars in 1 hr. or twenty 70-ton cars in 5 hr. under favorable conditions, that is, free-flowing coal, uninterrupted movement of cars away from and to the dumping point, and cars in good condition. From the discussion in Chapter 17, we will specify twin 12 by 14 ft. track hoppers and tracks on a 1 per cent downgrade for gravity movement of the cars. A train of ten 70-ton cars has a length of about 450 ft., so that the track should have ample length both sides of the track hoppers.

Flow from the hoppers to the conveyor must be controlled. A vibrating feeder has distinct advantages over either a reciprocating feeder or apron feeder, but with twin feeds the apron will be best. The apron speed (about 20 ft. per min.) to deliver 300 tons per hour need not be changed whether the flow is from one or both hoppers. If both hoppers are full, the coal will flow from the rear hopper only and will not feed from the front hopper until the other clears, but delivery to the belt will be steady at 300 tons per hour. If the operator controls the dumps first from one track and then from the other, there will be little delay in car movement. With two independent feeders each must

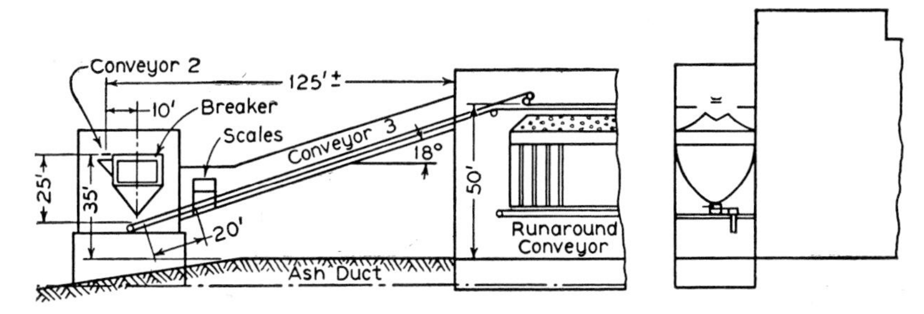


FIG. 20–13. Layout of breaker, automatic scales, conveyor 3, the bunker, and runaround distributing conveyor. View is section *A-A* in Fig. 20–12.

be geared to 150 tons per hour, and, if a delay occurs in either hopper, the handling rate is reduced to 150 tons per hour until the trouble is cleared. The ideal arrangement, if the necessary depth is permissible, is a single large track hopper and a single electromagnetic feeder adjusted to 300 tons per hour.

Before we consider the conveyor layout, we must determine the type of crusher. The job is to reduce mine-run coal to ¾-in. and under and to remove stray lumber, tramp iron, rags, hay, and other foreign matter. Either a hammermill or Bradford breaker will serve, and in view of the advantages in the combination machine we will specify a 7 by 14 ft. breaker with an internal 30 by 30 in. hammermill.

Tentatively assuming the elevation of the top run of the conveyor within the bunker building as 50 ft. above ground level, we can now consider the layout. In Fig. 20-14 with a minimum depth of pit and keeping within a slope of 18°, a height of 45 ft. is attained at a point 190 ft. from the center line between tracks, which gives us ample head for a chute to form an initial pile for reserve coal distribution. If at times clean ¾-in. coal may be received, a by-pass chute should be provided at the discharge from conveyor 2, so that the breaker hammermill can be by-passed. The breaker hammermill requires about 25 ft. vertically from its outlet to the conveyor feeding it, and we see

(Fig. 20-13) that we can locate the center line of conveyors 1 and 2 about 125 ft. from the end of the building. Tandem units are better than a single conveyor with a fixed tripper since snubbing the belt does not contribute to its life. We could incline conveyor 2, extend it rearward to just below ground level, and locate the breaker-hammer-mill between 1 and 2. Then a short inclined conveyor from beneath the breaker would form an initial pile, and coal would be cleaned before going to ground storage. Reclaimed coal would be delivered to the foot end of conveyor 2 unless it had become frozen and lumpy, then it would be reclaimed to the track hopper and passed again to the breaker.

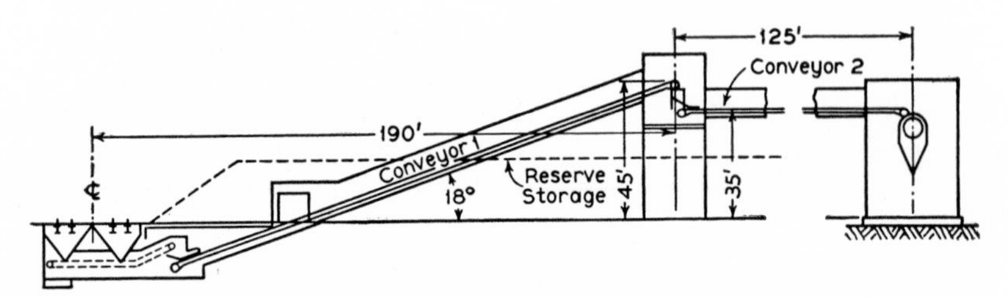


Fig. 20-14. Section *B-B*, Fig. 20-12. Conveyor 1 lifts the coal to an elevation at which it may be chuted to form an initial pile for spreading to reserve storage.

As to the arrangement within the bunker building, bunker capacity is largely a matter of architectural considerations, the larger the better — within limits — so that a major part of a shipment need not be diverted to ground storage, which more than doubles the per ton handling cost for the coal so diverted. The monolithic concrete bunker is highest in first cost, then comes the framed steel bunker with concrete lining, and then the suspension type. Considering the figures in Chapter 13, we will tentatively adopt the Ferro Inclave type suspension bunker with a minimum cross section of 25 by 25 ft., giving nicely steep sides and a capacity of about 15 tons per foot of length. The bunker height can be increased if desired by shifting the breaker toward the left (Fig. 20-13) and increasing the slope of conveyor 3 to 20°.

For the feed from bunker to the unit pulverizers we may have direct chutes with an auxiliary screw conveyor to make the coal in the bunker available for either boiler. If added boilers are a probability, we may have an auxiliary horizontal-runaround Redler conveyor. It can receive coal from any one of a succession of closely spaced bunker gates and will provide semi-automatic distribution to all pulverizer hoppers. A conveyor with a duct area of about 80 sq. in. will have a capacity of 10 tons per hour at 15 ft. per min., and can function for additional boilers, by slightly increasing its speed. With a variable-speed drive its speed may be closely adjusted to the rate of consumption so as to function for long periods without attention.

Removal of tramp iron by the breaker may not be sufficient protection. It does cull out fragments larger than 3/4 in., but nails, small nuts, and the like will pass through with the coal. Conveyor 3 might be split into two conveyors with a magnetic-head pulley on the first, but more effective separation can be secured by a short wide magnetic-head conveyor between the breaker and the foot end of 3.

**Reserve Coal Storage.** We have available alongside the tail tracks an area 200 ft. wide by 400 ft. long which with a depth of 20 ft. will give us a storage of 40,000 tons. Both the length and depth of the pile may be increased in emergency to provide about 80,000 tons. Since the coal is liable to spontaneous heating, it should be compacted to prevent air circulation, and so we will specify bulldozers for stocking out and reclaiming. Whether the added expense of a carryall is justified will depend on how active the in-and-out movements will be, a factor which the operators are in a better position to judge.

Coal will be spread out from the initial pile formed by conveyor 1 and reclaimed to the nearer track hopper.

**Ashes Disposal.** There is available for the disposal of about 24 tons of ashes per day an area adjacent to the river on the downstream side. For our layout a sluicing system fits in nicely. It provides dustless disposal, and the surplus water will cleanse as it filters through the soil to the river. If the disposal area, formed by banking up the earth around it, is at a lower level than the basement we can sluice direct. If it is at a higher level we may sluice to a sump and pump to storage.

Assuming that the ash hopper of the V-type dry-bottom water-walled pulverized-coal-fired furnace has a sloping floor, we must have for each hopper a jetting nozzle to flush the ashes out and a sluicing nozzle to convey them along the duct. The distance from the basement to the disposal area is about 400 ft., and to maintain the flow booster nozzles must be spaced about 60 ft. along its length. With water at 100-lb. pressure a jetting nozzle discharging 175 g.p.m. will flush ashes from the pit at the rate of 1 ton per minute. The sluicing nozzle should discharge 225 g.p.m. to move the mixture at that rate, and each booster nozzle contributes the same quantity; therefore the total water requirement is 1750 g.p.m. As a rule the requirement will be between 5 and 7 lb. of water per lb. of ashes.

Since the ash pits have a capacity of about 7 tons each, only two runs of 15 or 20 min. each day will be required to dispose of ashes. The ash sluice may be a concrete trench about 18 in. wide and deep, lined with corrosion-resisting U-plates and vapor-tight removable cover plates. If the sluice can thus be made direct, the cost of the ash-handling system is of course much less than if the ashes must be pumped from sump or surge pit; then a sump about 15 ft. deep would be provided, preferably midway between boilers, with a grid to catch clinkers too large for the pump. Again we would have the 175 g.p.m. jetting stream and 225 g.p.m. for sluicing to the sump, or a total of about 400 g.p.m. of ashes and water. To this must be added 500 g.p.m. of make-up water to condition the mixture for pumping. The disposal pump thus will have a capacity of 900 to 1000 g.p.m. which against a head of 50 ft. calls for a 20-hp. motor. The discharge line may be an 8-in. heavy cast-iron pipe. The head loss will be about 12 ft., and the velocity of flow about 6½ ft. per sec.

Usually it is desirable to have a duplicate or stand-by pump. Fly ash may be delivered to the sump pneumatically by a pipe line in which the air blast is induced by a venturi water jet near the sump end of the line.

A refinement in the coal-handling scheme is to eliminate the services of the man above the bunker by a series of electric eyes directed across the bunker at full-load level and connected to a bank of lamps in the conveyor control room — either in the breaker house or in the tower between conveyors 1 and 2. The tripper travel limits are remote-controlled from the same point. The attendant shifts the discharge from the tripper by observation of the lamps, which light up whenever a section of the bunker is filled nearly to capacity. When all the lamps are lighted, the bunker is filled, and the feeder is automatically stopped, or the discharge from conveyor 1 is automatically deflected to reserve storage.

Instead of the classic corrugated-steel sheathing and little windows commonly seen on conveyor bridges, consideration should be given to blank-steel or corrugated aluminum sides without windows. The bridges are all short span and do not require intermediate supports. The tower and breaker house should be of tile, brick, or similar attractive design. Engineers pay too little attention to making their work pleasing to the eye. The track layout must be worked out in cooperation with the railroad engineers, whose approval also is necessary for the girders across the track hoppers. The automatic scales should be located far enough from the loading point of conveyor 3 so that the readings will not be affected, 20 ft. is a minimum. If there is a possibility that oil-sprayed coal may be received at times, the belt covers must be one of the synthetics that resist the action of oil.

Figure 20-15 shows a plant where the coal- and ash-handling layouts were worked out closely along the lines just described. Flood level of the river was considerably higher than the level shown, which explains the height of the foundations. Incidently this is plant *H*, page 409.

Fig. 20–15. Associated Gas and Electric Company, Holland, New Jersey, station. Extensions are toward the left. Coal handling scheme (Hudson) engineered along the lines described in pages 423 to 429.

**Arching in the Bunker and Chutes.** With the increasing use of small bituminous coal (½ by 0), the difficult problem has arisen of maintaining the flow from the bunker and through the chutes to the pulverizers. This difficulty increases if the coal has been rained upon in ground storage and ground up by subsequent rolling with stocking-out and reclaiming track-type equipment. If thoroughly dry and not compacted, such coal has an angle of repose of about 45°, but with increasing percentages of surface moisture the repose angle increases to between 60 and 90°, and, as the bunker fills to capacity, the damp coal packs and frequently will not flow at all.

A thin suspended sheet of stainless steel substantially reduces arching in a hopper of moderate size but can scarcely have any practical value in a large storage bunker. The Richardson device depends on aerating pulverized material on the principle that aeration tends to make material flowable. As shown in Fig. 20-16, a 3/8-in. capped air pipe is mounted in each corner of the bin with 1/32-in. holes spaced 3-in. centers along a spiral path. Control is through a pressure gauge and pressure regulator, and a centrifugal water eliminator. It is questionable whether this would be effective with damp small coal. As

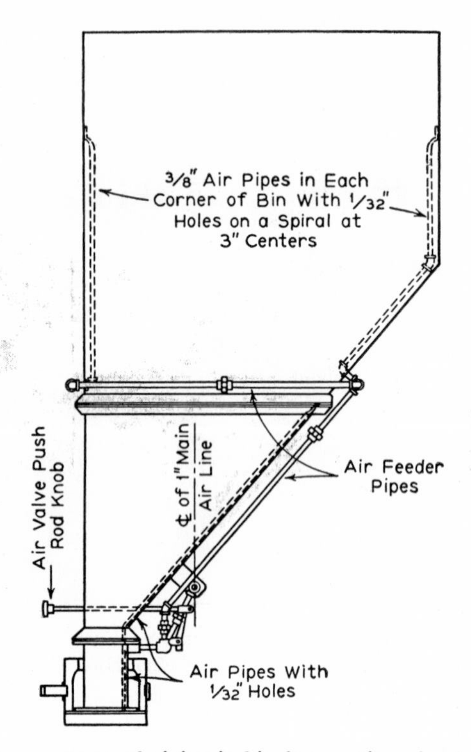


FIG. 20-16. Arrangement of piping in bin for aeration of pulverized material.

resistance to flow is less when the coal is freshly deposited, there is the possibility of passing it through a rotary dryer and then to dry-coal compartments in the bunker. It is impossible to dry incoming coal at the rate at which the conveying system delivers it, but freshly deposited coal could be dried at a reasonable rate corresponding to the consumption rate. However, such an auxiliary system involves, in addition to a costly dryer, an elevator and two horizontal runaround conveyors, one drawing coal from the bunker and feeding it to the dryer, the other distributing it to the mill chutes. It is a difficult problem.

In the chutes beneath the bunker the difficulty continues. Side thrust due to arching causes the coal to hang up. It has long been general practice to give a chute for wood chips, sand, gravel, and some bulk chemicals a gradually increasing diameter (truncated cone shape) to facilitate flow. This holds good with damp coal also, and coal in a widening chute will flow with a surface moisture content substantially higher than that at which it will stick in a cylindrical chute. Coal

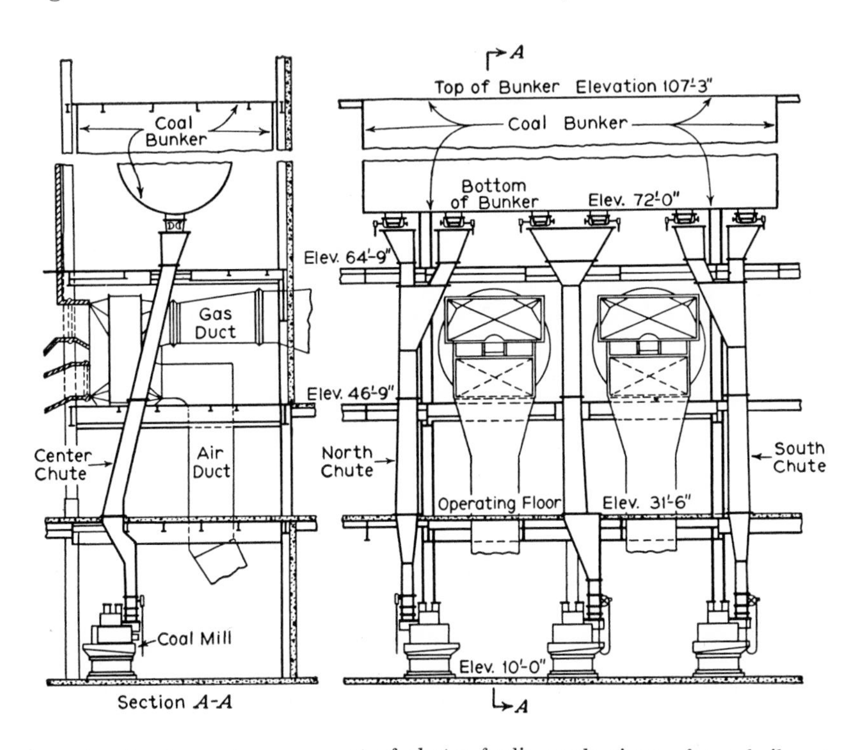


FIG. 20-17. General arrangement of chutes feeding pulverizers of one boiler at 200,000-kw. plant, as originally installed.

slides more readily on glass, aluminum, and stainless steel than on ordinary sheet steel, and with 10 or 12 per cent surface moisture it flows quite readily on these. Oil spraying has the good effect of shedding water from coal spread in ground storage but has little effect on flow through bunker chutes. Vibrating a chute has the effect of compacting the coal *standing* therein.

E. F. Wolf and H. L. vonHobenleiten investigated the problem in connection with the difficulties experienced at the Riverside Generating Station (Fig. 20-10) of the Consolidated Gas Electric Light and Power Company and their findings were reported in the ASME Transactions

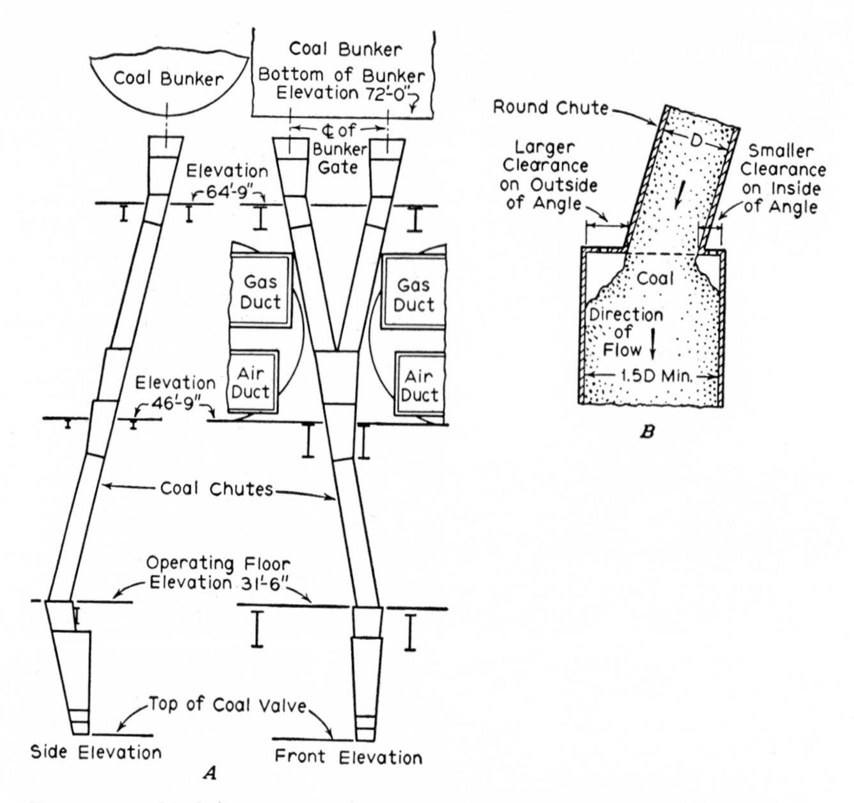


FIG. 20–18 (*A*) Middle chute, Fig. 20–17, as modified after research. (*B*) Diagram of "breakaway."

of October 1945, which we quote in part. The general arrangement of the chutes serving one boiler was as shown in Fig. 20-17. They selected the Y-chute for their investigation and followed the ingenious method of making translucent-Pyralin scale models which enabled them to observe how the coal acted, when it flowed, and where it hung up. As a result of their investigations they recommended:

Avoidance of sudden constrictions and sharp changes in direction.

Minimum angles of convergence of lines of flow, preferably approaching zero.

Minimum practical taper in hoppers.

Use of round chutes in preference to square or rectangular cross sections.

Maximum possible angle of inclination with horizontal throughout.

The Y of the central chute was formed with a "breakaway" (Fig. 20-18) which serves to permit the coal to realign itself.

Trials with full-size chutes have been promising, and the investigation is being extended. The problem is of growing importance and worthy of the attention of engineers in a position to conduct research. Among the possibilities is a chute with adjustable shelves of stainless steel (Fig. 13-9*C*) vibrated to secure a cascade from step to step, practically a series of vibrating plate feeders.

# CHAPTER 21

## SOME PROBLEMS AND SOLUTIONS

Every materials handling engineer occasionally runs up against a seemingly simple problem which develops unexpected kinks. A few of these experienced by the author are interesting.

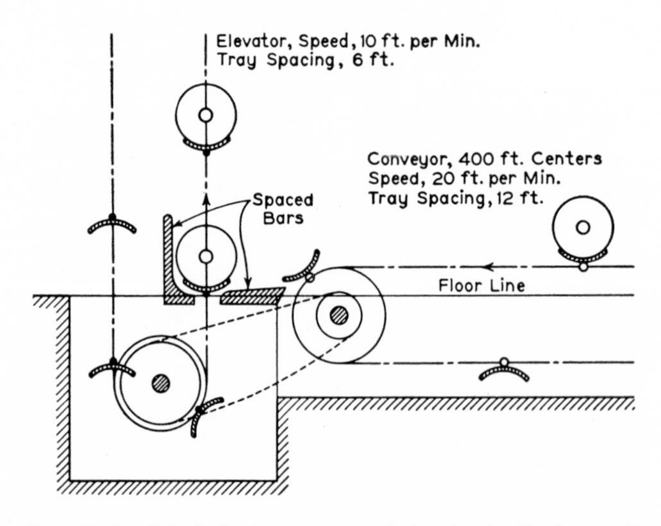


FIG. 21-1. Interlocked conveyor and elevator for linoleum rolls.

**Synchronized Tandem Units.** Figure 21-1 shows the transfer point between a horizontal conveyor and a tray elevator. The conveyor was a double strand machine of 400-ft. centers with 6-in. pitch roller chains having yoke attachments spaced 12-ft. centers on which rolls of linoleum are placed. Speed, 20 ft. per min. The tandem elevator with trays spaced 6-ft. centers had a speed of 10 ft. per min. The elevator element must be adjusted so that each tray passes the point where it receives the roll at just the right instant when the roll from the conveyor has reached a position upon the stationary cradle, so the two machines are mechanically interlocked. Once this adjustment has been made it is permanent, or should be. But it was not. The erector reported that the installation started up nicely, with the transfer of rolls as contemplated. However, succeeding reports stated that after several hours operation the trays failed to synchronize, and the rolls got tangled up in the elevator. Readjustment was made with the same result. The draftsman responsible for the design was sent to investigate. Obviously the only possible explanation was an error in the spacing of the yokes, but the erector was positive that this had been carefully checked. However, the draftsman chalked a link and checked the spacing of each passing yoke. It required about 40 min. for the chain to make a round trip, and, just as he noted the return of the chalked link he found a spacing that was 6 in. short. The erector had omitted a pair of links. That meant the conveyor gained 6 in. each round trip, and, although this would not cause immediate trouble, eventually the trays would be completely out of step.

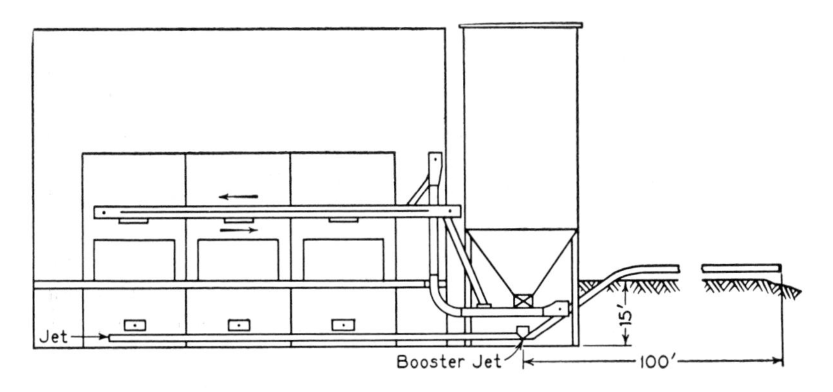


Fig. 21-2. Hydraulic ash conveyor with booster jet at upturn.

**Sluicing Ashes "Up-Hill."** Figure 21-2 outlines the coal- and ash-handling layout at a steam plant where it was desired to spread the ashes from the basement ash pits over an adjacent low area. The coal-handling and storage arrangement is conventional, with an L-path continuous-flow elevator taking coal from a silo and discharging to the upper run of a similar conveyor which feeds from the return run to the stoker hoppers and returns any surplus to the elevator, restricting the flow from the silo.

Water at high pressure was available, and so it was decided to attempt hydraulic ash disposal, which was risky because of the 15-ft. difference of level between the basement and the outside ground level. A 10-in. cast iron pipe was installed with ash inlets at each pit. A ⅝-in. nozzle at the far end flushed the ashes to the upturn, where a booster jet was to send the stream of ashes and water up and out to the disposal point. Starting up, the stream carried nicely to the upturn but backed up there and spouted out at the intakes. Happening to remove the cover plate at the upturn elbow, the engineer saw the stream immediately continue up the incline without any further trouble. The inrush of air due to the injector action of the booster jet aerated the stream, reduced its weight, and increased the velocity sufficiently to make the conveyor workable.

**Multiple Materials.** Many of the pulverized materials have characteristics that make them difficult. For instance, the clays are sluggish, tend to adhere to flights or buckets, and will not flow from storage. Their sticky qualities are annoying when it is necessary to handle several of them successively without admixture. This problem was presented at a plant in Indiana where the manufacturing process involves handling and storing in separate bins four finely pulverized and sluggish materials differing widely in weight, namely: zinc oxide, 30 lb. per cu. ft.; talc, 45 lb. per cu. ft.; whiting, 75 lb.; and barytes, 127 lb.

The materials are received in bags that must be cut to feed the contents to an L-path continuous-flow elevator, and so a capacity of 10 tons per hour will suffice, but there is the complication of wide weight variation. If the elevator is designed for 10 tons per hour of zinc oxide, it will be handling at the rate of 42 tons per hour when barytes are fed to the boot, calling for an elevator chain, drive group, and motor four times as strong for this material (which it so happens is much the smallest in annual volume) as for the zinc oxide. A variable-speed feeder will take care of this, or the cutting and loading squad can be reduced from four men to one. Reducing the speed is no solution: An elevator at 20 ft. per min. handling 10 tons per hour of the heavy material puts about four times the working load on the chain as 10 tons per hour at 80 ft. per min.

The continuous-flow system with L-path elevator and tandem conveyor installed was designed for 10 tons per hour of zinc oxide, but with the chain and drive suited for 25 tons per hour of whiting, and with feed restriction for the infrequent handling of heavy barytes. It was impossible to secure complete clearing of one material so that the next could be handled without admixture. A bucket elevator would be no better in this regard since the clay would stick to the buckets and would build up in the boot. The only way to secure complete discharge is by blowing out the duct with compressed air. This can be done with clays, but is not advisable with soybean meal, starch, sulphur, and similar explosive dusts. Distribution without intermingling can be improved by specifying separate screw conveyors, one for each bin, and a selective starting station at the platform which would prevent starting a conveyor unless the elevator chute is swung to the proper position for the material to be handled. Even then we must rely on the intelligence of the operator.

At a plant manufacturing a brand of packaged macaroni in short lengths, "elbow macaroni," the product comes from the ovens to a slow-speed belt conveyor to cool and harden. There was the risk that small pieces of non-magnetic metal, such as Monel metal, might get into the macaroni and be unremovable by a magnetic pulley. Even one such piece might result in costly damages. Positive removal was

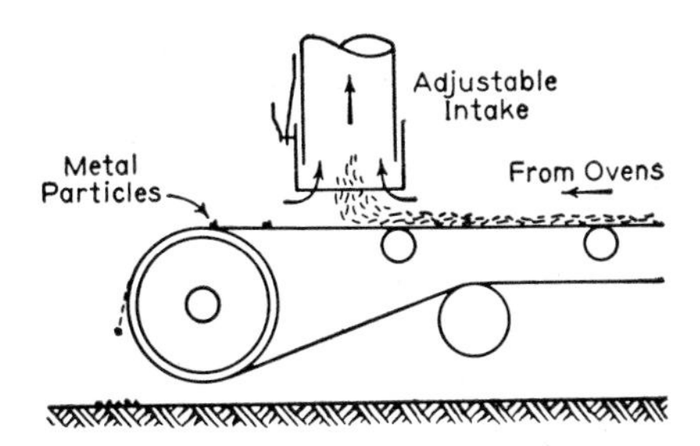


FIG. 21-3. Separation of metallic particles from "elbow macaroni."

secured by a pneumatic elevator (Fig. 21-3). The pipe has an adjustable end directly above the discharge end of the belt to give a lifting action just sufficient to lift the macaroni but not metal fragments which therefore spill to the floor. The scheme applies equally well to culling out undesired light material from a heavy product. A constant-pressure-variable-volume exhauster is preferable here to the usual constant volume type.

**The Reciprocating Grid as a Feeder.** A unique attempt to relieve a hammermill of useless work by combining the functions of a feeder and by-pass is shown in Fig. 21-4. Here 1½-in. slack coal is desired for the stokers. With the knowledge that at times larger sizes could be purchased advantageously, the hammermill was provided. The continuous-flow elevator is nearly 100-ft. centers and has a capacity of 40 tons per hour. The track hopper has a grating with 4-in. openings and a feeder in which the usual reciprocating plate is, instead, a reciprocating grid, so that the undersize may pass direct to the elevator, and only plus 1½ in. will go through the hammermill.

Actually the undersize immediately fills the duct, since a reciprocating grid has no feed control, and the output from the hammermill is blocked off until this machine stalls. In an effort to correct this, the chute from the reciprocating grid was led around to the lower duct. This gave but little improvement, because the 1½ by 0 coal ordinarily received backed up into the track hopper and then fed into the hammermill, making it necessary to operate both feeder and hammermill though the coal was already undersize. Since coal of the proper stoker size is nearly always available, the correction is to provide a reciprocating plate feeder with a removable plate or trap door for direct feed to the elevator unless crushing is needed. Incidently, the hammermill is an 18 by 15-in. at 1800 r.p.m. A two-roll 24 by 24-in. crusher at 100 r.p.m. would be better.

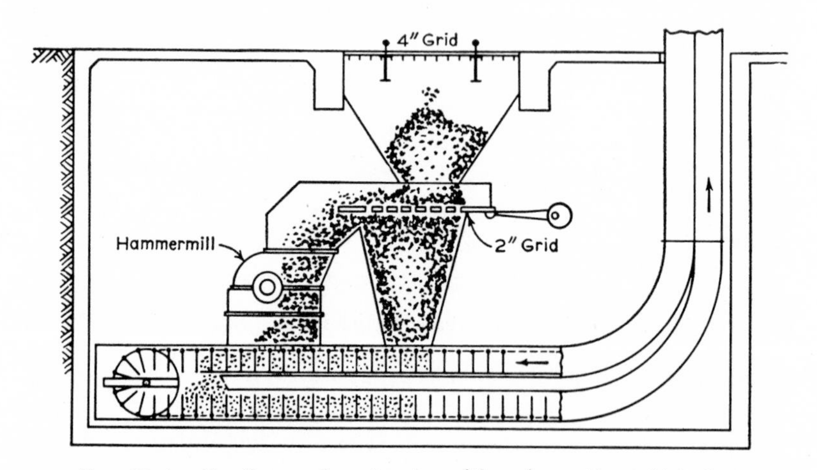


FIG. 21–4. Continuous-flow elevator with reciprocating-grid feeder.

Another detail in this layout which should be avoided when possible (it was not avoidable in this instance because of foundation interference) is that there is no accommodation for chain slack. The chain when operating is under a tension of about 11,000 lb. An elongation of 1 per cent under this loading causes an accumulation of about 12-in. slack across the feed gap in the partition plate. This, even though the take-ups are well tightened when the elevator is idle, produces a sag which brings the two runs of chain dangerously close together. This is a difficult condition to correct. Counterweighted ratchet take-ups might be installed, but this type of elevator when starting under load sometimes takes an extremely heavy starting pull which would leave the chain very taut. It is better when possible to have a short feed section ahead of a high elevator, which then can be a loop-type machine with automatic slack space where the return run enters the loop.

At a manufacturing plant in mass production of devices with small lacquered steel casings, it is necessary before applying the lacquer to remove all oil or grease from the metal. Immersion in a heavy gas, remotely related to mustard gas, cleanses the parts in a few seconds; then the lacquer is applied by dipping, after which it is necessary to allow time for the lacquer to dry before assembly continues. This requires about 10 min.

The layout for the machine for cleansing, lacquering, and drying, is shown in Fig. 21-5. An attendant hooks the parts to cross rods between two strands of chain at *A*. The parts then dip into the degreasing gas at *B*, which is so heavy it rests in the open-top tank like a liquid. The cleansed parts then dip into the lacquer bath *C* and

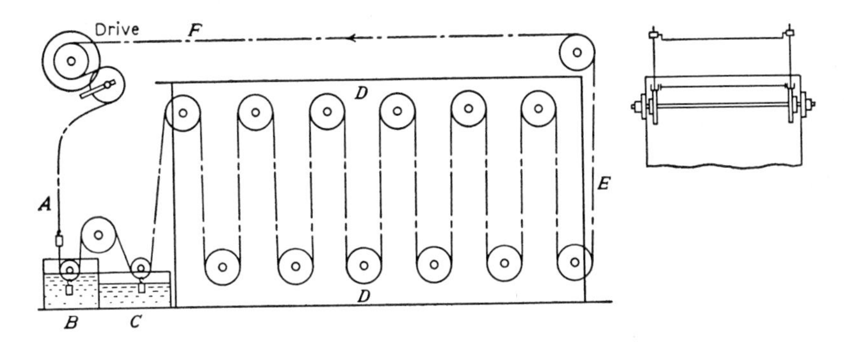


FIG. 21-5. Cleansing, lacquering, and drying machine for sheet-steel containers.

emerge to pass through the drying chamber *D* over and under a series of guide sprockets at 10 ft. per min. Finally they are removed at *E*.

Checking the work when the machine was put into operation, the author found that the input to the motor was 3 hp., although a reasonable assumption would be 1 hp. Toward the far end it was observed that the $1\frac{3}{16}$-in. sprocket shafts were deflecting sharply. The pull on each chain at *B* could hardly exceed 100 lb., but snubbing around 13 shafts evidently built up the pull to above 4000 lb., as deduced from the power required at the motor. Part of this build-up came from the friction in the rigid bearings and from friction in the dry chain joints as the links articulated, but it was due chiefly to binding in the far bearings under the accumulated tension. Ten pairs of self-aligning bearings reduced the power input to slightly over 1 hp., or a maximum chain pull of about 1500 lb., still showing considerable increase between *B* and *F* and illustrating the effect of bending unlubricated chains around multiple idler sprockets.

Even a simple layout sometimes develops some troublesome detail. One layout included a centrifugal-discharge elevator for a few tons per hour of finely pulverized zinc oxide. The discharge chute at the top had a 45° slope. This material has a peculiar characteristic of doing the unexpected, and here it persisted in building up a stalagmite-like pile where the flow from the elevator hit the chute, so that it was necessary to keep a man sweeping the chute clear. It appeared that an electric vibrator would be necessary, but a simple change eliminated the trouble. A square-foot section of the floor of the chute was cut away and replaced by a piece of tightly stretched canvas. The falling discharge maintained the canvas in vibration sufficiently to prevent build-up.

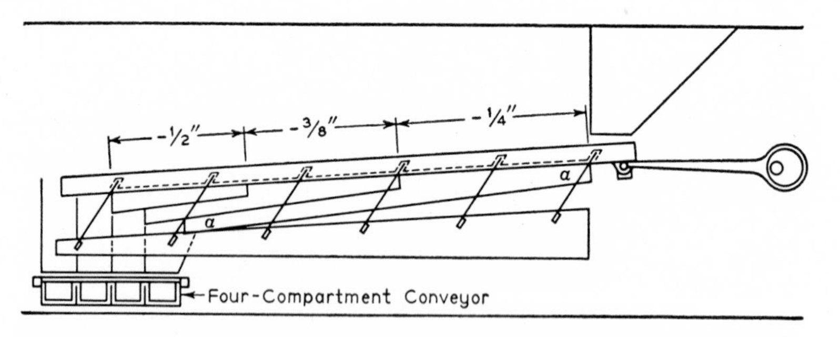


FIG. 21-6. Shaker screen for classifying washed coal screenings.

Sometimes the solution of a difficulty is found just in time to prevent the removal of the offending machine. Figure 21-6 is a diagram of a heavy grasshopper screen installed at a coal-preparation plant, whose function it was to screen out the smallest size of washed coal as rejects and then to separate the remainder into three sizes. The action of the inclined cantilever supports is to jounce the wet coal along the screens with very little blinding if the speed and throw of the eccentric drive are just right, but the damp fines built up on the tray (*a–a*) to a depth of about 3 in., bringing a destructive load on the supports. Hickory, laminated steel, and heavy spring steel were tried without success, and a replacement with some other type of screen was contemplated. As a final experiment the tray section was lined with a sheet of 24-gauge polished stainless steel. The trouble disappeared. The fines flowed along without noticeable build-up.

Occasionally the failure of an installation is due to inaccurate information furnished by the purchaser and again by failure of the engineer to foresee the rather obvious. Figure 21-7 shows the latter instance. Mine carloads are dumped to a shaker screen to cull out about 10 per cent of slack and chute the lump into railroad cars for shipment. Thus a belt conveyor and elevator good for 35 tons per hour were specified for the screenings, as the dumping rate was stated to be 200 tons per hour. As long as the stated conditions held, the installation functioned perfectly, but when the men back in the mine loaded cars with small stuff, nearly all of which passed through the screen, a conveyor and elevator of 200 tons per hour rather than 35 were required. The installation was rebuilt for that capacity.

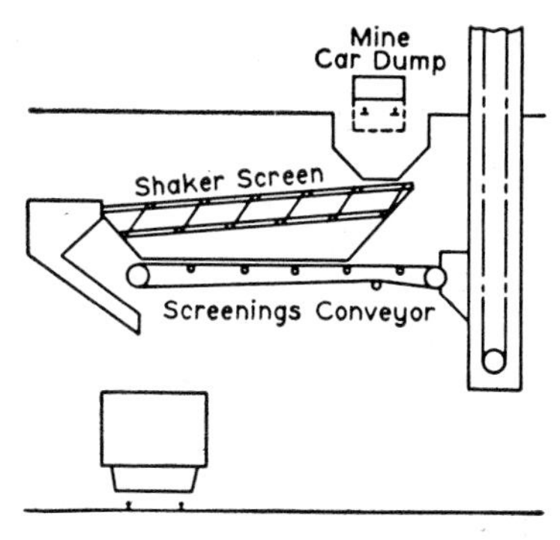


Fig. 21–7. Shaker screen, screenings conveyor, and elevator at mine dump.

**Handling Paper Rolls.** The materials handling scheme in a plant printing daily or weekly publications in large volume provides a most interesting series of problems since operations must follow a rigid schedule, and any interruption in the orderly flow completely upsets the timed mail and express shipments. Let us work through one section of the problem, the handling of the paper rolls from the cars, through ready storage, to the reels serving the presses, in a plant printing a weekly magazine (Fig. 21-8).

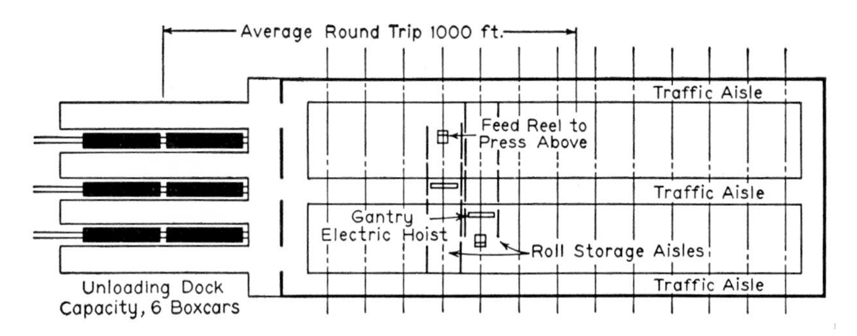


Fig. 21–8. General plan of hypothetical plant for discussion of unloading and distributing 3000-lb. paper rolls.

Unloading is a three-shift operation. Rolls weighing 3000 lb., wound on 6-in. core pipes, arrive in wide-door boxcars containing 21 rolls each, loaded crosswise. The cars are delivered at one end of the plant on three sidings with adjacent platforms opposite the long storage room, in four shifts of 6 cars each, or 24 cars per 24-hr. day. These rolls must be distributed to long storage aisles from which further movement to the press reels is by overhead bridge cranes. The traffic movement is 500 rolls per 24 hr. For unloading the cars the best equipment is the gooseneck-crane industrial truck with self-releasing grab. It functions to bring the rolls from within the car to skids on the platform alongside. One crane can unload a car in 2 hr., and so two cranes operate simultaneously. In view of the requirement of uninterrupted operation the requirements are:

| Equipment: | | |
|---|---|---|
| 2 gooseneck-crane trucks | $15,500 | (with grab and battery) |
| 2 spare or stand-by trucks | 12,000 | |
| 2 replacement batteries | 2,300 | |
| | $29,800 | (1946) |

Labor:
6 truck operators
12 men in cars to insert grabs
Total, 18 men

There are three possible methods for the transfer of the rolls from the platform through the storage aisles. The round trip averages 1000 ft.

*A*. By a heavy-duty variable-speed reversible pallet-conveyor flush with the floor and driven by a 15-hp. motor at 5 to 15 ft. per min. The rolls are to be lifted off at the proper points by the bridge cranes which function also to shift rolls to the press reels. The approximate cost of this conveyor (1946 prices) including foundation trench is $40,000. The goosenecks are too actively engaged to bring the rolls to the conveyor, and so two fork trucks do the transfer work. The requirements for distribution are:

| Equipment: | | |
|---|---|---|
| 2 fork trucks | $10,300 | (with battery) |
| 1 spare truck | 4,000 | |
| 2 replacement batteries | 2,300 | |
| 1 conveyor | 40,000 | |
| | $56,600 | |

Labor:
6 operators
3 conveyor maintenance
Total, 9 men
Plus a charge for the time of crane men

*B*. By fork trucks. The rolls on the skids on the platform are picked up and moved by 3000-lb.-capacity fork trucks which travel along the aisles to distribute them to the proper points. A truck can maneuver and average a round trip in 10 min., or five trips per 50-min. hr. The requirements for distribution are:

| Equipment: | | |
|---|---|---|
| 4 fork trucks | $20,600 | (with battery) |
| 2 spare trucks | 8,000 | |
| 4 replacement batteries | 4,600 | |
| | $33,200 | |

Labor:
12 operators

The objection to method $A$ is that it is difficult for the bridge cranes to engage the rolls as they pass beneath, and, should a roll get by without being lifted off at the proper aisle, the conveyor must be reversed to bring the roll back, but this is awkward as regards the back travel of the following rolls. The objection to method $B$ is that it involves 500 truck trips per day.

$C$. By tractor trains of 6 trailers, each trailer carrying 3 rolls. The aisles are sufficiently wide to permit travel and turning of 4-wheel-steer trailers. The number of trips per day is $500/6 \times 3 = 28$. The trailers will be brought to the storage lines and parked there until cleared by the bridge cranes, while the tractor returns for the next loaded train. The requirements for distribution are (the car-unloading goosenecks will place the rolls on the trailers instead of upon floor skids, but we will add two to assist unloading):

| Equipment: | |
|---|---|
| 2 goosenecks with grabs and batteries | $15,500 |
| 2 replacement batteries | 2,300 |
| 1 tractor with battery | 3,150 |
| 1 spare tractor | 2,000 |
| 1 replacement battery | 1,150 |
| 72 trailers | 18,000 |
| | $42,100 |

Labor:
6 operators
3 tractor operators
Plus a charge for time of crane men

All batteries are standardized as 18 cell, 23 plate.

This last method seems the best solution as involving a minimum traffic volume — slightly more than one trip per hour as against twenty trips per hour for the mechanized equipment — with low maintenance and battery charging cost. Method $A$ appears least desirable because it involves a 24-hr. per day operation of the conveyor, and, should it be down for lengthy repairs, as eventually it must be, there is no emergency method of maintaining distribution, and operations come to a stop.

## CHAPTER 22

# DUST-EXPLOSION HAZARDS

One factor in the engineering of materials-handling installations is recognized as of increasing importance; this is the explosion hazard from dusts. The danger in floating coal and grain dusts has long been recognized, but there are other dusts from materials now coming into general use, such as the plastics and metallic powders, that are quite as dangerous if not more so. In 1943, 41 dust explosions were

FIG. 22-1. After a dust explosion in a feed mill. (U. S. Bureau of Mines.)

reported in which 13 persons were killed and 44 injured, and the property loss exceeded $9,000,000. These occurred in metal-powder plants, grain elevators, woodworking plants, flour mills, starch factories, feed and cereal mills, cotton mills, and so on. After such an occurrence usually there is not much left of the plant, as is shown by Fig. 22-1, a feed mill.

The Bureau of Mines, United States Department of the Interior, has done extensive research on the general subject of dust explosions, described in various publications:

Technical Paper 617, " Characteristics of Fuel Pitches and Their Explosibility in Pulverized Form," by Irving Hartmann, H. C. Howarth, and H. P. Greenwald.

Report of Investigations 3722, " Inflammability and Explosibility of Metal Powders, " by Irving Hartmann, John Nagy, and Hylton R. Brown.

Report of Investigations 3751, " Inflammability and Explosibility of Powders used in the Plastics Industry, " by Irving Hartmann and John Nagy.

Information Circular 7309, " Industrial-Dust Explosions, " by Hylton R. Brown.

Report of Investigations 3924, " Effect of Relief Vents on Reduction of Pressures Developed by Dust Explosions, " by Irving Hartmann and John Nagy.

Other publications cover investigations on coal dust explosions supervised by G. S. Rice and H. P. Greenwald. Much of the material in the following discussion is quoted by permission from these reports.

Generally speaking, any combustible material in finely divided form may produce a dust explosion if aerated. To be dangerous there must be a certain percentage of dust to air; and in materials-handling installations the proportion of dust varies all through the range of too little to too much for the propagation of an explosion; somewhere along the line it may be just right. This is illustrated in the pneumatic coal-handling layout shown in Fig. 20-8, where the conditions are ideal for ignition.

When pulverized material is blown through the duct of a pneumatic conveyor into a steel receiver, a spark may be struck by a fragment of steel or a static discharge. Recently a pneumatic conveyor in Camden, New Jersey, handling wood dust from a pattern shop to a stoker hopper, blew up, injuring several men. It is, however, possible that this explosion was due to a flashback from the combustion chamber.

The laboratory tests by the Bureau of Mines showed that for 200-mesh coal dust the minimum concentration is 0.055 oz. per cu. ft. of air. In a chamber 10 by 10 by 10 ft. this means more than 3 lb. of coal dust in suspension before the dust-air mixture is explosive. But it is not necessary that an entire room or enclosure be filled uniformly with an explosive dust-air mixture before we can have a disaster. Accumulations of dust on machinery supports, roof beams, and so on, may be thrown into suspension by a jar, and, should this small volume be ignited, the pressure wave will stir up other accumulations, and an expanding dust cloud sufficiently dense for flame propagation may be formed throughout the room and along elevator casings or conveyor galleries leading from the room.

The amount of energy which might be liberated in the explosion of coal dust is perhaps indicated by the fact that, although the surface area per ton of 3 in. nut coal is only about 500 sq. ft., this increases to about 4000 sq. ft. for 3/8 by 0 in. coal and to an exposed area of 500,000 sq. ft. or more for coal pulverized to 200 mesh. The release of energy in the detonation of 1 ton of such a coal-air mixture, although almost infinitesimal in comparison with the imprisoned atomic energy which Professor Einstein calculated as 25 billion kw.-hr. per kg. (2.2 lb.), is impressive to contemplate (Fig. 22-2).

The research of the Bureau of Mines included the development of equipment by which it is possible to determine experimentally the ignition temperature, the relative inflammability, the ease of ignition, the limits of explosive concentration, and the rate of pressure rise.

In the Bureau of Mines data which follow, the maximum pressure and rate of pressure rise indicate to some extent the seriousness of the dust-explosion hazard. Some information has also been obtained on the venting requirements which must be provided in a building or enclosure to reduce explosion pressure. To propagate an explosion the concentration of dust in air must be between certain upper and lower limits. The minimum concentration is that at which there is barely enough dust in the air to propagate flame. The upper explosive limit exists when the complete combustion of a portion of the dust in all the oxygen available does not provide heat enough to raise the temperature of the entire dust cloud to ignition temperature. Usually the maximum intensity of the explosion will be with mixtures between these two limits. Most of the determinations on maximum explosion pressures and on rates of pressure rise were made with dust clouds of 0.1 and 0.5 oz. per cu. ft. concentration. The reason for choosing these comparatively dense clouds is that the minimum explosive concentration for some of the heavier dusts is not much below these values.

The unit of energy used for measuring the electrical spark energy for ignition of dust clouds is the joule which equals 1 watt-second, or 0.00095 B.T.U. The minuteness of this amount of energy needed in static sparks to ignite dust clouds shows the importance of proper grounding of equipment to prevent formation of static sparks. It is so small that if the ignition temperature is reached there can hardly fail to be sufficient energy for ignition to proceed.

**Carbonaceous Dusts.** Tests with 200 mesh coal gave:

Ignition temperature of dust cloud, 610° C
Relative inflammability, 90+
Minimum energy required for ignition of dust cloud, 0.04 joule
Minimum explosive concentration, 0.055 oz. per cu. ft. of air
Maximum pressure with 0.5 oz. per cu. ft. of air, 46 lb. per sq. in.
Maximum rate of pressure rise, 780 lb. per sq. in. per sec.

In addition to coal, tests have been made on various grain dusts, wood flour, powdered milk, spices, tobacco dust, powdered sugar, cocoa, leather dust, and insecticides. Explosion hazards ranged from low

FIG. 22–2. The above photographs, by the Explosions Research Section of the Bureau of Mines, illustrate the violence of dust explosions. *A* shows the explosion of 700 lb. of coal dust issuing from the pit mouth of their experimental mine seen at the right. *B* is from a photo taken when water was used in an attempt to extinguish burning magnesium dust in a storage shed. Explosive bursts of fire resulted which endangered nearby buildings.

to high, with coal in the middle group, as are the grain dusts. Cornstarch has a high rate, 3000 lb. per sq. in. per second.

**Metal Powders.** The bureau classifies these powders in decreasing risks as follows:

Zirconium heads the list because of its extreme ease of ignition and very high inflammability; however, it produces lower pressures and rates of pressure rise than do a number of others.

Magnesium and its alloys, Dowmetal, and magnesium aluminum have high inflammability, pressures, and rates of pressure rise, but their ignition temperatures are higher than those of some other metals that are less hazardous. Stamped aluminum ranks a little below magnesium and its alloys, and atomized aluminum is definitely below the stamped variety.

Titanium ranks only slightly below aluminum.

Antimony, manganese, zinc, silicon, and tin are in the range of the coal dusts.

Magnesium powder is a good example of the group of metal powders that have been found capable of forming explosive dust clouds in the air:

Ignition temperature of dust cloud, 520° C.
Relative inflammability, 90+
Minimum energy required for ignition of dust cloud, 0.02 joule
Minimum explosive concentration, 0.020 oz. per cu. ft. of air
Maximum pressure with 0.5 oz. per cu. ft. of air, 72 lb. per sq. in.
Maximum rate of pressure rise, 4760 lb. per sq. in. per sec.

**Plastic Powders.** Some of the phenolic-type resins can be used to illustrate the hazard of dust explosions in plants manufacturing or using plastics in powdered form. Laboratory tests gave:

Ignition temperature of dust cloud, 500° C.
Relative inflammability, 90+
Minimum energy required for ignition of dust cloud, 0.01 joule
Minimum explosive concentration, 0.025 oz. per cu. ft. of air
Maximum pressure with 0.5 oz. per cu. ft. of air, 61 lb. per sq. in.
Maximum rate of pressure rise, 3160 lb. per sq. in. per sec.

The following table gives the results with some powders used in the plastics industry. Data are for dust-cloud concentrations of 0.5 oz. per cu. ft. of air:

| | Ignition Temperature of Dust Cloud | Minimum Explosion Concentration, ounces per cubic foot | Maximum Pressure, pounds per square inch | Rate of Pressure Rise, pounds per square inch per second | |
|---|---|---|---|---|---|
| | | | | Average | Maximum |
| Resins: | | | | | |
| Shellac, resin, gum | 390° C. | 0.015 | 58 | 1240 | 2990 |
| Phenolic | 500 | 0.025 | 61 | 1370 | 3160 |
| Cellulose acetate | 410 | 0.035 | 68 | 800 | 1740 |
| Molding compounds: | | | | | |
| Cellulose compounds | 320 | 0.025 | 62 | 1180 | 2260 |
| Phenolic | 490 | 0.030 | 63 | 900 | 2080 |
| Synthetic rubber | 320 | 0.030 | 59 | 740 | 1870 |
| Fillers for molding compounds: | | | | | |
| Ground wood flour | 430 | 0.040 | 62 | 830 | 2080 |
| Ground cotton flock | 470 | 0.050 | 67 | 870 | 2990 |

Many of the plastics powders tested developed pressures exceeding 60 lb. per sq. in. or over 8500 lb. per sq. ft., an indication of the possibilities of widespread destruction which may result.

As a convenient comparison with coal, with dust-cloud concentrations of 0.5 oz. per cu. ft. of air:

| Dust | Relative Inflammability, per cent | Ignition Temperature of Dust Cloud, °F | Rate of Pressure Rise, pounds per square inch per second | |
|---|---|---|---|---|
| | | | Average | Maximum |
| Aluminum, stamped | 80 | 1195 | 2170 | 5700 |
| Magnesium, stamped | 90+ | 970 | 4390 | 4760 |
| Pittsburgh coal | 65 | 1130 | 370 | 780 |
| Cornstarch | 80 | 715 | 830 | 3000 |

Note the violence of the explosion of aluminum dust compared with that of coal dust.

**Prevention and Protection.** Safety lies in two directions: (1) through effective elimination of free dust and the sources of ignition by suitable ventilating and dust-collecting provision, approved wiring, dustproof switches, fully enclosed or explosion-proof motors where dust-laden air cannot be avoided, and grounding of metallic parts where static electricity is suspected. Sources of danger are open flames or lights, smoking, and steel-plate walk-ways. Gas- or coal-burning rotary dryers for dusty products liable to ignition or explosion should be operated where the atmosphere is as nearly as possible inert. If the air is recirculated it should be effectually cleansed before it is re-heated.

Emergency fire-extinguishing equipment may include talc, sand, or other inert dry material for smothering fires in magnesium, aluminum, and other metal powders, rather than water, carbon tetrachloride, and carbon dioxide pressure extinguishers, which sometimes tend to spread the fires in these dusts.

(2) Construction which will vent or release the explosive pressures should ignition occur. Venting of enclosures is by lightweight panels in side walls, roofs, elevator casings, conveyor-bridge housings and closed storage bins. The areas should be in as large a ratio to enclosed volume as can be arranged. Such pressure-release protection is of course more effective for dusts with a medium rate of pressure rise than for high-rate pressure-rise dusts.

Stair wells, elevator shafts, and floor openings should have emergency closures. Where the hazards are extreme the processes should be conducted in detached unit structures. All the above and other recommendations are covered by the rules of the National Fire Protection Association.

Safeguard conveyor and elevator belts against overheating or choking by automatic releases actuated by overloads or reduction below normal operating speed. Feed dusty material to a belt conveyor through a chute with a choke feed, or have an effective ventilating hood above the chute. Grinders, conveyors, elevators, dust collectors, or other equipment by which dust is produced, processed, or handled, should be dust tight or operated under slight vacuum. Good housekeeping is essential.

# APPENDIX 1

## NOMENCLATURE

Engineers whose work includes the selection or recommendation of material-handling equipment must be familiar with materials of construction involved in the various elements if they are to evaluate the competitive propositions offered them.

The specifications of the manufacturers almost invariably include a technical description of the make-up of the various parts — gears, shafts, chains, crusher rolls, structural-steel supports, etc. We will endeavor to cover the essential designations in order to indicate why they are so specified.

The work of the metallurgist has vastly improved the life and efficiency of modern material-handling equipment as compared with what was considered good practice a few years ago.

### FERROUS ALLOYS

**Wrought Iron and Ingot Iron.** Iron in nearly the pure state, containing only very small amounts of carbon and other elements, is called ingot iron. When the processing has been such as to retain slag in the metal, the product is wrought iron. These nearly pure irons are soft and relatively weak, but they are very ductile, can be worked both hot and cold, and are considered to have better rust resistance than mild steel.

**Carbon Steel.** Steel is classified as carbon steel when no minimum content is specified for aluminum, chromium, molybdenum, nickel, tungsten, and so on, and when the maximum content of copper specified does not exceed 0.40 per cent or when the maximum content for the following elements does not exceed: manganese 1.65 per cent, silicon 0.60 per cent, copper 0.60 per cent.

**Alloy steel.** Steel is classified as alloy steel when any minimum content is specified for aluminum, chromium, molybdenum, nickel, tungsten, and so on, and when the minimum content of copper specified exceeds 0.40 per cent or when the maximum content for any of the following elements exceeds: manganese 1.65 per cent, silicon 0.60 per cent, copper 0.60 per cent.

**Structural Steel.** Structural steel contains carbon up to about 0.25 per cent plus small amounts of manganese and silicon. Sulphur and phosphorus are present as impurities. Structural steel, sometimes called mild steel or machinery steel, is used in the form of bars, girders, channels, beams, plates, etc., for the fabrication of machinery supports and similar parts requiring a material of moderate strength and toughness which also can be fabricated easily by bending, punching, riveting, or welding. These steels are rarely heat treated, being used almost entirely in the " as-rolled " condition.

Several low-alloy structural steels of relatively high strength and consequently a higher strength-to-weight ratio than carbon steel are available. The improved strength is achieved by adding small percentages of such alloying elements as nickel, copper, chromium, molybdenum, vanadium, or phosphorus. Occasionally the manganese and silicon contents are raised above the amount usually present in ordinary structural steel and are used where weight saving is an important feature. Some which have better corrosion resistance than ordinary structural steel are useful for elevator buckets or other parts in contact with wet ore, high-sulphur coal, etc.

**Heat-Treated Wrought Steel.** These steels may contain carbon ranging from about 0.10 to about 0.85 per cent, and they depend for their properties upon heat treatment such as normalizing, annealing, or quenching and tempering. The carburizing steels are in a sense similar to structural steels in that their carbon content is low, rarely exceeding 0.25 per cent; hence they are ductile, tough, and fairly strong. By heating such steels to 1600–1750° F. while they are packed in a carbonaceous material, exposed to a carbonaceous gas, or immersed in a molten salt having carburizing characteristics, a surface layer of high-carbon steel is developed which has high hardness after subsequent heat treatment. The result is a material resistant to wear on the surface, backed by a strong tough core.

Gears subject to heavy wear, roller-bearing races, the teeth of sprockets, and conveyor chain links and pins are often made of carburized steel, usually alloyed with nickel, chromium, or molybdenum.

Cyaniding, in which parts are immersed in molten cyanide salt, also produces a hard surface containing both carbon and nitrogen. This case is relatively thin, rarely exceeding 0.01 in. in depth.

Nitriding consists of exposing steel parts to the action of ammonia gas at 900–1000° F.; it produces an extremely hard wear-resistant surface without the necessity for further heat treatment. Special alloy steels containing chromium, aluminum, molybdenum, and sometimes nickel are invariably used for nitrided parts.

The direct hardening steels, containing 0.25 to 0.55 per cent carbon, are employed in applications such as shafts, trunnions, highly stressed bolts, and other parts requiring high strength and some measure of toughness and resistance to shock. Readily machined in the as-rolled or annealed condition, these steels can be heat-treated by quenching and tempering to develop excellent strength characteristics.

The heat-treated steels are often alloyed to produce better combinations of properties. Most popular of the common alloying elements are nickel, chromium, molybdenum, vanadium, manganese, and silicon, added either singly or in combination. In general these alloy steels may be oil quenched instead of water quenched like carbon steels, with resultant lessening of the risk of distortion or cracking during heat treatment. They respond better to heat treatment in heavy sections, are more uniform in their hardening characteristics, and consequently develop a higher order of strength combined with toughness.

The 3½ per cent nickel steels find wide applications for shafting, bolts, crusher parts, etc., where strength and toughness are required. The lower-carbon varieties of this nickel steel remain tough at subzero temperatures where many other steels become brittle and so are useful for machinery operating under conditions of extreme cold.

The nickel-chromium, chromium-molybdenum, and chromium-vanadium steels are widely used for gears and for the side bars of conveyor chains, pins, keys, etc. Chromium-vanadium and silicon-manganese steels are widely used for springs.

Molybdenum, chromium-molybdenum, and nickel-chromium-molybdenum steels are particularly useful at temperatures up to about 1000° F. For this reason they are used for parts of conveyors of annealing furnaces operating at these moderately high temperatures.

The heavy-duty nickel-chromium and nickel-chromium-molybdenum steels are unexcelled for parts which must have high strength and toughness in heavy sections.

**SAE System of Designations.** The index system adopted by the Society of Automotive Engineers is widely used in designating the composition of steels. In this system the numerals are partly descriptive of the composition of the material. The first digit indicates the type to which the steel belongs; thus "1" indicates a carbon steel, "2" a nickel steel, and "3" a nickel-chromium steel. For the simple alloy steels the second digit generally indicates the approximate percentage of the predominant alloying element. Usually the last two or three digits indicate the average carbon content in "points" or hundredths of 1 per cent. Thus "2340" indicates a nickel steel of approximately 3 per cent nickel (3.25 to 3.75) and 0.40 per cent carbon (0.35 to 0.45). SAE 6150 is a chromium-vanadium steel containing about 0.50 per cent carbon, 1 per cent chromium, and 0.17 per cent vanadium. The letter "x" is used in numerous instances to denote variations in the range of elements. The basic numerals for the various types of SAE steels are as shown in the table below.

Chromium steel of the SAE 52100 type containing 1 per cent carbon and 1¼ per cent chromium is usually employed for ball bearings because of its extreme hardness and high resistance to crushing.

**Cast Steels.** Steel castings are generally employed for parts which can be economically cast into special shapes and which require moderate strength and toughness, or abrasion-resistant hardness. The carbon content may range from 0.15 per cent to about 0.60 per cent, depending on the service to which the part is subjected. As with

| Type of Steel | Numerals (and Digits) |
|---|---|
| Carbon steels | 1xxx |
| Plain carbon | 10xx |
| Free cutting (screw stock) | 11xx |
| Free cutting, manganese | X13xx |
| Manganese steels | 13xx |
| Nickel steels | 2xxx |
| 3.50% nickel | 23xx |
| 5.00% nickel | 25xx |
| Nickel-chromium steels | 3xxx |
| 1.25% nickel, 0.60% chromium | 31xxx |
| 1.75% nickel, 1.00% chromium | 32xx |
| 3.50% nickel, 1.50% chromium | 33xx |
| 3.00% nickel, 0.80% chromium | 34xx |
| Corrosion- and heat-resisting steels | 30xxx |
| Molybdenum steels | 4xxx |
| Chromium | 41xx |
| Chromium-nickel | 43xx |
| Nickel | 46xx and 48xx |
| Chromium steels | 5xxx |
| Low-chromium | 51xx |
| Medium-chromium | 52xxx |
| Corrosion- and heat-resisting | 51xxx |
| Chromium-vanadium steels | 6xxx |
| Silicon-manganese steels | 9xxx |

wrought steel, the lower the carbon content, the tougher, more ductile, and softer the steel; the higher-carbon varieties are characterized by great hardness and strength.

Alloying elements play the same important role in cast steel as in wrought steel, and for the same general reasons. Nickel, chromium, molybdenum, vanadium, and manganese are used to develop high strength and hardness with toughness and to improve response to heat treatment. The low- and medium-carbon moderately alloyed steels are strong and tough and have excellent resistance to shock and fatigue. Typical applications are for machinery frames and structural castings.

With somewhat raised carbon content, cast nickel-chromium steels are used for gears, cams, sheaves, sprockets, and miscellaneous castings requiring high strength. Oil-quenched and tempered, such steels are employed for parts subject to abrasion such as bucket teeth, conveyor chain links, cams, and rollers.

Higher-carbon steel castings which may be alloyed with nickel, chromium, molybdenum, manganese, and vanadium are used for heavy castings which must have high strength and hardness. Highly resistant to abrasion, they are useful for power-shovel teeth, tractor shoes, wearing plates, large gears, and pinions.

One widely used abrasion-resisting cast steel is Hadfield's manganese steel, containing about 10 to 14 per cent manganese with or without 3 to 5 per cent nickel. This steel is relatively soft initially but hardens remarkably under impact and heavy pressures to develop good abrasion resistance. The nickel-containing variety of this steel can be easily welded and is generally less subject to cracking upon heat treatment. It is used for crusher jaws, ore feeder aprons, and similar applications subject to abrasion under conditions of impact which permit the essential work-hardening action to take place.

Wartime regulations limited to a considerable extent the activities of the manufacturers through rigid restrictions in permitted materials, but these restrictions actually gave stimulus to the development of new designs, and the adoption of methods developed in other industries. Because of the necessity of conserving scarce alloying elements, a series of *national-emergency steels* were developed. These utilized the residual alloys in steel scrap, and some have proved valuable, such as the N.E.8600 series containing nickel, chromium, and molybdenum. The N.E.8620 is replacing some higher-alloy steels for carburizing, and the N.E.8640 is replacing some of the medium-carbon alloys. Those parts of conveying machinery subject to heavy abrasion are now made as hard as conditions permit. Case hardening is advantageous because file hardness is attained without too much risk of brittleness. Small parts such as ¾-in. pins and ½-in. wear plates can be made of carbon steel and be completely hardened. As the parts increase in size, additional hardenability is required, and this is attained by additional percentages of alloy. The trend now is toward selecting a steel for its hardenability rather than for its alloy content.

**Cast Irons.** The term cast iron is applied to a series of alloys of iron, silicon, and carbon which also contain appreciable percentages of other elements such as manganese, phosphorus, and sulphur. Most commercial cast irons contain between 2.50 and 3.75 per cent carbon, and silicon from about 0.25 to 3.00 per cent.

In gray iron, so called because of the gray appearance of its fracture, most of the carbon is present as graphite; hence gray iron can be considered an intimate mixture of steel and graphite. Relatively cheap and easily machined, it finds many applications for parts not subject to shock and a strength not above 20,000 to 35,000 lb. per sq. in. Nickel, chromium, molybdenum, and vanadium are the alloying elements generally used in gray cast iron. Suitably alloyed, and sometimes processed by special melting techniques, high-strength gray irons are produced with tensile strengths exceeding 60,000 lb. per sq. in. and toughness greater than that of ordinary gray iron, though not approaching that of steel. Chromium and nickel-chromium irons are used for stoker and grate bars and other applications requiring moderate resistance to elevated temperatures. These irons are also used for gears and other parts subject to wear as the graphite particles serve to some extent as a lubricant. The toughest of the gray irons are the nickel-molybdenum irons, often used for crankshafts and camshafts.

A special alloyed gray iron, containing about 14 per cent nickel, 7 per cent copper, and 2½ per cent chromium, has good resistance to corrosion and to the effects of elevated temperatures. These qualities make it useful for furnace doors, frames, and parts not subjected to heavy loads at high temperatures and for food conveyor tables and similar parts subject to corrosive attack.

When the silicon content is reduced to about 1 per cent or less, the carbon in cast iron remains chemically combined with iron instead of precipitating as graphite; hence the iron is called *white iron.* White or chilled cast iron is hard but brittle and is useful for parts which are not subject to shock but which must withstand abrasion, such as the wearing backs of pneumatic conveyor elbows. An alloyed white iron containing 4½ per cent nickel and 1½ per cent chromium is much harder and tougher than plain white iron and is extensively used for ball-mill liners, wear plates, coal-chute liners, sand-blast nozzles, and similar parts.

**Malleable iron** is white cast iron which has been annealed. Suitable heat treatment decomposes the chemically combined carbon to rosettes of graphite. This produces an iron with tensile strength of about 50,000 to 60,000 lb. per sq. in. and 10 to 25 per cent elongation. The ductility of malleable iron makes it excellent for chains, conveyor flights, elevator buckets, conveyor rollers, etc. Pearlitic malleable cast iron is a malleable iron with some carbon left in the combined form to produce greater strength and consequently reduced ductility.

**Heat- and Corrosion-Resisting Alloys.** The alloy widely known as *stainless steel* contains 18 per cent chromium and 8 per cent nickel, popularly called 18–8. There are a wide number of stainless and heat-resisting steels, containing chromium from about 11 to 32 per cent and nickel up to about 68 per cent. Molybdenum is sometimes added to about 3½ per cent, and columbium is occasionally used in small quantities to stabilize the carbon and provide resistance to intergranular corrosion. The low-carbon (about 0.10 per cent maximum) grades of 18–8 are suitable for welding.

In addition to 18–8, alloys containing 21 to 25 per cent chromium and 12 per cent nickel, or 25 per cent chromium and 20 per cent nickel, are widely used for corrosion-resisting applications in the form of sheets, bars, shapes, and castings. Conveyors handling food or chemicals may require the use of stainless steels to prevent contamination of the products. Many of the so-called stainless steels are also useful for elevated temperature conditions, being resistant to scaling and the effects of hot gases while maintaining load-carrying ability at temperatures that render ordinary steels weak and plastic. The 25–12 and 25–20 chromium-nickel alloys are so used. Alloys containing 35 per cent nickel and 15 per cent chromium, 60 to 70 per cent nickel with 12 to 17 per cent chromium, and 80 per cent nickel with 14 per cent chromium are also popular. The conveyors of continuous furnaces and those in steel mills make extensive use of such alloys. Where sulphurous atmospheres are encountered at high temperatures, alloys containing 17 to 30 per cent chromium, sometimes with 2 per cent nickel, are customarily employed.

**Special Iron Alloys.** There are a number of iron-base alloys, not falling into any of the foregoing classifications, which have uses suited to their special characteristics. Invar, an alloy containing 36 per cent nickel, 64 per cent iron, has a thermal coefficient of expansion which approaches zero at temperatures of about 250° F. This alloy is used for the low-expansion side of the bimetal strips for thermostats and for the parts of accurate measuring instruments subjected to heat. Certain other special nickel-iron compositions are used for glass-sealing alloys (Dumet, Platinite, Fernico, Kovar, and Fernichrome), for springs having a constant elastic modulus over a wide range of temperatures (Elinvar, Iso-Elastic), and for alloys of high magnetic permeability (Permalloy, Mumetal, Hypernik, etc.) used in long-distance telephone cables and loading coils. An alloy called Alnico, containing 20 per cent nickel, 12 per cent aluminum, and 5 per cent cobalt, is used for exceptionally strong permanent magnets.

## NON-FERROUS ALLOYS

**Aluminum Alloys.** Aluminum, having only one-third the weight of steel, is useful wherever saving in weight is an important factor. The pure metal is soft, ductile, and lacking in strength, but when it is alloyed with small amounts of copper, silicon, manganese, magnesium, zinc, or iron, better strength properties are secured. The most popular high-strength aluminum alloy, called Duralumin, contains 4 per cent copper, 0.5 per cent magnesium, 0.5 per cent manganese, and up to 15 per cent maximum each of iron and silicon. Tensile strength up to 65,000 lb. per sq. in., with an elongation of 13 per cent in 2 in., can be achieved by heat treating and cold working. Alclad is Duralumin with a surface layer of pure aluminum bonded to its core to secure better corrosion resistance.

Aluminum alloys may also be used to line conveyor chutes to prevent static sparking which might ignite the conveyed material, as when chuting sulphur into cargo vessels.

**Cadmium.** Cadmium is used chiefly as a protective coating, applied by electroplating, for steel parts subject to corrosion. On conveyor pins and links a very thin coating serves as a semi-permanent lubricant.

**Copper Alloys.** Because pure copper has the highest electrical conductivity of all commercial metals it is used extensively in electrical apparatus. Its high thermal conductivity makes it useful for heat exchangers, condensers, radiators, and cooking utensils.

**Brass** is the term applied to copper-base alloys in which zinc is the predominant alloying element, and **bronze** to alloys in which tin is the essential alloying element. These terms are sometimes confusing since many alloys of copper contain both zinc and tin. **Red brass** contains 85 per cent copper, 15 per cent zinc; it is generally employed for plumbing pipe, tubing, and flexible hose; **yellow brass,** 70 per cent copper, 30 per cent zinc, is used for tubing and spun or drawn shapes. With 1 per cent tin added the 30 per cent zinc alloy is known as Admiralty metal, used for condenser tubing.

Wrought tin bronze deoxidized with phosphorus, known as **phosphor bronze,** is used extensively for springs and diaphragms because of its high strength. Silicon, aluminum, and manganese are also used to impart strength to certain of the bronzes. One of the strongest and hardest copper alloys is produced by the addition of 2 per cent beryllium, making a useful alloy for non-sparking parts where risk of explosion exists.

Of the cast brasses and bronzes, the most generally popular compositions are red brass, containing 5 per cent each of zinc, tin, and lead; "G" bronze containing 10 per cent tin and 2 per cent zinc, and chill-cast gear bronze containing 11 per cent tin. The last is widely used for worm wheels. All these compositions sometimes contain up to 2 or 3 per cent nickel. An age-hardening cast nickel-bronze, used for gears, contains 5 per cent nickel, 5 per cent tin, and 2 per cent zinc. It has a tensile strength in excess of 75,000 lb. per sq. in. when heat treated.

The **nickel silvers** are a series of copper-zinc alloys containing nickel up to 30 per cent. The nickel serves to decolorize the alloy, producing a series of alloys varying in tint from pale pink and yellow through white to pale green, depending on the adjustment of the zinc content. Wrought nickel silver, used for silver-plated ware, springs, and chemical equipment, contains 18 per cent nickel and 18 per cent zinc.

**Cupro-nickel,** containing 70 per cent copper and 30 per cent nickel, is widely used for condenser tubing because it is resistant to corrosion and fouling by salt water. A variation of this alloy containing 25 per cent nickel is used for our 5 cent "nickels."

**Lead.** Pure lead sheet is used for lining chemical equipment exposed to sulphuric acid and lead pipe for plumbing and cable sheaths. Corrugated steel sheets clad with lead make an excellent sheathing for conveyor or elevator housings. Various soldering alloys are composed of lead with tin up to 50 per cent added to form a low-melting alloy with good bonding properties. **Lead-base babbitts** contain up to 20 per cent tin, 15 per cent antimony, and copper up to $1\frac{1}{2}$ per cent, and are extensively used for babbitted bearings.

**Magnesium Alloys.** Magnesium, having two-thirds the weight of aluminum, is the lightest available commercial metal. In the pure form its most common use is for flashlight powder, but when it is suitably alloyed with aluminum, zinc, and manganese a series of light alloys are produced in cast or wrought shapes useful where light weight without heavy stresses is of paramount importance.

**Nickel Alloys.** Pure nickel is extensively used in chemical and food-handling equipment to avoid corrosion and contamination. Nickel-clad steel plate is likewise used for this service. **Nickel plating** forms the base layer for most chromium plating. Heavy nickel plating is used to build up the worn parts of machinery, and a hard plate is available for applications requiring unusual resistance to abrasive wear.

The most widely known nickel-base alloy is **Monel,** containing 67 per cent nickel, 30 per cent copper, and the remainder mostly iron and manganese. This is primarily a corrosion-resistant alloy for handling acids, alkalies, brines, and food products. One grade of Monel metal with a strength in excess of 170,000 lb. per sq. in. is used for shafting, springs, and other parts requiring high strength in corrosive environments. Non-sparking tools are made of Monel.

An alloy containing 80 per cent nickel, 14 per cent chromium, and 6 per cent iron is known as **Inconel;** it has good strength, toughness, and resistance to corrosion and oxidation. Because of these qualities, even under high temperatures, it is used for furnace equipment, aircraft engine exhaust manifolds, and similar parts.

**Tin.** This metal is widely used for " tin plate," which is steel dipped in molten tin to provide a thin but corrosion-resistant coating suitable for contact with foodstuffs. **Terneplate** utilizes a thin lead-base coating containing up to 25 per cent tin. The tin-base bearing metals known commercially as babbitt metals are essentially alloys of tin, antimony, and copper, to which as much as 30 per cent lead may be added.

**Zinc.** Galvanized sheet is mild steel to which a thin protective surface layer of pure zinc has been added by hot dipping or by electrodeposition. The resultant product, being resistant to atmospheric corrosion and to some forms of chemical attack, is used for roofing material and for sheathing conveyor galleries. Corrugated sheathing of pure zinc tends to sag with time unless the studs are very closely spaced.

When alloyed with 4 per cent aluminum and up to 2½ per cent copper, zinc is utilized for die-casting such parts as meter housings, carburetors, fuel pumps, model parts, and small gear reducers.

## DEFINITION OF TERMS

Certain terms which are commonly used in connection with material-handling installations are grouped and discussed briefly in the following paragraphs.

**Abrasion.** The cutting, wearing, or chipping away of one material by another. Although the abrading material is usually the harder, it may itself be worn away, as in grinding wheels or ball-mill liners and balls. A resilient material like rubber or an inert soft material like lead or copper may sometimes resist abrasion by impingement better than a harder material; for example, in a pneumatic conveyor an elbow wearing back of lead will last longer than one of hard white iron.

**Corrosion.** Chemical attack on a metal or alloy, sometimes accelerated by electrolysis, in which event it is termed galvanic corrosion. A common form of corrosion is the rusting of iron or steel, where oxygen in the presence of moisture attacks the surface. To prevent or delay corrosion, alloys resistant to attack may be employed, or the surface of a vulnerable material may be protected with paint, rubber, lead, or with resistant metals applied by plating, tinning, or galvanizing.

**Erosion.** The wearing action of a stream of liquid or gas, such as the erosion of the bore or nozzle in a stream-jet conveyor. Abrasion, corrosion, and erosion may occur simultaneously.

**Cold Working.** Plastic deformation of a metal or alloy at room temperature, or some temperature low enough to insure hardening as a result of such deformation or working.

**Hot Working.** Plastic deformation of a metal or alloy at such high temperatures that no hardening takes place as a result of such deforming or working.

**Endurance limit,** also called **fatigue limit.** A limiting stress below which an alloy or metal will withstand without fracture an indefinitely large number of repetitions of such stress. Most failures of materials in service are fatigue failures, sometimes accelerated by various causes, resulting from stresses applied in excess of the endurance limit. Its value for steel is about 50 per cent of the ultimate tensile strength.

**Hardness, Brinell.** A measure of hardness obtained by pressing a steel ball into the surface of a metal or alloy under a definite load. The diameter of the resultant cuplike depression is measured and converted into a Brinell hardness number. Because of the relatively large area under the test ball this method is preferred for gray cast iron and other heterogeneous materials.

**Hardness, Rockwell.** A measure of hardness obtained by pressing a conical diamond penetrator or a hardened-steel ball into the surface of a metal or alloy under a definite load. The depth of the resulting depression is measured and converted to a Rockwell hardness number. This method, using a diamond penetrator, is particularly useful for hard steels.

**Hardness, Scleroscope.** A measure of hardness obtained by dropping a diamond-tipped hammer from a fixed height upon the surface of a metal or alloy, and measuring the height of rebound. This method is applicable for heavy parts requiring the use of a portable instrument and for finished surfaces which must not be marred by large indentations.

**Hardness, File.** An arbitrary method of determining whether a hardened surface is harder or softer than a testing file by determining whether the file " bites " the surface or slides over it. In the hands of an experienced operator, this is a useful test for the teeth of carburized gears, the pins of conveyor chains, and similar parts.

**Heat Treatment.** Any operation or combination of operations which involve heating or cooling of a metal or alloy in the solid state to secure certain desirable properties. Some of the common types of heat treatment are as follows:

(*a*) *Annealing.* Slow cooling after heating, usually in order to remove stresses, to induce softness or improve ductility, or to remove internal gases.

(*b*) *Normalizing.* Heating an iron-base alloy (usually steel) to approximately 100° F. above its critical temperature, followed by cooling to below that range in still air at ordinary temperature.

(*c*) *Quenching.* Rapid cooling of a metal or alloy by immersion in a liquid or gas. Usually applied to steel heated above its critical range and subsequently cooled by plunging into water or oil.

(*d*) *Tempering or Drawing.* Reheating hardened or quenched steel to some temperature below its critical range, followed by any desired rate of cooling.

(*e*) *Spheroidizing.* Any heat-treating process that produces a rounded or globular form of carbide, usually obtained by prolonged heating just below the critical range, followed by slow cooling. This treatment is useful to condition steel rod or wire for cold-drawing processes.

(*f*) *Flame Hardening.* A localized quenching operation obtained by heating the part to a temperature above the critical range by means of a blowtorch followed by rapid cooling with a jet of water, oil, or air. A typical use is for hardening gear and sprocket teeth without destroying toughness in the hub.

(*g*) *Induction Hardening.* A localized quenching operation, obtained by heating to some temperature above the critical range by placing the part within an electrical field, followed by rapid cooling with a jet of water, oil, or air. This process is useful for hardening the wearing surfaces of camshafts, crankshafts, etc.

**Tensile Tests.** The popular method for measuring the strength and ductility of metals and alloys. A specimen of suitable size and shape is pulled longitudinally until it ruptures. The usual test specimen is a round bar with thread-end grips, having a test section 0.505-in. in diameter and not less than 2 in. long. Flat plate tensile specimens are often used for structural steels and boiler plate. Some of the properties measured by the tensile test are as follows:

(*a*) *Ultimate Tensile Strength.* The load in pounds at which a specimen ruptures, divided by the original cross-section area.

(*b*) *Yield Point.* The load per unit of original cross section at which, in soft steel, a marked increase in deformation (elongation) takes place without further increase in load. In other steels and in non-ferrous metals, the yield point is more properly called yield strength and is the stress corresponding to some definite and arbitrarily chosen total deformation, such as 0.1 or 0.2 per cent permanent elongation. The yield point of heat-treated steel is about 60 to 80 per cent of the tensile strength; in cast iron it is very close to the tensile strength.

(*c*) *Proportional Limit.* The limiting load per unit of original cross section beyond which the increase in elongation is no longer proportional to the increase in stress. The proportional limit is slightly lower than the yield point.

(*d*) *Elastic Limit.* The maximum load per unit of original cross section which may be applied without causing permanent deformation, and for which only elastic deformation takes place. Upon release of the load, the specimen regains its original dimensions. This value is equivalent to, or lower than, the proportional limit.

(*e*) *Elongation.* The amount of permanent extension of a specimen after rupture in tension. It is usually measured as a percentage over a gauge length of 2 in., but an 8-in. length is often used for structural-steel-plate tensile specimens. Elongation is a measure of ductility and, indirectly, of toughness.

(*f*) *Reduction of Area.* The difference between the original cross-sectional area and the smallest area at the point of rupture, expressed as a percentage of the original area. This also is a measure of ductility and toughness.

(*g*) *Modulus of Elasticity.* The ratio, within the elastic limit, of the stress to the corresponding strain or elongation. It is expressed in pounds per square inch and may be considered to be the stress which would cause a 1-in. specimen to elongate to double its original length if purely elastic conditions prevailed. For steel, the modulus is generally considered to be 30,000,000 lb. per sq. in.

**Photoelasticity.** The behavior of conveyor and drive chains under stress, and the location and distribution or concentration of the stresses, are important factors in the design of these parts. Photoelasticity provides a photographic method of showing these stresses. Failure usually occurs in the region of localized stresses, and analytical methods often cannot be applied to determine their magnitude. In the photoelastic method a model of the part is machined from a flat piece of isotropic transparent material such as Bakelite. The model is loaded exactly as the original part would be in service. When polarized light from a mercury-vapor lamp is passed through the stressed model, a photograph shows a grouping of black and white bands which indicate the magnitude and distribution of the shearing stress in the model. This method offers an interesting field of research to the engineer to the end of improving the design of many details in machinery parts of conveyors, elevators, crushers, spring supports, etc.

## APPENDIX 2

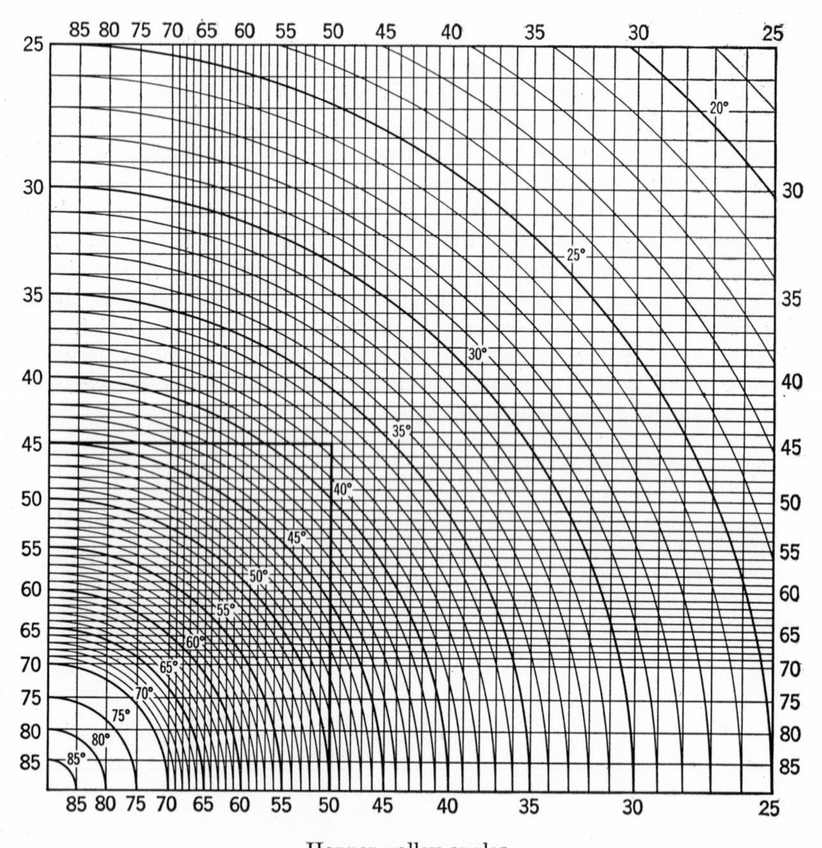


Hopper valley angles.

To find valley angle when the angles of the two adjacent sides are known: Enter chart with values of angles of sides read on vertical and horizontal scales. The intersection of these lines determines the corresponding valley angle as read on the circular arcs. Example: Given angle of one side = 45°. Angle of adjacent side = 50°. Intersection of 45° line with 50° line gives valley angle of 37° 30′.

# INDEX